QUANTITATIVE ANALYSIS
Elementary Principles and Practice

QUANTITATIVE ANALYSIS

Elementary Principles and Practice

HARVEY DIEHL, Ph.D.

Professor of Chemistry, Iowa State College

•

G. FREDERICK SMITH, Ph.D.

Professor of Chemistry, University of Illinois

JOHN WILEY & SONS, INC., NEW YORK

CHAPMAN & HALL, LIMITED, LONDON

Library of Congress Catalog Card Number: 52–11286

PRINTED IN THE UNITED STATES OF AMERICA

Preface

The value of the written record is that it enables us to do over, each time a little better, we would like to believe, those things which early experience found workable. Any new textbook, then, should enable us to duplicate our earlier efforts with somewhat greater facility and with somewhat better precision. In the last generation a profound change has come over the textbooks of quantitative analysis. Literally, they have become textbooks on physical chemistry. Although the procedures in a textbook of 1910 are often identical with those in one of 1950 (would that someone had devised a better method for sulfate in this interval!), theory has been added, and to such an extent that the book of 1950 is half theory. Much of this theory has been good; an unconscionable amount of it has been considerably less than germane to the subject of chemical analysis. The authors of this book are practicing analytical chemists whose chief delights in life have been to devise new methods of analysis and to teach the discipline, and the dignity, and the utility, of chemical analysis to college students. In these activities they have found theory useful, but they have also found descriptive chemistry and careful laboratory work indispensable. Naturally their writing reflects their own approach to the subject, emphasizing chemistry, paying perhaps as much attention to technique as to theory, and including only those items of theory of direct benefit to the working analyst.

This is not to say that theory has been ignored. Indeed, the electrochemical theory of oxidation-reduction has been made a dominant theme of the last half of the book, and an attempt has been made to correlate to it more concepts than is customary—oxidation-reduction titrations and indicators, electrodeposition and polarization, and the pH scale and neutralization reactions. Consistency in the explanation relating pH and neutralization reactions to the reduction-potential series has made it necessary to invert the pH scale as commonly presented with 14 at the top and 1 at the bottom. Precedent for the inverted form is already in the literature, and the justification is ample to cover the shock older chemists will experience in seeing pH 1 at the top of the scale. This will be harder on the teacher than on the pupil.

Qualitative analysis is disappearing as a separate course from the curricula of American colleges, and its position in general chemistry courses is shrinking. In the present book little is presupposed of qualitative analysis and theory begins with the solubility-product principle;

for those with qualitative analysis, this will be in the nature of review and Chapter 5 will be of small importance. Similarly the calculations (Chapter 4) begin at a level presupposing only general chemistry.

In the teaching of quantitative analysis in recent years there has been some tampering with the order in which the divisions of the subject have been taught. In this book gravimetric analysis is taken up first. For several years, the authors taught volumetric analysis before gravimetric, and then returned to the older method, gravimetric analysis first, with considerable relief. They have documented this argument in a discussion of the teaching of quantitative analysis in the first chapter of a companion booklet which gives the answers to the problems in this textbook.

Colorimetric analysis has undergone a spectacular growth in the last decade since the advent of commercial photoelectric instruments. At a conservative estimate, as many colorimetric analyses as volumetric analyses are now performed in industrial and research laboratories. In accord with this change in practice, colorimetry (Chapter 13) follows promptly after volumetric analysis, and it treats of photoelectric as well as Duboscq colorimeters, and of Beer's law, absorption spectra, and color filters, as well as of Nessler tubes.

The specificity of reagents and the methods of effecting the separation of one element from others before measurement is as important to the working analyst as the balance and the operations of filtering and titrating. Methods of effecting separations are discussed in considerable detail (Chapters 14 and 15) before the analysis of complex materials like brass and limestone are considered.

A chapter has been included on the measurement of pH, colorimetric as well as potentiometric methods, for, even in these days of commercial pH meters, the simple methods often find service when expensive equipment is lacking. The final chapter has to do with precision and accuracy, significant figures, and the rejection of data; because it comes last its importance is not to be discounted.

Gravimetric analysis, volumetric analysis, colorimetric analysis, separation methods, pH measurements, solubility product, neutralization theory, the electrochemistry of oxidation-reduction and electrodeposition, and a little elementary treatment of data—all this makes up a one-year course in quantitative analysis. Some theory, as much technique, and a lot of chemistry just about sums it up.

HARVEY DIEHL

Ames, Iowa

G. FREDERICK SMITH

Urbana, Illinois
September, 1952

Contents

vii

CHAPTER 1

On the Nature
of Quantitative Analysis

It may indeed be asserted that chemistry was elevated to a science by quantitative analysis, for it was the quantitative research work which led to the discovery of the laws which govern the combinations and transpositions of the elements—C. R. Fresenius.

The science of chemistry deals with the changes that matter undergoes when its environment is altered. In studying such changes two methods of attack are employed based on the general line of thinking adopted in approaching a given problem. The approach to a problem can be either analytic or synthetic. The analytic method is characterized by breaking down; the synthetic method, by building up. The analytic method seeks to find the pertinent factors of a problem or to identify the components of a material under study, to separate these factors and components, and to measure their quantity. The synthetic method attempts to correlate information, to bring together new combinations of matter and of ideas, and to create new matter or devise new concepts which unify apparently diverse phenomena. The analysis phase of scientific work demands close study, diligence, and care; the synthesis requires insight, imagination, and inspiration.

In any worthy scientific task both methods are used. Usually the analytic part comes first and the synthesis comes later. The analysis is often the drudgery, and the synthesis the crowning achievement in the form of a new species of matter or of an embracing concept which broadens our understanding of nature. The two processes must go on together, and usually with much overlapping. A new compound must be analyzed and its composition proved, and any new concept presents novel features which suggest extensions; the extensions then become a new problem, the elements of which must be segregated, identified, and measured. Fresh correlations can then be made, and the process starts all over again.

Analysis and synthesis thus alternate and are mutually interdependent. Examples of this are found in every field of science. In astronomy the extensive observations of Tycho Brahe on the motion of the planets was analytic in nature. The discovery by Kepler, which followed fairly quickly after Brahe's work, of the three laws of planetary motion was purely synthetic. The latter in turn was followed by observations of a more directed type, and these by the discovery by Newton of the underlying principle of gravitation. This again led to more exact observations by Flamsteed and others of the motions of the satellites and the comets, of the movements of the tides, and on the shape of the earth. This in time was followed by the great theoretical treatments of the motions of the celestial bodies by Legendre and Laplace.

In chemistry the early analytic phase lasted much longer than in astronomy. The problem was more complicated, for the number of different kinds of matter close at hand for immediate investigation was enormous and the reactions between them complex. The synthetic phase began only during the closing years of the eighteenth century when the analytic phase had proceeded far enough to make possible the elucidation of the nature of the combustion process. The multitudinous forms of matter and the complexity of individual materials make the analytic aspect of chemistry of unending interest. Chemistry is the one science in which the analytic aspect is emphasized as a major division of the science and is taught specifically and separately for itself. Analytical chemistry enters early into the training of a chemist, and is at once the training ground and the tool of the other branches of the science.

The analytic phase of the development of a science or the attack on a specific problem involves two stages, a qualitative stage and a quantitative stage. In the qualitative stage the component parts are isolated and identified; in the quantitative they are measured and their quantity is expressed by a number. The first stage calls for background knowledge, intuition, directed experimentation, and confirmatory tests. The results usually come quickly, and for the most part great care may not be essential—the very word *qualitative* carries a connotation of superficiality. The measurement stage, however, requires more elaborate equipment, demands close attention to detail, is time-consuming, and is often tedious and even exasperating. In the end, it gives information of greater significance, concrete, definite information on which the synthetic phase can be safely based and on which decisions can be made with assurance.

In the nature of things, then, the student of chemistry finds quantitative analysis more difficult than qualitative analysis. A quantitative analysis requires a considerable degree of care, often for an extended period of time, and such intense application and continuous concentration are often distasteful and even overwhelming after a quarter of a lifetime of wholly qualitative habits. Moreover, if the learning process is to have any resemblance to life outside the classroom and to science as it is practiced, the analyses chosen for laboratory experience must be of materials of unknown composition, materials which the student must actually analyze. The results cannot be secured with a pencil, and no amount of talk is a substitute for the labor of a true analysis, skillfully and conscientiously carried out and honestly interpreted.

As a discipline in manual dexterity, in the application of the intellect to the handling of an inanimate and often perverse nature, and in the exercise of personal integrity under sometimes trying circumstances, quantitative analysis is a subject without peer in the teaching of science. It develops poise and self reliance. It leads to an appreciation of the inflexibility of the physical laws of nature and brings an understanding of the great difficulties men have overcome to bring science to its present state. Students usually find quantitative analysis difficult. The rewards, even though partly intangible, are worth time and trouble, and the disappointments which sometimes follow long and exacting quantitative work should not produce more than momentary discouragement and should never be allowed to befog an intelligent appraisal of reality. There is nothing in an elementary course in quantitative analysis that cannot be mastered with reasonable diligence and average intelligence. One might almost take as a motto the foreword to that priceless gem among mathematics books, Thompson's *Calculus Made Easy:* "What one fool can do, another can also."

In quantitative analysis skillful laboratory work is a big part of the game. This manual-dexterity requirement is not severe. It is not the gifted touch of the artist or even the high perfection acquired by the dentist or surgeon, but rather the sure and steady hand of the carpenter and the machinist—preferably coupled with the neatness of a Dutch housekeeper. The details of the laboratory work in a beginning course have been well worked out, and a careful reading of the text material and an intelligent application of this knowledge to the laboratory work and to the solution of numerical problems are all that are needed. Creative thinking comes later, often for the first time, in the application of a method of analysis to some new problem.

Quantitative analysis has been called a bread-and-butter course. It has been likened to the grammar course in learning a language and to the practicing of scales in learning the piano. It has been called an art, a science, and a state of mind. It has also been called a variety of names not fit for print. There is a good deal of truth in all this. Quantitative analysis supplies the methods of sorting the good from the bad with certainty, and in the chemical industry it provides the criteria which decide whether a raw material meets specifications and whether the finished product should be released for sale. It decides whether a batch of chemical is a reagent-grade chemical or must be marketed at a lower rate as a technical or u.s.p. grade. In its daily working, quantitative analysis impartially sorts, rejects, or passes, informs and dictates, and its answers inevitably cheer or annoy, for the materials analyzed may be high in value or rich in effort and hope.

As the grammar or scale-practicing course of the science of chemistry, quantitative analysis is the first professional course in chemistry. It provides the chemist with tools he will use for the remainder of his professional days. He may not elect to specialize in analytical chemistry, but there is hardly a chemical subject he can touch without occasions to apply it.

Man's great urge is to create, and it is a rare fellow indeed who wants only to analyze. Even the professional analytical chemist seeks escape from this by devoting much of his time to working out new methods of analysis, for this is essentially a creative activity. The routine business of analysis he turns over to technicians, people who can weigh and titrate but who may have a meager and turbid concept of what the work is all about. G. E. F. Lundell, one of our great American analytical chemists and for a long period the chief chemist at the Bureau of Standards, thought it well to differentiate these two persons clearly: the determinator and the analyst. The determinators have little training in chemistry, have learned merely the manipulations, and devote their time to turning out a mass of essentially repetitious work. The analysts are chemists; they make certain that the samples are properly taken, that the methods employed are suitable, that the solutions are properly standardized, and the results properly evaluated; periodically they slip in known samples to check up on the activities of the determinators. The economics of labor and profit dictate that the industry work this way. The fresh college graduate on his first job may well find himself in the analytical laboratory the first few months. There, the opportunity to learn about the company's operation is unexcelled. But it should not be long before he is supervising the determinators and looking about for better methods of analyzing the company's products. The principal aim of the course in quantitative analysis is to prepare him to be able to do just this.

Of great value in approaching a new problem in chemical analysis is the habit of examining the methods and measurements critically to evaluate the probable accuracy with which they can be made. In spite of all the critical studies and the enormous effort which has been put into improving the procedures of quantitative analysis, it is rare that the results are any better than 1 part in 1000. Most analytical work in industrial and research laboratories is of the order of accuracy of 1 part in 500 or 1 part in 1000. On very rare occasions accuracy of 1 part in 10,000 is needed, and only one problem in the entire history of chemistry has justified the effort needed to secure an accuracy of 1 part in 100,000. There are certain physical measurements which can be made even more accurately, and some with astonishingly simple apparatus. The chemist will continue to envy the physicist in this, for nature has decreed that the chemist must be content with accuracy several decimals lower and that even this he may not achieve without struggle.

Quantitative analysis is quite largely an empirical business. The methods used must be critically examined, and there is no substitute for actually trying out a method in the laboratory. The best proof that a method is functioning properly is to secure a pure substance, duplicate the conditions, perform the analysis, and then repeat the whole process several times to see if the behavior is always the same. Theory helps; it makes progress more rapid and correlates apparently isolated facts which might otherwise be difficult to understand or remember. However, practically all quantitative analyses are carried out in aqueous solutions of relatively high concentration of electrolyte, and this is the one situation in chemistry where theory has been most inadequate. Moreover, the analyst himself brings on difficulties, for he is continually striving for accuracy in the next decimal place and naturally running ahead of theory. At the same time, most analyses are made on impure materials, and these introduce into the solutions substances whose effects on the methods cannot be predicted. Theory, then, must be tempered with a knowledge of its limitations, and the analytical chemist dare not get too far from experiment.

This book is about equally divided between theory and practice. The student should learn both. The descriptive material, the methods of analysis, and the techniques will help him on specific problems; the theory will broaden his understanding of nature and of the processes of measurement. With both he can direct the determinators with assurance, use the analytical literature with understanding, and enter the ranks of his great chemical forbears with appreciation.

CHAPTER 2

The General Operations
of Quantitative Analysis

In a quantitative analysis two measurements must be made, the first on the sample taken for the analysis and the second on some component of the sample, usually after it has been suitably separated from the other components of the sample. Both measurements may be simple measurements of mass, that is, weighings. The analysis is then called a *gravimetric analysis*. On the other hand, the final measurement may be a measurement of the volume of a solution of a certain chemical required to react with the component of the sample being determined; the analysis is then called a *volumetric analysis*. Thus, the subject of quantitative analysis is divided on the basis of the final measurement employed in the analysis, *colorimetric analysis* if a color is measured, *electrometric analysis* if an electrical indicating device is used, and so on through a considerable variety of methods. In the great majority of analyses, the first measurement is one of mass, that is, the mass (weight) of the sample, and the final measurement practically always involves a second measurement of mass, either directly or indirectly. Such analyses are therefore made on a weight basis, and the results are reported as per cent by weight.

In a gravimetric analysis both measurements are direct measurements of mass. For example, a sample of potassium acid sulfate and sodium chloride (a mixture commonly sold as a wash-bowl cleaner) is weighed out and dissolved in water. The sulfate is then precipitated as barium sulfate

$$KHSO_4 + BaCl_2 = BaSO_4 + HCl + KCl$$

The barium sulfate is filtered off on ashless paper, the paper and barium sulfate are placed in a weighed crucible, the water is driven off by heating, the paper is burned away, and the crucible and barium sulfate are weighed. The increase in weight of the crucible is the mass of barium sulfate obtained. By simple proportion with the molecular

6

weights of the substances involved, the weight of potassium acid sulfate present in the sample at the beginning can be calculated and hence also the per cent of potassium acid sulfate in the sample. The final measurement is the weighing of the barium sulfate. Such an analysis is a typical gravimetric analysis.

The same reaction can be used as a volumetric analysis; instead of weighing the barium sulfate produced, the amount of barium chloride required for the reaction is measured. This is best done by preparing a solution of barium chloride whose concentration is accurately known. The volume of this solution just necessary to carry out the reaction is then accurately measured. A method must be available for telling when an equivalent amount of the barium chloride solution has been added; an indicator, for example, may be introduced which changes color at the equivalence-point, or there may be dipped into the solution a suitable pair of electrodes which change potential at the equivalence-point and can be made to flash a light or ring a bell. Essentially, however, the volume of the barium chloride solution needed is measured, and the calculations are again based on a proportion between the weights of the substances involved and their molecular weights. Such a volumetric analysis also gives the results as per cent by weight. The sample taken for analysis was weighed and the barium chloride in the standard solution was weighed accurately when the solution was prepared.

In a *colorimetric analysis* the intensity of the light transmitted by a solution of a colored material is compared with a solution containing a known amount of the same material. In *spectrographic* analysis a measurement is made of the intensity of certain lines on a photograph of the spectrum of the material when placed in the electric arc. There are as many ways of making quantitative analyses as there are instruments or methods by which measurements of some precision can be made.

So far we have discussed only the measurements which must be made in a quantitative analysis, the measurement of the sample and the final measurement on some component of the sample. These measurements are only two steps in the process, however, for usually the component to be determined must be separated from the other substances present in the sample. Indeed, the very word *analysis* means "a taking apart." Even before the sample is weighed there are certain preliminary steps which must be taken and which if improperly carried out may vitiate the entire analysis. Since usually only a portion of a material will actually be subjected to analysis, it is necessary that the small portion chosen shall truly represent the whole. It is obvious that if the procedure of selecting the material to be actually analyzed is not properly carried out the analysis will mean little.

The principal steps in a quantitative analysis are:

1. Procuring the sample.
2. Crushing, grinding, and reducing the gross sample to a quantity which can be taken to the laboratory, and further grinding and reduction in the laboratory to a particle size suitable for the analysis.
3. Drying.
4. Weighing the sample for analysis.
5. Dissolving the sample.
6. Adjustment of conditions and separation of the component being determined from other substances present which would otherwise interfere in the final measurement.

Gravimetric	*Volumetric*	*Colorimetric*
7. Precipitation	7. Titration.	7. Production of color.
8. Digestion.	8. Standardization of volumetric solution.	8. Preparation of color standards.
9. Filtration.		9. Comparison of colored solutions.
10. Washing.		
11. Drying and ignition.		
12. Weighing.		
13. Calculation.	9. Calculation.	10. Calculation.

It is apparent that a gravimetric analysis involves a greater number of operations than a volumetric or a colorimetric analysis, and it is true that volumetric and colorimetric analyses in general are more rapid than gravimetric.

The most fundamental operation of all is the determination of mass, and a separate chapter is devoted to it, Chapter 3, "The Balance and Weighing." The techniques of carrying out operations 7 through 10 in volumetric and colorimetric analyses are discussed in Chapters 7 and 13. The operations common to all the methods of analysis and the final operations of gravimetric analysis are discussed in detail in the remainder of this chapter.

SAMPLING

If the material to be analyzed is homogeneous, that is, has the same composition throughout the mass, sampling is no problem. Any portion of the mass may be taken as the sample for the analysis. If the material is inhomogeneous, however, the problem is not so simple, for a small portion taken at one point may not at all represent the composition of the whole mass. Obviously, the problem is more difficult if the particles are large and if they vary greatly in composition from piece to piece. Under such conditions the sample first taken, the so-called *gross sample*, is quite large, and this large preliminary sample is subjected to a careful process of alternate crushing and dividing until a suitable amount of material of much smaller particle size remains.

Coal is notoriously difficult to sample; the particle size is large, individual pieces may be slate wholly different from coal, and the fine material in general runs much higher in ash than the coarse material. Coal is sampled by taking a gross sample of not less than 1000 pounds, the material being collected at various points throughout the shipment and preferably when the material is being moved. The gross sample is then crushed and divided in half by alternate shoveling. One half is rejected and the other half further crushed and again cut in half. This alternate crushing and dividing is continued until a sample of only 15 pounds of material about pea size is ready for the laboratory.[1]

Large bodies of liquid materials are sampled by *thief samplers*, which consist of several bottles fastened along a pole or together in a basket and fixed so that the bottles can be unplugged at various points in the liquid.

In the storage of samples care should be exercised to minimize changes which the sample may undergo on standing. Hygroscopic materials may pick up water from the atmosphere; alkaline materials may absorb carbon dioxide; and reducing materials may be oxidized by oxygen from the air. The sample may even react with its container.

The problem of securing a true sample which will faithfully represent the entire mass is often the most difficult part of the entire analysis. In an elementary course in quantitative analysis not much can be done to give the student first-hand experience in sampling because of the nature of the problem. The samples which are given out for analysis are finely divided and completely homogeneous. Any small portion may be taken directly for analysis. The student should remember, however, that this is rather an unusual case.

Crushing, Grinding, and Reduction of Gross Sample. If the gross sample is large, as in the case of coal, the crushing machinery must be adequate in size. Coal is easy to crush, and a concrete floor

[1] As might be expected the methods of sampling and analysis of a material as important as coal have been worked out with great care. The official method is that devised by the Bureau of Mines and the American Society for Testing Materials. The successive steps in reducing the gross sample of 1000 pounds are specified in exact detail; see ASTM Standard D21-40.

Fig. 1. Jaw crusher. Rear steel plate is stationary; front plate is given a reciprocating motion by eccentric and heavy flywheel. Space at bottom of jaws can be varied. Material can be reduced to 4 mesh.

Fig. 2. Roll crusher. Material drops between heavy iron rollers rotating in opposite directions at slightly different rates. Space between rollers can be varied. Material can be crushed to about 10 mesh or somewhat finer.

and a heavy iron tamper are all that are required. For harder materials a jaw crusher, Fig. 1, or a roll crusher, Fig. 2, is used. The 4-in. jaw crusher commonly found in laboratories will reduce the particles to about pea size. Further grinding is done by hand with a mortar and pestle if the amount is small or mechanically with the disk pulverizer,

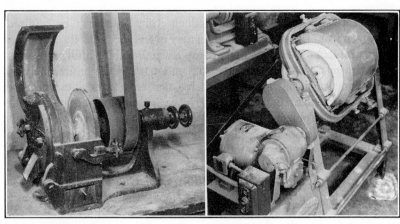

Fig. 3. Disk pulverizer. Cover plate open. Material enters opening at top left, passes between stationary (left) and rotating (right) cast-iron plates, slightly closer at bottom, and out chute at bottom right. Material can be reduced to 10 or 20 mesh.

Fig. 4. Ball mill. Material and balls are placed in porcelain crock and rotated about 45–60 r.p.m. Material may be reduced to 200 mesh or finer. Although the ball mill is excellent for grinding it does only a fair job of mixing.

Fig. 3, or ball mill, Fig. 4, if the amount is large. A ball mill is a porcelain crock which is filled one-third with material and one-third with steel or porcelain balls; the crock is rotated in a machine, and the continual pounding of the balls reduces the material to almost any degree of fineness desired. The contamination of the sample by material abraded from the balls usually is not serious.

The mortars and pestles commonly used in analytical work are made of glass, agate, or mullite, a hard silicate material, Fig. 5. Ex-

Fig. 5. Mortars. 1, mullite; 2, "diamond" mortar (actually steel); 3, glass; 4, agate.

ceptionally hard materials are crushed in a so-called diamond mortar made of steel. Only small amounts of material can be crushed. The steel pestle is struck with a hammer and rotated between blows.

Hand grinding is, of course, tedious, and machines have been devised to take over this chore (Fig. 6).

Fibrous materials, such as hay and other vegetable products, are reduced in size by the Wiley mill, Fig. 7, which has a number of rotating knives that chop the material into fine bits so that it may pass through the surrounding screen. Small laboratory hammer mills are available for grinding hard materials; in these machines a number of hammers are rotated at high speed and the material when sufficiently reduced in size passes through screens.

After each crushing operation the amount of material is reduced to avoid the labor of grinding the entire mass to the final fineness. The reduction in size can be made with a divided chute device called a riffle, Fig. 8, or by cone and quartering. In the latter method, the

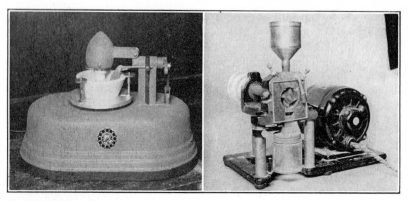

Fig. 6. Automatic mortar and pestle. Mortar and pestle are of mullite, a hard silicate material.   Fig. 7. Wiley mill, small size. Knives rotating at high speed chop up fibrous material which passes out screen at bottom.

material is piled into a cone by adding the material at the apex so that it slides uniformly in all directions. The cone is then flattened and divided into quarters. Diagonally opposite quarters are rejected, and the remaining quarters are taken for further crushing or for analysis.

Fig. 8.   Riffle.   Fig. 9.   Sieves.

Sieves (Fig. 9) are used to determine the size or range of sizes of finely divided materials. Sets of sieves [1] of various size openings are

[1] Sieves are usually made of brass wire. Sizes of wire and opening are specified by the American Society for Testing Materials; see ASTM Specification E11.

available in the following number of mesh per inch: 3½, 4, 5, 6, 7, 8, 10, 12, 14, 16, 18, 20, 25, 30, 40, 45, 50, 60, 70, 80, 100, 120, 140, 170, 200, 230, 270, 325, and 400. The entire mass of sample is seldom screened, as the segregation which may occur in the process is undesirable. Rather, a portion of the material is tested to determine the relative amounts which pass or are retained on various screens.

DRYING THE SAMPLE

Powders, which are finely divided and have a large surface area, adsorb moisture from the atmosphere. Such moisture must be removed from the material before it is analyzed so that the correct weight will be obtained for the sample taken for analysis. Adsorbed moisture is expelled from most powdered materials by heating the material in an oven at 110°, a period of at least 2 hours usually being required.

Strictly, the information desired about the material to be analyzed determines whether or not the material is to be dried before the analysis. Frequently the information desired indicates that the sample should be analyzed just as received. The water content of many materials, coal and soil among others, varies greatly, depending on the exposure to rain or to an atmosphere of low humidity. The water content of coal may run as high as 30 per cent, and an actual determination of the moisture content, conveniently combined with the drying operation, may be the most important part of the analysis. An analysis of coal as received will tell the buyer whether he is paying for coal or water; it might be a poor basis, however, for the comparison of one coal with another. Actually, the official methods for the analysis of coal call for a preliminary air drying of the entire sample received by the laboratory, and the loss in weight during this air-drying operation is measured. The air-drying operation consists in exposing the sample to the air of the laboratory at somewhat above room temperature and allowing the superficial water to evaporate until the sample is in equilibrium with the air of the laboratory and no further change in weight occurs. The analysis is then carried out on the *air-dried* material. The loss in weight on air drying being known, the results of the analyses made on the air-dried material can be calculated to the *as-received* basis.

Ores, minerals, and non-hygroscopic materials are usually analyzed without drying in most commercial work; they are dried at 110° to remove the last traces of adsorbed moisture in very careful work where the extra time required may be justified. Metal shavings and large crystals of non-hygroscopic materials need not be dried. Chemicals containing water of crystallization usually cannot be dried without expelling their crystal water. Obviously, materials which contain other volatile components may not be heated for drying. Certain materials may also undergo oxidation when warmed in contact with air, and their composition may thus be changed. It is apparent that the analyst must give some thought to such matters before beginning work.

After the sample is dried in the oven, it is stored in a desiccator, Figs. 10 and 11, charged with a drying agent such as anhydrous calcium

Fig. 10.   Desiccator.   Soft glass, older design.

chloride, anhydrous magnesium perchlorate, or anhydrous calcium sulfate.

The desiccator is primarily a convenient way to store the sample and carry it about the laboratory. When a desiccator is opened a portion of the air in it is exchanged with the moist air of the laboratory, and the time which elapses before the water vapor introduced is removed from the air in the desiccator depends on the efficiency of the drying agent and the ease with which the air can come into contact with the drying agent.

The drying agents commonly used are listed in Table 1. Calcium chloride, the most usual desiccant because of its very low cost, absorbs moisture very rapidly when fresh but does not remove the water as completely as some of the desiccants above it in the list. Thus, although it is fine for removing most of the water introduced by the fresh air entering a desiccator when opened, it is unsatisfactory when strong drying agents are to be placed in the desiccator; anhydrous barium chloride, for example, takes water away from partially hydrated calcium chloride in a matter of only an hour when they are together in a desiccator. In such a case there is no alternative but to charge the desiccator with a better desiccant, preferably anhydrous magnesium perchlorate.

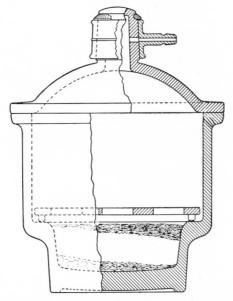

Fig. 11.   Desiccator.   Pyrex glass, newer design.

The shape of the desiccator has a good deal to do with the speed with which the water vapor is removed. The path the water molecules must travel to strike the desiccant should be as short and direct as possible. The newer desiccators, Fig. 11, are better than the older type in this respect. A variety of desiccators is shown in Fig. 12. Experiments have shown that even with the older-style desiccators 90 per cent of the water vapor is removed within 3 minutes and removal is essentially complete in 7 to 15 minutes, provided the desiccant is a satisfactory one, that is, anhydrous magnesium perchlorate, fresh barium oxide, or fresh anhydrous calcium chloride.

Metal desiccators, made of aluminum, are becoming increasingly popular. They are lighter than the glass desiccators, which are always of heavy construction, and their greater heat conduction reduces the

TABLE 1. COMMON DRYING AGENTS

Material	Chemical Composition		Trade Name	Capacity	Porosity	Residual Water (mg./l. of air)	Properties
	Anhydrous	Hydrated					
Phosphorus pentoxide	P_2O_5	HPO_3		Very low	Poor	0.0001	Rapidly becomes coated with a glaze of metaphosphoric acid.
Magnesium perchlorate, anhydrous	$Mg(ClO_4)_2$	$Mg(ClO_4)_2 \cdot 6H_2O$	Dehydrite Anhydrone	Very high	Very high	0.0001	Rapid; exceptionally high capacity; absorbs water, ammonia, ethyl alcohol, and certain unsaturated hydrocarbons.
Barium oxide	BaO	$BaO \cdot 10H_2O$		Moderate	Low	0.0001	Cheap; rapid when fresh; corrosive.
Potassium hydroxide	KOH	$KOH \cdot xH_2O$		Moderate	Poor	0.002	Cheap; liquefies.
Potassium hydroxide on fluffed mica	KOH	$KOH \cdot xH_2O$	Mikohbite	High	Very high		Cheap; does not liquefy.
Calcium sulfate	$CaSO_4 \cdot \frac{1}{2}H_2O$	$CaSO_4 \cdot 2H_2O$	Drierite	Moderate	High		Cheap; insoluble in organic solvents.
Silica, activated	SiO_2	$SiO_2 \cdot xH_2O$	Silica gel	Low	Very high	0.004	Cheap.
Aluminum oxide	Al_2O_3	$Al_2O_3 \cdot xH_2O$		Low	Very high	0.003	
Calcium chloride	$CaCl_2 \cdot 2H_2O$	$CaCl_2 \cdot 6H_2O$		High	Very high		Cheap; rapid when fresh.
Sodium hydroxide plus calcium oxide	$CaO + NaOH$	$Ca(OH)_2 + NaOH \cdot xH_2O$	Soda-lime	High	High	0.2	Cheap.
Copper sulfate	$CuSO_4$	$CuSO_4 \cdot 5H_2O$		High	Low	1.40	Changes color, gray to blue.

time needed to cool a hot object to the temperature of a balance. A small aluminum desiccator (Fig. 12, number 6) which can be carried in one hand and has provision for the storage of four crucibles has been aptly called by the manufacturer a Desicooler.

When it is desirable or necessary to dry a material at room temperature, the process can be greatly speeded by evacuating the desiccator.

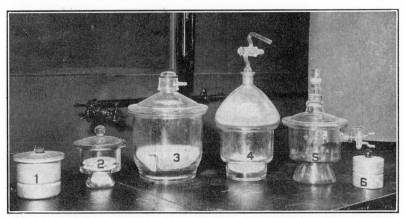

Fig. 12. Various types of desiccators. 1, Aluminum; 2, soft glass, small size, old form; 3, pyrex, vacuum; 4, pyrex, can be evacuated, drying agent above and below; 5, vacuum desiccator designed for filtration; 6, aluminum.

The larger, soft-glass desiccators of conventional design and perforated for the insertion of a vacuum line occasionally collapse when evacuated and are therefore hazardous. The newer Pyrex desiccators are structurally better designed, and even the larger models may be safely evacuated. The path traveled by the gas molecules from object to desiccant is shortened in these models, and the great increase at lower pressures of the mean free path of the gas molecules, that is, the average distance the molecules travel between collisions, greatly accelerates the drying. A larger surface of the desiccant is exposed in the newer desiccators, and this also speeds up the process.

Procedure for Drying the Sample. Determine if the analysis is to be made on the as-received basis, air-dried basis, or oven-dried basis (110°, moisture free). Decide also if the sample will stand drying at 110° without undergoing decomposition, oxidation, or the release of some volatile component.

If the sample is to be dried at 110°, place it in a weighing bottle and place the weighing bottle uncovered in a beaker. Cover the beaker with a cover glass, using three glass hooks to raise the cover glass off the beaker slightly; this will allow the escape of steam. Place the beaker in the drying oven and leave it at least 2 hours or preferably overnight. Then remove the beaker from the drying oven and transfer the weighing bottle and sample to a desiccator suitably charged with anhydrous calcium chloride, anhydrous calcium sulfate, or anhydrous magnesium perchlorate.

WEIGHING THE SAMPLE

Samples of hygroscopic materials are best weighed by difference. The bottle and material are first weighed, the sample for analysis is removed with a spatula, and the bottle again weighed. The loss in weight of the bottle and material is the weight of the sample taken. This is the best procedure for hygroscopic and finely divided materials which gain weight on contact with moist air, for the material is exposed only briefly when the sample is actually removed. The weight of the sample taken will be only approximately the size desired, but its weight will be known exactly.

Metal turnings, non-hygroscopic materials, and even finely divided ores at times of low humidity, may be poured directly on a balanced cover glass or metal weighing scoop for weighing. Since only one weighing is involved this is a more rapid procedure than weighing by difference. It has the additional merit that the weight of material taken can be easily made quite close to the weight desired for the sample.

How accurately the sample must be weighed depends on the accuracy desired in the analysis and on the size of the sample. Most analytical work has an inherent accuracy of about 1 part in 1000. If a sample of about 1 g. is taken, it is apparent that the sample need be weighed to only 1 mg., that is, 1 in the third decimal place, to equal the accuracy of the chemical part of the analysis. In practice, the weighing would be made to within 1 or 2 in the next decimal place, for if the sample is weighed by difference there are two uncertainties in its weight and the errors in the two weighings may not cancel; by carrying out the weighing to the fourth decimal place, the error in the weighing will be definitely smaller than other errors in the analysis. Many analyses of importance commercially are carried out with a much lower accuracy, particularly where the component determined is only a small part of the material being analyzed. For example, the carbon content of steel is usually 1 per cent or less, and the results are seldom required to better than 0.01 per cent carbon. This is a relative error of only 1 part in 100, and in weighing a 1-g. sample for such an analysis it would be a waste of time to weigh more accurately than to 5 or 10 mg.

Procedure for Weighing a Sample by Difference. Remove the stopper from the weighing bottle containing the dried material momentarily to insure that the air inside is at atmospheric pressure. Place the bottle on the left pan of the balance and weigh it as accurately as is required for the analysis, usually to 0.1 mg. Pick up the weighing bottle, using a strip of paper or chamois finger coverings to protect it from fingerprints. Hold the bottle over the beaker in which the sample is to be placed, remove the stopper, and shake it briefly so that any particles on it will fall into the beaker. With a clean spatula transfer to the beaker a quantity of the material estimated to be about the weight desired for the sample. Leaving the spatula in the beaker, replace the stopper, and return the bottle to the balance. Using a small brush, sweep any particles clinging to the spatula into the beaker. Remove the spatula from the beaker and cover the beaker with a cover glass. Weigh the bottle. The weight of sample taken is the difference between the two weights. The second weight is used in weighing the second sample, so that three weighings are required for two samples.

DISSOLVING THE SAMPLE

Many salts, the strong acids and bases, and many weak acids and bases are soluble in water and present no problem in securing a solution in which the operations involved in a chemical analysis can be carried out. Metallic materials, minerals, and many commercial products require treatment with acids or sometimes fusions with acid or basic fluxes.

Oxide ores will usually dissolve in hydrochloric acid. Some oxides, aluminum oxide which has been ignited at a high temperature, for example, must first be fused with sodium carbonate, after which the melt may be dissolved in hydrochloric acid. The fusion with sodium carbonate is carried out in a platinum crucible.

Silicates such as glass and rock also require fusion with sodium carbonate. The fusion converts the silicate and any silica present to sodium, calcium, aluminum, and other metal silicates which then dissolve readily in hydrochloric acid.

Metals below hydrogen in the electromotive series can only be dissolved in an oxidizing acid such as nitric acid or a mixture of nitric acid and hydrochloric acid. Metals above hydrogen in the electromotive series will dissolve in non-oxidizing acids such as sulfuric acid, hydrochloric acid, and dilute perchloric acid. There are certain exceptions to this rule, for sometimes the action is so slow as to be impracticable; an insoluble coating is formed which stops the action; or the metal surface is rendered impassive by some little understood electrolytic phenomenon. The action of sulfuric acid on metallic zinc, for example, is extremely slow, and the action of sulfuric acid on metallic lead is quickly stopped because of the formation of a film of insoluble

TABLE 2. ELECTROMOTIVE SERIES

(Standard Reduction Potentials)

Metal	E^0 (volts [a])	Metal	E^0 (volts [a])
Au	+1.4	Co	−0.277
Pt	+1.2	Cd	−0.402
Ag	+0.7995	Fe	−0.440
Hg	+0.7986	Cr	−0.71
Cu	+0.3448	Zn	−0.762
Bi	+0.32	Mn	−1.05
Sb	+0.212	Al	−1.67
H	0.0000	Mg	−2.34
Pb	−0.126	Na	−2.712
Sn	−0.136	Ca	−2.87
Ni	−0.250	K	−2.922

[a] A more detailed electromotive series and an explanation of the meaning of E^0 is found in Chapter 10 dealing with oxidation-reduction theory, page 236.

lead sulfate. Perchloric acid, on the contrary, easily dissolves metallic lead because the lead perchlorate formed is very soluble.

Certain metals, notably aluminum and zinc, can be dissolved in sodium hydroxide.

Stainless steel is rapidly dissolved by treatment with hot, 72 per cent perchloric acid.

A few general rules should be observed in taking materials into solution for analysis. Some materials may be volatilized during the process. Carbon dioxide and hydrogen sulfide will be lost on dissolving a carbonate or sulfide in acid, arsenic may be lost as volatile arsenic trichloride from hydrochloric acid solutions, and mercury salts are volatilized from hot acid solutions. In general, only the minimum amount of the solvent needed to effect the solution should be used; this will reduce the amount of foreign materials present in the solution during the analysis and improve the purity of precipitates formed during the analysis. When possible volatile acids should be used as solvents; the excess acid can then be removed by evaporation. Hydrochloric acid and nitric acid can be easily removed by evaporation. Perchloric acid can also be boiled away (boiling point 204° for the constant-boiling 72 per cent acid), but its condensation on wood flues produces a hazard. Sulfuric acid and phosphoric acid are not readily volatilized and can be added when it is necessary to insure the complete expulsion of some more volatile acid.

PRELIMINARY OPERATIONS

By preliminary operations are meant those chemical reactions and adjustments in conditions which must be made before a precipitation can be made or a titration carried out. Quite commonly some change in the acidity of the solution must be made; for example, in the precipitation of barium sulfate some acid must be present in the solution to prevent the precipitation of barium carbonate; but too much acid cannot be tolerated as it increases the solubility of the barium sulfate beyond the permissible point. Often the valence state of an element must be changed. In the gravimetric determination of iron by precipitation as ferric hydroxide, iron present in the ferrous state partially escapes precipitation; a few minutes' boiling with a little nitric acid rapidly oxidizes the ferrous iron to the ferric state.

Often it is necessary to remove one element from the solution before another can be determined. Calcium must be precipitated as calcium oxalate and removed before magnesium can be determined, for example. Such separations are really part of the preliminary operations, but they are so important that they frequently consume a major part of the time required for the analysis, and are so intimately connected with the chemistry of the analysis that they will not be discussed in detail at this point. Rather, in each of the individual chemical analyses studied, the preliminary separations necessary are dealt with in detail, and Chapter 14 is devoted to the general methods and principles of separating one chemical from another.

PRECIPITATION AND DIGESTION

The precipitates chosen for quantitative analysis must, of course, be sufficiently insoluble so that all the material being determined is removed from the solution. In general, since weighings are made to 0.1 mg., the precipitate should be sufficiently insoluble so that less than this quantity of material will be left in solution.

There are certain ways in which the solubility of compounds can be reduced. An excess of the precipitating agent generally reduces the solubility. This is the so-called *common-ion effect*, which is discussed in detail in Chapter 5 dealing with the solubility-product principle. A great excess of the precipitating agent often causes an increase in the solubility of a material so that the common-ion effect cannot be pushed too far, usually not beyond about 0.2 M in the common ion. The solubility can also be reduced by lowering the temperature, for in general the solubility increases with temperature. It is sometimes permissible to reduce solubility by the addition of a miscible solvent such as alcohol; the solubility of other materials present in the solution is also reduced by this process, however, and precipitation of these may be undesirable.

The solubility of salts is usually increased by the presence of foreign electrolytes, a phenomenon known as the *diverse-ion effect*. For this reason the amounts of reagents used and of foreign materials introduced into the solution during the course of an analysis should be kept at a minimum.

The precipitation of an insoluble compound should usually be made rather slowly and from a hot solution if permissible. Material precipitates more slowly this way, and the crystals are usually larger and purer.

When first formed the particles of a precipitate are frequently so small that they will pass through filter paper. When left in contact with the solution for some time, especially when the solution is hot, the particles of a precipitate become larger, settle rapidly when stirred, and can be filtered readily. The process of facilitating crystal growth by keeping precipitate and solution hot together for a period is known as *digestion*. It has been demonstrated that the solubility of fine crystals is greater than that of larger crystals of the same material. As a result of this the fine crystals dissolve and the large crystals grow larger. Usually a digestion of 1 to 2 hours will render a crystalline precipitate easily filterable. However, digestion is of little benefit with non-crystalline materials, ferric hydroxide, for example, and heating the solution beyond the few minutes required to cause the precipitate to coagulate is of no value.

FILTRATION

In quantitative work, precipitates may be filtered using either ashless filter paper or porous-bottom filtering crucibles. The choice between the two is dictated principally by the ease of reduction of the precipitate to be filtered. Fairly strong reducing conditions prevail when filter paper is burned away. At high temperatures, carbon and organic matter from the filter paper and carbon monoxide are capable of reducing many materials. Silver chloride, for example, is readily reduced to metallic silver. The effect of such reduction on the results of a quantitative analysis is obvious. In such cases porous-bottom filtering crucibles must be used.

Solutions should be filtered while hot if the solubility of the precipitate is low enough to permit this; the viscosity of a liquid is much less when the liquid is hot, and consequently the filtration proceeds more rapidly.

Filter Paper and Its Use. The filter paper used for quantitative work must burn away without leaving a weighable residue of ash.

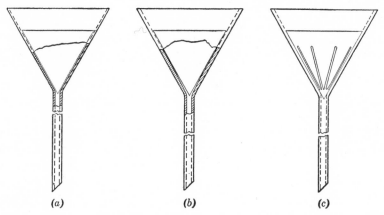

(a)   (b)   (c)

Fig. 13. Funnels. *a*, Ordinary 60° funnel; *b*, "58" funnel of Kimball Glass Co.; *c*, fluted 60° funnel of Corning Glass Co.

Ashless filter paper is available for this purpose. It is paper that has been treated with hydrofluoric acid, which removes any silica present by the formation of fluosilicic acid, H_2SiF_6. Such ashless filter paper is available in several grades of fineness.[1] Coarse or loose papers are used for gelatinous and flocculent precipitates such as ferric hydroxide and aluminum hydroxide. A medium grade is satisfactory for most precipitates. A hard or tightly pressed paper is used for very finely divided precipitates, silica, for example.

The disk of filter paper is first folded in half and then folded in half again. The paper is opened into the form of a cone. The angle at the apex of the cone is exactly 60°, so that the paper cone will exactly fit a glass funnel having a 60° angle. Carefully made glass funnels are cast on a mold and have an angle of exactly 60°; the upper edge of such high-quality funnels is usually ground flat in contrast to the simple fire polishing used to finish cheaper funnels. The glass com-

---

[1] Whatman filter papers bearing a black label have been treated with hydrofluoric acid. Whatman No. 41 is a coarse paper, No. 40 a medium, and No. 42 a hard or fine paper.

panies have introduced specially designed funnels which filter more rapidly than the conventional 60° funnel (see Fig. 13).

Gelatinous precipitates such as ferric hydroxide and aluminum hydroxide are difficult to filter because they clog the pores of the filter paper. The addition of filter-paper pulp to the solution before such substances are precipitated greatly improves the rate of filtration and the effectiveness of the washing. The precipitate as it is formed

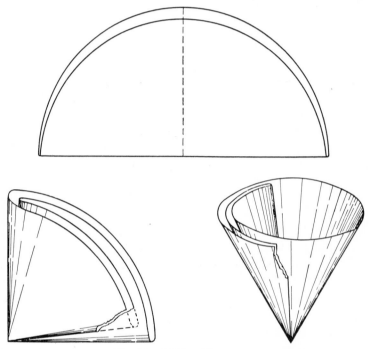

Fig. 14.   Folding filter paper.

becomes attached to the fibers of the paper pulp, and the precipitate is kept from coagulating into a curdy, impervious mass. The wash water penetrates the mass more easily, and the subsequent ignition is easier for, although there is more paper to burn away, the porous character of the remaining mass brings it into contact with air more rapidly because of the increased rate of diffusion.

Ashless filter pulp can be purchased in the form of tablets weighing about 1 g. A portion of such a tablet disintegrates rapidly when shaken with water and is then ready for addition to the solution. Ordinary filter paper can be used, but it is more difficult to disburse. A sheet of 11-cm. paper weighs about 1 g. and is about equivalent to one tablet.

The sheet may be disintegrated by boiling it with distilled water or by poking it about in a test tube with 1 or 2 ml. of concentrated nitric acid with a stirring rod. If a large amount of filter-paper pulp is needed a pad of filter-paper disks can be disintegrated rapidly in water in a Waring blender.

Procedure for Filtering with Paper. Fold the disk of paper in half and then in quarters, creasing it lightly (Fig. 14). Tear off the corner of the outside fold at the top to break up the easy channel for air down

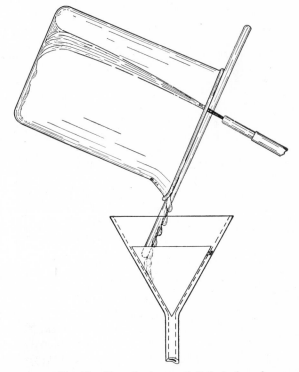

Fig. 15. Transferring precipitate to funnel.

the fold next to the funnel. Open the paper into a cone and fit it into the funnel. Pour distilled water from a wash bottle into the paper and with the finger smooth the paper down to the glass and press down the loose fold. The paper should fit the glass snugly all around with no air bubbles between the glass and paper. The stem of the funnel should fill with water and remain full even after the water has drained from the paper.

Place the receiving beaker below the funnel with the stem touching the side of the beaker; water will then run from the funnel into the beaker without splashing; this is important if the filtrate is to be used subsequently.

Pour the solution from a beaker into the funnel, holding a stirring rod against the beaker so that the liquid runs down the rod and enters the funnel without splashing. Pour as much of the liquid as possible

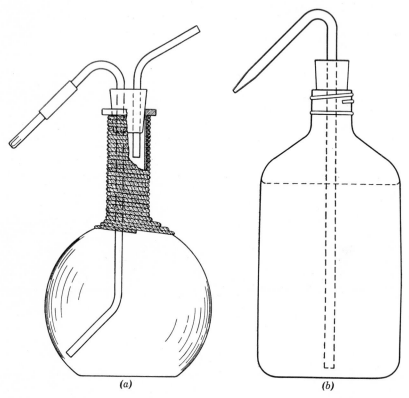

(a)   *(b)*

Fig. 16. Wash bottles. *a*, Conventional type, using glass flask; *b*, collapsible polyethylene bottle.

into the funnel without stirring up the precipitate. Filtration will be faster if little or no precipitate is on the paper, and washing is more effective if the wash water can be added to the precipitate in the beaker and the precipitate and wash water vigorously stirred together. After washing by decantation this way two or three times, transfer the precipitate to the funnel. Hold the beaker in the left hand with the stirring rod across the beaker and extending into the funnel, Fig. 15.

Direct a stream of wash water from the wash bottle to the bottom of the beaker in such a manner as to wash the precipitate down the beaker and rod into the funnel. This is the critical part of the process, and care should be exercised that every bit of precipitate finds its way into the funnel and not onto the funnel support or the table top. Using a rubber-tipped stirring rod (policeman) rub loose the film of precipitate adhering to the beaker and stirring rod. Wash this precipitate into the funnel. It may be well at this stage to wipe the outside of the beaker clean with a moist rag so that inspection of the beaker for remaining particles of the precipitate may be thorough. Finally, wash the precipitate with small portions of the wash solution, allowing the water to drain completely from the funnel before adding the next portion.

Porous-Bottom Filtering Crucibles. *Filtration with Suction.* A precipitate that is easily reduced must be filtered and ignited on a

Fig. 17. Porous-bottom filtering crucibles. Available in quartz, glass, platinum, and porcelain.

porous-bottom filtering crucible so that when ignited it does not come in contact with hot carbon or carbon monoxide. Filtering crucibles are made of glass with fritted glass bottoms, of quartz with sintered quartz bottoms, and of glazed porcelain with porous porcelain bottoms [1] (Fig. 17). The glass and porcelain crucibles are much less expensive

[1] The earliest form of filtering crucible, the Gooch crucible, was simply a glazed porcelain crucible having a bottom perforated by numerous small holes. A mat of asbestos fibers placed in the bottom of the crucible served as the filtering medium. It is virtually impossible to pour liquid through such an asbestos mat without losing an appreciable amount of the fine asbestos fibers. Most specimens of asbestos change on ignition and are somewhat soluble in acids. The Gooch crucible is no longer used very much. A later filtering crucible, the Monroe crucible, consisted of a platinum crucible having a perforated bottom; a spongy mass of platinum was used as the filtration medium, its porosity being regulated by the amount of burnishing given the mass The Monroe crucible, although free of some of the objectionable features of the Gooch crucible, is little used.

than the quartz crucibles and are available in various pore sizes,
Table 3.

TABLE 3. POROSITY OF GLASS FILTERING CRUCIBLES

| Designation | | | Pore Diameter | | |
Corning Pyrex	Jena	Porosity	Range (microns)	Mean (microns)	Principal Uses
EC	G1	Extra coarse	100–200	160	Very coarse precipitates; support for filter pulp; gas dispersion.
C	G2	Coarse	40–50	40	Coarse precipitates; clarification of viscous liquids and mercury; gas dispersion.
M	G3	Medium	20–30	20	Crystalline precipitates in general; gas dispersion; extraction thimbles.
F	G4	Fine	5–10	5	Finely crystalline precipitates, barium sulfate, silver chloride.
UF	G5	Ultrafine	1.5–2	1.2	Clarification of biological solutions.

Glass filtering crucibles may be used for precipitates which need not
later be heated above 450° or 500°. Porcelain filtering crucibles will
withstand bright red heat and are suitable for filtering such precipitates
as magnesium ammonium phosphate which must be heated to the full
heat of the Meker burner (900°) for conversion to magnesium pyrophosphate, the substance actually weighed. Quartz crucibles with
fritted quartz bottoms may be heated to 1100–1200°.

The suction required for using filtering crucibles is most easily
obtained with a water aspirator. The apparatus required for filtration
with a filtering crucible is shown in Fig. 18. The empty bottle is placed
between the aspirator and the filtering flask as a trap in case the water
flows backward into the suction line because of a decrease in the
water pressure. Another apparatus for filtration with suction is the
modified desiccator shown in Fig. 19; this assembly is particularly
convenient when the filtrate is to be used for further work.

Before a filtering crucible is used to filter a precipitate, it should be
cleaned and dried or ignited in the same manner in which it and the
precipitate are to be treated later. The ignition of crucibles and precipitates is discussed in detail in the next section; briefly, however, a

filtering crucible should be placed inside another, ordinary crucible during ignition over a burner to keep the gases of the flame away from the porous bottom.

The cleaning of porous-bottom filtering crucibles often presents something of a problem. In general the methods discussed earlier in

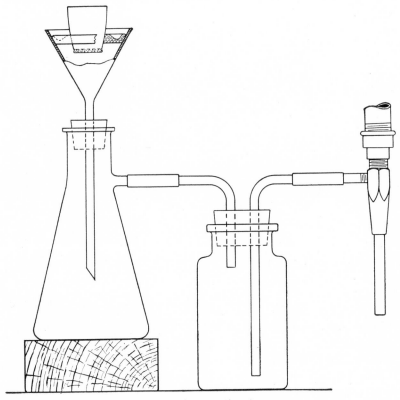

Fig. 18. Suction filtration.

connection with the dissolution of the samples for analysis can be effectively employed, always keeping in mind that the crucibles themselves are silicates and are attacked by hydrofluoric acid and strong alkalies. Silicious residues may be removed by actual treatment with dilute hydrofluoric acid, working on the basis that the time of contact will be short and the precipitate more rapidly dissolved because of its finer size. Barium sulfate precipitates may be dissolved in boiling, concentrated sulfuric acid which converts the barium sulfate to barium acid sulfate. Barium sulfate may also be dissolved out of a crucible by a solution of sodium ethylenediaminetetracetic acid (Versene). Organic materials can be burned away with hot nitric acid; silver chloride can be dissolved in ammonia, and so on through the great bag of tricks available to the ingenious chemist. Cleaning solution, however, is a poor thing to put in a porous-bottom filtering crucible; once chromic oxide is formed in the pores it is practically impossible to remove.

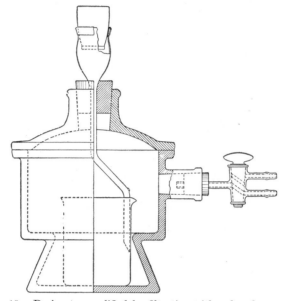

Fig. 19.   Desiccator modified for filtration with reduced pressure.

One minor disadvantage of porous-bottom filtering crucibles is their slightly hygroscopic character. The large surface area of the finely divided porous plate causes the adsorption of moisture. That this is significant in humid weather can be readily detected by a gradual increase in weight during the weighing of a crucible taken from a desiccator out into a humid atmosphere. This source of error can be avoided by weighing the crucible inside a ground-glass-stoppered weighing bottle. This is only necessary in very refined work.

WASHING PRECIPITATES.   WASH SOLUTIONS

If a precipitate is to be weighed, obviously all the foreign material present in the solution from which it has been precipitated must be washed away. Occasionally water alone may be used as the wash solution, but usually some material is dissolved in the wash water to reduce the solubility of the precipitate or to prevent it from becoming colloidal. The material added to the wash water must itself leave no weighable residue, that is, it must be volatile at the temperature at which the precipitate is later dried or ignited. In practice, this limits the materials which may be added to wash solutions to ammonium hydroxide, ammonium salts, hydrochloric acid, and nitric acid.

To minimize loss of precipitate by solution in the wash water advantage is taken of the common-ion effect or the addition of a miscible liquid such as alcohol. Because the common ion must be derived from an ammonium salt, the technique of using the common-ion effect is limited to the determination of cations and then only to those salts where the anion used forms a volatile salt with ammonium ion. For example, silver may be determined by precipitation as silver chloride and the silver chloride washed with a solution of ammonium chloride; but, in the determination of lead by precipitation of lead molybdate, lead molybdate cannot be washed with ammonium molybdate because the ammonium molybdate leaves a residue on ignition.

The addition of alcohol to the wash water also has its limitations. Besides reducing the solubility of the precipitate it may also throw out of solution other salts present. Occasionally when quick drying is necessary a final wash with alcohol or acetone is made.

Some precipitates, particularly the insoluble hydrated oxides (hydroxides) like ferric hydroxide, become colloidal and pass through the filter. This is known as *peptization*. This phenomenon occurs toward the end of the washing when the last of the electrolyte is being removed. It can be prevented by having an electrolyte in the wash water. Ammonium hydroxide and ammonium chloride or nitrate are the electrolytes commonly used, hydroxide for washing insoluble metal hydroxides and chloride or nitrate for washing insoluble salts.

Normally, water is slightly acid owing to the presence of dissolved carbon dioxide. When water is used as wash liquid this acidity causes some precipitates to dissolve; for example, magnesium ammonium phosphate is precipitated from a neutral or slightly basic solution and in even weakly acid solutions dissolves according to the reaction $MgNH_4PO_4 + H_2O = MgHPO_4 + NH_4OH$. The addition of a little ammonium hydroxide to the wash water drives this reaction to the left and effectively prevents the dissolution of the magnesium ammonium phosphate.

The mechanics of washing deserve special attention. It is best to remove as much of the liquid as possible before adding the next portion of the wash water. The effectiveness of a washing increases directly with the volume of the wash water used, but increases with the power of the number of washings made. Thus, four washings with 2.5-ml. portions are a great deal more effective than a single washing with a 10-ml. portion. Crystalline precipitates can usually be washed effectively on the filter. Gelatinous materials such as ferric hydroxide, however, become compact on the filter, and the wash water passes through channels in the mass and does not come in contact with the main body of the precipitate; in these cases as much of the washing as possible should be done in the beaker, stirring up the precipitate vigorously with the wash solution, allowing the precipitate to settle, and decanting off the liquid.

The tip of the wash bottle, Fig. 16, should have only a small opening, so that only a fine stream of water will issue from it. The tip should be fire-polished so that no particles of glass will break away from it and fall into the funnel. When washing a precipitate on a filter paper, direct the fine stream of water at the top of the filter paper and simultaneously rotate the funnel through a turn and a half so that the part of the paper three layers thick is covered twice. Allow the liquid to drain away completely before repeating the washing. By keeping the total volume of wash water low, the loss of precipitate by solubility will be lower, the amount of filtrate which may later have to be evaporated away is less, and the time taken for the washing is reduced.

If a convenient qualitative test is available for some material present in the solution which must be washed out, the liquid coming through the filter can be so tested and the washing discontinued when the test fails.

DRYING AND IGNITING PRECIPITATES

If a precipitate is to be weighed and the results of an analysis calculated from the weight, it is obvious that the precipitate must be dry and that it must be of definite composition. Not much can be done at this stage about the purity of the precipitate, although sometimes, notably with silica, stannic oxide, and tungstic oxide, the amount of impurity is later determined and subtracted from the weight of the precipitate to obtain the true weight of the precipitate.

Removing water from crystalline material is often something of a problem. The water may not be merely on the surface (adsorbed) but may be trapped inside the crystal. Certain crystals, in growing, form cavities which close over, trapping the mother liquor within the crystal. This is called *occlusion*. Occluded water is not removed by drying at 110°. If the crystal is heated to a high enough temperature the steam pressure generated bursts the crystal and the water is driven off;

potassium perchlorate, a notorious offender with respect to occlusion, bursts at a temperature about 310°; at this temperature the crystal is so violently shattered that particles of the salt are thrown out of the crucible if the crucible is not large enough. Non-volatile impurities in the solution which are occluded in the precipitate remain behind when the precipitate is ignited and increase the weight of the precipitate. For this reason precipitates that occlude the mother liquor seriously should be dissolved and reprecipitated under such conditions that little foreign material, preferably only volatile ammonium salts, is present in the solution.

The problem of eliminating water from materials to be weighed is so serious that in the most exacting analytical work, such as in the determination of atomic weights, it is a general rule that the only permissible methods of analysis are those in which the materials may be melted and the absence of water thus guaranteed.

At a red heat, see Table 4, the absence of water is pretty well assured and precipitates which are not decomposed or are not volatilized are

TABLE 4. APPROXIMATE TEMPERATURES [a]

Color	Approximate Temperature (°C.)	Obtained by
Barely visible red	550	Bunsen-type burner
Visible red	600	Bunsen-type burner
Cherry red	800	Meker-type burner
Bright cherry red	900	Meker-type burner, with surrounding chimney
Bright red	1000	Electric muffle, ordinary resistance wire
Bright orange	1100	Electric muffle, globar elements

[a] All temperatures through this book are in degrees centigrade.

ignited [1] at such temperatures. Besides volatilizing away any water and any ammonium salts which may be present, the ignition may cause a change in the composition of the precipitate; for example, magnesium ammonium phosphate, $MgNH_4PO_4$, is converted to magnesium pyrophosphate, $Mg_2P_2O_7$, and calcium oxalate is converted to calcium carbonate (525°) or to calcium oxide (800°). A change in the crystal form of the precipitate may also occur; for example, aluminum oxide

[1] The word ignite, from the Latin *ignare*, strictly means to set fire to. In chemical work it has the meaning to heat to a high temperature.

is converted from the γ form to the α form which is non-hygroscopic and a better form for weighing.

One of the most serious problems in igniting precipitates prior to weighing is the prevention of any reduction of the precipitate by carbon of the filter paper or carbon monoxide from the burner flame. The ease of reduction varies enormously. Elements at the negative end of the electromotive series, Table 2, are reduced with difficulty, and

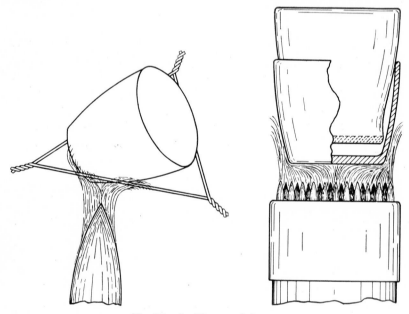

Fig. 20.   Igniting precipitates.

the ignition of their oxides presents no problem; aluminum oxide, calcium oxide, and magnesium oxide are examples of such very stable oxides. At the other extreme are materials with which great care must be exercised: silver salts which are very easily reduced and mercury compounds which can be hardly heated at all. Even with an element at the negative end of the electromotive series it should be remembered that the anion with which it is associated may be susceptible to reduction; barium sulfate, for example, is reduced to barium sulfide fairly readily.

Easily reduced materials should not be filtered on paper but on porous-bottom filtering crucibles. Preferably, such precipitates should be ignited in an electric muffle and the absence of any reducing gases thus insured. When a burner must be used the crucible should be inclined, Fig. 20, and the flame kept toward the back so that air may.

diffuse into the crucible. Porous-bottom filtering crucibles must be placed inside another ordinary crucible to protect the bottoms from reducing gases.

Although most precipitates are ignited in porcelain crucibles, platinum and quartz crucibles are also frequently used. Platinum has little mechanical strength when heated to a red heat and must be handled carefully; in addition it is pervious to hydrogen and carbon monoxide; these gases pass through it readily and thus can cause reduction of material in the crucible. Certain metals formed on reduction, notably iron, tin, copper, and silver, alloy with platinum and thus ruin platinum crucibles. It is best never to ignite in platinumware any material which is easily reduced, but if it must be done an electric muffle should be used.

Crucibles of the size used in ordinary analytical work can be heated to about 800° with Meker-type burners operating on natural gas. Some elevation of this temperature can be secured by enclosing the crucible in a chimney of firebrick or more simply a cylinder of asbestos paper.

The crucible to be used for the ignition of a precipitate should be given a heat treatment identical with the ignition to be carried out with the precipitate later. Usually this ignition need not take so long, its principal objective being to burn away fingerprints and drive off any water on the surface of the crucible. Any markings to identify the crucible should be put on before this ignition.

Procedure for Igniting Precipitates. Mark the crucible so that it may be easily identified later. The top may be scratched with a file or the sides marked with iron or cobalt salts which leave stains when ignited.[1] Clean and dry the crucible and heat it to the full heat of a Meker burner for 5 or 10 minutes. Treat the cover similarly if it is to be weighed. When the crucible has cooled almost to the point where it can be touched by hand safely, transfer it to a desiccator for final cooling. After the crucible has cooled to room temperature, weigh it. Transfer the filter paper and precipitate to the crucible carefully, lifting the paper at the point where it is three layers thick. Wipe out the funnel with a small piece of wet filter paper. If time is available place the crucible and paper in the drying oven at 110° for 1 hour to drive off most of the water. Otherwise heat the crucible with a burner

---

[1] A satisfactory marking ink for porcelainware can be made as follows: Grind together 1 g. potassium carbonate, 1 g. borax, 2 g. litharge, and 2 g. cobalt nitrate (previously dried at 100° for 1 hour). To the fine powder add 5 or 6 drops of glycerine. With continued grinding add water a few drops at a time until the suspension flows well from a pen. Write the figures desired on the porcelainware lightly and heat the vessel to a red heat for a few minutes. A blue figure fused into the vessel will appear.

slowly, being careful that the rapid generation of steam does not violently disrupt the paper and eject some of the precipitate from the crucible. Place the cover on the crucible and heat gently below a dull red heat to carbonize the filter paper. Inflammable gases will escape from the crucible, and tar and carbon will be deposited on the cover and crucible. When the paper has been charred remove the lid, incline the crucible to provide free access to air (Fig. 20), and place the flame so that it strikes only the bottom part of the crucible. The filter paper should glow like a cigarette but not break into flame, which might carry away mechanically fine particles of the precipitate. Gradually increase the flame and rotate the crucible occasionally so that the carbon and tar are burned away. Treat the cover the same way if it is to be weighed. Continue the ignition 20 or 30 minutes, then cool and transfer to a desiccator. Weigh the crucible only after it has cooled to the temperature of the balance.

When igniting porous-bottom filtering crucibles, heat them slowly for the first few minutes to drive the steam from the pores gradually. When using a burner to ignite the crucibles, place the crucible inside an ordinary porcelain crucible to prevent direct contact of the flame with the porous bottom; otherwise, in a reducing flame, carbon may be deposited in the pores and change the weight of the crucible. Even in the oxidizing part of the flame, easily reduced materials in the crucible may be reduced if this precaution is not taken.

MISCELLANEOUS NOTES ON TECHNIQUE IN THE ANALYTICAL LABORATORY

Glassware. Apparatus made of ordinary soda-lime glass (soft glass) has all but disappeared from the laboratory. Soft-glass bottles and some soft-glass volumetric flasks may remain in service, but the beakers, test tubes, and flasks in which chemical reactions are carried out are invariably made of Pyrex or other brand of boro-silicate glass having a small coefficient of expansion. Boro-silicate glassware is more resistant to chemical attack than soft glass and will stand considerable abuse from mechanical and thermal shock.

A new line of glassware, called Vycor, has been introduced by the Corning Glass Works of Corning, N. Y. Vycor is almost pure silica and will stand essentially the same treatment that quartz will stand. Transparent crucibles of Vycor may be ignited at the full heat of the Meker burner. A Vycor flask containing boiling, concentrated sulfuric acid, temperature 250°, can be plunged directly into ice water with safety. Vycor ware is thus indicated where any sudden change in temperature is called for.

Glass, either soft or Pyrex, is quite resistant to attack by all acids except hydrofluoric acid, and evaporations and reactions involving acid solutions can be carried out in glass without danger of contamination. Glassware is attacked by alkali, however. Pyrex is much more resistant to alkali than soft glass, and mildly alkaline solutions can be heated in Pyrex for short periods without causing appreciable attack. The Corning Glass Works makes a boron-free glass of unusually high resistance to alkali, Corning No. 7280. This glass will not stand the thermal and mechanical shock of Pyrex or Vycor and is available in somewhat fewer shapes but is ideal where resistance to alkali or freedom from boron is required. For hot, concentrated alkalies vessels of platinum must be used. Alkaline fusions, that is, fusions with sodium hydroxide or potassium hydroxide, must be made in crucibles of silver or gold; such fusions attack platinum. Fusions with sodium carbonate, however, may be made in platinum crucibles.

Handling Hot Vessels. Beaker tongs are convenient for handling hot beakers but they are clumsy when the space is confined, as on a

Fig. 21.   Rubber finger caps for handling hot vessels.

hot plate crowded with beakers. In such a place the rubber finger caps shown in Fig. 21 are convenient. Three such caps are made from 25-mm. rubber tubing having a wall thickness of 3 mm. Lengths of about 35 mm. are cut off, and a V-shaped cut about 25 mm. long and an opening of 20 mm. at the top of the V, made by flattening out the tubing and snipping off a corner with a scissors. This relieves the tension when the finger is inserted.

The neck of a wash bottle in which hot liquids are handled should be insulated. This can be conveniently done by wrapping heavy cord around the neck of the flask. Carpenter's chalk line is good. Place a U-shaped fold of cord vertically along the neck of the wash bottle (Fig. 22), with the closed end of the loop at the top. Starting at the bottom of the neck, wrap the cord around the neck snugly, thrusting the coils against each other and continuing until the entire neck is covered. Slip the cord through the loop at the top. Pull the cord which makes the loop so that the loop and other end are drawn under the coils. This puts the whole system under tension and prevents the cord from unwinding. Cut off the cord ends which protrude. The winding takes only a short time, is inexpensive, and may be quickly replaced.

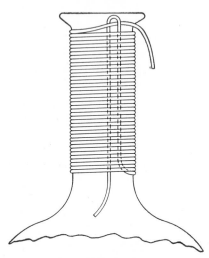

Fig. 22.   Insulating the neck of a wash bottle.

Evaporation. Probably the most time-consuming operation in general analytical work is evaporation. Precipitations are usually carried out in dilute solution to minimize contamination, and more water is added in the operations of transferring the precipitate to the filter and washing. If the filtrate is to be used for a further determination it is usually necessary to reduce the volume before proceeding. Frequently it is necessary to evaporate to remove an excess of a volatile reagent such as nitric acid or hydrochloric acid or even some undesirable component of the sample. Evaporations cannot often be side-stepped, and the few simple tricks which greatly speed the process should be utilized fully.

Evaporations and digestions are best carried out in a well-ventilated hood on a steam-heated or electrically heated hot plate. Electrically heated hot plates are available commercially in a variety of sizes, up to large plates which will accommodate twenty to thirty beakers at once.

The ease with which electrically heated hot plates can be regulated is a great advantage. High-pressure steam hot plates are particularly good in being inexpensive to operate and in requiring practically no maintainance.

The cleanliness which is essential at all times in analytical work extends even to the outsides of beakers and flasks. Particles of rust acquired by a beaker from a rusty hot plate can all too easily find their way into a funnel during a filtration. Rusty hot plates are an abomination and should be cleaned or discarded. In actual practice a sheet of asbestos placed on the hot plate will keep the glassware clean and is an effective compromise between the brevity of mortal life and the high cost of fighting the terrific corrosion of chemical laboratories by replacement. The use of a sand bath for evaporation would seem to violate the cleanliness rule but is nevertheless common practice. The advantage lies in the smoother and more rapid evaporation which is obtained by keeping the walls of the beaker hot by heaping sand around the beaker. A sand bath is most conveniently heated electrically, the top of the hot plate being provided

Fig. 23. Twin cover-glass supports to speed evaporation.

with a shallow trough in which a 2-in. layer of sand can be placed. Sand does not adhere to glassware if the glassware is clean and dry, but the necessity of wiping every bit of sand off the beaker after removing it from a sand bath should be obvious.

Evaporations are best made at or just below the boiling temperature. The beaker should be covered to keep out the dust and to retain any material which may spray from the solution. The cover glass should be elevated slightly above the rim of the beaker; hooks made of glass rod, three to a beaker, do this well but have an annoying proclivity of finding their way into the beaker. The twin watch-glass supports shown in Fig. 23 are better for the purpose. Special cover glasses with radial ribs which raise the cover glass above the rim of the beaker are also available.

Water condensed on the lower side of the cover glass during an evaporation forms a drop which eventually falls and spatters the solution about. This is especially bad toward the end of an evaporation in which the residue in the beaker is concentrated sulfuric acid. A good plan is to leave a stirring rod in the solution, placed diagonally across the beaker from the lip. The drop then strikes the stirring rod and runs smoothly into the solution.

In general it is well not to fill a beaker more than half full, especially if an evaporation is to be hastened by actually boiling the solution. Otherwise, spray from the bursting bubbles may carry material out of the beaker. When time is not such a critical factor, the evaporation should be allowed to proceed quietly below the boiling point. "Bumping" is liable to occur when a solution is heated to the boiling point; this is caused by local superheating and a sudden conversion of a considerable amount of water to steam. Bumping may be avoided by passing a fine stream of air through the solution or where permissible by adding a few small pieces of carborundum to the solution, which act as nuclei on which bubble formation may begin.

The Use and Care of Platinumware. There are certain reactions which cannot be carried out in glassware and for which platinum utensils are about the only possible containers. These reactions are chiefly the fusions with sodium carbonate and the reactions with hydrofluoric acid. Platinum can be readily fabricated into wire and sheet and is used about the laboratory in various forms. The principal platinum vessels used in chemical analysis are crucibles, evaporating dishes, gauze electrodes, and boats, Fig. 24, which are available in a variety of sizes. Platinum is attacked by many substances at high temperatures and by a few even at room temperature or the temperature of boiling aqueous solutions. A strongly oxidizing acid, such as a mixture of nitric acid and hydrochloric acid, or of nitric acid and a chlorate or bromate, dissolves platinum rapidly. Free chlorine and bromine also attack it rapidly.

Although platinum is the ideal material in which to carry out fusions with sodium carbonate or potassium carbonate, the attack on platinum by the hydroxides, peroxides, cyanides, and nitrates of the alkali metals (lithium, sodium, and potassium) and barium is rapid enough that these substances should not be heated in a platinum vessel.

Also included in the list of materials which should not be heated in platinum are: all sulfides; mixtures of free sulfur and a hydroxide or carbonate; compounds of phosphorus and arsenic; all metals; any material that is readily reduced with the formation of a metal.

At high temperatures metals form alloys with platinum and spoil platinum vessels. This rules out metallic materials and substances which can be reduced to a metal by carbon from a filter paper or carbon monoxide from a gas flame, such as lead oxide, silver chloride, lead sulfate, or stannic oxide. At high temperature platinum is quite pervious, and the gases of a burner flame diffuse through it quite readily, producing a reducing atmosphere within the vessel. If a crucible is open, diffusion of air into the crucible is so rapid that the effects of the

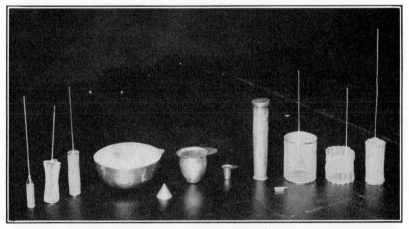

Fig. 24.   Common pieces of platinumware.

reducing gases may not be appreciable. In a covered crucible heated by a gas flame the reducing atmosphere present is strong enough to reduce ferric oxide at least partially to metallic iron and sodium sulfate to sodium sulfide. Even in a sodium carbonate fusion some reduction seems to occur. In general, then, ignitions should be carried out with the crucible uncovered and in a slanting position with free access to air.

Platinum becomes brittle when heated in contact with a reducing flame, because of the formation of a carbide of platinum. A platinum crucible should therefore be placed so that the inner cone of the burner flame does not touch it; whenever possible a Meker burner should be used since it has only a small inner cone and the flame is uniform.

When the surface of a platinum crucible becomes gray or crystalline it should be polished with sand or powdered pumice. Stains which are not readily removed by sand can usually be removed by fusing potassium bisulfate, sodium bisulfate, or borax in the crucible. Boiling with hydrochloric acid or with nitric acid (but never with a mixture of the two) will usually help. If these treatments fail, heating with a mixture of equal parts of concentrated hydrofluoric and hydrochloric acids or fusion with potassium acid fluoride may work. Iron stains are readily removed by heating a covered crucible containing a gram of ammonium chloride at the full heat of a burner.

Platinum crucibles should always be kept polished, and should not be bent or injured in any way. If they become deformed, they should be reshaped on a wood form of the same style. Attempts to rub out a dent with a glass rod usually makes matters worse.

A large part of the cost of a platinum vessel is the intrinsic value of the platinum in it. In the accidental situations where a platinum vessel is damaged or dissolved, the platinum can be easily recovered and a new vessel obtained for the cost of fabrication. The recovery involves simply converting the platinum to chlorplatinic acid, H_2PtCl_6, by boiling it with a mixture of nitric and hydrochloric acids and precipitating it as ammonium chlorplatinate, which is fairly insoluble and can be filtered off and shipped to the companies manufacturing platinumware.

Magnetic Stirring. Mechanical stirring is a great aid in volumetric analysis, particularly when the end-point of the titration is

Fig. 25. Magnetic stirring. Glass-enclosed magnet placed in beaker is caused to rotate by spinning magnet driven by motor in box.

Fig. 26. Magnetic stirring. Beaker shown is wrapped with electric resistance ribbon so that the beaker can be heated and stirred at the same time.

being determined potentiometrically or when the end-point must be approached slowly. The magnetic stirrer is particularly convenient. It consists of a small electric motor mounted in a box with the armature in a vertical position. A small, powerful permanent magnet, usually of alnico, is mounted crosswise on the shaft of the motor so that it rotates just below the top of the box. The solution to be stirred is placed on the box, and a rotor is dropped into the solution. The rotor consists of a piece of iron sealed in a short glass tube. As the motor rotates the permanent magnet, the rotor also turns and sets the liquid in motion. The rate of stirring may be regulated by varying the speed of the motor. These devices are on the market; two commercial makes are shown in Figs. 25 and 26.

PERCHLORIC ACID

Perchloric acid, $HClO_4$, is a strong acid which is as useful in chemical analysis as hydrochloric acid, sulfuric acid, or nitric acid. Perchloric acid has unique properties that enable it to effect certain reactions in which the other strong acids fail. These same properties demand that knowledge and care be exercised in its use.

Composition and Physical Properties. Perchloric acid is marketed as the 72 per cent acid, which is a constant boiling mixture (azeotrope) having a composition corresponding closely to the dihydrate, $HClO_4 \cdot 2H_2O$ (theoretically 73.6 per cent $HClO_4$). When a dilute solution of perchloric acid is boiled, the temperature rises gradually to 203° and the acid remaining in the vessel concentrates to about 72 per cent; at this point the temperature remains constant and the acid distilling has the same composition as the acid remaining in the vessel. Commercial perchloric acid, the 72 per cent, constant-boiling acid, is perfectly stable and is better referred to as *perchloric acid dihydrate*.

Anhydrous perchloric acid can be prepared, but it is unstable and can be stored safely only at liquid-air temperatures. Perchloric acid monohydrate is a crystalline solid at room temperature and is presumed to be oxonium perchlorate, H_3OClO_4; it can be stored at room temperature. Neither the anhydrous form nor the monohydrate is produced by simply boiling a water solution of perchloric acid to concentrate it. Neither material is available commercially and neither finds use in chemical analysis.

Chemical Properties. Perchloric acid, when hot and concentrated, *is a powerful oxidizing agent.* At ordinary temperatures, whether dilute or concentrated, it *is not an oxidizing agent.* Hot and concentrated, perchloric acid *is also a powerful dehydrating agent.* These properties, coupled with unusual solubility relationships among the metal perchlorates, makes perchloric acid unique among the strong acids.

The oxygen of perchloric acid is so firmly bound to the chlorine atom that none is available at room temperatures for oxidation reactions. Thus, metallic iron, unless finely powdered, dissolves in perchloric acid at room temperature with the formation of ferrous perchlorate and the evolution of hydrogen. At a higher temperature and with concentrated acid, 60 to 72 per cent, ferric perchlorate is formed. The oxidizing power of perchloric acid increases gradually when a dilute solution of the acid is boiled; water distills away, the acid concentrates toward 72 per cent, and the temperature rises. The oxidizing power is thus brought to bear gradually and in a manner that can be carefully controlled. The reduction potential (see Chapter 10 for meaning) of hot, 72 per cent perchloric acid is estimated from certain reactions to be about 1.9 to 2.0 volts; perchloric acid under these conditions is thus one of the most powerful oxidizing agents known. It will oxidize chromic salts to chromic acid and cerous sulfate to sulfatoceric acid (quadrivalent cerium); chromic acid and sulfatoceric acid are themselves very strong oxidizing agents.

The powerful dehydrating action of perchloric acid arises from its comparatively high boiling point, 203°, and the distillation of the perchloric acid azeotrope on boiling. Any water present in material mixed with perchloric acid is extracted on heating to form this constant-boiling mixture. Use of this dehydrating action of perchloric acid is made in the determination of silica.

The perchlorates of all the metals are soluble in water; the least soluble, very curiously, are those of the alkali metals potassium, rubidium, and cesium. The metal perchlorates are also soluble in many organic solvents, especially the alcohols, ketones, esters, and glycols. In all cases the increase in solubility with increase in temperature is high, often a tenfold increase between 0 and 100°.

As a solvent for metals and alloys perchloric acid is superior to the other strong acids. All the perchlorates of the metals are soluble, and this fact, coupled with the high boiling temperature and the oxidizing power of perchloric acid dihydrate, makes the action of the acid almost irresistable. Perchloric acid dissolves stainless steel and ferrochrome readily, oxidizing the chromium to chromic acid. Unlike sulfuric acid, which fails to dissolve metallic lead because of the formation of a coating of insoluble lead sulfate, perchloric acid acts rapidly on lead, forming lead perchlorate which is soluble.

The perchlorate ion is much more stable than the ions of any of the other oxygen-containing acids of the halogens. The alkali metal perchlorates are decomposed only when heated to 350 to 400°. The perchlorate ion is not reduced electrolytically. Perchlorates and perchloric acid are made from sodium perchlorate produced by the electrolytic oxidation of sodium chlorate, and it is not necessary to have in the electrolysis cell a porous diaphragm separating the solutions surrounding the anode and the cathode. The oxidation of the chlorate at the anode is made complete without such a membrane because the perchlorate is not reduced at the cathode.

Boiling perchloric acid dihydrate undergoes slow decomposition according to the reactions

$$4HClO_4 = 2Cl_2 + 7O_2 + 2H_2O \quad \text{(principal reaction)}$$

$$2HClO_4 = Cl_2 + 3O_2 + H_2O_2 \quad \text{(minor reaction)}$$

A small amount of ozone may also be formed. These reactions are important in explaining certain phenomena which occur when 72 per cent perchloric acid is used for oxidation.

Applications in Analytical Chemistry. Because of its unusual properties perchloric acid finds many uses in chemical analysis:

1. As a solvent for metals and alloys.

2. As a dehydrating agent, particularly in the determination of silica in iron and steel and in cement and other silicate materials.

3. As an oxidizing agent, especially in the determination of chromium in steel, ferrochrome, chromite, leather, and chromatized catgut.

4. In combination with nitric acid for the destruction of organic matter, especially in preparation for the determination of calcium, arsenic, iron, copper, and other metals in such materials; also in the determination of sulfur in coal and rubber. See page 403.

5. As a solvent for sulfide ores, for the determination of copper and other metals.

6. In the separation and determination of the alkali metals sodium and potassium.

7. In combination with hydrochloric acid in the separation of chromium from other metals by distillation of chromyl chloride.

8. In the isolation of fluoride prior to its determination, by distillation as hydrofluosilicic acid.

9. As a deproteinization reagent in food analysis, for example, in the determination of butterfat in dairy products.

10. As an adjunct to increase the reduction potential of cerate salts in volumetric analysis.

11. As a primary standard acid; vacuum-distilled perchloric acid dihydrate contains exactly 73.606 per cent $HClO_4$.

12. Indirectly in the manufacture of anhydrous magnesium perchlorate, the best of the absorbents for water in analytical work.

13. As a strong, standard acid for the titration of bases.

14. As a strong acid dissolved in anhydrous acetic acid for the titration of bases in non-aqueous solvents.

All the applications of perchloric acid mentioned above are in routine use in industrial and testing laboratories.

Hazards and Precautions in the Use of Perchloric Acid. Perchloric acid dihydrate (72 per cent perchloric acid) is not hazardous to make; it is perfectly stable on storage; and it may be boiled with perfect safety as long as organic matter is absent.

At room temperature perchloric acid may be mixed with organic matter safely, but such a mixture should never be heated. Note that the wet oxidation of organic matter begins with a mixture of nitric acid and perchloric acid.

Some troubles have been experienced when perchloric acid fumes have been allowed to collect on wood hoods and ductwork, especially where coal or organic dusts have accumulated. Routine operations involving many solutions in which perchloric acid is being boiled should be carried out in hoods made entirely of stone or transite with provision for washing down the ducts occasionally. Usually it is not necessary to boil away perchloric acid, and a cover glass on a beaker or a reflux head in a flask, Fig. 72, page 305, is sufficient to condense the acid and prevent its escape. When it is necessary to boil away appreciable amounts of perchloric acid, the glass hood shown in Fig. 83, page 369, is very convenient.

CHAPTER 3

The Balance and Weighing

The equal-arm balance is an extraordinary machine. Using the balances commonly found in analytical laboratories an operator with a little experience can determine the weight of an object weighing 100 g. to within 0.0001 g., that is, to within 1 in the fourth decimal place. This is an uncertainty of only 1 part in 1,000,000. Measurements of such accuracy can be equaled or surpassed in the measurement of only two other physical properties.[1] An even more remarkable aspect of the weighing operation is that it can be carried out in a very few minutes. The chemist does well, then, to approach the balance with respect, if indeed not with awe. The balance is an instrument which enables him to perform an extraordinary operation in a remarkably short time.

The primary feature of the construction of the analytical balance is that the distances between the central knife edge and the outer knife edges are equal. It is astonishing how closely the balance makers can locate the knife edges on the beam to make the two distances the same, the common analytical balances manufactured having the arms equal in length within 1 part in 100,000. Although methods, described later in this chapter, are known for eliminating the effect of any difference in the lengths of the arms by making two weighings, this is an unnecessary consideration in all but the most refined analytical work.

A typical analytical balance, capable of weighing objects up to 100 g.

[1] Radio frequency can be measured with an uncertainty of only 1 in 10^7, and the wave length of the cadmium red line has been determined in terms of the standard meter to within 1 in 10^8. A comparison of the wave lengths of the cadmium red line and the lines of the isotope of mercury of mass 198 has been made with an estimated error of 1 in 10^9. No chemical analysis has ever been carried out with an accuracy greater than 1 in 10^6, and the ordinary analytical work of industrial and research laboratories is done with an accuracy of only 1 in 10^3. The balance, then, is capable of far better work than the chemist is ever likely to demand of it. Actually, the greatest source of error in making weighings resides in the values of the weights used.

in mass to within 0.0001 g., is shown in Fig. 27. The details of construction of the balance are shown in Fig. 28.

The knife edges of the analytical balance are made of agate and bear on flat agate plates. Agate is extremely hard, and the knife edges stay

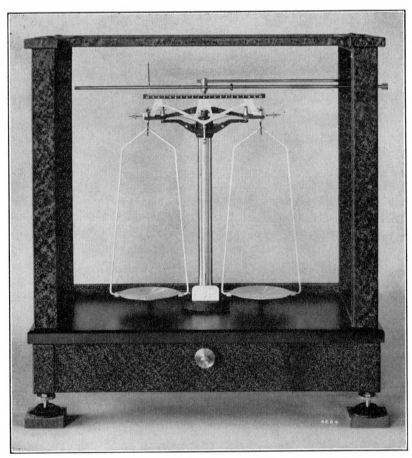

Fig. 27.   Ainsworth balance, Type LC.   (*Courtesy of Wm. Ainsworth & Sons, Inc.*).

sharp for a long time. Agate is brittle, however, and the knife edges can be easily chipped by mechnical shock. For this reason balances are equipped with a beam-arresting mechanism by which the knife edges and plates are separated when the beam is not in use or when objects and weights are being moved on and off the pans. The beam arrest and the pan supports are operated by knobs at the front of the balance.

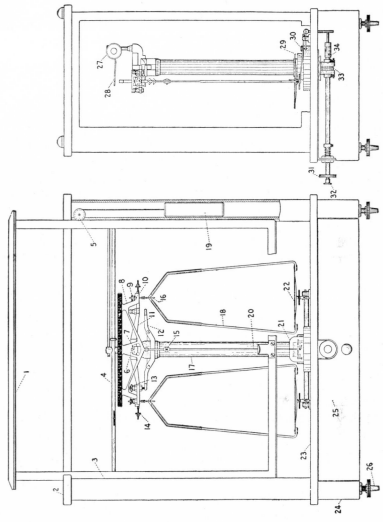

Fig. 28. Details of construction of balance. 1, Door; 2, case top; 3, end frame; 4, rider rod; 5, door pulley; 6, center edge; 7, center bearing; 8, beam; 9, end bearing; 10, end edge; 11, drop lever; 12, drop-lever support; 13, beam support; 14, equilibrium adjuster; 15, gravity bob; 16, stirrup; 17, column; 18, hanger wire; 19, door counterweight; 20, pointer; 21, index plate; 22, hanger plate; 23, sub-base; 24, base; 25, drawer; 26, leveling screw; 27, rider bushing; 28, rider arm; 29, pan arrest; 30, pan-arrest adjusting screw; 31, operating thumbpiece; 32, pan arrest button; 33, drop-lever operating mechanism; 34, pan-arrest lock. (*Courtesy Wm. Ainsworth & Sons, Inc.*)

The nuts at the ends of the beam are used to change the center of swings of the balance; they are useful and easy to manipulate. The nut on the pointer is used to adjust the sensitivity of the balance and is moved only under extraordinary circumstances.

The balance is constructed so that all three of the knife edges lie in the same plane. If the beam is not rigid enough to maintain this, the sensitivity of the balance changes widely and erratically with varying load.

The sensitivity of the equal-arm balance increases with the length of the arm. In the design of a balance, however, there is a distinct limit to increasing the sensitivity by making the arm length longer, for the longer the arm the more slowly the balance swings.[1]

The sensitivity also increases with decreasing weight; for this reason lightweight alloys are used and a triangular, cutaway construction is adopted for the beam.

A third factor enters into the sensitivity of the equal-arm balance: the distance between the central knife edge and the center of gravity. As this distance is decreased the sensitivity increases. This factor gives the balance designer an opportunity to exercise his ingenuity. By locating a large portion of the beam above the knife edges the sensitivity can be greatly improved. The center of gravity must remain, of course, below the central knife edge if the balance is to swing like a pendulum. But it can be, and is, brought up to within a hair's breadth of the knife edge. Moreover, an adjustment is provided whereby this distance can be varied; the nut on the pointer can be moved up and down. The student is warned away from this adjustment, however, for a little movement of the nut changes the sensitivity considerably; the manufacturer sets the nut properly, and unless there is a very good reason for change it is best to leave the nut strictly alone.

The relation between the sensitivity of the balance and the three factors discussed above are developed in mathematical form in the section following Fig. 29. The final mathematical equation is a concise statement of the manner in which sensitivity is determined by the length of the balance arm, the weight of the beam, and the position of the center of gravity. In practice it is more convenient to express

---

[1] The period of oscillation of the balance, considered as a compound pendulum, is given by the expression

$$t = \pi\sqrt{(Wk^2 + 2PL)/WGg}$$

in which t is the time, W is the weight of the beam, k is the radius of gyration, P is the weight of pan and object on it, G is the distance between the center of gravity and the central knife edge, g is the acceleration of gravity, and L is the distance between the central and outer knife edges.

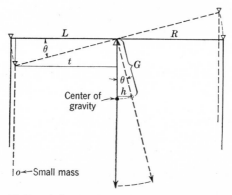

Fig. 29. The sensitivity of the equal-arm balance. The balance behaves essentially as a pendulum with its mass W located at the center of gravity. A small mass, o, placed on one pan causes a movement of the system so that the center of gravity is no longer directly below the central knife edge. Remembering from physics that force is equal to mass times acceleration (G, the acceleration of gravity in this case) and that moment is equal to force times length of lever arm, the opposing moments which constitute the new equilibrium are the small, added mass o times the perpendicular distance t from the direction of the force to the central knife edge, that is, ot, and the mass W acting through the perpendicular distance h. Setting these moments equal

$$ot = Wh$$

From the figure it is apparent that

$$t = L \cos \theta \qquad \text{and} \qquad h = G \sin \theta$$

so that

$$oL \cos \theta = WG \sin \theta$$

$$\frac{\sin \theta}{\cos \theta} = \frac{oL}{WG}$$

$$\tan \theta = \frac{oL}{WG}$$

For the small angles involved in the swinging of a balance

$$\tan \theta = \theta \text{ (in radians)}$$

and therefore

$$\theta = \frac{oL}{WG}$$

Thus, the displacement of the center of swings of the equal-arm balance (the sensitivity) is directly proportional to the weight added to one side and directly proportional to the length of the balance arm; it is inversely proportional to the mass of the system (beam, pans, and load) and inversely proportional to the distance between the center of gravity and the central knife edge.

the sensitivity of a balance in terms of divisions on the scale over which the pointer swings rather than angular measure for a given load.

Center of Swings and Zero Point.   In effect the balance is a pendulum oscillating back and forth about the central knife edge. The center of gravity must, of course, be below the central knife edge; if it were above the central knife edge the balance would fall to one side and remain there.

Because of friction of the knife edges and air resistance, each swing is smaller than the one before. The damping of the oscillations is so small, however, that it is hopelessly impractical to wait until the balance stops swinging to decide if the loads on the two sides are equal. It is necessary therefore to average the swings to obtain the center of swings or rest point. In doing this, an odd number of readings on one side are averaged and an even number of readings on the other side are averaged and these averages are averaged with due regard for sign. This gives the center of swings or the place where the balance would come to rest if allowed to swing long enough.

Example.   After neglecting the first swing of the pointer across the scale

the following readings were taken and the center of swings calculated:

$$
\begin{array}{ll}
-4.2 & \\
-3.8 & +6.0 \\
-3.3 & +5.8 \\
\hline
-3.8 & +5.9 \\
     & -3.8 \\
\hline
     & 2\underline{|+2.1} \\
     & +1.05
\end{array}
$$

The center of swings was thus 1 scale division to the right of center.

The zero point is the center of swings of the balance with no load. It is not necessary that the zero point fall on the center of the scale. It can be made to do so by rotating the nuts on the ends of the beam. Unless the zero point is more than 2 scale divisions (s.d.) from the center of the scale the balance is used without further adjustment. The weights are manipulated in making a weighing until the center of swings coincides with the zero point. The zero point may change from time to time because of accumulation of dust or changes in temperature. In making a long series of weighings it is best to check the zero point occasionally during the work.

Sensitivity. The sensitivity of a balance is expressed as the number of scale divisions which the center of swings is shifted by a 1-mg. load. To determine the sensitivity it is first necessary to find the center of swings. A 1-mg. weight is then added to one side of the balance; this is most conveniently done by setting the rider at the 1.0 mg. position. The center of swings is again found. The difference of the two values obtained for the center of swings is the sensitivity in scale divisions per milligram.

Example. The zero point of a certain balance was -1.0. The rider was set at 1.0 mg. on the right side. The new center of swings was found to be -3.5. The shift was therefore 2.5 s.d. The sensitivity with no load on the balance was therefore 2.5 s.d. per mg.

The sensitivity of the balances commonly used for analytical work is in the range 1.5 to 5 s.d. per mg. As mentioned earlier, the sensitivity of the balance decreases with load. The sensitivity of a well-con-

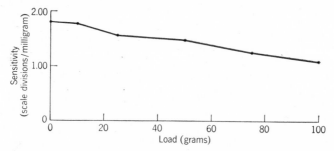

Fig. 30. Variation of sensitivity with load.

structed balance when carrying full load should not be less than 40 per cent of the sensitivity with no load. In Fig. 30 is shown the variation in sensitivity with load of a good analytical balance of a type commonly used by students in quantitative-analysis courses.

Weights. The weights used in analytical work are made of either brass or stainless steel. Brass weights are gold plated and then covered with a hard, non-hygroscopic lacquer. The weights are usually constructed in two pieces, the body of the weight and the handle which is screwed into it. Beneath the handle is a cavity in which are placed pieces of fine wire to bring the weight to its exact value. Metric weights are, of course, commonly used, and the weights in a set are arranged 50 grams (abbreviated g.), 20 g., 20 g., 10 g., 5 g., 2 g., 2 g., 1 g.; or alternatively 50 g., 30 g., 20 g., 10 g., 5 g., 3 g., 2 g., 1 g. A little thought will show that some combination of these weights will give every number from 1 to 100 without exception.

The same system is employed for the fractional weights, those below 1 g. The fractional weights are usually made of aluminum and some-

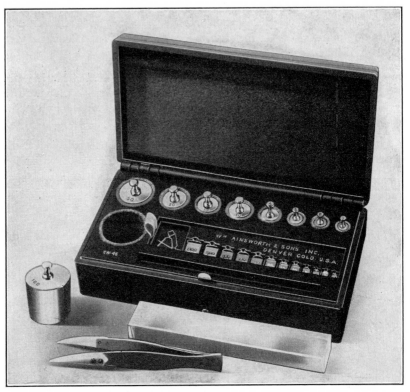

Fig. 31. Set of metric weights, stainless steel, Class S. (*Courtesy of Wm. Ainsworth & Sons, Inc.*)

times of tantalum or platinum. The smallest fractional weight is usually 10 milligrams (abbreviated mg.), that is, 0.0100 g.

Below 10 mg. the weights are too small to handle conveniently, and a small movable platinum wire, or rider, is moved along the beam to obtain the smaller weights, that is, milligrams and tenths of milligrams (the third and fourth decimal places). The rider weighs 10 mg. and acts as a 10-mg. weight when placed at the 10 mark directly above the right knife edge. The whole numbers on the beam are thus milligrams, and the fine divisions tenths of milligrams (fourth decimal place).[1]

Finding the proper location of the rider is about the longest part of the time required for a weighing. Various schemes have been tried

Fig. 32. Chainomatic balance. See Fig. 33 for detail. (*Courtesy of Wm. Ainsworth & Sons, Inc.*)

to supplant the rider and smaller weights in an effort to speed the final steps in the weighing process. In the chainomatic balance, Figs. 32 and 33, the weight up to 100 mg. is added to the beam by means of a fine, gold chain suspended between the beam and a movable block traveling up and down a nearby post. The block can be moved up and

[1] On some balances the beam is divided into 5, or sometimes into 6 or 12 divisions. A 5-, 6-, or 12-mg. rider should be used with these balances, respectively. The proper weight of rider is determined by the number directly above the knife edge.

down by turning a wheel on the right side of the balance. As the block is lowered more of the chain is suspended from the balance, thus increasing the weight on the right-hand side of the balance. The post upon which the block travels is calibrated in milligrams and by means

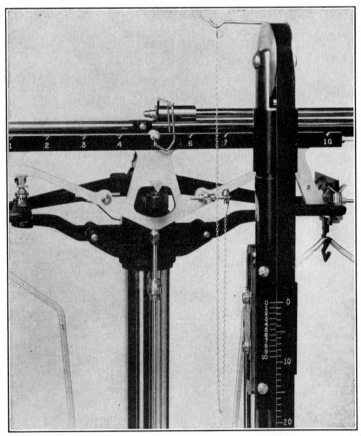

Fig. 33.   Close-up view of chainomatic balance.   (*Courtesy of Wm. Ainsworth & Sons, Inc.*)

of a vernier reads to 0.1 mg. The position of the block may be changed without interrupting the swinging of the beam, and just as with the rider balances, the position of the block is adjusted until the center of swings coincides with the zero point.

Care of the Balance. The balance should be located in a room separate from the laboratory to protect it from corrosion. Preferably the room should be lighted from the north so that direct and shifting sunlight does not fall on the balance or cause rapid changes in the temperature of the room. The balance should be located on a solid support free from vibration. Ideally it should be in a large case which

Fig. 34. Balance case, open.

may be closed when the balance is not in use to protect it from dust and fumes; the hinged case shown in Fig. 34 is a good arrangement.

The analytical balance is provided with screw legs and a spirit level so that the balance may be made level when placed in a new position.

To reduce wear on the knife edges the beam should be raised on the beam arrests whenever the balance is not in use. The beam should always be raised off the knife edges when an object or weights are being moved on the pans; the knife edges, which are made of agate, may otherwise be seriously damaged. The beam-arresting mechanism should be operated slowly to avoid damaging the agate knife edges, which are brittle.

Powdered materials should never be placed on the balance pan. Indeed, the best plan is to keep a pair of carefully balanced cover glasses on the pans at all times. Volatile or corrosive substances should always be weighed in closed containers such as ground glass weighing bottles or stoppered flasks.

Objects being weighed must first be cooled to the temperature of the balance. Hot or very cold objects induce air currents in the balance case which seriously affect the weighing and cause one arm of the balance to expand, shifting the zero point.

Serious damage may result from overloading a balance. The safe load which may be carried by a balance is one which will not decrease the sensitivity below 40 per cent of the sensitivity with no load. The safe load which an ordinary analytical balance, such as the Ainsworth student balance, will carry is about 100 g.

Weights should be handled with a forceps only. Weights should not be left standing on the balance pan, and the weight box should be kept closed when not in use.

The pans should not oscillate during the weighing.

Attention should be paid when replacing a rider that a new rider has the proper weight.

At the end of a weighing, the pans should be left empty, the pans and floor of the balance clean, the beam arrests raised, the door of the balance case closed, the weights all returned to the box, and the weight box closed.

Making a Weighing. When making a weighing the object is always placed on the left pan of the balance and the weights on the right pan.[1] The rider, which is part of the weights, is placed at various positions on the right side of the beam as the weighing demands. The weights and the rider are adjusted until the center of swings is the same as the center of swings with no load, that is, the zero point.

The weights must not be manipulated when the beam is resting on the knife edges. The violent jarring which occurs when this is done may damage the agate knife edges. The usual procedure is to lower the pan supports first and then the beam arrest. Often when

---

[1] This is simply tradition, probably started because the right-hand pan was easier for most people to reach. On the equal-arm balance it does not matter on which side the object and on which side the weights are placed. Weights and rider should be used on the same side, however, to avoid confusion.

lowering the pan supports the pans begin to swing; this is not good and is most easily stopped by bringing the pan supports up gradually until the felt covering of the pan supports just touch the pans and stop the swinging. Usually the balance will begin to oscillate as soon as the beam arrest is lowered; on one side, the beam support carries the balance on a ball which fits into a cup and the suction produced on lowering the arrest should start the balance swinging.

The usual practice is to start with weights heavier than the object and work from the heavier to the lighter weights, systematically. The longest part of the time taken for the weighing will be the final step of locating the rider. The sensitivity of the balance can be used at this point to speed the process.

Example. The zero point of a certain balance was -0.1 and the sensitivity 2.5 s.d. per mg. In weighing a crucible (on the left pan), the following weights were on the right pan: 10, 5, 1, 0.2, 0.05, and 0.01. With the rider at 3.7 the center of swings was found to be $+2.5$. To bring the center of swings to the zero point is a shift of $2.5 + 0.1$, or 2.6 s.d.

$$\frac{2.6 \text{ s.d.}}{2.5 \text{ s.d./mg.}} = 1.04 \text{ mg.}$$

The rider was then placed at 4.7 (3.7 + 1.0), and a new center of swings found to be -0.3. The rider was then moved to 4.6, and the center of swings found to be -0.1. This coincided with the zero point, and the weights were then totaled and the weight 16.2646 entered in the notebook.

At the conclusion of the weighing, the weights on the balance should be added and the number written in the laboratory record book. As a check, the weights missing from the box should also be added, the rider reading added to the sum, and this total used to confirm the number already recorded.

LABORATORY WORK WITH THE BALANCE

1. Read the preceding material in this chapter. Identify the various parts of the balance: beam, knife edges, stirrups, pans, pointer, beam arrest, pan supports, rider, rider hook, level, and so on. Learn what is meant by center of swings, zero point, and sensitivity.

2. Find the zero point of the balance, proceeding as follows: Lift the rider off the beam or set it at zero. Lower the pan supports, raising them once or twice gently to stop any oscillation of the pans. Release the beam arrest gently. Neglect the first swing of the pointer and then take three readings on the left and two on the right. Average the readings on each side and then average the averages, making sure the signs are handled correctly. Repeat the determination two or three

times to see how reproducible the zero point is. Observe whether the zero point is changed when the pans are swinging somewhat.

3. Lift the rider off the beam and again determine the zero point, but this time lower the beam arrest slowly so that the balance swings not more than 2 or 3 s.d. on each side of the zero point. Note that the damping is so small that the zero point can be obtained by averaging small swings to each side.

4. Rotate the knob on one end of the beam one complete revolution and again determine the zero point. Now, knowing how much the zero point is shifted by rotating the nut, change it again so as to bring the zero point to the very center of the scale.

5. Determine the sensitivity of the balance. Place the rider at the 1-mg. mark and find the center of swings. Calculate the number of scale divisions between the zero point and this new center of swings. This gives the sensitivity in scale divisions equal to 1 mg. For most analytical balances this will fall between 1.5 and 6 s.d. per mg. Repeat the determination to see how closely the sensitivity can be duplicated.

6. Place a 10-g. weight on each pan and place the rider at 0, or lift it off the beam. Find the center of swings. Theoretically, the center of swings will be the same as the zero point, but it may not be because the two weights may not have exactly the same weight. Place the rider at the 1-mg. mark and find the center of swings. Compare the sensitivity with this 10-g. load with that with no load.

7. Return to the data of step 5. Using the difference between the zero point and the center of swings with 10-g. weights on each pan and the sensitivity at 10-g. load, calculate the difference in the weight of the two 10-g. weights. Note which is the lighter of the two.

8. Determine the sensitivity with loads of 20 g., 50 g., and 100 g. Tabulate these in your record book.

9. Obtain a porcelain crucible and cover. Weigh the crucible alone, placing the crucible on the left-hand pan and the weights on the right. Handle the weights with the forceps. Change the weights only when the beam arrest is up and the beam is not resting on the knife edge; the knife edge may be seriously damaged otherwise. Start with the heavier weights and work down systematically to the lighter weights. Finally, move the rider until the center of swings coincides with the zero point. The values obtained for the sensitivity can be used to find how far the rider should be moved during the weighing as described in the preceding section. Add the weights making sure that the decimal point is correct for each weight and for the rider reading. Add the weights missing from the weight box as a check. Enter the weight in the record book.

10. Weigh the crucible cover.

11. Weigh the crucible and cover together. The weights obtained should equal the sum of the weights obtained for the crucible and cover separately.

Temperature, Electrical, and Surface Effects. The object being weighed must be at the temperature of the balance, otherwise convection currents are set up which affect the oscillation of the balance. Also, heat on one side of the balance causes unequal expansion of the arms and shifts the zero point.

Objects which are non-conductors of electricity, glass vessels, for example, often carry a static charge which causes the balance to become erratic in operation. This effect is sometimes as much as 20 mg. It is particularly troublesome in winter and in times of low humidity. Such troubles can usually be avoided by reducing the handling of the object to the minimum and by avoiding any wiping of the object with cloth, as is sometimes done with the mistaken notion of removing moisture from the surface. Various methods of dispelling electrical charges have been tried. Radioactive materials are sometimes placed in the balance case; the radiation ionizes the air in the balance case and causes the static charge to leak away. Grounding a statically charged body helps only slightly; the charge is collected on the corners of the surface and does not pass quickly from one part of the object to another. The usual answer to the problem of dispelling a static charge on an object being weighed is time. Ultimately the charge will leak away, but the time required may be anything from a few seconds to 15 or 20 minutes.

Objects with large surfaces present a special problem because of the moisture which collects on the surface by adsorption. In making a series of weighings in a relatively short period of time, as, for example, in weighing a series of samples from a weighing bottle, this is of no consequence, as the film of adsorbed water will remain constant throughout. In case the weighings are made a few hours or longer apart, a change in humidity may occur, causing a change in the film of adsorbed water. This might happen, for example, with a glass absorption bulb weighed one day, used in an operation, and weighed again the next day. Such trouble may be eliminated by the use of a counterpoise, an identical object having the same surface area, which is placed on the right pan of the balance. The counterpoise is really part of the weights and is treated just as carefully. The film of moisture on the counterpoise changes in the same manner as that on the object, and the effects cancel.

Effect of Latitude and Altitude on Weighings. From physics we have the simple relations: Force = Mass × Acceleration; Moment = Force × Length lever arm.

In the case of the equal-arm balance there are two moments (in opposing directions) about the central knife edge, the lever arms are the distances between the knife edges, the masses involved are the objects on the pans, and the acceleration is the acceleration of gravity. When in balance, then,

$$OLg = WRg$$

in which L and R are the lengths of the left and right balance arms, respectively, and O and W are the masses of the object and weights, respectively. The term g cancels, and thus the comparison of the masses O and W is independent of the acceleration of gravity and hence independent of latitude and altitude. Thus, the equal-arm balance will give the same result at New York City, Denver, and at the North Pole, although there is considerable difference in the distance of each place from the center of the earth and hence in the acceleration of gravity.

Correction to Weight in Vacuum. According to Archimedes' principle an object immersed in a fluid is buoyed up by a force equal to the weight of the fluid displaced. An object on an equal-arm balance is thus buoyed up by a force equal to the air it displaces. The weights are also buoyed up, but since the volumes of air displaced by the object and by the weights are not usually equal the buoyant effects are not the same. If the object has a lower density than the weights, it will displace more air, the buoyant effect on it will be greater than on the weights, and it will appear to weigh less than if it were weighed in a vacuum or weighed with weights having the same density. Conversely, if the object has the greater density the weight in air will be greater than the weight in vacuum; this is so of a platinum crucible, for example, for platinum has a greater density (21.4) than brass weights (8.4).

The weight in vacuum may be calculated from the apparent weight (weight in air) if the densities of the object, weights, and air are known. The volumes of the object and weights are W_v/d_o and W_a/d_w, respectively, where W_v is the weight of the object in vacuum and W_a is the apparent weight as indicated by the weights. The difference between these two volumes multiplied by the density of air d_a gives the difference in the buoyant effects.

$$\text{Difference in buoyant forces} = \left[\frac{W_v}{d_o} - \frac{W_a}{d_w} \right] d_a$$

Inasmuch as d_a is a small number (0.0012) and the difference in the two volumes is small, W_a may be substituted for W_v without introducing appreciable error. The final equation then becomes

$$W_v = W_a + W_a \left[\frac{d_a}{d_o} - \frac{d_a}{d_w} \right]$$

If the density of the weights is greater than the density of the object, the correction to the apparent weight is positive, in agreement with the argument developed above.

The weight in vacuum of 1000.00 g. of water weighed in air with brass weights is

$$W_v = 1000.00 + 1000.00 \left[\frac{0.0012}{1.00} - \frac{0.0012}{8.4} \right] = 1001.06$$

that is, the correction amounts to about 1 part in 1000 for water. It is less for salts and solids, for their density is greater than 1 for the most part. In general, however, if accuracy greater than 1 part in 1000 or 1 part in 5000 is needed, the correction to weight in vacuum must be applied.

For the density of air, the value of 0.0012 used above is a good average value. A more precise value may be obtained from the barometric pressure, temperature, and relative humidity by the following equation

$$d_a = \frac{0.001,293}{1 + 0.003,670t} \cdot \frac{P - 0.37h}{760}$$

in which t is the temperature in °C., P is the barometric pressure in millimeters of mercury, and h is the vapor pressure of water at the temperature t multiplied by the relative humidity expressed as a fraction.

The density of brass weights is usually assumed to be 8.4. The fractional weights are usually made of some other metal (aluminum, tantalum, platinum), but their mass is usually a small part of the whole so that it is safe to consider them as having a density of 8.4. The density of the stainless steel weights coming into common use is 7.8.

TABLE 5.   DENSITY OF MATERIALS USED AS WEIGHTS

Aluminum	2.7	Tantalum	16.6
Brass	8.4	Platinum	21.4
Stainless steel	7.8	Quartz	2.65

Making Highly Accurate Weighings. *Inequality in Lengths of Balance Arms.* Within the limits that machinists can work, the arms of the balance are made equal in length. Assuming that a skilled machinist can place the knife edges on the beam to within 0.000,05 in. and assuming that the length of the arms of the balance are each 5 in., the uncertainty in the length of the arm is thus 1 part in 100,000. Most chemical analyses are carried out with an accuracy less than 1 part in 1000, and only occasionally are analyses made with an accuracy of 1 part in 10,000. For most analytical work, then, a simple weighing is good enough. For work of high accuracy provision must be made for eliminating the difference in the lengths of the balance arms. There are two ways of doing this; both involve making two weighings.

Double Weighing Method of Gauss. The object is first weighed with the object O on the left pan and the weights W on the right. The object is then weighed again with the object on the right and the weights W', on the left. The moments about the central knife edge in the two cases are $OL = WR$ and $W'L = OR$. By multiplying opposite sides of these equations together we obtained $O^2LR = WW'LR$ and $O = \sqrt{WW'}$. W and W' are large numbers, usually six figures, and the arithmetic of multiplying two large numbers together and extracting the square root of the product is cumbersome. A satisfactory approximation is $O = (W + W')/2$; that is, the arithmetic mean is a satisfactory approximation to the geometric mean.

The ratio of the lengths of the balance arms can also be obtained from such a double weighing. Again using the equations $OL = WR$ and $W'L = OR$, but multiplying the corresponding sides together, gives $OW'L^2 = OWR^2$, so that $R/L = \sqrt{W'/W}$. Once this ratio has been determined only one weighing need be made, for then $O = W(R/L)$, and the weight obtained can simply be multiplied by the ratio R/L.

Substitution Method. A second method of eliminating any difference in the length of the balance arms makes use of a tare in the first weighing. The object is simply balanced with some other object, most conveniently a second set of weights, although sand or star dust would do. The object is then removed and the tare weighed:

$$OL = TR$$
$$WL = TR$$

so that $$OL = WL$$

and $$O = W$$

Because of its convenience this method is used in the calibration of a set of weights.

CALIBRATION OF WEIGHTS

It is rarely necessary in analytical work to know the exact masses of the weights used. The results of analyses are expressed as percentages, and it is merely sufficient that the weights have the correct relative values among themselves, that is, the 2-g. weight must be exactly twice the mass of the 1-g. weight, and so on. Duplicate weights in a set are differentiated by a punch mark or indentation on the top of one weight of the pair.

In calibrating a set of weights the various weights are compared with each other, starting with the smallest weight. One of the 0.01-g. weights is assumed to have exactly the value 0.010,00 g., and the other weights are referred to it. Thus, the 0.01-g. weight, designated (0.01), is first compared with the (0.01′). It is then also compared with the (0.01″) weight and then with the rider. The (0.02) weight is then compared with (0.01) + (0.01′); then, (0.05) is compared with (0.02) + (0.01) + (0.01′) + (0.01″). This process is continued until all the weights in the set have been compared with the lower weights. The data is assembled in tabular form as shown in Table 6.

In making the actual comparison of the weights it is necessary to use one of the two methods described previously for making precise weighings; that is, a method must be used which eliminates the effect of any difference in the lengths of the balance arms. The substitution method has been most frequently employed, although the accuracy which can be secured by the transposition method is greater.

When the substitution method is used, the tare required is simply the corresponding weights of a second set. Thus, the (0.01) weight of the set being calibrated is placed on the left pan and $(0.01)_T$, the tare taken from another set, is placed on the right pan and the center of swings is found. The (0.01) weight is then replaced by (0.01′), and the new center of swings is found. The number of scale divisions' difference in the two centers of swings divided by the sensitivity in scale divisions per milligram gives the difference in mass of the two weights. One of the weights, say (0.01), is assumed to have a mass 0.010,00 g., and the value of (0.01′) is obtained in terms of it. In a similar manner the value of (0.01″) in terms of (0.01) is obtained. Then a new tare is taken and (0.02) compared with (0.01) + (0.01′), and so on.

In the transposition method the center of swings is determined first with (0.01) on the left and (0.01′) on the right. The positions are then reversed, and a new center of swings is found. The difference in the center of swings divided by the sensitivity in scale divisions per

TABLE 6. CALIBRATION OF A SET OF WEIGHTS

Comparison was made by the double weighing method. The weight designated (0.01) was used as preliminary standard. The final values are based on the 10-g. weight, assuming it to have a value of 10.000,00.

Designation of Weight	Compared with	Difference in Weight $\left(\dfrac{R_2 - R_1}{2s} \right)$	Value on Preliminary Standard (grams)	Aliquot Part of 10.028,27 grams	Correction (milligrams)	True Value (grams)
(0.01)			0.010,00	0.010,03	−0.03	0.009,97
(0.01′)	(0.01)	+0.03	0.010,03	0.010,03	0.00	0.010,00
(0.01″)	(0.01)	+0.03	0.010,03	0.010,03	0.00	0.010,00
(0.02)	(0.01′) + (0.01″)	+0.03	0.020,09	0.020,06	+0.03	0.020,03
(0.05)	(0.02) + (0.01) + (0.01′) + (0.01″)	+0.03	0.050,18	0.050,14	+0.04	0.050,04
(0.1)	(0.05) + (0.02) + (0.01) + (0.01′) + (0.01″)	−0.05	0.100,28	0.100,28	0.00	0.100,00
(0.1′)	(0.05) + (0.02) + (0.01) + (0.01′) + (0.01″)	−0.09	0.100,24	0.100,28	−0.04	0.099,96
(0.2)	(0.1) + (0.1′)	+0.06	0.200,58	0.200,57	+0.01	0.200,01
(0.5)	(0.2) + (0.1) + (0.1′) + (0.05) + (0.02) + (0.01) + (0.01′) + (0.01″)	−0.02	0.501,41	0.501,41	0.00	0.500,00
(1)	(0.5) + (0.2) + (0.1) + (0.1′) + (0.05) + (0.02) + (0.01) + (0.01′) + (0.01″)	+0.14	1.002,98	1.002,83	+0.15	1.000,15
(2)	(1) + (0.5) + (0.2) + (0.1) + (0.1′) + (0.05) + (0.02) + (0.01) + (0.01′) + (0.01″)	−0.21	2.005,61	2.005,65	−0.04	1.999,96
(2′)	(1) + (0.5) + (0.2) + (0.1) + (0.1′) + (0.05) + (0.02) + (0.01) + (0.01′) + (0.01″)	−0.15	2.005,67	2.005,65	+0.02	2.000,02
(5)	(2) + (2′) + (1)	+0.02	5.014,28	5.014,14	+0.14	5.000,14
(10′)	(5) + (2) + (2′) + (1)	−0.36	10.028,18	10.028,27	−0.09	9.999,91
(10)	(10′)	+0.09	10.028,27	10.000,00	0.00	10.000,00
(20)	(10) + (10′)	−0.26	20.056,19	20.056,54	−0.35	19.999,65
(50)	(20) + (10) + (10′) + (5) + (2) + (2′) + (1)	−0.25	50.140,93	50.141,35	−0.42	49.999,58
(100)	(50) + (20) + (10) + (10′) + (5) + (2) + (2′) + (1)	−0.52	100.281,59	100.282,70	−1.11	99.998,89

milligram and divided by two gives the difference in the masses of the two weights:

$$\text{Difference in weight} = \frac{R_2 - R_1}{2s}$$

R_1 and R_2 are the centers of swings and s is the sensitivity in scale divisions per milligram. Care must be taken that this difference is added to the proper weight. It is best to adopt a formal procedure to escape confusion. For example, if weight A is on the left and weight B on the right, the center of swings is designated as R_1; reversed, the center of swings is R_2. Then

$$B = A + \frac{R_2 - R_1}{2s}$$

The first data obtained in the calibration given in Table 6 were:

Left	Right	Center of Swings
(0.01)	(0.01′)	−0.35
(0.01′)	(0.01)	−0.2

so that
$$(0.01') = (0.01) + \frac{-0.2 - (-0.35)}{2(2.5)}$$

$$= (0.01) + 0.03 \text{ mg.}$$

As before, (0.01) is assumed to have a mass of 0.010,00 g. and the values of (0.01′), (0.01″), (0.02), and so on, are determined in terms of it. In either the substitution or the transposition method two weighings are necessary for each comparison of two weights. Since the observed difference is divided by 2 in the transposition method, the accuracy is double that of the substitution method.

As observed in column 4 of Table 6 the apparent values of the weights on the assumption that the weight designated (0.01) is correct depart farther and farther from the nominal values as the calibration progresses. By taking one of the larger weights as the basis for the set, the size of the corrections can be reduced to small numbers which are more convenient to handle. The 10-g. weight is usually chosen as the standard; it may be given the arbitrary value of 10.0000 g. or its actual mass if a way of determining its actual mass is available (comparison with a standard 10-g. mass). The change to the basis of the larger weight is made by use of the formula

$$d_2 = (W + d_1) - (W/R)(R + c_1 - c_2)$$

where W = any weight in set; R = final standard; d_1 = correction for W in terms of preliminary standard; d_2 = correction for W in terms of final standard; c_1 = correction for R in terms of preliminary standard; c_2 = correction for R in terms of final standard; $(W + d_1)$ represents W in terms of the preliminary standard; $(R + c_1)$ represents R in terms of the preliminary standard; $c_2 = 0$ if the final standard is assumed to have exactly the nominal value rather than its absolute mass.

The term $(W/R)(R + c_1 - c_2)$ is the aliquot part of the final standard (column 5 of Table 6). Thus, the correction on the 0.020-g. weight of the set described in Table 6 is

$$d_2 = (0.020,09) - (0.020,00/10.000,00)(10.028,27)$$

$$= 0.020,09 - 0.020,06 = +0.000,03$$

Note that the actual mass of the 0.020-g. weight is greater than the aliquot part of the final standard, and that the correction is positive. When the weight is actually used the nominal value is low and the correction is therefore positive.

BUREAU OF STANDARDS CLASSIFICATION OF WEIGHTS

The National Bureau of Standards, Washington, D. C., groups weights into six classes. Weights for commercial use are placed in

TABLE 7. U. S. BUREAU OF STANDARDS TOLERANCES FOR LABORATORY WEIGHTS

Denomination	Classes M and S (milligrams)	Class S2 (milligrams)
1 kg.	5	25
500 g.	3	15
200	1.0	5
100	0.5	2.5
50	0.3	1.5
26	0.2	1.0
20	0.2	1.0
13	0.15	0.75
10	0.15	0.75
5	0.15	0.75
2	0.10	0.50
1	0.10	0.50
500 mg.	0.05	0.25
200	0.05	0.25
100	0.05	0.25
50	0.03	0.15
20	0.03	0.15
10	0.02	0.10
5	0.02	0.10
2	0.01	0.05
1	0.01	0.05

classes A, B, and C. Weights for laboratory use are placed in classes M, S, and S2.

Class M weights are weights of the highest precision and are used for the most reliable reference standards and for weighings of extreme precision, 1 p.p.m. or better. Class M weights must be constructed of only a single piece.

Class S weights are high-grade "analytical" weights. They must be made with the same tolerances as class M weights but may be of two-piece construction.

Class S2 weights are weights of medium quality and are referred to as "second-quality analytical" or "student" weights. The tolerances are five times those of class S.

The Bureau of Standards will calibrate single weights or sets of weights for a fee. If a set conforms to the specifications and tolerances of Table 7, the Bureau issues a "certificate" giving the corrections and true weights. For weights not conforming to the requirements it issues a "report."

PROBLEMS

1. Of nine pennies, eight are identical in weight, and one is slightly heavier than the others. Using the balance only twice it is possible to pick out the heavy penny. Tell how this is done.

2. (a) Sets of weights have eight weights: 50, 20, 20, 10, 5, 2, 2, 1, and some combination of the weights will give every number from 1 to 110. It is possible to devise a set in which only seven weights will give every number from 1 to 127. Tell how this is done.

(b) If the weights may be placed on both pans it is possible to devise a set of weights with less than seven weights. Show how this is done and determine how many weights are needed and what range of numbers is covered.

3. In the double-weighing method of Gauss the inequality in the lengths of the arms of a balance is eliminated and the true value of the weight of the object is obtained by $O = \sqrt{WW'}$. Prove that the arithmetic mean is a satisfactory approximation to the geometric mean. *Hint:* let $W' = W + a$, and expand using the binomial theorem. Rearrange the first two terms of the expansion to give the arithmetic mean, and the next term will be the error.

4. In an actual experiment a 10-g. weight was placed on the left pan of a balance and a second 10-g. weight, designated 10′, was placed on the right pan; the center of swings was found. The weights were then exchanged and it was found that an additional 0.50 mg. had to be added to the right side to return the center of swings to that of the first weighing. Calculate the weight of the 10′-g. weight assuming that the 10-g. weight has the mass 10.000,00 g.

5. Using the data of Problem 4, calculate the ratio of the lengths of the balance arms R/L. In extracting the square root make use of the binomial theorem after casting into the form $R/L = (10)^{1/2}(10 + 0.000,50)^{-1/2}$. *Ans.:* 0.999,975. Check the answer of Problem 4 using this ratio.

6. Calculate the correction to weight in vacuum to be applied to 1 g. of water when weighed in air (density, 0.001,20) with stainless-steel weights (density, 7.82). Repeat the calculation for 1-g. masses of materials having densities of 0.5, 2.5, 5.0, 7.8, 10.0, 15.0, and 20.0. Plot the results on graph paper.

7. A platinum crucible weighing 20.0000 g. was exactly balanced by a nickel crucible on an equal-arm balance. Calculate the difference in the weights of the two crucibles in vacuum. The densities of platinum, nickel, and air, respectively, are 21.45, 8.90, and 0.0012.

8. A set of stainless-steel weights, stated by the manufacturer to meet class S specifications, was sent to the Bureau of Standards for calibration, and the following report was returned to the purchaser.

Report on Set of Metric Weights

Designation	Apparent Mass vs. Brass		True Mass	
	Correction	Value	Correction	Value
(100 g)	0.0 mg	100.000 0 g	+1.0 mg	100.001 0 g
(50 ")	+0.1 "	50.000 1 "	+0.6 "	50.000 6 "
(20 ")*	0.0 "	20.000 0 "	+0.2 "	20.000 2 "
(20 ")	−0.2 "	19.999 8 "	0.0 "	20.000 0 "
(10 ")	+0.40 "	10.000 40 "	+0.50 "	10.000 50 "
(5 ")	+0.30 "	5.000 30 "	+0.35 "	5.000 35 "
(2 ")*	−0.20 "	1.999 80 "	−0.15 "	1.999 85 "
(2 ")	+0.15 "	2.000 15 "	+0.15 "	2.000 15 "
(1 ")	+0.05 "	1.000 05 "	+0.05 "	1.000 05 "
(500 mg)	−0.03 "	0.499 97 "	−0.07 "	0.499 93 "
(200 ") ·	+0.01 "	0.200 01 "	0.00 "	0.200 00 "
(200 ")	0.00 "	0.200 00 "	−0.01 "	0.199 99 "
(100 ")	+0.01 "	0.100 01 "	0.00 "	0.100 00 "
(50 ")	0.00 "	0.050 00 "	0.00 "	0.050 00 "
(20 ") ·	+0.07 "	0.020 07 "	+0.08 "	0.020 08 "
(20 ")	−0.07 "	0.019 93 "	−0.07 "	0.019 93 "
(10 ")	+0.16 "	0.010 16 "	+0.16 "	0.010 16 "
(5 ")	+0.04 "	0.050 04 "	+0.04 "	0.005 04 "

(*a*) Pick out the weights which do not meet class S tolerances; also the one which does not meet class S2 tolerances.

(*b*) A sample was weighed by difference using this set, and the following uncorrected weights were obtained by simply adding the nominal values of the weights used.

15.5150 g.

14.1600 g.

———

1.3550 g.

An accuracy of 1 part in 1000 was desired. Decide if it was necessary to apply the corrections to the weights.

9. It is apparent that, if the sensitivity of a balance is to be constant irrespective of the weight of the objects which may be weighed on it, the load on the balance must somehow be maintained constant. Devise a method by means of which this might be done.

CHAPTER 4

The Calculations

in Gravimetric Analysis

$\cdots$ This led the way to the combinations of gases, and to the *number* of atoms entering into such combinations. Other bodies besides elastic fluids—namely, liquids and solids—were subject to investigation, in consequence of their combining with elastic fluids. Thus a train of investigation was laid for determining the *number* and *weight* of all chemical elementary principles which enter into any sort of combination one with another—*John Dalton.*

PERCENTAGE FROM A GRAVIMETRIC ANALYSIS

The results of a gravimetric analysis are computed by a simple proportion of the weights of the materials involved and their molecular weights. Thus, if a sample containing potassium sulfate was weighed out, dissolved, the sulfate precipitated as barium sulfate, and the barium sulfate filtered off, ignited, and weighed, the calculations would be

$$K_2SO_4 + BaCl_2 = BaSO_4 + 2NaCl$$
$$\underset{174.3}{\underset{\text{Mol. wt.}}{}} \qquad \underset{233.4}{\underset{\text{Mol. wt.}}{}}$$

$$\frac{\text{Wt. } K_2SO_4}{\text{Mol. wt. } K_2SO_4} = \frac{\text{Wt. } BaSO_4}{\text{Mol. wt. } BaSO_4}$$

$$\text{Wt. } K_2SO_4 = (\text{Wt. } BaSO_4)\left[\frac{\text{Mol. wt. } K_2SO_4}{\text{Mol. wt. } BaSO_4}\right]$$

Having thus obtained the weight of potassium sulfate in the sample the per cent of potassium sulfate may be calculated:

$$\text{Per cent } K_2SO_4 = \frac{(\text{Wt. } K_2SO_4)100}{\text{Wt. sample}}$$

Combining the two steps gives

$$\text{Per cent } K_2SO_4 = \frac{(\text{Wt. BaSO}_4)\left[\dfrac{\text{Mol. wt. } K_2SO_4}{\text{Mol. wt. BaSO}_4}\right](100)}{\text{Wt. sample}}$$

The results, of course, do not need to be reported as the same material which was present in the sample; for example, the per cent of sulfur in the sample in the problem just discussed may be desired, in which case the calculations would be made as follows:

$$\text{Per cent } S = \frac{(\text{Wt. BaSO}_4)\left[\dfrac{\text{Mol. wt. } S}{\text{Mol. wt. BaSO}_4}\right](100)}{\text{Wt. sample}}$$

The ratio of the molecular weights of the two materials involved,

$$\left[\frac{K_2SO_4}{BaSO_4}\right] \quad \text{or} \quad \left[\frac{S}{BaSO_4}\right]$$

in the problem just mentioned, is called a *gravimetric conversion factor*. The molecular weight of the substance sought appears in the numerator, the molecular weight of the substance weighed appears in the denominator. The same numbers of the common atom must appear in the numerator as in the denominator. In the cases just mentioned sulfur is the common atom and there is 1 atom of sulfur in the numerator and 1 atom in the denominator. If the per cent ferric sulfate, $Fe_2(SO_4)_3$, in the sample were being reported, the gravimetric conversion factor used would be

$$\left[\frac{Fe_2(SO_4)_3}{3BaSO_4}\right]$$

for obviously 1 molecule of ferric sulfate yields 3 molecules of barium sulfate.

In general, then, the results of a gravimetric analysis are calculated by the formula

$$\text{Per cent } A = \frac{(\text{Wt. } B)\left[\dfrac{x(\text{Mol. wt. } A)}{y(\text{Mol. wt. } B)}\right](100)}{\text{Wt. sample}}$$

in which x and y are chosen so that the numerator and denominator contain the same number of the atom common to A and B, or, somewhat more correctly, x and y are the coefficients of A and B in the chemical equation showing the conversion of substance B into substance A. On some occasions there may be no atom common to substances B and A. For example, it is possible to determine the potassium ferricyanide in a sample by converting it to silver ferricyanide and then converting the silver ferricyanide to silver chloride, the silver chloride being the substance weighed

$$K_3Fe(CN)_6 + 3AgNO_3 = Ag_3Fe(CN)_6 + 3KNO_3$$

$$Ag_3Fe(CN)_6 + 3KCl = 3AgCl + K_3Fe(CN)_6$$

If the results are to be reported as the per cent of potassium ferricyanide, the conversion factor to be used is $[K_3Fe(CN)_6/3AgCl]$.

Gravimetric conversion factors have been calculated for all the common analyses the analytical chemist is called on to make; an extensive table of them will be found in any good handbook of chemistry.

In some gravimetric analyses the final step involves the volatilization of a substance, the loss in weight being measured by weighing the crucible before and after the volatilization operation. Thus, on ignition at 800°, calcium carbonate is decomposed to calcium oxide and carbon dioxide: $CaCO_3 = CaO + CO_2$. The loss in weight can be used to calculate the calcium in the sample, using the general formula developed above and keeping in mind that the loss in weight is carbon dioxide:

$$\text{Per cent Ca} = \frac{(\text{Loss in weight}) \left[\dfrac{Ca}{CO_2}\right] 100}{\text{Wt. sample}}$$

There is obviously no point in this case of first calculating the weight of calcium carbonate and then the weight of calcium oxide from it.

PROBLEMS

1. Indicate, but do not calculate, the gravimetric conversion factors for converting: (*a*) silver chloride to potassium chloride; (*b*) magnesium pyroarsenate to magnesium phosphate; (*c*) magnesium pyrophosphate to phosphorus pentoxide; (*d*) carbon dioxide to calcium carbonate; (*e*) calcium carbonate to carbon dioxide.

2. Indicate, but do not calculate, the gravimetric conversion factors to be used in the following analyses:

Weighed	*Result Reported as*
(*a*) $CaCO_3$	CaO
(*b*) Mn_3O_4	MnO_2
(*c*) Fe_2O_3	Fe_2O_3
(*d*) Fe_2O_3	Fe_3O_4
(*e*) $(NH_4)_3PO_4 \cdot 12MoO_3$	P_2O_5

3. Calculate the numerical values of the following conversion factors and then check the values in one of the chemistry handbooks: (a) potassium perchlorate to potassium oxide; (b) lead chromate to lead.

4. A sample weighing 0.5550 g. containing sodium sulfate and sodium chloride on analysis for sulfate gave 0.7500 g. of barium sulfate. Calculate: (a) the weight of sodium sulfate; (b) the per cent sodium sulfate; and (c) the per cent sulfur in the sample.

5. A sample of orthoclase, a potassium-containing silicate, weighing 0.7568 g., yielded 0.5200 g. of potassium perchlorate on analysis. Calculate the per cent of potassium oxide (K_2O) in the sample.

6. A mixture of calcium carbonate and calcium sulfate weighing 1.0000 g. was ignited at 900°, which converts the carbonate to oxide. The loss in weight was 0.3450 g. Write the equation expressing this dissociation reaction. Calculate the per cent of calcium carbonate in the sample.

7. Calcium oxalate decomposes on being heated at 800° according to the reaction $CaC_2O_4 = CaO + CO + CO_2$. Indicate the conversion factors which would be used in computing the per cent of calcium oxalate in a sample from (a) the weight of carbon monoxide evolved; (b) the weight of carbon dioxide evolved; (c) the loss in weight which occurs on ignition; and (d) the weight of calcium oxide remaining. Criticize the statement made in paragraph 2 of this chapter: The same number of common atoms must appear in the numerator as in the denominator.

8. The carbon dioxide content of a sample of dolomite, a naturally occurring carbonate of calcium and magnesium, was determined by treating the mineral with hydrochloric acid and collecting the carbon dioxide evolved in a weighed tube containing sodium hydroxide. The increase in weight of this tube represents the carbon dioxide absorbed: $2NaOH + CO_2 = Na_2CO_3 + H_2O$. A sample weighing 1.0000 g. gave 0.4500 g. of carbon dioxide. Calculate the per cent of calcium carbonate in the sample assuming that all the carbon dioxide was present as calcium carbonate. Repeat the calculation assuming all the carbon dioxide to be present as magnesium carbonate.

9. The iron in a sample of Mohr's salt, $Fe(NH_4)_2(SO_4)_2 \cdot 6H_2O$, was determined gravimetrically. A sample weighing 0.6580 g. gave 0.1270 g. of ferric oxide. Calculate the purity of the salt.

10. A sample of Mohr's salt was analyzed as described in the preceding problem, but a sample of the same weight gave 0.1640 g. of ferric oxide. Calculate the purity of the salt and explain why the answer obtained may be reasonable.

11. A sample of pure ferric sulfate weighing 0.7960 g. was dissolved, and the iron was precipitated as ferric hydroxide and ignited to ferric oxide. Calculate the weight of ferric oxide which should have been obtained.

FACTOR WEIGHTS

The calculation following a gravimetric analysis is materially simplified by the use of a particular value for the weight of the sample taken for analysis. By making the weight of the sample equal to some multiple of the gravimetric conversion factor, some of the terms cancel and the per cent of the constituent being determined can be computed from the weight of the final substance by inspection. This is most easily seen by making use of the formula previously developed for calculating the results of a gravimetric analysis

$$\text{Per cent } A = \frac{(\text{Wt. } B)F(100)}{\text{Wt. sample}}$$

in which F is the gravimetric factor for converting the weight of substance B (the material finally weighed as the result of the analysis) into the weight of A. If the weight of the sample taken for analysis is equal to the conversion factor F in grams, these terms cancel and the per cent of A is found by multiplying the weight of B by 100. This simplification is commonly used in commercial laboratories when a large number of determinations are being made for the same constituent.

As an example, consider the determination of nickel in steel. Nickel is determined gravimetrically by precipitation and final weighing as the scarlet nickel dimethylglyoxime compound. The factor for converting the weight of this compound into the weight of nickel is 0.2032. If a sample weighing 0.2032 g. is taken for analysis the results of the analysis will be calculated by

$$\text{Per cent Ni} = \frac{(\text{Wt. Ni dimethylglyoxime})(0.2032)(100)}{0.2032}$$

that is, the weight of the precipitate multiplied by 100 gives the per cent of nickel in the sample directly.

If a factor weight is too small to be suitable as a sample weight in grams, the size of the sample may be increased by some simple multiple and the number 100 as used above changed accordingly. Thus, sodium is precipitated and weighed as the slightly soluble triple acetate, $NaMg(UO_2)_3(C_2H_3O_2)_9 \cdot 6.5H_2O$, which contains 1.528 per cent sodium. A sample weight equal to the factor weight in grams, 0.015,28 g., is too small to permit an accurate analysis; one a hundred times larger is more satisfactory. In this case the per cent of sodium would be calculated by

$$\text{Per cent Na} = \frac{(\text{Wt. triple acetate})(0.015,28)(100)}{1.528}$$

$$= (\text{Wt. triple acetate})$$

In commercial practice a slug of metal weighing exactly the factor weight in grams is often used as the weight in weighing out the sample; the sample is poured onto a metal scoop on the balance pan so that sample and slug just balance. The final adjustment is made by adding material from a spatula or removing it with a small brush.

PROBLEMS

Feb. 8

1. The factor for converting nickel dimethylglyoxime into nickel is 0.2032. The nickel in a sample of steel weighing 0.2032 g. was precipitated with dimethylglyoxime, filtered, dried, and weighed. The material so obtained weighed 0.1725 g. Calculate (mentally) the per cent of nickel in the sample. $Na_3\,PO_4$

2. Calculate the weight of a material containing trisodium phosphate which should be taken so that the percentage of trisodium phosphate in the sample is equal to the weight in grams of magnesium pyrophosphate obtained multiplied by 100. $Mg_2P_2O_7$

3. Calculate the weight of sample to be taken so that each 10 mg. of barium sulfate obtained equals 1 per cent of sulfur in the sample.

4. Lead ores are commonly analyzed by converting the lead to lead chromate. What weight of sample should be taken so that each 5 mg. of lead chromate is equal to 2 per cent lead?

B

5. Phosphorus is often weighed as the so-called "yellow precipitate" $(NH_4)_3PO_4 \cdot 12MoO_3$, containing 1.64 per cent phosphorus. Using a sample 50 times the factor weight in grams calculate the number by which the weight of yellow precipitate must be multiplied to give the per cent of phosphorus.

CALCULATION TO DRY BASIS

Coal, soils, plant fiber, and animal tissues and certain other materials gain or lose water to the air during the time between sampling and analysis. This gain or loss depends on the nature of the material and its state of subdivision. It becomes particularly serious during the crushing and grinding operations which precede the analysis. For this reason the sample as received at the laboratory is frequently air dried to bring it into equilibrium with the atmosphere. After that, changes in the moisture content will be relatively insignificant and the analyses to be made on the material can be carried out without further concern for the constancy in the composition of the sample. It is necessary to distinguish, therefore, between results on the "as-received" basis and on the "air-dried" basis. The analyses will be made on the air-dried basis, but the results on the as-received basis will more often be of greater interest.

The air-drying operation in the case of coal is carried out on the entire sample received at the laboratory, usually about 5 lb. The coal, about 8 mesh in size, is placed on large pans, weighed, and placed in an oven 10° to 15° above room temperature until the loss in weight is no longer greater than 0.1 per cent per hour. By determining the loss in weight in this air-drying step it becomes possible to convert the results of analyses on the air-dried basis to results on the as-received basis. It is apparent that the per cent of a constituent will increase as water is lost from the sample during the air-drying operation and therefore that the per cent of some constituent A on the air-dried basis will be greater than that on the as-received basis. The relation between these values becomes apparent by considering a weighed amount of the as-received material which is first air dried and then analyzed for a substance, A:

$$\text{Per cent air-drying loss} = \frac{100(\text{Wt. lost on air drying})}{\text{Original wt.}}$$

$$\text{Per cent } A_{\text{Air dried}} = \frac{(\text{Wt. } A)100}{\text{Original wt.} - \text{Wt. lost on air drying}}$$

$$\text{Per cent } A_{\text{As received}} = \frac{(\text{Wt. } A)100}{\text{Original wt.}}$$

Combination of these equations gives

$$\text{Per cent } A_{\text{As received}} = \text{Per cent } A_{\text{Air dried}}$$

$$- \text{Per cent } A_{\text{Air dried}} \left[\frac{\text{Per cent air-drying loss}}{100} \right]$$

In the special case where moisture is being determined a further quantity of water may be expelled from the air-dried sample by heating at 100°. The moisture on the as-received basis is then the sum of the air-drying loss plus the moisture determined on the air-dried sample and converted to the as-received basis:

$$\text{Per cent water}_{\text{As received}}$$

$$= \text{Per cent air-drying loss} + \text{Per cent water}_{\text{Air dried}}$$

$$- \text{Per cent water}_{\text{Air dried}} \left[\frac{\text{Per cent air-drying loss}}{100} \right]$$

PROBLEMS

1. The air-drying loss on a sample of coal was found to be 10.5 per cent. The air-dried sample was found to contain 4.52 per cent sulfur. Calculate the per cent of sulfur in the coal as received.

2. The same coal mentioned in Problem 1 was also analyzed for other constituents. The moisture remaining in the air-dried sample was determined by heating the sample at 100° for 1 hour; this additional loss was found to be 3.63 per cent. Calculate the total moisture in the coal as received. This particular coal was selling for $14.25 per ton. Calculate how much was paid for the water in a ton of coal.

3. The heating value of the coal of Problem 1 was found in the air-dried sample to be 11,820 B.t.u. per lb. Calculate the heating value on the as-received basis.

4. Combine the first three equations of paragraph 2 of this section to give the final equation for converting results on the air-dried basis to results on the as-received basis.

5. A sample of clay was analyzed as received and found to contain 21.3 per cent aluminum oxide (Al_2O_3) and 6.77 per cent water (oven drying at 150°). Calculate the per cent of aluminum oxide in the sample on the oven-dried basis.

6. A sample of corn was found to contain 6.70 per cent protein and 24.5 per cent moisture. Calculate the per cent of protein if the moisture content is reduced to 10.0 per cent.

7. A sample of superphosphate to be used as fertilizer was analyzed for moisture and for phosphorus. A sample weighing 0.8005 g. lost 0.0125 g. on oven drying. Another sample weighing 0.7300 g. gave 0.2975 g. of magnesium pyrophosphate ($Mg_2P_2O_7$). Calculate the per cent of phosphorus pentoxide (P_2O_5) in the oven-dried material.

8. A specimen of maple wood flooring was suspected of not being sufficiently kiln-dried for immediate use in construction. A sample was taken by boring twenty-six $\frac{3}{4}$-in. holes half through the board. Half the coarse shavings were ground to pass a 40-mesh sieve in a Wiley mill. A third sample consisted of a 2-in. length of the board. All three samples were then dried to constant weight at 110°. The block sample lost 6.57 per cent, indicating its moisture content; the coarse shavings upon similar treatment lost 6.12 per cent; the 40-mesh sawdust lost 5.78 per cent. Explain these differences in moisture content.

PROBLEMS INVOLVING THE SPECIFIC GRAVITY OF SOLUTIONS

Aqueous solutions of acids are generally marketed commercially on the basis of their specific gravity, which is a convenient and accurate measure of the composition or strength of the solution. In using such reagents or other chemicals which are themselves liquids or are dispensed in aqueous solution, it is often more convenient to measure out the reagents by volume rather than by weight. In calculating the volume of reagent required for a specific purpose three steps are usually involved. At the start, it is well to distinguish clearly between specific gravity and density.

Specific gravity is the number of times heavier an object is than an equal volume of water at the same temperature; specific gravity is simply a number and has no dimensions. Density is weight per unit volume and has dimensions, grams per milliliter, pounds per cubic foot, or pounds per gallon. If the density of water can be taken as one,[1] which is usually the case, the specific gravity may be set equal to

[1] The error in doing this is about 2 parts in 1000 at 20° and 4 parts in 1000 at 30°, the density of water at these temperatures being 0.998,23 and 0.995,68, respectively; see Table 10, page 158.

the density in grams per milliliter. The fundamental relation

$$\text{Density} = \frac{\text{Wt. of solution}}{\text{Vol. of solution}}$$

may then be used.

The three steps involved in calculating the volume of liquid reagent to be taken for a specific purpose are: (*a*) calculation of weight of pure chemical required; (*b*) calculation of weight of solution required; and (*c*) calculation of volume of solution required.

Example. Calculate the volume of commercial perchloric acid, sp. gr. 1.71, 72 per cent $HClO_4$, required to prepare 1 l. of 0.10 N perchloric acid.

Step a. The equivalent weight of perchloric acid is 100.5, so that 10.05 g. of $HClO_4$ chemical is required.

Step b.

$$(\text{Wt. of chemical}) = \left[\frac{\text{Per cent of chemical in solution}}{100} \right] (\text{Wt. of solution})$$

$$10.05 = (0.72)(\text{Wt. of 72 per cent solution})$$

Wt. of 72 per cent
solution   = 13.95 g.

Step c.

Vol. of 72 per cent solution = 13.95/1.71 = 8.17 ml.

In some problems the order in which these steps are taken may be reversed, and of course they may all be combined algebraically into one arithmetical computation if desired.

The specific gravities of commercial acids and of ammonia are given in the Appendix, Table A1.

PROBLEMS

1. Phosphoric acid is marketed as "syrupy phosphoric acid" containing 85 per cent H_3PO_4, sp. gr. 1.69. Calculate the volume of this solution required to prepare 5 l. of 1.000 M phosphoric acid solution.

2. Calculate the normality of concentrated nitric acid, sp. gr. 1.42, 72 per cent HNO_3. For convenience place this figure in a new column in Table A1 in the Appendix.

3. Calculate the number of gallons of hydrochloric acid, sp. gr. 1.19, 37 per cent HCl, required to dissolve 500 lb. of limestone consisting of 98 per cent calcium carbonate and 2 per cent insoluble matter (silica and silicate rock). One gallon of water weighs 8.338 lb.

4. Find the volume of commercial ammonia, sp. gr. 0.90, 28 per cent NH_3, which is required to neutralize 150 ml. of sulfuric acid, sp. gr. 1.51, 60.7 per cent H_2SO_4.

5. Aqueous ammonia, sp. gr. 0.90, contains 28 per cent ammonia (NH_3). Calculate the per cent of ammonium hydroxide in the solution assuming all the ammonia to be present in solution as the hydroxide.

6. The specific gravity of 100 per cent (by weight) ethyl alcohol is 0.7939; the specific gravity of a 50 per cent (by weight) alcohol-water mixture is 0.9344. Calculate the decrease in total volume on mixing 100 g. of water with 100 g. of ethyl alcohol.

7. The specific gravity of a solution containing 13.38 per cent sodium thiosulfate is 1.1145. Calculate (a) the grams of sodium thiosulfate per liter and (b) the pounds of sodium thiosulfate per gallon. One gallon of water weighs 8.338 pounds.

8. One hundred pounds of ammonium chloride, 98.0 per cent pure, was dissolved in water and treated with an excess of sodium hydroxide to displace the ammonia. The ammonia evolved was passed through a tower of lump potassium hydroxide to dry it and then absorbed completely by passage into 20.0 gallons of water. Calculate the per cent of ammonia in the resulting solution. Find the specific gravity of this solution, using a handbook of chemistry, and calculate the volume of the solution. One gallon of water weighs 8.338 pounds.

CALCULATION OF EMPIRICAL FORMULAS

An empirical formula can be calculated from the percentage composition of a material. An empirical formula gives the ratio of the numbers of the different kinds of atoms in the molecule but does not tell the actual number of each. Thus, a compound of carbon, hydrogen and oxygen was found by analysis to contain 26.10 per cent carbon, 4.35 per cent hydrogen, and 69.55 per cent oxygen. The percentage of each material is divided by the respective atomic weight

$$\frac{\text{Per cent carbon}}{\text{At. wt. carbon}} = \frac{26.10}{12} = 2.175$$

$$\frac{\text{Per cent hydrogen}}{\text{At. wt. hydrogen}} = \frac{4.35}{1} = 4.35$$

$$\frac{\text{Per cent oxygen}}{\text{At. wt. oxygen}} = \frac{69.55}{16} = 4.37$$

The smallest of these numbers can be divided into the others almost exactly a whole number of times, and the ratios of carbon, hydrogen, and oxygen are therefore 1:2:2. The empirical formula of the compound is thus CH_2O_2. This may not be the actual formula of the compound, for it might equally well be $C_2H_4O_4$ or $C_3H_6O_6$ or some still higher multiple of CH_2O_2. To establish the actual formula a determination of the molecular weight of the compound is required. The molecular weight can be obtained from a measurement of the gas density of the material (the weight required to occupy 22.4 l. at standard pressure and temperature is the gram molecular weight), or of the depression of the freezing point, or of the elevation of the boiling point of a solution of the material. A chemical analysis alone can only give the empirical formula of a compound and cannot establish the true formula.

The results of the analyses of rocks and other silicates, and of many minerals and commercial products which are salts of oxygen-containing acids are reported often as the per cent of the oxide rather than the per cent of the element. The sum of the percentages of the various oxides composing the material will add up to 100. Given the per cent of oxides of a material the empirical formula may be calculated as above by dividing the percentages by the molecular weights of the respective oxides. Thus, the mineral dolomite was found on analysis to contain 30.5 per cent calcium oxide, 21.8 per cent magnesium oxide, and 47.7 per cent carbon dioxide. Without calculating the per cent of elemental calcium or magnesium in the material the empirical formula is determined as follows:

$$\frac{\text{Per cent CaO}}{\text{Mol. wt. CaO}} = \frac{30.5}{56} = 0.545$$

$$\frac{\text{Per cent MgO}}{\text{Mol. wt. MgO}} = \frac{21.8}{40} = 0.545$$

$$\frac{\text{Per cent CO}_2}{\text{Mol. wt. CO}_2} = \frac{47.7}{44} = 1.085$$

The least common denominator is 0.545, and the ratios are obviously $CaO:MgO:CO_2 = 1:1:2$. This is written chemically as $CaO \cdot MgO \cdot 2CO_2$ or as $CaMg(CO_3)_2$.

PROBLEMS

1. A compound of oxygen and hydrogen was found to contain 11.1 per cent hydrogen and 88.9 per cent óxygen. Determine the empirical formula of the compound.

2. A pure material was found on analysis to be 100 per cent oxygen. Determine the empirical formula of the material. Name the possibilities as to the identity of the material.

3. A pure salt resembling ammonium chloride was analyzed and found to contain 13.80 per cent nitrogen, 3.94 per cent hydrogen, and 35.00 per cent chloride. It is assumed that the remainder of the material was oxygen (for which there is no convenient method of analysis). Determine the empirical formula of the material. A solution of the material was found to conduct electricity about like a solu-

tion of sodium chloride, and a measurement of its freezing point showed that the same lowering was obtained with 1.010 g. of the material per l. of solution as with 0.585 g. of sodium chloride per l. Identify the material.

4. The mineral emerald was analyzed, and the results were reported as usual in silicate analyses as the percentage of oxides: 14.0 per cent beryllium oxide (BeO), 19.0 per cent aluminum oxide (Al_2O_3), and 67.0 per cent silica (SiO_2). Calculate the empirical formula of the mineral. Do not calculate the per cent of metal in each oxide but find the empirical formula in terms of the oxides.

THE COMPOSITION OF MIXTURES OF SOLIDS

The ultimate composition of a mixture of materials can be calculated from the weights of the components mixed without difficulty, if there is no element common to the components. Thus, if sodium chloride is mixed with potassium sulfate the per cent of chloride in the mixture is simply

$$\text{Per cent Cl} = \frac{(\text{Wt. NaCl}) \left[\dfrac{\text{Cl}}{\text{NaCl}}\right] 100}{\text{Wt. NaCl} + \text{Wt. } K_2SO_4}$$

The per cent of chloride in the mixture could vary from 0 (all potassium sulfate) to 60.66 [all sodium chloride, 100(Cl/NaCl)].

If it is desired to compute the per cent of an element common to both components of the mixture the problem is a bit more complicated. It is necessary to calculate the weight of the element in each component and to add these amounts. Thus, the chloride content of a mixture of sodium chloride and potassium chloride is calculated in the following manner:

$$\text{Wt. Cl in NaCl} = (\text{Wt. NaCl}) \left[\frac{\text{Cl}}{\text{NaCl}}\right]$$

$$\text{Wt. Cl in KCl} = (\text{Wt. KCl}) \left[\frac{\text{Cl}}{\text{KCl}}\right]$$

$$\text{Per cent Cl} = \frac{(\text{Wt. NaCl}) \left[\dfrac{\text{Cl}}{\text{NaCl}}\right] + (\text{Wt. KCl}) \left[\dfrac{\text{Cl}}{\text{KCl}}\right]}{\text{Wt. NaCl} + \text{Wt. KCl}}$$

The amounts of the salts mixed may be expressed in per cent, in which case the equation becomes

$$\text{Per cent Cl} = (\text{Per cent NaCl}) \left[\frac{\text{Cl}}{\text{NaCl}}\right] + (\text{Per cent KCl}) \left[\frac{\text{Cl}}{\text{KCl}}\right]$$

If only the two salts are mixed it is apparent that

$$(\text{Per cent KCl}) = 100 - (\text{Per cent NaCl})$$

so that   Per cent Cl = $(\text{Per cent NaCl}) \left[\dfrac{\text{Cl}}{\text{NaCl}}\right]$

$$+ \; [100 - (\text{Per cent NaCl})] \left[\dfrac{\text{Cl}}{\text{KCl}}\right]$$

or   Per cent Cl = $(\text{Per cent NaCl}) \left\{ \left[\dfrac{\text{Cl}}{\text{NaCl}}\right] - \left[\dfrac{\text{Cl}}{\text{KCl}}\right] \right\} + 100 \left[\dfrac{\text{Cl}}{\text{KCl}}\right]$

This is the equation of the form $y = mx + b$, a straight line. A graph of this function, Fig. 35, is useful if the chloride content of a number of mixtures of these particular salts must be calculated.

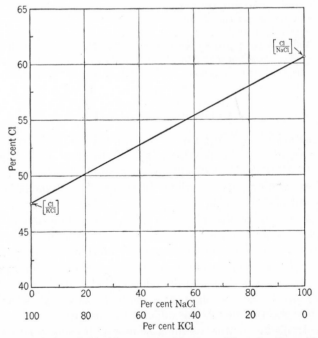

Fig. 35.   Variation of chloride content with composition of sodium chloride-potassium chloride mixtures.

The composition of mixtures is occasionally expressed in the ratio of parts of one component to parts of another. This refers to parts by weight and should be handled as shown above. In certain types of chemical work it is desired to have a certain ratio between the numbers of molecules of each component. A mixture containing equimolecular quantities of sodium chloride and potassium chloride would contain 58.46 parts by weight of sodium chloride and 74.56 parts by weight of potassium chloride, the molecular weights being 58.46 and 74.56.

PROBLEMS

1. Calculate the per cent of sulfur in a mixture consisting of 30 per cent calcium sulfate and 70 per cent barium sulfate.

2. Calculate the per cent of total sulfur in a mixture prepared by mixing 5 parts (by weight) of sulfur with 2 parts of barium sulfate.

3. Show by means of a graph how the per cent of potassium in mixtures of potassium chloride and potassium sulfate varies with the composition of the mixture. Indicate on the graph the compositions corresponding to (a) equal parts by weight, and (b) equimolecular amounts of the two salts.

4. A metallurgist has an ingot weighing 5.00 kg. of a brass containing 65.5 per cent copper. Compute the weight of pure copper he should melt with the brass to bring the copper content to 70.0 per cent.

5. The composition of two iron ores is, respectively, 55.0 and 40.5 per cent iron and 0.35 and 0.78 per cent phosphorus pentoxide. Calculate the weight of the second ore which should be added to 5.00 tons of the first so that the mixture contains 50.0 per cent iron. Calculate the per cent of phosphorus pentoxide in the mixture.

√ INDIRECT ANALYSIS

Two metals in a mixture can be determined indirectly by weighing them together in one chemical form and then together in a second form. A mixture of calcium and strontium, for example, can be weighed first as calcium chloride plus strontium chloride and then converted to the sulfates and weighed again. Or, the second piece of data can involve the anion content of the mixture. Thus, the sodium and potassium in a mixture of the two can be determined by converting them to their chlorides for weighing and subsequently determining the chloride in the mixture. As far as the mathematics is concerned it is only necessary to have two pieces of data and the relations between them to solve for two unknowns. At first sight such methods sound attractive, especially when the two metals are difficult to separate, as they are in a calcium-strontium mixture or in a sodium-potassium mixture. Unfortunately, because of the nature of the calculations, errors in the measurements become greatly magnified, and in general such indirect analyses are rather unsatisfactory. The limitations on the method can be seen by following through the calculations.

In the method of determining sodium and potassium just outlined the data consist of the weight of the sample, the weight of sodium chloride and the weight of silver chloride obtained from the mixture. The unknowns are the weights of sodium and potassium in the sample.

The weight of sodium multiplied by the conversion factor [NaCl/Na] gives the weight of sodium chloride in the mixture of combined chlorides, and similar relations give the weights of potassium chloride and of silver chloride. This leads to the equations

$$(\text{Wt. Na})[\text{NaCl/Na}] + (\text{Wt. K})[\text{KCl/K}] = (\text{Wt. NaCl} + \text{KCl})$$

$$(\text{Wt. Na})[\text{AgCl/Na}] + (\text{Wt. K})[\text{AgCl/K}] = (\text{Wt. AgCl})$$

Solution of these equations algebraically gives

$$\text{Wt. Na} = \frac{(\text{Wt. NaCl} + \text{KCl})[\text{AgCl/K}] - (\text{Wt. AgCl})[\text{KCl/K}]}{[\text{NaCl/Na}][\text{AgCl/K}] - [\text{KCl/K}][\text{AgCl/Na}]}$$

$$\text{Wt. K} = \frac{(\text{Wt. NaCl} + \text{KCl})[\text{AgCl/Na}] - (\text{Wt. AgCl})[\text{NaCl/Na}]}{[\text{KCl/K}][\text{AgCl/Na}] - [\text{NaCl/Na}][\text{AgCl/K}]}$$

Thus, in one such analysis a sample weighing 1.0103 g. gave 0.8214 g. of sodium chloride plus potassium chloride, and the mixture subsequently yielded 1.8713 g. of silver chloride. Substituting these data and the various molecular weights in the above formulas yields for the weight of sodium 0.2170 g. and for the potassium 0.1415 g. From these values the percentages of the two metals in the sample can easily be calculated.

This is an unusually favorable case because of the high ratio of the atomic weights of potassium to sodium and of silver to potassium and sodium. Usually in the process of taking the differences involved in these calculations the experimental errors become greatly magnified, particularly if the atomic weights of the metals are not greatly separated.

Many such indirect methods of analysis can be devised. In general, methods for making calculations can be derived by making use of the appropriate conversion factors and simultaneous equations in a manner similar to that employed in the example above.

PROBLEMS

1. A mixture of 0.2500 g. of lithium chloride and 0.1000 g. of potassium chloride was treated with an excess of sulfuric acid and ignited gently to drive off the sulfuric acid and render the remaining sulfates anhydrous. Calculate the weight of the combined sulfates obtained.

2. The sodium and potassium in a sample weighing 1.0103 g. was converted quantitatively to a mixture of sodium chloride and potassium chloride, and the mixture was subsequently treated with sulfuric acid to convert the chlorides to the anhydrous sulfates. The weight of the combined chlorides was 0.8214 g.; the weight of the combined sulfates 0.8949 g. Calculate the per cent of sodium and of potassium in the sample.

CHAPTER 5

Mass Action and
the Solubility-Product Principle

··· and in view of these facts we may well consider the solubility product constant an approximate empirical principle, much in the same way as so many other important principles concerning electrolytes are still simply empirical—Julius Stieglitz.

Practically all chemical reactions are reversible. Even those which are normally considered to be complete, such as the neutralization of a strong acid with a strong base, come to equilibrium and stop somewhat short of absolute completion. The reversible character of chemical reactions and the factors which determine the amounts of reactants and products are matters of great moment. In the large-scale manufacture of chemicals the monetary value of a product usually demands that the reactions used be forced as far as practically possible in the direction which will increase the yield. In analytical chemistry such necessity is even greater, for the results of analyses can only be of significance when reactions are employed whose equilibria lie close to 100 per cent in one direction.

Temperature, of course, has a great effect on the rate at which reactions take place and influences greatly the amounts of reactants and products remaining when equilibrium has been established. Pressure also has an effect on the equilibrium conditions, particularly in reactions involving gases. The concentrations of the reactants and the products also play a big part. Thus, in the reaction

$$A + B = C + D$$

an increase in the amount of either A or B in the reacting mixture will cause the reaction to go further to the right. Conversely, a greater concentration of either C or D will shift the equilibrium to the left. This effect is known as the law of mass action. It is a special case of the Le Châtelier principle, which states that, when a stress is applied to a system, the system moves so as to relieve the stress.

The quantitative expression of the law of mass action is derived from a consideration of the rates at which the forward and back reactions take place. A reaction of A with B occurs whenever A and B collide with sufficient energy. The number of such collisions depends on the numbers of molecules of A and of B in a given volume of the reaction mixture. If the number of molecules of A is doubled the probability of a given molecule of B colliding with a molecule of A is doubled. Instead of dealing with the actual numbers of the molecules involved, it is more convenient to use molar concentrations. The number of molecules in 1 gram molecular weight is the same for every material (Avogadro's number, 6.06×10^{23}). Molar concentration is, therefore, a measure of the number of molecules in a liter and can be used wherever the type of calculation or thinking is based on the numbers of molecules in a given volume. The molar concentration of a material is denoted by brackets enclosing the formula of the material; thus the molar concentration of material A is denoted by $[A]$.

The foregoing statement that the rate of formation of C (and at the same time of D) is proportional to the molar concentrations of the reactants A and B can be expressed mathematically

$$R_C = k_1[A][B]$$

in which R_C is the increase in the molar concentration of C in a given interval of time. The reverse reaction in a similar manner is proportional to the molar concentrations of C and of D

$$-R_C = k_2[C][D]$$

the negative sign indicating decrease in the concentration of C. The constants k_1 and k_2 are called rate constants. They do not have the same values, for the forward and reverse reactions do not proceed at the same rate. When the reaction is over and equilibrium has been established the rate at which C (and at the same time D) is being formed is just equal to the rate at which it is being used up in the reverse reaction; that is

$$R_C = -R_C$$

Therefore $$k_1[A][B] = k_2[C][D]$$

and $$K = \frac{k_1}{k_2} = \frac{[C][D]}{[A][B]}$$

the new constant K being the equilibrium constant of the reaction.

The situation is somewhat more complicated if two or more molecules of a substance enter the reaction. Thus, for the reaction

$$2A + B = A_2B$$

the number of collisions of B with A to form the intermediate AB is proportional to the number of molecules of A and of B present. The number of collisions of the intermediate AB with A is not proportional to the number of molecules of A but to this number minus 1, for 1 molecule of A has already reacted with B and has been removed from the solution. The rate at which B reacts with A is thus proportional to $n(n - 1)$ if n is the number of molecules of A. The actual number of molecules of A even in extremely dilute solutions is very large, and n is indistinguishable from $n - 1$. The rate at which B reacts with A, then, is proportional to n^2. The rate at which A_2B forms, then, is proportional to the molar concentration of A squared and to the molar concentration of B

$$R_{A_2B} = k_1[A]^2[B]$$

The rate at which the reverse reaction takes place is proportional to the number of molecules of A_2B (molar concentration of A_2B)

$$-R_{A_2B} = k_2[A_2B]$$

At equilibrium the rates of formation and decomposition are equal

$$R_{A_2B} = -R_{A_2B}$$

and

$$k_1[A]^2[B] = k_2[A_2B]$$

$$K = \frac{k_1}{k_2} = \frac{[A_2B]}{[A]^2[B]}$$

K being the equilibrium constant. The molar concentration of A, the substance which enters the reaction twice, is squared. In general, the equilibrium constant is defined as the product of the molar concentrations of the products of the reaction divided by the molar concentrations of the reactants, each concentration being raised to the power indicated by the number of molecules appearing in the balanced equation. Thus, for the general reaction

$$aA + bB = cC + dD$$

$$K = \frac{[C]^c[D]^d}{[A]^a[B]^b}$$

The mass-action principle can be applied to the ionization of electrolytes, the ionization reaction being a reversible one. For example, the extent of ionization of acetic acid

$$HC_2H_3O_2 = H^+ + C_2H_3O_2^-$$

is expressed quantitatively by the so-called acid dissociation constant

$$K_A = \frac{[H^+][C_2H_3O_2^-]}{[HC_2H_3O_2]} = 1.75 \times 10^{-5}$$

Considerable use is made of such constants and equilibrium expressions in volumetric analysis, especially in reactions between acids and bases. In gravimetric analysis the mass-action law is applied to the equilibrium between solids and solutions saturated with them. This application of the mass-action law is known as the *solubility-product principle.*

The Solubility-Product Principle. Between a crystal and a solution with which it is in contact there exists a continual exchange of ions. Some ions are always leaving the crystal to enter the solution and some are always returning to the crystal, but at all times the crystal and the solution remain electrically neutral. Consider a compound having the general formula, A_xB_y, which ionizes

$$A_xB_y = xA^{y+} + yB^{x-}$$

to give x positively charged ions of A and y negatively charged ions of B. Whenever x positive ions dissolve, y negative ions must also dissolve to maintain the electrical neutrality of the solution and crystal.

The crystal surface is considered to be a layer of ions, laid down in some regular pattern, there being x ions of A for every y ions of B in the surface layer. The rate at which the ions pass from the crystal into the solution depends on the area M of the crystal surface:

$$\text{Rate of solution} = k_1M$$

The rate at which the ions are deposited on the crystal, x ions of A and y ions of B more or less simultaneously, also depends on the area of the surface exposed. It also depends on the numbers of the ions in solution. Obviously if the number of ions of A in the solution is doubled, the chances of depositing the first ion of A in a certain interval of time is also doubled. The rate at which the first ion of A is deposited is proportional, then, to the number of ions of A, n_A, in the solution:

$$\text{Rate of deposition of } A_1 = k'n_A$$

The rate at which the second ion is deposited is proportional to $n_A - 1$, since 1 molecule of A was removed when the first ion of A was deposited:

$$\text{Rate of deposition of } A_2 = k''(n_A - 1)$$

In a similar manner

$$\text{Rate of deposition of } A_3 = k'''(n_A - 2)$$

$$\cdot \ \cdot \ \cdot \ \cdot \ \cdot \ \cdot \ \cdot \ \cdot \ \cdot \ \cdot \ \cdot \ \cdot \ \cdot \ \cdot \ \cdot \ \cdot \ \cdot \ \cdot \ \cdot$$

$$\text{Rate of deposition of } A_x = k^{x'}[n_A - (x - 1)]$$

The rate at which the deposition of the first two ions of A takes place is proportional to the product [1] $n_A(n_A - 1)$. The rate at which the first three are deposited is proportional to $n_A(n_A - 1)(n_A - 2)$. In general, the rate for x ions of A is proportional to $n_A(n_A - 1)(n_A - 2)$ $\cdots [n_A - (X - 1)]$. The number of ions present even in exceedingly dilute solutions is very great (Avogadro's number is 6.06×10^{23}), and there is little difference between n_A and n_A minus a very small number such as x; consequently the rate of deposition of x ions of A is proportional to n_A raised to the x power, $n_A{}^x$.

The same reasoning is extended to the negatively charged ions B. The rate of deposition of y ions of B is proportional to $n_B{}^y$. The rate of deposition of x ions of A and y ions of B is thus proportional to the surface M and to $n_A{}^x$ and to $n_B{}^y$.

$$\text{Rate of deposition of } A_xB_y = k_2Mn_A{}^xn_B{}^y$$

When the solution has become saturated and equilibrium has been reached the rate at which the material is dissolving just equals the rate at which it is depositing, and therefore

$$k_1M = k_2Mn_A{}^xn_B{}^y$$

from which
$$K = \frac{k_1}{k_2} = n_A{}^xn_B{}^y$$

It is more convenient to use molar concentration, which is directly proportional to the number of molecules than the number of molecules themselves. Rewriting this equation in terms of molar concentrations gives

$$S_{A_xB_y} = [A]^x[B]^y$$

The constant $S_{A_xB_y}$ is called the solubility product of the substance A_xB_y. It is equal to the product of the molar concentrations of the

[1] This is an application of the general rules of permutation. There are three ways of traveling from Chicago to Detroit by rail (via Pennsylvania, Michigan Central, or Grand Trunk) and two ways of traveling from Detroit to Buffalo (Michigan Central through Ontario, and New York Central south of Lake Erie); the number of ways of traveling from Chicago to Buffalo via Detroit is 3×2 or 6, since for each of the first three ways of making the trip to Detroit either of two ways could be used to continue on to Buffalo.

ions involved each raised to a power equal to the number of ions furnished by the compound on ionizing. The solubility-product principle applies only to slightly soluble materials, and the numerical value is good only at the temperature specified. The solubility-product expression and the numerical values of the constant at room temperature for a few typical, insoluble salts are given in the accompanying table. A more extensive table of solubility products is given in the Appendix, Table A2.

Silver chloride $\qquad S_{AgCl} = [Ag^+][Cl^-] = 1.7 \times 10^{-10} \left(\dfrac{moles}{liter}\right)^2$

Silver chromate $\qquad S_{Ag_2CrO_4} = [Ag^+]^2[CrO_4^=] = 1.1 \times 10^{-12} \left(\dfrac{moles}{liter}\right)^3$

Silver phosphate $\qquad S_{Ag_3PO_4} = [Ag^+]^3[PO_4^\equiv] = 1.4 \times 10^{-18} \left(\dfrac{moles}{liter}\right)^4$

Calcium fluoride $\qquad S_{CaF_2} = [Ca^{++}][F^-]^2 = 3.9 \times 10^{-11} \left(\dfrac{moles}{liter}\right)^3$

Calcium sulfate $\qquad S_{CaSO_4} = [Ca^{++}][SO_4^=] = 6.1 \times 10^{-5} \left(\dfrac{moles}{liter}\right)^2$

Lead phosphate $\qquad S_{Pb_3(PO_4)_2} = [Pb^{++}]^3[PO_4^\equiv]^2 = 1.5 \times 10^{-32} \left(\dfrac{moles}{liter}\right)^5$

Aluminum hydroxide $\qquad S_{Al(OH)_3} = [Al^{+++}][OH^-]^3 = 3.7 \times 10^{-15} \left(\dfrac{moles}{liter}\right)^4$

Arsenic sulfide $\qquad S_{As_2S_3} = [As^{+++}]^2[S^=]^3 = 1.1 \times 10^{-33} \left(\dfrac{moles}{liter}\right)^5$

The dimensions of the solubility-product constant vary from compound to compound. Thus, for silver chloride which furnishes two ions, the solubility-product constant has the dimensions (moles/liter) $\times$ (moles/liter) or (moles/liter)^2. For silver chromate, which gives three ions, the solubility-product constant has the dimensions (moles/liter)^3. In general, the dimensions of the solubility-product constant are moles per liter raised to a power equal to the number of ions formed by the ionization of the compound when dissolved.

Since the solubility product is a constant at a given temperature it can be used for calculating the amount of dissolved material present in solution when different amounts of one ion are present in excess (common-ion effect). This is the principal use of the solubility-product law. The solubility product is not a direct measure of the solubility of a material and cannot be used directly for determining even relative solubilities except for compounds of the same valence type, that is, compounds having the same general formula, AB, AB_2, A_3B, and so on.

In connection with the use of molar concentration in equilibrium calculations it should be noted that when an electrolyte is dissolved in water the molar concentration of the compound and of the ions in the solution may not be the same. In a 1 M solution of sodium chloride, the salt being completely ionized, the solution is also 1 M in sodium ions and 1 M in chloride ions. In a 1 M solution of barium chloride, however, the molar concentration of the barium is 1 M, but 2 gram molecular weights of chloride are present and the solution is 2 M in chloride. These relations can be expressed in mathematical form

1 M NaCl	1 M BaCl$_2$	1 M Na$_3$PO$_4$
[NaCl] = 1	[BaCl$_2$] = 1	[Na$_3$PO$_4$] = 1
[NaCl] = [Na$^+$] = [Cl$^-$]	[Ba^{++}] = [BaCl$_2$] = 1	[Na$^+$] = 3[Na$_3$PO$_4$]
	[Cl$^-$] = 2[Ba^{++}] = 2	[Na$^+$] = 3[PO$_4$$^=$]
		[PO$_4$$^=$] = [Na$_3PO_4$]

In practice, the solubility of a material is determined experimentally and the solubility product calculated. Thus, it has been found that a saturated solution of barium sulfate contains 0.0023 g. of barium sulfate per l. The molecular weight of barium sulfate is 233. The solution is therefore $0.0023/233 = 1.0 \times 10^{-5}$ M in barium sulfate. Since each barium sulfate molecule consists of 1 barium atom and 1 sulfate radical the concentrations of the barium ion and of the sulfate ion are both also 1.0×10^{-5}:

$$[\text{BaSO}_4] = \frac{0.0023}{233} = 1.0 \times 10^{-5}$$

$$[\text{Ba}^{++}] = 1.0 \times 10^{-5} \qquad [\text{SO}_4{}^=] = 1.0 \times 10^{-5}$$

$$S_{\text{BaSO}_4} = [\text{Ba}^{++}][\text{SO}_4{}^=] = (1.0 \times 10^{-5})(1.0 \times 10^{-5})$$

$$= 1.0 \times 10^{-10} \left(\frac{\text{moles}}{\text{liter}}\right)^2$$

that is, the solubility product of barium sulfate is 1.0×10^{-10} (moles/liter)^2.

The solubility of strontium fluoride has been found to be 0.114 g. per l. Its molecular weight is 126, so that the molar concentration of a saturated solution is $[\text{SrF}_2] = 9.05 \times 10^{-4}$. In this solution

$$[\text{Sr}^{++}] = [\text{SrF}_2] \qquad \text{and} \qquad [\text{F}^-] = 2[\text{SrF}_2]$$

$$= 9.05 \times 10^{-4} \qquad\qquad\qquad = 2 \times 9.05 \times 10^{-4}$$

The solubility product then becomes

$$S_{SrF_2} = [Sr^{++}][F^-]^2$$

$$= (9.05 \times 10^{-4})(2 \times 9.05 \times 10^{-4})^2$$

$$= 3.0 \times 10^{-9} \left(\frac{moles}{liter}\right)^3$$

Given the numerical value of the solubility product, the calculation can be reversed. Thus, the solubility product of silver chromate is

$$S_{Ag_2CrO_4} = [Ag^+]^2[CrO_4^=] = 2 \times 10^{-12} \left(\frac{moles}{liter}\right)^3$$

In a saturated water solution the following relations hold for the concentrations of the silver ion, the chromate ion, and the dissolved silver chromate

$$[Ag^+] = 2[CrO_4^=] \quad [Ag^+] = 2[Ag_2CrO_4] \quad [Ag_2CrO_4] = [CrO_4^=]$$

Since we are interested ultimately in finding the concentration of dissolved silver chromate the concentrations of silver and chromate appearing in the solubility-product expression may be replaced by the concentrations of silver chromate just given. This yields

$$S_{Ag_2CrO_4} = (2[Ag_2CrO_4])^2[Ag_2CrO_4] = 2 \times 10^{-12}$$

$$[Ag_2CrO_4]^3 = \tfrac{2}{4} \times 10^{-12}$$

$$[Ag_2CrO_4] = \sqrt[3]{0.5 \times 10^{-12}} = \sqrt[3]{500 \times 10^{-15}}$$

$$[Ag_2CrO_4] = 7.9 \times 10^{-5}$$

or, since the molecular weight of silver chromate is 332, the amount of dissolved silver chromate in a saturated solution is $7.9 \times 10^{-5} \times 332$ = 0.0261 g. Ag_2CrO_4 per l.

The Common-Ion Effect. Because the solubility product of a given material is a constant at a given temperature, it follows that if the concentration of one of the ions is increased the concentration of the other must fall. As mentioned above, in a saturated solution of barium sulfate, the molar concentration of the barium ion and of the sulfate ion are equal and have a numerical value of 1.0×10^{-5}. If the sulfate concentration is increased to 1×10^{-4} M by the addition of potassium sulfate, the barium-ion concentration must drop to 1×10^{-6} M so that the product of the two always equals the solubility-product constant, 1×10^{-10} (moles/liter)^2. Some barium is precipitated as barium sulfate to bring this about. Conversely, if barium chloride is added to a saturated solution of barium sulfate, some barium sulfate will precipitate, and, when equilibrium has been established, the molar concentrations of the barium and sulfate ions when multiplied together give a value of 1×10^{-10} (moles/liter)^2. This is known as the *common-ion effect*. Obviously it is of great value, for it provides a practical way of materially reducing the solubility of precipitates and of securing complete precipitation, a matter of importance in gravimetric analysis.

As an illustration of the common-ion effect, the experimentally measured solubilities of thallous chloride, TlCl, in solutions of various salts are given in Table 8. The data are plotted in Fig. 36 for the

TABLE 8. SOLUBILITY OF THALLOUS CHLORIDE IN THE PRESENCE OF OTHER SALTS, IN MOLES PER LITER AT 25°

| Concentration of Other Salt Equivalents per Liter ^{a} | Other Salt Present | | | | | | |
| | Chloride Common Ion | | | Thallous Common Ion | | No Common Ion | |
	KCl	HCl	BaCl₂	TlNO₃	Tl₂SO₄	KNO₃	K₂SO₄
0	0.016,07	0.016,07	0.016,07	0.016,07	0.016,07	0.016,07	0.016,07
0.020					0.010,34	0.017,16	0.017,79
0.025	0.008,69	0.008,66	0.008,98	0.008,80			
0.050	0.005,90	0.005,83	0.006,18	0.006,24	0.006,77	0.018,26	0.019,42
0.100	0.003,96	0.003,83	0.004,16	0.004,22	0.004,68	0.019,61	0.021,37
0.200	0.002,68	0.002,53	0.002,82				
0.300						0.023,13	0.026,00
1.000						0.030,72	0.034,16

^{a} Equal to molar concentration for KCl, HCl, BaCl₂, TlNO₃; equal to one-half molar concentration for Tl₂SO₄ and K₂SO₄.

solutions containing potassium chloride, the total chloride (chloride from potassium chloride plus that from dissolved thallous chloride) being plotted as the abscissa. The solubility calculated on the assumption that the solubility-product law holds is shown in the dotted curve. As will be seen the agreement is not exact, the decrease in solubility being less than that calculated.

Limitations of the Solubility-Product Principle. The principle of mass action can be applied in qualitative fashion in almost every branch of chemistry. Quantitative calculations based on it, however, are exact only under certain conditions. This is also true of the solubility-product principle and its corollary, the common-ion effect, which are simple, special cases of the mass-action law. The solubility-product principles applies only to insoluble materials; it is of no value for soluble salts such as sodium chloride and potassium sulfate. The principle works best in very dilute solutions and is of no value if the concentration of the common ion exceeds 0.1 M. In general, also, the principle applies more exactly to the simpler types of electrolytes, AB, A_2B and AB_2, than to the more complex types.

These restrictions are unfortunate, of course, for many practical cases arising in analytical work cannot be accurately handled in a

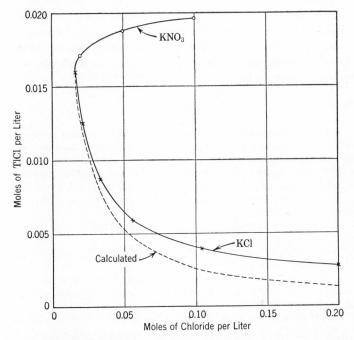

Fig. 36. The solubility of thallous chloride in solutions containing the common ion chloride and the diverse ions potassium and nitrate.

quantitative manner. One important application is in deciding the amount of excess reactant which can be added to advantage in precipitating an insoluble compound. The common ion cannot be pushed beyond 0.2 M, for at greater concentrations of common ion the solubility of many salts begins to increase.

The solubility product makes no mention of the rate at which equilibrium will be reached. In the case of small amounts of materials the time required for a precipitate to form and settle out completely may be quite appreciable. After the addition of sulfate to a solution less than 0.0001 M in barium ion it takes almost an hour for barium sulfate to precipitate at room temperature.

Diverse-Ion Effect. The solubility of a slightly soluble salt is increased by the presence in solution of electrolytes which have no common ion with the insoluble material. This is clearly seen in the case of thallous chloride, Table 8 and Fig. 36, which give the solubility of thallous chloride in solutions containing potassium nitrate and potassium sulfate. This is known as the diverse-ion effect. A quantitative treatment of the increase in solubility by foreign electrolytes has been worked out (a result of the interionic attraction theory), but the study of this is left for the course in physical chemistry. It is important, however, to note that, the less foreign salt introduced into the solution during the course of an analysis, the more complete precipitation is likely to be.

PROBLEMS

1. Write the mathematical expression defining the solubility product of each of the following materials: silver chloride, cuprous molybdate, thallous ferricyanide, thallous ferrocyanide, and barium ferrocyanide.

2. Write the mathematical expression defining the solubility product of each of the following salts and look up the numerical value of each in Table A2 on solubility-product values in the Appendix: barium iodate, strontium chromate, lead phosphate, and arsenious sulfide.

3. Go through the reasoning that leads to the formulation of the solubility-product law, using as example calcium hydroxide.

4. The solubility of lead chloride in water at 0° is 0.673 g. per 100 ml. Calculate the solubility product at this temperature.

5. A measurement of the amount of lead in a liter of water saturated with lead sulfate at 25° gave a value of 0.0314 g. of Pb per l. Calculate the solubility product of lead sulfate at this temperature.

6. At 20° silver arsenate dissolves in water to give a saturated solution containing 8.5×10^{-4} g. of Ag_3AsO_4 per 100 ml. Calculate its solubility product.

7. Calculate the solubility products of silver chloride at 10° and 100°, the solubility in grams per liter of silver chloride being 0.000,895 and 0.0208 at these temperatures respectively.

8. The solubility product of cuprous chloride, CuCl, is 1.8×10^{-7} (moles/liter)^2. Calculate the molar concentration of a saturated cuprous chloride solution.

9. The solubility product of lead fluoride at 25° is 3.7×10^{-8} (moles/liter)^3. Calculate the solubility of lead fluoride in (a) moles per liter and (b) grams per liter.

10. Calculate the amount of silver, in grams, present in 100 ml. of a saturated solution of silver phosphate. $S_{Ag_3PO_4} = 1.4 \times 10^{-18}$ (moles/liter)^4.

11. Using the solubility product of barium arsenate, $Ba_3(AsO_4)_2$, given in the Appendix, Table A2, calculate the solubility of barium arsenate in grams per liter.

12. Calculate the number of milliliters of water at 25° required to dissolve 1 g. of cupric sulfide. $S_{CuS} = 8.5 \times 10^{-45}$ (moles/liter)^2(25°).

13. List the following silver salts in the order of their solubility in grams of silver per 100 ml. of water: silver chloride, $S_{AgCl} = 1.7 \times 10^{-10}$ (moles/liter)^2;

silver chromate, $S_{Ag_2CrO_4} = 1.1 \times 10^{-12}$ (moles/liter)^3; silver carbonate, $S_{Ag_2CO_3}$ $= 8.2 \times 10^{-12}$ (moles/liter)^3; silver cyanide, $S_{AgCN} = 2.7 \times 10^{-12}$ (moles/liter)^2.

14. Arrange the following compounds in order of their decreasing solubility in water: cuprous iodide, lanthanum iodate, lead carbonate, and lead iodate. See Table A2 on solubility-product values in the Appendix.

15. Calculate the amount of silver remaining in 500 ml. of solution from which silver chloride was precipitated by the addition of sufficient sodium chloride to make the final concentration of chloride 0.05 M. $S_{AgCl} = 1.0 \times 10^{-10}$ (moles/liter)^2.

16. The solubility of thallous chloride, TlCl, is 0.016,07 moles/liter. Calculate its solubility product. Calculate the concentration of thallous chloride in solutions saturated with thallous chloride and containing thallous nitrate sufficient to make a total thallous-ion concentration of 0.025, 0.050, 0.075, and 0.100 M. Plot these points using [TlCl] as ordinate and [Tl$^+$] as abscissa. On the same graph plot the data of Table 8 for the actual solubility of thallous chloride in solutions of thallous nitrate; to get the total thallous concentration it will be necessary to add the concentrations of thallous ions derived from the chloride and from the nitrate. The curves should appear much like those in Fig. 36.

17. Calculate the solubility product of thallous chloride in a solution 1.00 M in potassium nitrate. See Table 8 for data.

18. Calculate the molar solubility of (a) magnesium fluoride, and (b) the fluoride ion in water saturated with magnesium fluoride. $S_{MgF_2} = 7 \times 10^{-9}$ (moles/liter)^3. Calculate also the molar concentration of magnesium fluoride in saturated solutions having the following total concentrations of fluoride ion: 0.0030 M, 0.0040 M, 0.0060 M, and 0.0080 M. Plot the results on graph paper, making the molar concentration of magnesium fluoride the ordinate and the molar concentration of fluoride the abscissa.

19. Continue the work of Problem 18 by calculating the molar concentration of magnesium fluoride in solutions saturated with this salt and having a total concentration of magnesium ion of 0.0012 M, 0.0020 M, 0.0050 M, and 0.010 M. Plot the results using the molar concentration of magnesium fluoride as ordinate and the molar concentration of magnesium as abscissa. Use the same numerical scales. Explain why the slopes of the two curves differ. Tell which of the two common ions is more effective in reducing the solubility of magnesium fluoride.

20. Using the data of Problem 18 plot log [MgF$_2$] against log [F$^-$]. Determine the slope and the intercept of the straight line so obtained. Since in Problem 17 [Mg^{++}] = [MgF$_2$], the solubility product may be written [MgF$_2$][F$^-$]^2 = S_{MgF_2}. Taking the logarithm of each side of this equation log [MgF$_2$] = -2 log [F$^-$] $+$ log S_{MgF_2}. This is the equation of a straight line, $y = mx + b$, if log [MgF$_2$] is taken as y and log [F$^-$] as x. The slope of the line is -2.

CHAPTER 6

Typical Gravimetric Determinations

··· The analyst must be an expert manufacturer of pure chemicals, for on this ability the success of his gravimetric determinations depends—*Lundell*.

In Chapter 2, which deals with the general operations of quantitative analysis, are listed the various steps in carrying out gravimetric, volumetric, and colorimetric analyses. Chapters 4 and 5 deal with the calculations of gravimetric analysis and the factors related to the solubility of precipitates. We now turn our attention to the immediate practical problems of actually carrying out the gravimetric determination of specific elements. It turns out that in practically all cases the weighing operation is the most accurate part of the process, that the mechanical operations of transfer, filtration, and ignition can be carried out without significant loss, and that the greatest errors arise in the chemistry of the precipitation process.

Loss of material resulting from the solubility of precipitates is one of the most serious errors in gravimetric work. The solubility of many materials can be greatly decreased by taking advantage of the common-ion effect, but too great an excess of reagent often reverses the effect and results in an increase in the solubility. Thus, the indiscriminate addition of reagent, on the theory that if a little is good, more is better, may be detrimental, and conservation of reagents often promotes accuracy as well as economy. The magnitude of the diverse-ion effect, by which the solubility of materials is increased by the presence of salts having no common ion, cannot even be estimated in most practical cases. The effect is very real, however, and throughout an analysis it is wise to use only as little of the various reagents as is necessary and to avoid loading the solution with foreign salts.

It is unfortunate that relatively few reagents are known that are completely specific. The sulfate ion may be thought of as a reagent for barium, but it is hardly a specific reagent because the sulfates of lead and strontium are also insoluble and that of calcium is sparingly soluble. In the presence of these interfering elements it is apparent

98

that the barium cannot be precipitated as barium sulfate but must be precipitated as some other salt which will separate it from the other alkaline-earth elements and lead. Such limitations on the methods which must be employed to effect the proper separations frequently introduce additional steps into the analysis, for the separation may not leave the element in a form suitable for weighing. Thus, the analysis of a mixture of barium, lead, strontium, and calcium is usually handled by first precipitating the lead as the sulfide; in the filtrate the hydrogen sulfide is then removed by boiling; the acidity is adjusted by buffering with acetate; and the barium is precipitated as the chromate to separate it from the strontium and the calcium. Barium chromate, like barium sulfate, is a suitable form in which to weigh barium, but lead sulfide is not a satisfactory form in which to weigh lead, owing to contamination by free sulfur. Rather the lead sulfide must be converted to lead sulfate for weighing, an extra operation.

Unfortunately, the effects of foreign materials are not limited to increasing the solubility of precipitates or to reacting in an undesirable fashion with the precipitating agent. Frequently a foreign material will be carried down with a precipitate even though it does not itself form an insoluble compound with the reagent. This entrainment of foreign materials comes about in at least three distinctly different ways: occlusion, adsorption, and coprecipitation.

The term *occlusion* refers to a purely mechanical entrainment in which the crystals of the precipitate actually enclose or trap a portion of the mother liquor. Obviously, vigorous agitation should be instrumental in reducing the amount of materials carried down in this fashion, and this is true in the cases of the metal hydroxides and silver chloride, which are finely crystalline in character. In other precipitates, particularly those in which the crystals tend to grow to relatively large size, the mother liquor and any materials dissolved in it are tightly enclosed in cavities in the crystal, and mere stirring will not free the trapped solution. In the case of potassium perchlorate, a notorious offender in this respect, the trapped liquid is only removed by heating the salt to 310°, at which temperature the steam pressure developed is sufficient to burst the crystal. In cases of this sort, the only way to secure a pure precipitate is to filter off the precipitate, dissolve it, and precipitate it a second time; the reprecipitation is made from a solution which has a much lower concentration of foreign material and hence the amount of non-volatile foreign material trapped in the interstices of the crystalline mass is less. Obviously, the loss of the precipitate itself by solubility will limit the number of such reprecipitations that can be performed.

Adsorption is the retention of foreign material on the surface of a solid. Finely divided materials have a much greater surface area and hence adsorb a much greater amount of foreign material. This is a subject that has received a good deal of study, and a few rules have been found by which the nature of the ions which will be adsorbed on various types of precipitates can be predicted. In general the amount of adsorbed material increases with the concentration of the foreign material in the solution. In many cases the precipitate can be filtered off, dissolved, and reprecipitated, and the amount of foreign material carried down by adsorption materially reduced.

The term *coprecipitation* is used to designate the process by which material is carried down as a definite part of the crystalline structure of the precipitate. Thus, in the case of barium sulfate precipitated from a solution containing potassium, it is found that a portion of the barium in the crystal is replaced by potassium. Two atoms of potassium weigh less than an atom of barium, so that the coprecipitation of potassium leads to low results. This is especially unfortunate, for the determination of sulfate is an important analysis and no method of dissolving the barium sulfate for reprecipitation is available. Even worse, barium sulfate also carries down with it certain common negative ions, principally nitrate and chlorate. These lead to high results, for they leave a residue of barium oxide in the barium sulfate when the barium sulfate is ignited. As in the case of adsorption, the amount of material coprecipitated depends not only on the specific nature of the ions involved but also on the concentration of the foreign material in solution. Reprecipitation again will reduce the amount of material coprecipitated.

The form in which an element is precipitated may not be the same as that in which it is finally weighed. The composition of the precipitate may not be definite, or it may undergo a change on being dried. The metal hydroxides such as those of ferric iron and aluminum are of rather indefinite composition and are referred to in the literature as hydrated oxides rather than hydroxides. They are converted to the oxides for weighing. Metal sulfides are not good forms for weighing; they are usually contaminated with sulfur and tend to pass into oxides or sulfates on drying. Usually salt hydrates are not satisfactory forms for weighing, the water of hydration being too easily lost.

Essentially, the chemical form in which an element is precipitated should provide a separation of the element from any interfering elements present; essentially also, the form in which an element is weighed should be of definite composition and suitable for weighing, that is, reasonably non-hygroscopic and stable toward the atmosphere.

The principal forms in which the common elements are precipitated and the forms in which they are weighed are given in Table 9.

TABLE 9. THE FORMS IN WHICH THE COMMON ELEMENTS ARE PRECIPITATED AND WEIGHED

Element	Form in which Precipitated	Elements from which Separated	Principal Interfering Elements	Form in which Weighed
Na	$NaMg(UO_2)_3$ $(C_2H_3O_2)_9 \cdot$ 6.5H_2O	Ca, Mg, K, NH_4^+, $SO_4^=$	Li, $PO_4^=$	$NaMg(UO_2)_3$ $(C_2H_3O_2)_9 \cdot$ 6.5 H_2O
	NaCl	Li	Rb, Cs, heavy metals	NaCl
K	$KClO_4$	Na, Li, Ca, Mg, Ba	Rb, Cs	$KClO_4$
	K_2PtCl_6	Na, Li	Rb, Cs, heavy metals	K_2PtCl_6, Pt^0
Cu	Cu^0 by electro-deposition	Pb, Cd, Zn	Sb, Sn, As, Ag, Bi, Hg	Cu^0
	CuCNS	Most metals	Hg_2^{++}, Ag	CuO, CuCNS
Ag	AgCl	Most metals	Hg_2^{++}, Cu^+	AgCl
Mg	$MgNH_4PO_4$	Na, K, NH_4^+	All other metals	$Mg_2P_2O_7$
Ca	CaC_2O_4	Mg, Na, K, NH_4^+	All other metals	$CaCO_3$, CaO
Ba	$BaSO_4$	Most metals	Ca, Sr, Pb	$BaSO_4$
	$BaCrO_4$	Ca, Sr		$BaCrO_4$
Zn	ZnS	Ni, Mn, Fe, Al, Cr, Ca, Mg, Na	Acid hydrogen sulfide group	ZnO
	$ZnNH_4PO_4$	Na, K, NH_4^+, Ni	All other metals	$Zn_2P_2O_7$
Cd	CdS	Zn, Fe, Al, Co, Ni, Mn, Ca, Na, K	Acid hydrogen sulfide group	$CdSO_4$
	$CdNH_4PO_4$	Na, K, NH_4^+	All other metals	$Cd_2P_2O_7$
Hg	Hg^0 by chemical reduction	Most common metals	Cu, Ag, Pt	Hg^0
	HgS	Fe, Al, Ni, Co, Mn, Ca	Acid hydrogen sulfide group	HgS
Al	$Al(OH)_3$	Fe^{++}, Mn, Ca	Fe^{+++}, Ti, Zn, acid hydrogen sulfide group	Al_2O_3
Si	SiO_2	Most metals	H_2SnO_3, WO_3	SiO_2
Ti	$TiO_2 \cdot xH_2O$ (pH 1.5, SO_2)	Fe, Al	Zr, Th	TiO_2
Sn	H_2SnO_3	Fe, Pb, Zn, Cu	Sb, SiO_2	SnO_2
Pb	$PbSO_4$	Most common metals	Ca, Sr, Ba	$PbSO_4$
	PbO_2	Most common metals	Ag, Bi, Mn, As, Sn, $PO_4^=$, Cl^-	PbO_2
As	$MgNH_4AsO_4$	Na, K, NH_4^+	$PO_4^=$, all heavy metals	$Mg_2As_2O_7$
Bi	BiOCl	Most heavy metals	Ag, As, Sn, Sb	BiOCl
S	$BaSO_4$	Cl^-, anions of weak acids	NO_3^-, ClO_3^-	$BaSO_4$
Cl	AgCl	NO_3^-	Br^-, I^-, CN^-, CNS^-	AgCl
Br	AgBr	NO_3^-	Cl^-, I^-, CN^-, CNS^-	AgBr
Mn	MnO_2	Fe, Ni, Zn, Cu	Sn, W	Mn_3O_4
	$MnNH_4PO_4$	Na, K, NH_4^+	All heavy metals	$Mn_2P_2O_7$
Fe	$Fe(OH)_3$	Na, K, Ca, Mg	Al, Cr, Co, Ni, Zn, Cu, $PO_4^=$	Fe_2O_3
Ni	Ni dimethyl-glyoxime	Fe, Co, all metals	Fe^{+++} and Co together, Cu, Pd	Ni dimethyl-glyoxime

THE DETERMINATION OF WATER BY LOSS IN WEIGHT ON HEATING

The determination of the water present in a material by measuring the loss in weight on heating the material to a temperature sufficient to expel the water is reliable only when it is certain that no other volatile constituents are present. A carbonate, for example, may give off carbon dioxide, or a mercury compound metallic mercury, and the situation may be further complicated by the oxidation and loss of such carbonaceous material as carbon dioxide, or of sulfur as sulfur dioxide or trioxide. With such materials the sample must be heated in a closed system and the water absorbed in anhydrous magnesium perchlorate and weighed. When no secondary reaction can take place on heating the sample to a temperature high enough to drive off the water, the loss in weight may be quite a satisfactory method of determining the water present in the material. The water in barium chloride dihydrate, $BaCl_2 \cdot 2H_2O$, can be determined in this way.

Hydrated salts have a vapor pressure similar to the vapor pressure of water or of aqueous solutions. The vapor pressures of water and of barium chloride dihydrate at various temperatures are shown graphically in Fig. 37.

Each gas present in a mixture of gases behaves independently of the others, exerting its own partial pressure. The sum of the partial pressures of the gases comprising the mixture is the total pressure of the gas. Thus, water vapor present in air exerts a partial pressure of its own just like the oxygen, nitrogen, argon, and carbon dioxide which are also present. When air is brought into contact with liquid water, the amount of water vapor in the air increases by evaporation to a certain maximum value depending on the temperature; that is, the partial pressure of the water in the air increases to the vapor pressure, after which evaporation stops. Normally the atmosphere is not saturated with water vapor, the fraction actually present of the amount at saturation being the relative humidity, usually expressed as a percentage. Relative humidity is thus the actual partial pressure of the water vapor divided by the vapor pressure and multiplied by 100. If the partial pressure of the water in the atmosphere exceeds the vapor pressure, as might be the case temporarily when air saturated with water vapor is cooled, liquid water will condense out of the air.

A hydrated salt behaves in a manner quite similar. At 25° the vapor pressure of barium chloride dihydrate is 5.7 mm. (Fig. 37). The vapor pressure of water at 25° is 23.7 mm. In air at 25° having a relative humidity of 20 per cent the partial pressure of the water vapor is 4.7

mm. The dihydrate would lose water to such air since its vapor pressure is greater than the partial pressure of the water vapor. The loss of water by hydrated crystals in this manner is known as *efflorescence*.

Anhydrous barium chloride has zero vapor pressure. If a little water is added to it, some dihydrate is immediately formed and the

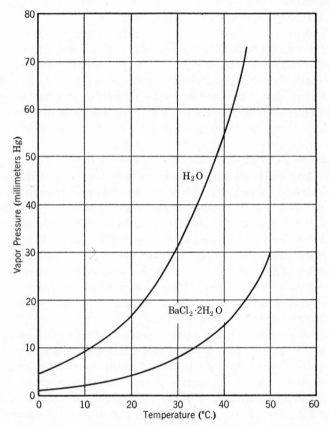

Fig. 37. The vapor pressures of water and of barium chloride dihydrate at various temperatures.

vapor pressure rises to that of the dihydrate at the prevailing temperature. As more water is added the vapor pressure remains constant as the anhydrous barium chloride is gradually converted to the dihydrate. After all of the anhydrous form has been converted to the dihydrate, the further addition of water causes the formation of a saturated solution of barium chloride (deliquescence) and the vapor pressure rises again.

The loss of water from the dihydrate takes place more rapidly at higher temperatures because the vapor pressure of the salt increases rapidly with temperature. The relative humidity of the air falls as the air is heated because the vapor pressure of water rises, but the actual water present in the air does not increase. At 100° the dehydration takes several hours. For practical purposes a temperature above 200° and even as high as a low red heat (550°) is used to effect the dehydration. No secondary reactions occur, and at room temperature and average humidity neither the hydrate nor the anhydrous barium chloride changes weight sufficiently rapidly on exposure to air to make the weighing a difficult problem. However, on standing for some time in a desiccator charged with calcium chloride, anhydrous barium chloride will take water away from the calcium chloride and gain significantly in weight; such gain is usually negligible in times up to 1 hour.

Procedure for the Determination of Water in Barium Chloride Dihydrate. Clean and mark a porcelain crucible and cover using the marking fluid described on page 35. Place the crucible in a triangle on a ring stand and heat for 10 minutes at the full heat of a Meker or Bunsen burner. Cool, and while it is still too hot to touch transfer the crucible and lid to a desiccator by means of tongs. Allow about 30 minutes for the crucible and cover to cool to room temperature and weigh them accurately. The crucible and cover when weighed must be at the same temperature as the balance. Heat the crucible and cover again for 5 minutes, cool as before, and weigh again. The second weight should check the first within 0.0002 g.

Weigh approximately 1 g. of the sample containing barium chloride dihydrate in the crucible. To do this, place both crucible and cover on the left-hand pan of the balance and weigh them accurately. Place approximately 1 g. of the sample in the crucible and weigh crucible, sample, and lid accurately. It is not necessary to use a sample weighing exactly 1 g., but the exact weight of the sample must be known.

Arrange a Bunsen-type burner and two rings on a ring stand as shown in Fig. 38. Place the lower ring about 9 cm. above the top of the burner and the second ring 9 cm. above the lower ring. Place a wire screen (about 6 mesh per cm.) on the lower ring and adjust the burner to give a non-luminous flame (no yellow flame) with an inner blue cone 4 to 5 cm. in height. Adjust the burner so that the wire screen is heated to redness over an area about 5 cm. in diameter. Place the covered crucible containing the sample in the triangle in the upper ring directly above the red spot on the wire screen. Provided there are no air drafts affecting the area, this arrangement will raise the temperature of the crucible to about 250°. Heat the covered crucible and contents for 15 minutes, cool, and transfer to a desiccator, placing the lid on the crucible in the desiccator. When the crucible has cooled to room temperature, weigh the crucible and sample with

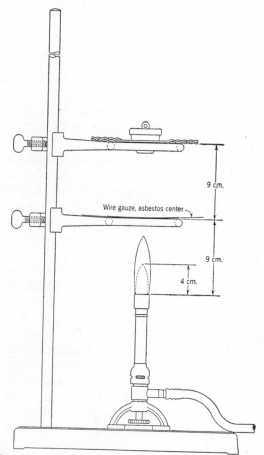

Fig. 38. Dehydration of barium chloride dihydrate.

the lid on. Make the weighing fairly promptly. Heat the crucible and sample for another 15 minutes, cool, and weigh again. The two weights should check within 0.0004 g. If the desiccator is charged with calcium chloride, the sample must not be left in the desiccator more than 45 minutes before weighing, as anhydrous barium chloride will take water away from the calcium chloride; this would, of course, lead to low results in the determination of the water in the sample. The sample may be left indefinitely in a desiccator charged with anhydrous magnesium perchlorate, which is a much better drying agent than calcium chloride.

From the loss in weight of the sample, calculate the per cent of water in the sample. Pure barium chloride dihydrate, $BaCl_2 \cdot 2H_2O$, contains 14.75 per cent water.

THE PRECIPITATION OF BARIUM SULFATE

Sulfur in the form of the sulfate radical may be determined by precipitation as barium sulfate

$$Na_2SO_4 + BaCl_2 = BaSO_4 + 2NaCl$$

The precipitation is made from a solution slightly acidified with hydrochloric acid. From a neutral or alkaline solution barium carbonate may be precipitated, because of absorption of carbon dioxide from the atmosphere; in fairly strong hydrochloric acid solutions the solubility of barium sulfate is so greatly increased that precipitation is incomplete. Barium sulfate is stable at high temperatures and is ignited before weighing at the full heat of the Meker burner.

Although the determination of sulfate is one of the most common and important analyses made and it is almost invariably carried out by the precipitation of barium sulfate, the determination is none too satisfactory. Coprecipitation with barium sulfate, both of certain anions and certain cations, is very serious. Of the anions, nitrate and chlorate are particularly troublesome.[1] Barium nitrate or barium chlorate carried down in addition to the barium sulfate yields barium oxide on ignition and thus causes the results to be high. Nitric acid may be eliminated before the precipitation by evaporating the solution to dryness with hydrochloric acid. The chlorate is also eliminated by this treatment, for chloric acid is decomposed by boiling with 20 per cent hydrochloric acid.

Certain cations are also coprecipitated by barium sulfate. Aluminum and ferric iron are carried down, and large amounts of sodium and potassium in solution cause serious trouble. These cations replace the barium in the precipitate and cause low results because their equivalent weight is less than that of barium.

[1] The permanganate ion is also extensively coprecipitated with barium sulfate. Barium sulfate precipitated in the presence of permanganate is actually colored purple. No amount of washing will remove the color, showing how intimately the permanganate ions are mingled with the sulfate in the crystal lattice.

The coprecipitation of ferric iron is due, at least in part, to the precipitation of the barium salt of disulfatoferric acid. Ferric iron in a solution containing sulfuric acid is practically colorless (in contrast to the yellow color of a solution of ferric chloride) owing to the formation of disulfatoferric acid, $HFe(SO_4)_2$; the barium salt of this acid, $Ba[Fe(SO_4)_2]_2$, is quite insoluble and is precipitated along with the barium sulfate. On ignition of a precipitate of barium sulfate contaminated with barium disulfatoferrate, the disulfatoferrate is decomposed with the loss of sulfur trioxide

$$BaSO_4 = No \ change$$

$$Ba[Fe(SO_4)_2]_2 = BaSO_4 + Fe_2O_3 + 3SO_3$$

This decomposition leads to low results for sulfate, of course. The sulfates of potassium and sodium are not decomposed by ignition and the coprecipitation of potassium and sodium also leads to low results because the equivalent weights of the metals are lower than the equivalent weight of barium.

Barium sulfate when strongly heated with carbon is reduced to barium sulfide, $BaSO_4 + 2C = BaS + 2CO_2$. This reaction is used commercially as the first step in obtaining barium compounds from the mineral barite (barium sulfate) and may cause trouble in analytical work during the process of burning away the filter paper. The final ignition should be conducted with free access to air, preferably in an electric muffle.

Sulfur in any material can be determined by precipitation as barium sulfate provided a satisfactory way can be found to convert the sulfur to sulfate. In most cases this is not too difficult. Sulfite, thiosulfate, and the various thionates and thionites can be oxidized to sulfate in acid solution by treatment with potassium permanganate; the excess of permanganate is reduced by heating the hydrochloric acid solution before the barium sulfate is precipitated. The sulfur in sulfide minerals such as pyrite, FeS_2, and chalcopyrite, $CuFeS_2$, is converted directly to sulfate by fusion with sodium peroxide, although sometimes the ore may be simply dissolved in nitric acid or in a mixture of nitric and hydrochloric acids. Soluble sulfides can be oxidized to sulfate very conveniently in ammoniacal solution by hydrogen peroxide. A persulfate, for example, $K_2S_2O_8$, must be reduced to sulfate; this can be most easily effected by heating it in solution with hydroxylammonium chloride, formaldehyde, or some other reducing agent, or simply by boiling a solution of the persulfate for 10 minutes after acidifying it with hydrochloric acid.

Barium is also determined by precipitation as barium sulfate. Lead also may be separated and determined as the sulfate. Strontium sulfate is somewhat more soluble (15 mg. per 100 ml. of water at room temperature) than is permissible for a precipitate to be used for a gravimetric determination; when strontium is precipitated as the sulfate, alcohol is added to reduce the solubility.

Procedure for the Determination of Sulfate. Dry the material obtained for analysis for at least 2 hours in the oven at 110°. Cool, and store the weighing bottle containing the dried material in a desiccator. Weigh exactly into 600-ml. beakers three samples such that the weights fall between 0.40 and 0.60 g. in each case. This is best done by weighing by difference from the weighing bottle (page 18), but if the salt is not hygroscopic the sample may be weighed out on a scoop and brushed carefully into the beakers. Add 200 ml. of water and 1 ml. of concentrated hydrochloric acid to each sample. Place cover glasses on the beakers and heat the solutions to a gentle boil.

For each sample, using its exact weight, calculate the weight of barium chloride, $BaCl_2$, equivalent to the amount taken, assuming that the sample is pure potassium sulfate. From the weight of barium chloride necessary in each case calculate the volume of 0.25 M barium chloride solution which will contain this amount of barium chloride (each milliliter of 0.25 M barium chloride contains 0.052 g. of barium chloride). Remove the cover glass, first washing down the lower side with a stream of water from the wash bottle to return to the solution any material which may have splashed on to the cover glass. With continuous stirring add over a period of 3 to 5 minutes from a delivery pipet the volume of 0.25 M barium chloride calculated plus a 30 per cent excess (for example, a sample weighing 0.4000 g. requires 0.478 g. of barium chloride or 9.2 ml. of 0.25 M barium chloride solution; add 9.2 + 2.8, or 12.0 ml.).

Replace the cover glass and keep the solution hot for 2 hours using either a low flame or a hot plate. The solution need not boil during this digestion, and longer digestion, even overnight, does no harm provided the solution does not evaporate to dryness. After the crystals have grown sufficiently so that the precipitate settles rapidly, leaving the liquid clear, test for completeness of precipitation by adding a few drops of barium chloride solution. If a turbidity appears where the drops strike the solution add 5 ml. more of the barium chloride solution and test again later. After digestion allow the solution to cool to room temperature.

Filter the barium sulfate, using a medium, ashless paper (Whatman No. 40, for example). Pour as much liquid as possible through the filter before transferring any precipitate. Hold the stirring rod against the lip of the beaker so that the solution runs down the rod and enters the funnel without splashing. Do not fill the funnel to more than 5 mm. below the top of the paper. When removing the stirring rod from the beaker, hold the beaker and rod over the funnel so that if any solution or particles drop off the rod they will fall into the funnel. When all the solution has passed through the filter hold the beaker and stirring rod in one hand with the rod across the top of the beaker and extending into the funnel. With a stream of water from the wash bottle, sluice the precipitate into the funnel. Be careful not to spatter any particles out of the funnel. With a rubber-tipped stirring rod rub loose any barium sulfate clinging to the walls of the beaker and the stirring rod. Wash this into the funnel. If the outside of the beaker is dirty, go over it with a moist rag so that particles of barium sulfate will not escape detection. Wash the beaker once or twice further with small portions of water. Wash the precipitate on the filter with several small portions of water, allowing the funnel to drain completely between washings. The washings are best made by directing the stream of wash water at the top of the filter paper and rotating the funnel a turn and a half so that the portion of the filter paper which has three thicknesses of paper is wetted twice. Collect a few milliliters of the wash water and test it for chloride by adding a few drops of silver nitrate. Test the distilled water itself to see if it contains chloride. When the washings are free of chloride, discontinue the washing.

Transfer the filter paper and precipitate to a porcelain crucible previously ignited and weighed. Wipe out the funnel with a bit of moist filter paper and add this to the filter paper in the crucible. If time permits dry the filter in the oven at 100°. If not, proceed directly to charring the paper, but heat more slowly at first so that the steam formed will not eject material from the crucible. Place a lid on the crucible and heat it gently with a burner flame, gradually raising the temperature until the escaping gases burn. Heat gently until combustible gases are no longer given off. Remove the cover and incline the crucible at about a 45° angle. Place the burner so that the flame strikes the lower half of the crucible. The black residue of the paper should burn away like a cigarette but should not break into flame. Rotate the crucible with the tongs occasionally. After all the carbon has burned away continue the ignition for 15 minutes at the full heat of a Meker burner, keeping the crucible in an inclined position and the flame back toward the bottom of the crucible so that air can diffuse freely over the barium sulfate. The hottest part of the flame of a grid-type burner is just at the tip of the blue cone, so that the lowest point of the crucible should just touch the top of the bank of blue cones about 5 mm. above the burner. Cool the crucible and contents to room temperature and transfer to the desiccator 2 or 3 minutes after turning off the burner.

After 30 minutes weigh the crucible and barium sulfate. Ignite the crucible and barium sulfate again, keeping the crucible tilted and the flame toward the bottom of the crucible so that air may diffuse freely into the crucible. Cool in the desiccator for 30 minutes and weigh again. The weight should check the previous weight within 0.3 or 0.4 mg. From the weight of barium sulfate and the weight of the sample calculate the per cent of sulfur trioxide in the sample. The factor for converting barium sulfate to sulfur trioxide is 0.3430.

If it is suspected that reduction occurred during the ignition, moisten the precipitate with one or two drops of concentrated sulfuric acid. Heat the crucible carefully to expel the sulfuric acid and then ignite for 10 minutes or so at the full heat of the burner.

PROBLEMS

1. Write equations for the reactions involved in the determination of sulfate as barium sulfate, starting with a mixture of sodium sulfate and sodium carbonate.

2. Tell what error results in the determination of sulfur if the barium sulfate is precipitated from a highly acid solution. Explain why any hydrochloric acid is needed at all.

3. Describe how the test for completeness of precipitation of sulfate as barium sulfate is carried out.

4. Explain what is meant by filtering by decantation.

5. Tell how a stirring rod is used when filtering and explain the purpose of the rubber policeman.

6. Explain what error is introduced if the precipitate of barium sulfate is not washed completely free of barium chloride.

7. Show by an equation what may occur if the temperature becomes too high before all the filter paper has been burned away during the ignition of barium sulfate.

8. Calculate the conversion factor for converting barium sulfate to sulfur trioxide.

9. A sample of a soluble sulfate weighing 0.5301 g. gave 0.4271 g. of barium sulfate on analysis. Calculate the result of this analysis expressing the result as (a) per cent sulfur trioxide, and (b) per cent sulfur.

10. Tell how the presence of various anions (negative radicals) present in the solution affects the result of the determination of sulfate as barium sulfate.

11. List three metals that may be determined by precipitation as sulfate.

12. Write equations for the reactions involved in the determination of the sodium sulfite in a mixture of this salt with sodium chloride.

13. The potassium persulfate, $K_2S_2O_8$, in a sample weighing 0.9000 g. was reduced to sulfate, and the sulfate was precipitated as barium sulfate, of which 0.9320 g. was obtained. Tell how the preliminary reduction was probably made

and write equations for the reactions involved. Calculate the per cent of potassium persulfate in the sample. Do not proceed by calculating first the weight of potassium sulfate formed and from this the weight of potassium persulfate, but use the proper gravimetric conversion factor to convert weight of barium sulfate directly to weight of potassium persulfate.

14. A sample of pyrite, FeS_2, weighing 0.9000 g. was treated with hydrochloric acid in a closed flask, and the hydrogen sulfide evolved bubbled through a solution of ammonia and hydrogen peroxide which oxidized the sulfur to sulfate. Later this solution was acidified, and the sulfate was precipitated as barium sulfate, of which 1.5700 g. was obtained. Write equations for the sequence of reactions involved. Calculate the per cent of FeS_2 in the sample.

15. Calculate the volume of 0.25 M barium chloride solution required to precipitate the sulfate in a 1.00-g. sample, assuming that the sample is pure potassium sulfate.

16. In Problem 15, decide whether it would take more or less barium chloride if the sample is assumed to be pure sodium sulfate.

17. Determine what weight of sample should be taken for an analysis such that the weight in grams of barium sulfate obtained multiplied by ten gives the per cent of sulfur in the sample.

18. The sulfate in a 1.0000-g. sample containing potassium sulfate and potassium chloride was precipitated as barium sulfate. The precipitate obtained weighed 0.8750 g. but was found to contain 0.0335 g. of potassium. Calculate the error introduced into the per cent of sulfur trioxide in the sample by this replacement of barium by potassium.

19. A pure, crystalline acid was found on analysis to be composed of 1.8 per cent hydrogen and 28.0 per cent sulfur, the remainder of the compound being oxygen. Calculate the empirical formula of the compound.

20. Exactly 5.0 ml. of a photographic fixing solution ("hypo") was pipetted into a beaker, diluted, acidified with hydrochloric acid, the thiosulfate oxidized with permanganate, the excess permanganate destroyed by boiling, and the sulfate precipitated. The barium sulfate obtained weighed 1.180 g. Calculate the concentration of sodium thiosulfate in the solution in grams per liter.

21. The little-known compound disulfatoferric acid, $HFe(SO_4)_2 \cdot 4H_2O$, is a white, crystalline solid. Calculate (a) the residue of ferric oxide remaining on ignition of 1.000 g. of this material, and (b) the weight of barium sulfate which would be derived from 1.000 g. of the material.

THE PRECIPITATION OF SILVER CHLORIDE

Either the chloride ion or the silver ion may be determined by precipitation as silver chloride. In the determination of chloride, silver nitrate is added as the precipitating agent and a slight excess is used to take advantage of the common-ion effect to decrease the solubility of the silver chloride. If silver is being determined, either sodium chloride or hydrochloric acid is used as the precipitating agent and the excess chloride ion serves as the common ion (solubility-product principle, Chapter 5).

The determination of chloride is one of the most important in the field of quantitative analysis because of the abundance of the element chlorine in nature and its importance in commerce. Fortunately the precipitation of silver chloride can be carried out with great precision and accuracy. The process is subject to few inherent errors, and even these can be obviated by properly adjusting the conditions under which the determination is performed.

Silver chloride is affected by light. The exact nature of the reaction is not too well understood. The overall effect is the liberation of chlorine and the formation of metallic silver, although a subchloride, Ag_2Cl, may be involved:

$$AgCl \xrightarrow{\text{Light}} Ag^0 + Cl_2$$

This photochemical decomposition of silver chloride causes low results if silver is being determined but high results if chloride is being determined. In the determination of silver an excess of chloride is present in the solution and the liberated chlorine simply escapes; the precipitate weighs less than it should, and the results are low. In the determination of chloride, silver ions are in excess and the liberated chlorine reacts with them with the formation of more silver chloride. The precipitate then consists of all of the silver chloride which should be present and some free silver; the precipitate weighs more than it should and the results for chloride are high. This trouble is more serious in the case of the chloride determination because the fresh silver chloride formed is further affected by light and the entire process is repeated. However, in ordinary analytical work it is usually sufficient to avoid direct sunlight and very strong artificial illumination. In highly accurate work such as the determination of the atomic weights of the metals (commonly done by analyzing their chlorides) the precipitation is carried out in a dark room.

The solubility of silver chloride is increased considerably in strong hydrochloric acid solutions and in hot water; hence the precipitation should be made from solutions only weakly acid, and the solution should be cooled to room temperature before filtering.

Silver is positive to hydrogen in the electromotive series, Table 2, page 20. Silver salts are easily reduced to metallic silver. Silver chloride should, therefore, not be filtered on paper but on a porous-bottom filtering crucible.

Silver chloride melts without decomposition at 455°. In ordinary analytical work silver chloride is usually dried at 110° before weighing, but in very precise work, such as the determination of atomic weights, it is actually fused to insure the expulsion of water.

Other Applications. The oxygen-containing acids of chlorine can be reduced to chloride and the chloride precipitated as silver chloride. Hypochlorite (ClO^-), chlorite (ClO_2^-), and chlorate (ClO_3^-) can be reduced conveniently with sulfur dioxide, but no convenient method of reducing the very stable perchlorate ion (ClO_4^-) is known.

Silver bromide is also insoluble in acid solutions and serves for the determination of bromide and indirectly of bromate.

Silver iodide is the least soluble of the silver halides and may be used for the determination of iodide and indirectly for hypoiodite, iodate, and periodate. The reduction of these oxygen-containing acids is also readily effected with a sulfite or sulfur dioxide.

Silver cyanide and silver thiocyanate are also insoluble and are suitable precipitates for gravimetric work. In practice, however, these determinations are usually carried out volumetrically.

Procedure for the Gravimetric Determination of Chloride. Dry the material for analysis for at least 2 hours at 110°. Weigh samples of approximately 0.7 g. into 400-ml. beakers. Dissolve each sample in 200 ml. of water and add 0.5 ml. of concentrated nitric acid. Heat the solution to boiling and with constant stirring add 40 ml. of 0.25 M silver nitrate. Continue the heating for a few minutes, and when the precipitate has coagulated sufficiently test for completeness of precipitation by adding a little silver nitrate solution. Cool the solution to room temperature before filtering.

Filter the silver chloride on a porous-bottom filtering crucible which has been previously dried at 110° and weighed. See page 27 for the technique of filtering with these crucibles. Decant off the supernatant liquid and wash the precipitate several times in the beaker, beating the precipitate up vigorously with the wash water. As wash water use distilled water containing 0.5 ml. of concentrated nitric acid per 200 ml. Finally, transfer the precipitate to the filtering crucible and wash five or six times more. Place the crucible in a beaker, cover with a cover glass, and place in a drying oven at 120° for 2 hours or more. After cooling to room temperature weigh the crucible and silver chloride.

Calculate the per cent of chlorine in the sample. The factor for converting silver chloride to chlorine is 0.247,37.

PROBLEMS

1. Write equations for the reactions involved in the determination of the chlorine in a sample containing potassium chlorate and sodium carbonate.

2. A mixture of sodium chloride and sodium carbonate was acidified with nitric acid, and the chloride was precipitated as silver chloride. A sample of

0.7000 g. gave 1.1950 g. of silver chloride. Calculate the per cent of sodium chloride in the sample.

3. Calculate the weight of sample that must be taken so that the weight in grams of the silver chloride obtained multiplied by 100 is equal to the per cent of potassium chloride in the sample.

4. A sample of chlorobenzene, C_6H_5Cl, weighing 0.5000 g. was decomposed, and the chloride was converted to silver chloride of which 0.5730 g. was obtained. Calculate the per cent of chlorobenzene in the sample.

5. Name all the known oxygen-containing acids of the halogens and indicate the valence of the halogen in each.

6. Calculate the volume of 0.25 M silver nitrate solution required to precipitate the chloride in 0.7 g. of potassium chloride as silver chloride.

7. In the analysis of a 1.0000-g. sample of calcium chloride by precipitation with silver nitrate, 1.3078 g. of silver chloride was obtained. Assuming that calcium chloride was the only chloride present, calculate the per cent of calcium in the sample.

8. A pure compound, $KClO_x$, was analyzed for chlorine. A sample weighing 1.000 g. gave 1.170 g. of silver chloride. Determine the formula of the compound.

9. A pure compound, $KClO_x$, was analyzed for potassium. A sample weighing 1.000 g. gave 1.130 g. of potassium perchlorate. Find the value of x.

10. A sample of silver bromide weighing 0.5000 g. was heated in a stream of chlorine which displaces the bromine, forming silver chloride. Calculate the loss in weight.

11. A mixture of crystalline, hydrated barium chloride and sodium chloride was found on analysis to contain 39.5 per cent chloride and 40.8 per cent barium. Calculate (a) the per cent of sodium chloride in the sample and (b) the apparent number of molecules of water of crystallization per molecule of barium chloride.

12. A double salt occurring in the natural salt beds at Stassfurt, Germany, has the following composition: 9.76 per cent magnesium, 15.70 per cent potassium, 38.58 per cent sulfate ($SO_4^=$), 14.24 per cent chloride, and 21.70 per cent water. Determine the empirical formula of the salt and decide which salts compose the compound.

13. Calculate the weight of silver sulfate required to react exactly with 0.2083 g. of anhydrous barium chloride. Calculate also the weight of precipitate formed.

THE DETERMINATION OF SILICA

We must distinguish immediately between *silicon, silica,* and *silicate.* Silicon is the name of the element; it does not occur in nature as the free element, although silicon metal has been made. Silica is silicon dioxide, SiO_2; it occurs widely in nature as the mineral quartz and is the principal component of sand and sandstone. Silicates are salts of the oxygen acid of silicon, silicic acid. Silicates occur in an almost bewildering variety in nature, making up the rocks of the earth's crust.

Silicon in all forms is determined by conversion to silica. The problems are centered about how to convert silicates to silicic acid, how to dehydrate the silicic acid to silica to render it insoluble, and how to correct the impure silica so obtained for the elements it carries down with it.

Decomposition of Insoluble Silicates. Silicates are classed as soluble or insoluble depending on whether or not they dissolve in hydrochloric acid. The insoluble silicates have a high ratio of base metal oxide to silica; the acid, insoluble silicates have a low ratio. Variation in this ratio arises because of the property of silica of combining with different amounts of water to give the various silicic acids, H_4SiO_4, $H_6Si_2O_7$, H_2SiO_3, and so on. The metal salts of these acids may be written as a combination of oxides

$$Na_4SiO_4 = 2Na_2O \cdot SiO_2$$

$$Na_6Si_2O_7 = 3Na_2O \cdot 2SiO_2$$

$$Na_2SiO_3 = Na_2O \cdot SiO_2$$

$$Na_4Si_3O_8 = 2Na_2O \cdot 3SiO_2$$

$$Na_2Si_2O_5 = Na_2O \cdot 2SiO_2$$

In naturally occurring silicates, the metallic component may be a single metal, but it is more often a combination of metals; thus the feldspar series consists of albite, $NaAlSi_3O_8$, and orthoclase, $KAlSi_3O_8$, with a variety of transitions from one to the other by replacement of the alkali metals in part by each other or by alkaline earth metals. A typical mica has the formula $H_2K(Mg, Fe)_3(Al, Fe)(SiO_4)_3$; beryl has the formula $3BeO \cdot Al_2O_3 \cdot 6SiO_2$. Most of the naturally occurring silicates are insoluble in hydrochloric acid and are thus classed as acidic or insoluble silicates. When the ratio of base metal oxide to silica is high the silicate is decomposed by hydrochloric acid and is spoken of as a basic or soluble silicate. Portland cement is a typical example.

The problem of decomposing an acidic or insoluble silicate is simply one of increasing the proportion of base metal oxide. This involves addition of an alkali, usually by fusion with sodium carbonate. The fusion is carried out in a platinum crucible and the melt subsequently dissolved in hydrochloric acid. The acid silicate is thus converted to a basic silicate, and the hydrochloric acid converts it to metal chloride and silicic acid.

Dehydration of Silica. Silicic acid, formed on acidifying a basic silicate, decomposes immediately, in part precipitating silica. To render all the silicon present insoluble, it is necessary to dehydrate the silicic acid remaining in solution and also the hydrated silica already precipitated. There are three ways of doing this: evaporation to dryness with hydrochloric acid followed by baking; evaporation with sulfuric acid followed by short boiling; evaporation and boiling with perchloric acid.

The hydrochloric acid dehydration is commonly used in the analysis of limestone and silicate rock. The baking following the evaporation should be made on a low-temperature hot plate around 130° to 150° or in a drying oven at 140°. The residue is treated with strong hydrochloric acid to dissolve any basic salts formed, and then diluted and filtered without delay. If the total amount of silica is small, say less than 10 mg., and if the filtration is made within a few minutes, one dehydration is usually sufficient. For larger amounts of silica the amount of silica which redissolves is appreciable, and a second or even a third dehydration is necessary; obviously the silica precipitated in the first dehydration must be filtered off before the second dehydration is made.

Dehydration with sulfuric acid is not applicable to silicate and limestone analyses because insoluble calcium sulfate is formed. The sulfuric acid dehydration was used for the determination of silicon in steel for many years but has gradually been displaced by the perchloric acid method. Prolonged heating of ferric sulfate with hot sulfuric acid converts ferric sulfate to an anhydrous form which redissolves in hot water only very slowly. Nickel and aluminum salts behave the same way. The sulfuric acid must be heated for 2 to 3 minutes after dense white fumes of sulfuric acid appear to effect the dehydration. If the mixture is cooled to 80° to 90° rapidly and water is added quickly to dilute the solution, less difficulty is experienced in getting the salts back into solution. As in the other methods of dehydrating silica, the filtration must be made without delay after the dilution.

Hot, concentrated (72 per cent) perchloric acid is a powerful oxidizing and dehydrating agent. A dilute solution of perchloric acid has neither oxidizing nor reducing properties. If a dilute solution of perchloric acid is boiled, water is expelled and the temperature gradually rises to 203°, at which point a mixture of constant composition boils away; this is the "concentrated" perchloric acid which is marketed. It contains 72 per cent perchloric acid, corresponding to the dihydrate $HClO_4 \cdot 2H_2O$, and is an exceptionally powerful oxidizing and dehydrating agent. It, itself, is perfectly stable, but it will react violently with organic material such as filter paper.[1] At the boiling temperature this acid rapidly takes the water away from silicic acid, leaving anhydrous silica behind. One of the remarkable features of perchloric acid is that all its salts are soluble. After the dehydration, which can be effected completely in a very few minutes after the temperature has reached the boiling point of the constant boiling acid (203°), the mixture is cooled and diluted with water. The metal perchlorates dissolve instantly, leaving behind white, well-dehydrated silica, containing practically no impurities. A few precautions should be observed. The perchloric acid should be carefully washed from the paper or trouble may be experienced when the paper is later burned away. A little perchloric acid left on the paper will cause deflagration which may be violent enough to throw some of the silica out of the crucible. If the paper is moistened with 2 per cent ammonia after the last washing, any perchloric acid left is converted to ammonium perchlorate; the paper will then burn away easily and quietly.

Dehydrated silica has a pronounced tendency to revert to silicic acid in contact with water. Therefore, after the dehydrated mixture is taken up with water to dissolve the foreign salts, the silica must be filtered off promptly. If the amount of silica is greater than 10 mg., sufficient silica will redissolve to make necessary another dehydration. The perchloric acid method is better than the other two methods in this regard, for the metal perchlorates pass instantly into solution and less time elapses before the filtration can be made. Obviously the silica which has been rendered insoluble must be filtered off before the succeeding dehydration is made.

Correction of Silica for Impurities. Silica precipitated by acid is gelatinous and adsorbs metal ions badly, especially iron and aluminum. The impure silica obtained on ignition must be corrected for these impurities. This is done by treating the silica in a platinum crucible with hydrofluoric acid,[2] which converts it to volatile silicon tetrafluoride, $SiO_2 + 4HF = SiF_4 + 2H_2O$. The metal impurities are converted to fluorides but must be returned to oxides, that is, to the same form in which they were weighed as impurities in the silica. This is done by adding a little sulfuric acid and heating to expel the excess hydrofluoric and sulfuric acids. The metal sulfates are then heated strongly, which decomposes them, leaving the oxides. The

---

[1] If a material is suspected of containing organic matter, the evaporation should be begun with a mixture of dilute perchloric acid and nitric acid; the easily oxidizable organic material will be oxidized by the nitric acid before the perchloric acid becomes concentrated and begins to function as an oxidizing agent.

[2] See footnote, page 119, regarding the hazard in the use of hydrofluoric acid.

reactions which an impurity of iron undergoes are:

$$Fe_2O_3 + 6HF = 2FeF_3 + 3H_2O$$

$$2FeF_3 + 3H_2SO_4 = Fe_2(SO_4)_3 + 6HF$$

$$Fe_2(SO_4)_3 = Fe_2O_3 + 3SO_3$$

The reactions for aluminum and titanium are similar. The loss in weight on this treatment is, thus, the silica volatilized. The residue should not be more than a few milligrams and in the perchloric acid dehydration will usually be less than 0.1 mg.

Calcium sulfate is not decomposed at a temperature which can be obtained with a Meker burner. If calcium is present as impurity in the silica, the precipitate should be treated with a few drops of sulfuric acid before the first ignition so that it will be weighed as sulfate in the first place.

Procedure for the Determination of Silica in a Soluble Silicate (Portland Cement). Dry the finely powdered material for analysis at least 2 hours at 110°. Weigh accurately samples of approximately 0.5 g. into 400-ml. beakers. To each sample add 10 ml. of water and 10 ml. of concentrated hydrochloric acid. Heat the mixture gently and stir occasionally until the material has completely decomposed. Evaporate the solution to dryness on a hot plate, continuing the evaporation until the solid residue, beaker, and cover glass are completely dry. Add 5 ml. of concentrated hydrochloric acid to dissolve the basic salts and then 20 ml. of water. Cover and warm until all the salts have dissolved, leaving a precipitate of fine silica. Dilute to about 100 ml. and filter, using a hard paper (Whatman No. 42, for example). Wash with dilute hydrochloric acid (1:99) until no trace of yellow ferric iron remains on the paper, and then wash two or three times with water.

Evaporate the filtrate to dryness again, and as before take up with hydrochloric acid and water. Filter through a new filter paper and again wash with dilute hydrochloric acid and finally with water.

Transfer both filters to a crucible previously ignited and weighed; if only impure silica is desired a porcelain crucible is satisfactory, but if the silica is to be corrected for impurities a platinum crucible is necessary. See page 40 for the use and care of platinumware. Dry and burn away the papers, keeping the temperature low until the paper is burned away. Be careful not to allow the paper to break into flame, as silica is light and easily swept away in the gas stream. Finally, ignite the precipitate at the full heat of the burner for 20 minutes. Cool the crucible and silica in a desiccator and weigh. Calculate the per cent of impure silica, SiO_2, if this is to be reported.

Moisten the silica in the platinum crucible with a drop or two of sulfuric acid. Add about 5 ml. of hydrofluoric acid,[1] pouring the acid directly from the polyethylene bottle into the crucible unless a plastic graduated cylinder is available. Evaporate cautiously to dryness, using a good hood. Fume away the sulfuric acid and heat at the full heat of a Meker burner for 5 minutes. Cool and weigh. The loss in weight represents the pure silica in the sample. Report the results as per cent silica, SiO_2 (corrected). If R_2O_3 (iron and aluminum) are to be determined on the same sample, fuse the residue with a little sodium carbonate, dissolve the melt in dilute hydrochloric acid, and add the solution to the filtrate from the silica; alternatively the weight of the residue from the hydrofluoric acid-sulfuric acid treatment may be simply added to the weight of the ammonia precipitate (R_2O_3).

PROBLEMS

1. Look up in a handbook of chemistry or in a textbook on mineralogy the chemical composition of the following minerals, and class each as silica or a silicate: albite, orthoclase, mica, quartz, tridymite, beryl, topaz, garnet, crystobalite.

2. The silicon in a sample of steel weighing 3.000 g. was converted to silica. The silica when first obtained weighed 0.0120 g. The residue after the hydrofluoric acid-sulfuric acid treatment weighed 0.0013 g. Calculate the per cent of silicon in the sample.

3. On standing in a glass bottle ammonia attacks the glass and becomes contaminated with sodium, calcium, and silica. Tell how to determine the amount of silica in such ammonia.

4. Calculate the volume of hydrofluoric acid, 48 per cent HF, required to convert 0.20 g. of silica to silicon tetrafluoride. The catalogs of the chemical manufacturers do not give the specific gravity of commercial hydrofluoric acid as they do for other common acids; suggest a reason for this and assume a likely specific gravity for this acid.

5. Students occasionally obtain an increase in weight on treating impure silica with hydrofluoric acid and sulfuric acid. An experienced instructor will immediately ask: "How did you measure out the hydrofluoric acid?" Explain the reason for this question.

6. The ash of plant material runs as high as 80 per cent silica. Discuss the technique and precautions to be exercised in the direct determination ("wet ashing") of plant material using perchloric acid dehydration.

[1] Precautions must be taken in the use of hydrofluoric acid. Unlike other strong acids, hydrofluoric acid causes no pain when it comes in contact with the skin, the acid apparently acting as a local anesthetic. Pain begins after a few hours of contact and is accompanied by serious swelling and inflammation, which spread. Severe burns may require amputation. Great care should therefore be taken to avoid breathing hydrofluoric acid vapors or spattering the acid on the skin, and any acid touching the skin should be washed off immediately with water. A wise precaution is to wash the hands after every use of hydrofluoric acid.

7. A sample of silica sand, weighing 1.000 g. and known to contain 0.05 per cent ferric oxide, 0.01 per cent titanium oxide, and 0.15 per cent calcium oxide, is to be treated with hydrofluoric acid and sulfuric acid in a platinum crucible, and the residue is to be ignited over a Meker-type burner. Calculate the weight to be expected for the ignited residue.

8. Sandstone is essentially finely divided quartz with a small amount of silicate binder. Calculate the weight of sodium carbonate required to convert 1.0 g. of sandstone to a soluble sodium silicate assumed to be Na_4SiO_4.

9. Describe a scheme for determining the silica and the water content of colloidal silica ("silica gel," a common drying agent), bearing in mind that the colloidal silica is prepared from crude sodium silicate by acidifying and carries considerable other inorganic materials as impurities.

10. A silicate rock was found on analysis to consist of 11.8 per cent Na_2O, 19.2 per cent Al_2O_3, and 69.0 per cent SiO_2. Calculate the formula of the mineral.

11. Dissolved silica in natural waters (river and well water) may run as high as 5 p.p.m. (present as silicic acid). Calculate the volume of water sample to be taken for a reasonably accurate (1 per cent relative error) gravimetric determination of silica in such a water. Assume that the error in weighing the silica is 0.2 mg.

THE PRECIPITATION OF FERRIC HYDROXIDE

When ammonia is added to solutions of ferric salts hydrated ferric oxide is precipitated. This is usually called ferric hydroxide, although the composition does not correspond to the formula $Fe(OH)_3$ but contains a smaller and variable amount of water: $2FeCl_3 + 6NH_4OH = Fe_2O_3 \cdot xH_2O + 6NH_4Cl$. Ferric hydroxide is extremely insoluble and is filtered off and ignited to ferric oxide for weighing: $Fe_2O_3 \cdot xH_2O = Fe_2O_3 + xH_2O$.

This is, of course, a rather general reaction, for other metals are also precipitated by ammonia. Such metals are known as weak bases because their hydroxides are insoluble in weakly acid solutions, in contrast to the strong bases whose hydroxides are either soluble or are precipitated only in alkaline solutions.[1] The most common of these metals are aluminum, trivalent chromium, and titanium, which are also precipitated as hydrated oxides. Manganese is precipitated as hydrated manganese dioxide, $MnO_2 \cdot xH_2O$, if an oxidizing agent is present. The hydrated oxides on ignition give Al_2O_3, Cr_2O_3, TiO_2, and Mn_3O_4, respectively; each of these elements and ferric iron can be determined in this way if all the others are absent.

[1] There is a smooth transition from the weak bases such as ferric hydroxide to the strong bases such as sodium hydroxide, but the explanation involves the concept of pH which is taken up in volumetric analysis. This subject and the principles involved in the separation of the weak bases from stronger bases is taken up again in Chapter 14

Obviously then, precipitation with ammonia is a method for iron only when aluminum, chromium, titanium, manganese and several rarer elements are absent. Unfortunately, this is often not the case. Hematite, Fe_2O_3, the most common ore of iron, contains as impurities silica, appreciable amounts of aluminum and manganese, and small amounts of titanium. The silica can be filtered off after the ore has been dissolved in hydrochloric acid, but the iron must be first separated by some other chemical process from the aluminum, manganese, and titanium, unless the sum of all four is desired.

Ferrous iron is not completely precipitated by ammonia, so that provision must be made to insure that all the iron is in the ferric state; heating with a little nitric acid or bromine water will do this.

Magnetite, Fe_3O_4, the black oxide of iron, which is of some importance as an ore, gives a mixture of ferric and ferrous chlorides on solution, and the oxidation treatment must not be omitted.

Ferric hydroxides and the other hydrated oxides, in general, are gelatinous in character and carry down other materials when precipitated. Fortunately, ferric hydroxide is readily soluble in hydrochloric acid, and a reprecipitation of the ferric hydroxide can often be used to free it of the impurities carried down in the first precipitation. The separation of iron from copper by ammonia precipitation would appear to be possible since copper forms the well-known deep blue, soluble tetramminocupric ion with ammonia. Actually, however, the separation is quite poor, and even after two or three reprecipitations the ferric hydroxide still contains a significant amount of copper. Where the drop of ammonia strikes the solution both cupric hydroxide and ferric hydroxide precipitate and the gelatinous ferric hydroxide encloses the cupric hydroxide, effectively preventing ammonia from redissolving the cupric hydroxide even though the solution later becomes quite strongly ammoniacal. Other bivalent metals such as zinc, cadmium, cobalt, and nickel behave similarly.

Ferric phosphate and ferric arsenate are less soluble than ferric hydroxide and are precipitated in preference to the hydroxide. In the common ores of iron, there is usually a small amount of phosphate but, of course, not nearly enough to be equivalent to the iron. Ferric phosphate is unchanged on ignition, so that the final material is ferric phosphate plus ferric oxide.

Certain organic compounds, notably glycerol, mannitol and other sugars, citric acid, and tartaric acid, have the property of forming very stable, soluble non-ionized compounds with iron. These non-ionic compounds are so stable that they actually prevent the precipitation of ferric hydroxide.[1] Such materials must first be removed by boiling the solution with nitric acid or with nitric and hydrochloric acids.

Ferric hydroxide becomes colloidal when electrolytes are absent. If water is used as wash water, toward the end of the filtration and washing when the electrolyte has been removed ferric hydroxide will suddenly peptize and begin to pass through the filter paper. A little ammonium salt in the wash water will prevent this. Ammonium nitrate is usually chosen; ammonium chloride is not satisfactory as the ammonium chloride left on the precipitate causes a loss of iron during the ignition, owing to the formation and volatilization of ferric chloride.

Iron oxide is rather easily reduced to the metal, and care must be exercised in burning away the paper and igniting the precipitate to avoid this. If reduction has been suspected, treatment with a few drops of nitric acid followed by ignition to remove the excess acid and convert the nitrate to oxide will take care of the matter.

Ferric oxide does not have precisely the composition Fe_2O_3 but contains some excess oxygen, perhaps due to the formation of a little higher oxide as the amount is too great to be explained by adsorption. The amount of excess oxygen varies with the time and temperature of ignition and with the kind of gas surrounding the ferric oxide during ignition, but the results are always high. Using a Meker-type burner and natural gas (ignition temperature about 800°) the results will be high by about the following values:

Per Cent Fe in Sample	Per Cent Fe Error
100	0.6
50	0.4
20	0.2
10	0.1

Procedure for the Gravimetric Determination of Iron. If the material for analysis is an ore, dry it at least 2 hours at 110°. If the material is a salt mixture, find out if it needs to be dried; sometimes the drying may not be permissible as ferrous salts are oxidized by air. Weigh exactly samples of about 0.5 to 1.0 g. into 400-ml. beakers. To each sample add 5 ml. of water and 10 ml. of concentrated hydrochloric acid.

[1] The importance of this in biochemistry is apparent when it is remembered that the contents of the intestines are approximately neutral, so that iron present would normally be completely precipitated as highly insoluble ferric hydroxide. The presence of such polyhydroxy compounds capable of forming soluble non-ionized compounds with ferric iron make the iron available to the body.

Heat gently to dissolve the sample. If a residue remains, dilute the solution to 50 ml. and filter, using a medium paper. Wash the filter repeatedly with dilute hydrochloric acid (1:100) until all the yellow ferric chloride has been removed. If the residue on the paper is practically colorless it may be considered to be silica and need not be considered further. If an appreciable amount of dark material remains, it may contain iron and may require special treatment.[1]

Dilute the solution with distilled water to 125 to 150 ml., add 1 or 2 ml. of nitric acid to the solution and boil for a minute or two to oxidize all the iron to the ferric state. Heat the solution to boiling and add dilute, filtered ammonia (1:3) to the solution slowly, with stirring. Continue the addition until the solution is slightly alkaline and smells faintly of ammonia. In testing for this, wash down the cover glass and walls of the beaker with a stream of water from the wash bottle and dip the end of a strip of litmus paper into the solution, washing it off on withdrawing it. Keep the solution hot for 10 minutes, then filter through a loose, ashless paper. Transfer as little of the precipitate as possible and wash the precipitate in the beaker a number of times by beating it up with the wash water and decanting off the liquid after the precipitate has settled. As wash water use a 1 per cent solution of ammonium nitrate. Finally, transfer the precipitate to the funnel, scrub out the beaker with a policeman, and wash the precipitate a few more times.

Transfer the paper and ferric hydroxide to a porcelain crucible previously ignited and weighed. Dry and burn away the paper, being careful not to heat the ferric oxide and paper hotter than necessary to char and burn away the paper. Ignite the precipitate 20 minutes in the full heat of a Meker burner with the crucible inclined and the flame toward the bottom of the crucible. Cool and weigh. Report the per cent of iron in the sample. The factor for converting ferric oxide to iron is 0.6994.

---

[1] If it is necessary to recover iron in the residue, transfer the paper and residue to a platinum crucible and burn away the paper. Cool and add to the crucible about 0.5 ml. of hydrofluoric acid and 3 drops of concentrated sulfuric acid. See the footnote on page 119 regarding the precautions to be observed when using hydrofluoric acid. Heat the crucible carefully in a good hood to drive off silicon tetrafluoride and the excess hydrofluoric acid and sulfuric acid. Cool the crucible and add 0.3 g. of sodium carbonate. Heat the crucible to fuse the sodium carbonate and with the tongs carefully incline and rotate the crucible to bring the melt in contact with all of the residue. Cool and transfer to a beaker. Add water and hydrochloric acid to dissolve the melt. Add the solution to the main solution of the sample and proceed to the precipitation.

PROBLEMS

1. Give the mineral name and composition of the principal ores of iron.

2. In the gravimetric determination of iron, explain (a) why the solution must be filtered before the iron is precipitated, and (b) why the solution is treated with nitric acid before the precipitation.

3. List at least four other elements, excluding the members of the hydrogen sulfide group, which will precipitate with hydrated ferric oxide if present in the solution. Show in what form they would be weighed after ignition.

4. Explain why the precipitate of hydrated ferric oxide should be filtered within a few hours after precipitation.

5. Give equations for two undesirable possible reactions which could occur during the ignition of ferric oxide, and indicate how to avoid them.

6. The factor for converting ferric oxide to iron is 0.6994. Show how this is calculated and check this value, using logarithms for the calculation.

7. A sample of iron ore weighing 0.3497 g. gave 0.3580 g. of ferric oxide. Calculate the per cent of iron in the sample. Could the ore have been a hematite in this case?

8. Calculate the weight of sample which should be taken such that each 10 mg. of ferric oxide obtained represents 1 per cent of iron in the sample.

9. Ferric oxide is reduced to metallic iron by ignition in a stream of hydrogen gas, but aluminum oxide is not. A mixture of these oxides obtained from a sample weighing 1.5000 g. lost 0.1000 g. on ignition in hydrogen. Calculate the per cent of iron in the sample.

10. The ferric oxide obtained from a sample of iron ore weighing 0.8000 g. contained 0.0100 g. of metallic iron resulting from partial reduction of the ferric oxide. Calculate the error in the per cent of iron in the sample. Begin by calculating the weight of ferric oxide equivalent to the metallic iron formed.

11. On ignition at a sufficiently high temperature, Mohr's salt, $Fe(NH_4)_2(SO_4)_2 \cdot 6H_2O$, can be converted to ferric oxide. Calculate how much salt should be taken to leave a residue of 1.00 g. of ferric oxide.

12. Calculate the change in weight of 1.0000 g. of ferroso-ferric oxide, Fe_3O_4, on conversion to ferric oxide, Fe_2O_3.

13. The aluminum in a sample of alum, presumably $Al_2(NH_4)_2(SO_4)_4 \cdot 24H_2O$, was determined gravimetrically. A sample weighing 1.0000 g. gave 0.1223 g. of aluminum oxide. Show that the sample had apparently lost some of the water of crystallization and calculate the number of molecules of water lost. First, calculate the per cent purity of the alum, and then make another calculation assuming 100 per cent purity and finding the apparent molecular weight.

THE PRECIPITATION OF CALCIUM OXALATE

Practically all the oxalates of the metals are insoluble in neutral solution. The exceptions are those of the alkali metals and magnesium. Many metals can thus be precipitated as the oxalate, and in the absence of better methods such precipitation is used for the determination of certain of them, notably calcium, zinc, and the rare earths.

Like the salt of any weak acid and a metal, calcium oxalate is soluble in strong acids, and is only precipitated from a neutral solution. The precipitation is usually made by adding ammonia to an acid solution containing a calcium salt and oxalic acid:

$$CaCl_2 + H_2C_2O_4 + 2NH_4OH = CaC_2O_4 + 2NH_4Cl + 2H_2O$$

Calcium oxalate is precipitated as a monohydrate, $CaC_2O_4 \cdot H_2O$, but the hydrate is not a satisfactory form for weighing. It is therefore converted to calcium carbonate

$$CaC_2O_4 \xrightarrow{500-525°} CaCO_3 + CO$$

or to calcium oxide

$$CaCO_3 \xrightarrow{800°} CaO + CO_2$$

The ignition to the carbonate requires that the temperature be controlled accurately between 500° and 525°. Above 525° the carbonate begins to decompose to the oxide. In practice it is necessary to use an electric muffle, preferably with automatic temperature control. If such a muffle is available this is the best method, as calcium carbonate is not hygroscopic and presents no trouble in weighing.

The conversion to calcium oxide is complete at 800°. This temperature can just be secured with a Meker burner with natural gas; it is best to place the crucible in a chimney of asbestos paper or fire brick; this will raise the temperature to 900° or so. Calcium oxide is hygroscopic and gains weight on exposure to moist air. If the weighing is prolonged the calcium oxide may gain appreciably in weight while on the balance. A second ignition is then made, and the second weighing is made more rapidly, the weight already being known to within a few milligrams. Moreover, after ignition the weighing should not be delayed any longer than the time just needed to cool the crucible to room temperature. Calcium oxide will gain weight in the desiccator, absorbing the water and carbon dioxide from the air introduced into the desiccator on opening and taking water from the calcium chloride dihydrate in the desiccator.

The precipitation of calcium oxalate is not a separation of calcium from any metals but sodium, potassium, ammonium, and magnesium. The separation from magnesium is not sharp if much magnesium is present. Two precipitations are usually necessary.

One curious feature of the precipitation of calcium oxalate in the presence of magnesium is that enough oxalate must be added to combine with the magnesium as well as with the calcium; otherwise the precipitation of calcium is incomplete. This is generally assumed to be due to the formation of non-ionized soluble magnesium oxalate.

After the separation of calcium as the oxalate, the determination is frequently concluded volumetrically. The precipitate of calcium oxalate is dissolved in sulfuric acid, and the oxalic acid is titrated with potassium permanganate.

Procedure for the Determination of Calcium. If the material is a naturally occurring mineral such as limestone, dolomite, or a silicate rock, silica and R_2O_3 (iron, aluminum, titanium, and manganese) must be removed before the calcium is precipitated. The following procedure is applicable to soluble calcium salts or to calcium carbonate which can be put into solution by treatment with acids. The only other cations which may be present are magnesium, ammonium, and the alkali metals.

Weigh exactly samples of approximately 0.5 g. into 400-ml. beakers. Dissolve each sample in 10 ml. of water and 10 ml. of concentrated hydrochloric acid. Dilute the solution to about 175 ml. Add a solution of 1.1 g. of ammonium oxalate, $(NH_4)_2C_2O_4 \cdot H_2O$, or 1.0 g. of oxalic acid, $H_2C_2O_4 \cdot 2H_2O$, dissolved in about 25 ml. of water. A part of the calcium oxalate may precipitate when the oxalate is added. Add 2 drops of methyl red and heat the solution to boiling. Add filtered, dilute ammonia (1:3) dropwise with stirring until the indicator becomes yellow, and add a few drops in excess. Digest the precipitate and solution for 1.5 hours, keeping the solution hot but not necessarily boiling. Cool to room temperature. Filter the calcium oxalate, using a filtering crucible if the calcium oxalate is to be converted to calcium carbonate for weighing, or either paper or a filtering crucible if it is to be ignited to the oxide. Wash the precipitate with a solution containing 1.0 g. ammonium oxalate per l. until it is free of chloride. In testing the solution for chloride, collect a few milliliters of the filtrate in a clean test tube, add 2 drops of nitric acid and then a little silver nitrate (test the wash water to be sure it is chloride free). Use small portions of wash water and allow the liquid to drain away before adding more.

If the sample contains an appreciable amount of magnesium the calcium oxalate should be dissolved and reprecipitated. Difficulty is usually experienced in attempting to dissolve calcium oxalate in hydrochloric acid, and unless there is only relatively little precipitate it is best to ignite the oxalate to the oxide and to dissolve the oxide in hydrochloric acid. In this case the first filtration should be made on paper. Transfer the filter paper to a platinum crucible, dry and burn away the paper, and convert the calcium oxalate to calcium oxide at the full heat of a Meker burner for 15 minutes. Cool the crucible and place it in a 400-ml. beaker. Add water to the crucible cautiously with a cover glass in place. Finally, add 5 ml. of concentrated hydrochloric acid, and after all the calcium hydroxide has passed into solution dilute to 125 ml. Remove the platinum crucible with a stirring rod, washing crucible and rod carefully with a stream of water from the wash bottle. Reprecipitate the calcium as described above.

Ignition to Calcium Carbonate. Place the filtering crucible in an electric muffle at 500° to 525° for 1.5 hours. The temperature must be within this range, and it must be remembered that the front and back of the muffle may not be at the same temperature as the thermocouple in the center. Cool and weigh the filtering crucible and calcium carbonate. Moisten the precipitate with a drop of a saturated solution of ammonium carbonate, and place in the muffle again for 20 minutes. The weight should not change on this treatment. Report the per cent of calcium oxide. The factor for converting calcium carbonate to calcium oxide is 0.5603.

Ignition to Calcium Oxide. Transfer the paper and calcium oxalate to a weighed crucible, preferably of platinum although porcelain will be satisfactory. Dry and burn away the paper and ignite at the full heat of a Meker burner with the crucible in a chimney of some sort. Chimneys of fire brick can be purchased from the supply house, but cylinders of asbestos paper are easy to make and will last for a few determinations. Make the cylinder about 3 to 4 cm. larger in diameter than the crucible, and cut slots up from the bottom so it will rest on the wire triangle and extend below the crucible 2 cm.

If an electric muffle is available ignite the precipitate at 1000° to 1100°; at this higher temperature calcium oxide is "dead burned" and not as hygroscopic as when ignited at the lower temperature of a burner ("soft burned").

After removing the crucible from the burner or electric muffle allow it to cool almost until it can be touched with the hand, and then place it in a desiccator. As soon as it has reached room temperature, weigh it. Do not delay more than 30 minutes as calcium oxide will absorb water from the fresh air in the desiccator and later will extract it from the calcium chloride in the desiccator. Carry out the weighing as rapidly as possible. Ignite the crucible as before for 20 minutes, cool, and weigh again. This time have the weights already on the balance so that only the final adjustment of the rider is necessary and the weighing can be made quickly. A third ignition may be necessary if the weight is found to be increasing rapidly when the weighing is complete.

Report the per cent of calcium oxide.

PROBLEMS

1. A sample of limestone was ignited to convert the carbonate to oxide. A sample weighing 0.6000 g. lost 0.1960 g. Calculate the per cent of calcium carbonate in the sample, assuming the loss to be due entirely to carbon dioxide derived from calcium carbonate.

2. The calcium in a sample of very pure calcium metal weighing 0.7500 g. was precipitated as the oxalate and weighed as the carbonate. The result obtained was 99.0 per cent calcium. Assuming that all of the error in the determination was in the ignition, calculate the weight of calcium oxide in the calcium carbonate weighed.

3. Calculate the weight of carbon monoxide expelled on igniting 1.00 g. of anhydrous calcium oxalate.

4. Calculate the amount of calcium in grams per liter present in a solution which is 0.05 M in oxalate and saturated with calcium oxalate. See Appendix, Table A2, for values of solubility-product constants.

5. Calculate the weight of sample which should be taken so that each 5 mg. of calcium carbonate, $CaCO_3$, obtained will correspond to 0.28 per cent calcium oxide, CaO.

6. Give the principal steps in the analysis of a tooth powder known to consist of a mixture of calcium carbonate and silica.

7. Outline a method for the determination of calcium oxalate in a mixture of calcium carbonate and calcium oxalate.

8. A mixture of calcium oxide and calcium carbonate is to be analyzed for calcium carbonate. Tell how this can be done.

9. Give the principal steps in the analysis of blast-furnace slag, which is a silicate of iron and calcium, for silica, iron, and calcium. The silicate is soluble in hydrochloric acid.

THE PRECIPITATION OF MAGNESIUM AMMONIUM PHOSPHATE

The double salt magnesium ammonium phosphate, $MgNH_4PO_4$, is quite insoluble. It is used in the determination of both magnesium and phosphate. In either case the precipitate is usually ignited and weighed as magnesium pyrophosphate, $Mg_2P_2O_7$. The reactions involved in the determination are

$$MgCl_2 + NH_4H_2PO_4 + 2NH_4OH + 4H_2O$$

$$= MgNH_4PO_4 \cdot 6H_2O + 2NH_4Cl$$

$$2MgNH_4PO_4 = Mg_2P_2O_7 + 2NH_3 + H_2O$$

Being the salt of a weak acid, magnesium ammonium phosphate is soluble in solutions containing strong acids. The precipitation is effected by neutralizing the solution containing magnesium, phosphate, and ammonium chloride with ammonia. In the determination of magnesium an excess of diammonium phosphate is present; in the determination of phosphate an excess of magnesium chloride is present. An excess of ammonia is added after the precipitation, as the solubility of the double salt is greatly decreased by an excess of ammonium hydroxide.

The solubility of magnesium ammonium phosphate increases rapidly as the acidity of the solution is increased. In a neutral solution hydrolysis becomes appreciable: $MgNH_4PO_4 + H_2O = MgHPO_4 + NH_4OH$, and therefore a dilute ammonia solution is used in transferring the precipitate to the filter and in washing it.

Attempts have been made to weigh the precipitate as the hexahydrate. The difficulty of removing the superficial water without driving off any of the water of crystallization makes this a rather uncertain procedure, however, and it is better to ignite the precipitate to the pyrophosphate for weighing. The conversion of magnesium ammonium phosphate to the pyrophosphate is rapid at 1000° to 1100°. Above 1200° the compound begins to lose weight.

Unfortunately the composition of magnesium ammonium phosphate is altered appreciably by the method of precipitation and by the presence of foreign salts, particularly those of ammonium and potassium.

It is possible to precipitate magnesium ammonium phosphate by the addition of the phosphate to a neutral or slightly alkaline solution containing the magnesium salt and ammonium chloride. This procedure leads invariably to high results for magnesium, and a reprecipitation using the correct method of precipitation will then yield low results. The precipitation should, therefore, never be made by the addition of phosphate to an ammoniacal solution of a magnesium salt.

A large amount of ammonium salts in the solution causes the results to be high. This is generally explained as resulting from coprecipitation of ammonium phosphate which gives metaphosphoric acid, HPO_3, on ignition and from the precipitation of another double phosphate, $Mg(NH_4)_4(PO_4)_2$, which gives magnesium metaphosphate on ignition. Fortunately, a reprecipitation of the magnesium ammonium phosphate precipitated under such conditions yields a precipitate having the correct composition. Inasmuch as magnesium is usually determined about last in the systematic analysis of a limestone or silicate, large amounts of ammonium salts are frequently present with the magnesium, having accumulated from the various reagents added during the course of the analysis. The ammonium salts may be destroyed by several evaporations with nitric and hydrochloric acids. It is usually more satisfactory, however, to carry out the precipitation without destroying the ammonium salts and to reprecipitate the magnesium ammonium phosphate.

When precipitated from a solution containing potassium salts, the ammonium ion of the double phosphate is replaced in part by the potassium ion which has about the same atomic radius and fits into the crystal structure well. On ignition the potassium is not volatilized like the ammonium ion, and the increased weight leads to high results. A reprecipitation of the magnesium ammonium phosphate eliminates this error. Very large amounts of sodium in the solution cause the same trouble.

Filter paper can be used for magnesium ammonium phosphate, but if the ignition is not properly carried out some reduction of precipitate may occur. It is more satisfactory to use porous-bottom filtering crucibles.

Interfering Materials and Other Applications. Practically all the phosphates of metals other than those of the alkali metals (lithium, sodium, and potassium) and ammonium are insoluble in neutral solution. In the precipitation of magnesium as the double phosphate, then, the phosphates of any heavy metals present are also precipitated. Thus, the precipitation of magnesium as the ammonium phosphate serves only to separate the magnesium from the alkali metals and ammonium. It is for this reason that the determination of magnesium is deferred to the very end of the analysis of a limestone or a silicate.

Oxalate, which is used to precipitate calcium, is often present in the magnesium solution. Its presence tends to delay the precipitation somewhat, but with the period of standing recommended in the procedure the loss is negligible. Citric acid, which is often added to hold in solution small amounts of iron and aluminum, does not interfere with the determination of either magnesium or phosphate.

A number of bivalent metals, manganese, zinc, cadmium, cobalt, and beryllium, form similar double ammonium phosphates which are sufficiently insoluble in neutral solution to serve for the determination of these metals once they are separated from other heavy metals. The determination of manganese can be made by using the procedure for magnesium. Zinc, cadmium, and cobalt, however, form double salts which are soluble in ammonia because of the formation of stable, non-ionized compounds of these metals with ammonia, and the precipitation must be made from a strictly neutral solution; the solution is usually buffered with a mixture of diammonium hydrogen phosphate and ammonium dihydrogen phosphate which holds the solution close to the neutral point (pH 7).

The chemistry of arsenic is quite similar to that of phosphorus; in the quinquivalent state, for example, the two form the corresponding acids; H_3PO_4, H_3AsO_4; HPO_3, $HAsO_3$; and $H_4P_2O_7$, $H_4As_2O_7$. The solubilities of the corresponding salts are about the same. Double arsenates are also formed with magnesium and the bivalent metals just mentioned, $(M)NH_4AsO_4$. On ignition they yield the corresponding pyroarsenates, $(M)_2As_2O_7$. Magnesium can be determined as magnesium pyroarsenate. Arsenates, then, will interfere in the determination of phosphate, and, in the presence of arsenate, magnesium cannot be determined as the pyrophosphate. The arsenic may be removed from the solution by precipitation from a strong hydrochloric acid solution as the sulfide.

Procedure for the Determination of Magnesium. Weigh accurately a sample of such size that it contains approximately 0.1 g. of magnesium or less. Dissolve the sample, and to the nearly neutral solution add 5 to 10 ml. of concentrated hydrochloric acid. Dilute the solution to 150 ml. To this solution, which should be at room temperature or preferably cooler (cool in ice), add 10 ml. of a solution containing 25 g. of diammonium phosphate, $(NH_4)_2HPO_4$, per 100 ml. Add a few drops of methyl red indicator. Add filtered ammonium hydroxide, with stirring, until the indicator has turned distinctly yellow. Stir for a few minutes and then add an additional 5 ml. of concentrated ammonium hydroxide. Allow the solution to stand at least 4 hours or overnight.

Filter the magnesium ammonium phosphate on a porous-bottom filtering crucible previously washed, ignited, and weighed. Decant the supernatant liquid through the filter and then transfer the precipitate to the filter. Loosen the precipitate from the beaker with a rubber-tipped stirring rod. Wash the precipitate with dilute ammonium hydroxide (5:100) until the filtrate is free of chloride (acidify the sample of filtrate taken for the test with nitric acid before adding the silver nitrate). Use only as much of the wash water as is just necessary to effect the washing. Dry the precipitate in the drying oven or over a low flame. Place the filtering crucible in a larger porcelain crucible to protect the porous bottom and precipitate from the flame. Heat the precipitate rather slowly at first, and then finally ignite it at the full heat of a Meker burner for 1 hour. Cool and weigh. Ignite the precipitate again for 30 minutes and again cool and weigh. The loss in weight should not be greater than 0.3 mg. If an electric muffle is available carry out the ignition in it at 1000°; constant weight will be attained rapidly at this temperature. The magnesium pyrophosphate is usually quite dark in color after the ignition.

If the sample or original solution containing the magnesium contained a large amount of ammonium or potassium salts, it is necessary to reprecipitate the magnesium ammonium phosphate. Even though excessive amounts of potassium and ammonium were absent from the original solution, better results are obtained if a reprecipitation is made. The excess of ammonium and phosphate ions can be better controlled. If a reprecipitation is to be made, paper should be used for the first filtration. Dissolve the precipitate in 50 ml. of warm, dilute hydrochloric acid (1:9) and wash the paper thoroughly with hot, dilute hydrochloric acid (1:99). Dilute the solution to 125 to 150 ml., add 0.25 g. of diammonium phosphate, cool, and precipitate the magnesium as described above. After a minimum of 4 hours' standing, filter on a porous-bottom filtering crucible and complete the determination as before.

From the weight of magnesium pyrophosphate calculate the per cent of magnesium oxide in the sample; the conversion factor is 0.3623.

Procedure for the Determination of Phosphate. Dry the material for analysis at 110° for at least 2 hours. Weigh accurately samples of 0.7 g. into 400-ml. beakers. Dissolve each sample in 25 ml. of water containing 5 to 10 ml. of concentrated hydrochloric acid. Dilute the solution to 125 to 150 ml.

Prepare a solution of 50 g. of magnesium chloride, $MgCl_2 \cdot 6H_2O$, and 100 g. of ammonium chloride in 500 ml. of water. Make the solution slightly ammoniacal and allow it to stand overnight. Filter the solution and acidify the filtrate with hydrochloric acid. Add 5 ml. of concentrated hydrochloric acid in excess and dilute to 1 l. This solution is referred to as *magnesia mixture*.

Add 10 ml. of magnesia-mixture solution for each 0.2 g. of phosphorus pentoxide (P_2O_5) in the sample; assume that the sample contains 30 per cent phosphorus pentoxide. Cool the solution to room temperature or preferably lower by immersing in ice. Add a few drops of methyl red indicator. Add filtered, concentrated ammonium hydroxide slowly and with constant stirring until the color of the indicator has become distinctly yellow. Stir for a few minutes and then add 5 to 10 ml. of ammonium hydroxide. Allow the mixture to stand at least 4 hours or preferably overnight.

Filter the magnesium ammonium phosphate on a porous-bottom filtering crucible previously washed, ignited, and weighed. Decant the supernatant liquid through the filter and then transfer the precipitate to the filter. Loosen the precipitate from the beaker with a rubber-tipped stirring rod. Wash the precipitate with dilute ammonium hydroxide (5:100) until the filtrate is free of chloride (acidify the sample of filtrate taken for the test with nitric acid before adding the silver nitrate). Use only as much of the wash water as is just necessary to effect the washing properly, keeping the volume small to minimize the solubility loss. Dry the precipitate in the drying oven or over a low flame. Place the filtering crucible in a larger porcelain crucible to protect the porous bottom and precipitate from the flame. Heat the crucible rather slowly at first and then finally ignite it at the full heat of a Meker burner for 1 hour. Cool and weigh. Ignite the precipitate again for 30 minutes, and again cool and weigh. The loss in weight should not be greater than 0.3 mg. If an electric muffle is available carry out the ignition in it at 1000°; constant weight will be obtained rapidly at this temperature. The magnesium pyrophosphate is usually quite dark in color after the ignition.

If the sample being analyzed contained a large amount of ammonium or potassium salts, it is necessary to reprecipitate the magnesium ammonium phosphate. Even though excessive amounts of these elements were absent from the original solution, better results are obtained if a reprecipitation is made. The excess of ammonium and magnesium ions can be better controlled, and the precipitate has more nearly the correct composition. If a reprecipitation is to be made the first filtration should be made through paper. Dissolve the precipitate in 50 ml. of warm, dilute hydrochloric acid (1:9) and wash the paper thoroughly with hot, dilute hydrochloric acid (1:99). Dilute the solution to 125 to 150 ml., add 2 ml. of magnesia mixture, cool the solution and carry out the precipitation as described above. After a minimum of 4 hours' standing, filter on a porous-bottom filtering crucible and complete the determination as before.

From the weight of the magnesium pyrophosphate calculate the per cent of phosphorus pentoxide in the sample; the conversion factor is 0.6377.

PROBLEMS

1. Write the equations for the reactions involved in the determination of magnesium, starting with magnesium carbonate.

2. Explain why a dilute solution of ammonia is chosen as a wash solution for magnesium ammonium phosphate.

3. Discuss the similarities of the potassium ion and the ammonium ion. Look up the solubilities of corresponding salts in a handbook.

4. Summarize the errors which are inherent in the determination of magnesium as the pyrophosphate. Tell whether each gives high or low results.

5. Phosphate rock consists essentially of the mineral apatite, $Ca_5F(PO_4)_3$. A sample of phosphate rock from Tennessee was analyzed for phosphorus. A sample weighing 1.0000 g. gave 0.6100 g. of magnesium pyrophosphate. Calculate (a) the

per cent of phosphorus pentoxide, and (b) the per cent of apatite in the sample.

6. The magnesium in a sample weighing 0.4900 g. was determined as the pyrophosphate, of which 0.2220 g. was obtained. Calculate the per cent of magnesium in the sample.

7. Calculate the weight of sample which should be taken such that each 2 mg. of magnesium pyrophosphate represents 0.5 per cent of phosphorus pentoxide.

8. A magnesium mineral was found by analysis to be composed of 69.2 per cent magnesium oxide and 30.8 per cent water. Determine the empirical formula of the mineral.

9. Calculate the weight of pyrophosphoric acid which could be obtained from 1.000 g. of orthophosphoric acid.

10. Outline a procedure for the determination of the magnesium in the medicinal preparation, milk of magnesia, which is a suspension of magnesium hydroxide in water.

11. The molar solubility of cadmium ammonium phosphate in a neutral solution is about 1.0×10^{-6}. Calculate the weight in grams per liter of (a) cadmium, and (b) phosphorus pentoxide in a saturated solution.

12. Outline a method for the determination of calcium, magnesium, and arsenic in a mixture containing calcium and magnesium arsenates. The mixture is soluble in hydrochloric acid.

13. Devise a scheme for the determination of magnesium, zinc, arsenic, and phosphorus in a mixture of hydrated arsenates and phosphates of magnesium and zinc.

14. The calcium chloride used on roads is a crude, hydrated salt known to contain silica and magnesium chloride. Outline a scheme of analysis to determine its content of water, silica, calcium, magnesium, and chloride.

15. Devise a scheme for the analysis of Dowmetal, an alloy approximately 85 per cent magnesium and 15 per cent aluminum.

CHAPTER 7

Volumetric Analysis

Although the Atomic Theory is almost as old as the hills, no one before Dalton used the theory of atoms to explain chemical phenomena. His great achievement was that he was the first to introduce the idea of quantity into chemistry. He showed that the weights of the atoms of different elements are not identical, but different, and that combination amongst them takes place in simple proportions—*Sir Henry E. Roscoe.*

The process of determining the amount of a substance by measuring the volume of a solution of a second substance which reacts with it in some definite and complete fashion is known as a *volumetric analysis*. The solution of the second substance must be of some known concentration and is referred to as a *standard solution*. The process of carrying out the reaction is known as a *titration*, the standard solution being added from a buret. The verb *to titrate* is derived from the French word, *titrer*, to standardize or label. Volumetric analysis is often spoken of as *titrimetric analysis*.

It is essential in any volumetric analysis that some method be available for detecting when just sufficient standard solution has been added to react completely with the substance being determined; that is, some method must be available for finding the end-point. The commonest method of doing this is by the addition of a substance which changes color at the conclusion of the reaction. A great many natural and synthetic organic materials are known, which change color more or less abruptly on passing from an acid solution to a basic solution and can serve as indicators in titrations involving acids and bases. For certain reasons, however, not all such substances are equally suitable. In addition to indicators which change color at the end-point there are some twenty or thirty other ways of finding the end-point, some chemical in nature and others operating on some characteristic physical property of the solution; these will be mentioned in various places in the text.

It is also important, of course, that the end-point as marked by the indicator or one of the other devices mentioned come at the right point in the reaction, that is, exactly when equivalent amounts of the two substances have been mixed. We distinguish, then, between *end-point* and *equivalence-point*, the end-point being the point marked by the indicator and the equivalence-point being the point corresponding to the mixing of exactly the necessary amounts of the two substances involved. It is most desirable that the two should be identical, but for various reasons this is often far from the case.

In a very real sense the process of volumetric analysis is a comparison process, for the strength of the standard solutions used is usually determined by the titration of a pure material, called a *primary standard*, which has a composition identical or at least quite similar to the substance being determined. It is not even necessary to know the weights of the sample and of the primary standard provided exactly the same weight of the two were selected for two successive titrations with the standard solution.

Obviously any reaction to be used for volumetric analysis must be a reaction which can be made to go in one direction completely and stoichiometrically. Stoichiometrically means that there is a definite, whole-number ratio between the numbers of molecules of the substances entering the reaction. Occasionally it is possible to utilize a reaction for which a definite chemical equation cannot be written but which proceeds to the same extent each time if the conditions of temperature, acidity, and the concentrations of the various reagents are reproduced closely; in such a titration it is necessary to standardize the standard solution against a pure material under exactly the same conditions. Such an empirical method is only used when a reaction that proceeds stoichiometrically is not available.

The reactions which are employed in volumetric analysis can be classified into three general types: neutralization reactions, oxidation-reduction reactions, and precipitation and non-ionized-compound formation reactions. Neutralization reactions are those involving acids and bases, or, more generally, those involving hydrogen and hydroxyl ions; the standard solutions used are acids and bases. Oxidation-reduction reactions are those in which changes in valence or oxidation number occur; iron is oxidized from a valence of 2 to a valence of 3 by a standard solution of potassium permanganate, and arsenic is oxidized from arsenious acid to arsenic acid by standard iodine solution. Precipitation and non-ionized-compound formation reactions are those involving the formation of an insoluble material or a soluble material which is not dissociated into ions. Chloride can be titrated with silver nitrate, and sulfate with barium chloride, but unfortunately satisfactory indicators are not available for many similar and otherwise satisfactory precipitation reactions. Non-ionized-compound formation is sometimes referred to as complex-ion formation; this term is inappropriate because the term "complex ion" has been used indiscriminately to cover reactions whose nature has not been well understood, whereas reactions used in volumetric analysis must of necessity be clean cut and well established. An illustration of such a reaction is the determination of cyanide by the reaction

$$2NaCN + AgNO_3 = NaAg(CN)_2 + NaNO_3$$

The compound $NaAg(CN)_2$ is ionized into Na^+ and $Ag(CN)_2^-$ ions, but $Ag(CN)_2^-$ is not further ionized to any appreciable extent into Ag^+ and CN^- ions, and therefore the reaction above goes completely to the right and can be used for the determination of cyanide.

All three types of volumetric reactions just outlined are of great importance in chemical analysis as applied to problems in chemical research and in the chemical industry. Precipitation and non-ionized-compound formation reactions are of somewhat less importance than the other two types. An excellent theoretical background has been developed for each of these three types of reactions, and the theory of each will be discussed in separate chapters preceding the detailed treatment of the specific volumetric methods; thus, Chapter 8 deals with the theory of neutralization reactions; Chapter 9 with the practical aspects and applications of neutralization reactions. The remainder of the present chapter is devoted to certain aspects of volumetric analysis which are common to all three types of reactions: the general properties of primary standards, the normal system and calculations of volumetric analysis, the mechanics of titration, and the calibration of volumetric apparatus.

PRIMARY STANDARDS

Do not descend into a well on an old rope—Turkish proverb.

A volumetric analysis is carried out by adding to the substance being determined a solution of a second substance with which it reacts quickly and completely. The exact volume of the second substance required to effect the reaction is measured accurately. The concentration of the solution of this second material must be accurately known. If this material can be obtained in highly pure form the solution can be prepared by weighing out the necessary amount of the material, dissolving it, and diluting it exactly to a certain volume. Unfortunately, the majority of the materials used as standard solutions do not have properties which permit preparing the standard solution in this way. Sodium hydroxide is never pure but carries with it water and sodium carbonate; concentrated sulfuric acid contains about 5 per cent water; potassium permanganate is usually contaminated with manganese dioxide; barium chloride has water of crystallization the amount of which varies with the conditions of storage; and so on. In these cases the standard solution is made up approximately, using the best materials available, and its strength is determined by titration of a weighed amount of another material which can be obtained in pure form. Thus, sodium hydroxide solutions are standardized against sulfamic acid or potassium acid phthalate, sulfuric acid against sodium carbonate, and potassium permanganate against sodium oxalate.

A substance which can be obtained in pure form and which has certain other characteristics which permit it to be weighed out and made into a standard solution or titrated to establish the concentration of another standard solution is known as a *primary standard*. The characteristics which a primary standard should possess are:

1. *Purity*. The material should be available commercially in highly pure form, or at least an easy method should exist for its purification. Preferably the purity should be 100 per cent, but often a lesser purity, provided it be accurately known, is acceptable. It should be possible to test for the impurities.

2. *Stability*. The material should keep indefinitely without change. It should not absorb water or carbon dioxide from the atmosphere. It should be able to withstand drying at temperatures sufficient to drive off adsorbed water (usually 110–120°). In order to insure complete freedom from occluded moisture it is desirable that the material can be fused without decomposition.

3. *Chemistry*. The material should react quickly and stoichiometrically with the solution being standardized, and there must be a convenient way of finding the equivalence-point.

4. *High equivalent weight*. A high equivalent weight is desirable although not necessary; the greater the equivalent weight the larger the amount of material which must be weighed out for an analysis and the lower the relative error in the analysis, caused by the error in weighing.

The number of substances which meet all these requirements is quite limited. Compounds containing water of crystallization are usually unsatisfactory, for such water molecules are often not firmly bound to the molecule and are lost to dry air and reabsorbed from air of high humidity. Thus, oxalic acid crystallizes as a dihydrate, $H_2C_2O_4 \cdot 2H_2O$, but is not a primary standard because part of the 2 molecules of water is lost when the dihydrate is exposed to air. However, ferrous ethylenediammonium sulfate, which crystallizes with 4 molecules of water, does not lose its water to dry air and in fact must be heated to 50° before its water is expelled. In this case, although the material cannot be heated to 110° for drying, the equivalent weight is so high that traces of water adsorbed on the surface are an insignificant part of the total weight of material taken.

The most insidious impurity affecting primary-standard material is liquid water trapped inside the crystal. It is difficult to prove the presence or absence of such water by any direct method. In work of exceptional accuracy only those materials are employed as primary standards which can be melted and from which the water is thus guaranteed to be absent.

Obviously the primary standard must not gain or lose weight while being weighed out. Such an effect might be brought about by the absorption of carbon dioxide as well as water. When it is necessary to use a liquid primary standard, loss by evaporation must be prevented by carrying out the weighing in a closed vessel and performing the transferring operations quickly.

With respect to the third requirement listed above, it is best if the reaction of the primary standard and the solution proceed completely in such a fashion that the reaction can be expressed by a definite chemical equation. Occasionally this is not possible, and yet if the standardization and the later determination of the unknown are carried out in exactly the same way, for the same constituent, the results may be satisfactory. A material of the same composition as that being analyzed is then used to standardize the volumetric solutions. The composition of this material must be accurately known. Thus, in the determination of iron in iron ore, an ore whose iron content has been previously determined very accurately can be used in effect as a primary standard. Whenever possible, however, primary standards are used whose reactions are stoichiometric with the materials being standardized.

THE NORMAL SYSTEM AND CALCULATIONS IN VOLUMETRIC ANALYSIS

Several systems of expressing the concentration of solutions are in common use. Two of the systems are based on atomic or molecular weights and are more useful in chemical work than the methods based on straight weight or percentage. *Molar concentration* is defined as the number of gram molecular weights of a substance dissolved in 1 l. of solution. *Normal concentration* is defined as the number of gram equivalent weights of a substance dissolved in 1 l. of solution. Molar concentration is used in equilibrium problems, for mass-action effects depend directly on the number of molecules involved and molar concentration is directly proportional to the number of molecules in solution. Normal concentration is based on equivalent weight and is especially useful in analytical work, particularly in volumetric analysis where it greatly simplifies the calculations. The equivalent weight of a substance varies with the reaction in which the material is involved. Thus, in a neutralization reaction it may be different than in an oxidation-reduction reaction or in a reaction involving precipitation or the formation of a non-ionized compound. Indeed, it may not even be the same in all neutralization reactions in which the material may take part.

Equivalent weight in neutralization reactions is defined as the molecular weight divided by the number of replaceable hydrogen atoms which the substance contains, reacts with, or is derived from. Thus, the equivalent weights of hydrochloric acid, sulfuric acid, and sodium hydroxide are their molecular weights divided by 1, 2, and 1, respectively

$$\frac{HCl}{1} \qquad \frac{H_2SO_4}{2} \qquad \frac{NaOH}{1} \qquad \frac{Ba(OH)_2}{2}$$

and the equivalent weight of barium hydroxide is the molecular weight divided by 2, because it requires 2 replaceable hydrogen atoms for neutralization. On the other hand, the equivalent weight of phosphoric acid may be the molecular weight, one-half the molecular weight, or one-third the molecular weight, depending on the reaction in which it is involved.

$$H_3PO_4 + NaOH = NaH_2PO_4 + H_2O \qquad \frac{H_3PO_4}{1}$$

$$H_3PO_4 + 2NaOH = Na_2HPO_4 + 2H_2O \qquad \frac{H_3PO_4}{2}$$

$$H_3PO_4 + 3NaOH = Na_3PO_4 + 3H_2O \qquad \frac{H_3PO_4}{3}$$

The equivalent weight of salts is determined by the number of replaceable hydrogen atoms with which they react or which were involved in their formation.

$$Na_2CO_3 + HCl = NaHCO_3 + NaCl \qquad \frac{Na_2CO_3}{1} \quad \frac{NaCl}{1}$$

$$Na_2CO_3 + 2HCl = H_2CO_3 + 2NaCl \qquad \frac{Na_2CO_3}{2} \quad \frac{NaCl}{1}$$

$$H_2SO_4 + BaCl_2 = BaSO_4 + 2HCl \qquad \frac{BaSO_4}{2}$$

$$HCl + AgNO_3 = AgCl + HNO_3 \qquad \frac{AgCl}{1}$$

The solubility of the material has nothing to do with the equivalent weight; thus, although a 1 M solution of barium sulfate cannot conceivably be made, the equivalent weight of barium sulfate in the reaction above is one-half the molecular weight.

As a consequence of the definition of a normal solution the following are true statements:

One liter of 1 N sodium hydroxide will exactly react with 1 l. of 1 N hydrochloric acid.

One liter of 1 N sodium hydroxide will exactly react with 1 l. of 1 N sulfuric acid.

For by definition, 1 l. of 1 N sulfuric acid contains one-half a gram molecular weight, or 49 g., which is the amount just necessary to react with the 40 g. of sodium hydroxide in 1 l. of 1 N sodium hydroxide.

One liter of 1 N barium hydroxide will exactly react with 1 l. of 1 N hydrochloric acid.

One liter of any 1 N base will exactly react with 1 l. of any 1 N acid.

The reasoning is the same.

A milliequivalent weight (m. e. wt.) is one-thousandth of an equivalent weight. A gram milliequivalent weight is the amount of material in 1 ml. of a 1 N solution. Since most volumetric work is done with burets reading in milliliters, the milliequivalent weight is the quantity most frequently used. The milliequivalent weight of sodium hydroxide is 0.040,05, of sulfuric acid, 0.049,04, of barium hydroxide, 0.085,96.

Most volumetric work is done with solutions less than 1 N. Conversion of a given volume of solution of some normality to volume of exactly 1 N is conveniently made by the relation

$$(ml._1)(N_1) = (ml._2)(N_2)$$

or simply milliliters times normality equals milliliters of 1 N.

Since 1 ml. of a 1 N solution contains 1 milliequivalent weight, the weight of a dissolved substance A in a given volume of a solution of known normality is obtained by

$$g_A = (ml._A)(N_A)(m. e. wt._A)$$

Thus, 50.0 ml. of 0.1500 N sodium hydroxide contains

$$(50.0)(0.1500)(0.040,05) = 0.3004 \text{ g. of NaOH}$$

In a titration some substance A is caused to react with another substance B made up as a standard solution. The exact volume of the solution of B required is measured with a buret. The volume of liquid in which A is dissolved in the flask or beaker need not be known. This is fortunate because the volume would change as the standard solution is added, and it is desirable to wash down the walls of the flask toward the end of the titration. If some method is available for deciding when enough B has been added to react exactly with all of A, the amount of A can be calculated from the volume of the standard solution of B used, its normality, and the milliequivalent weight of A:

$$g_A = (\text{ml.}_B)(N_B)(\text{m. e. wt.}_A)$$

This comes about from the definition of normal solution and the consequence that 1 l. of an exactly 1 N solution of any base will exactly react with 1 l. of a 1 N solution of any acid.

As an example, suppose a sample containing hydrochloric acid and weighing 10.000 g. is taken, is diluted somewhat with water, indicator solution is added, and the acid is titrated with standard sodium hydroxide, 0.1500 N. The volume in the flask at the end-point will not be known, but the volume of standard sodium hydroxide, delivered from a buret, will be known exactly; say 45.00 ml. was used. The volume of 1 N sodium hydroxide would be (45.00)(0.1500), or 6.75 ml. If the hydrochloric acid present had been exactly 1 N its volume would have been 6.75 ml. The weight of hydrogen chloride present in the sample is then (6.75)(0.036,45) = 0.2454 g., the milliequivalent weight of hydrochloric acid being 0.036,45. Irrespective of the volume in which the hydrochloric acid was dissolved, it is apparent that the weight present is 0.2454 g. Since the weight of the original sample was 10.000 g., the per cent of hydrochloric acid (HCl) in the sample may be calculated:

$$\frac{0.2454}{10.000} \; 100 = 2.45 \text{ per cent HCl}$$

By gathering together all the preceding steps it is seen that this result was obtained from

$$\frac{(45.0)(0.1500)(0.036,45)}{10.000} \; 100 = 2.45 \text{ per cent HCl}$$

or

$$\text{Per cent HCl} = \frac{(\text{ml.}_{\text{NaOH}})(N_{\text{NaOH}})(\text{m. e. wt.}_{\text{HCl}})100}{\text{Wt. sample}}$$

or, more generally, where A is the substance being determined and B is the standard solution

$$\text{Per cent } A = \frac{(\text{ml.}_B)(N_B)(\text{m. e. wt.}_A)100}{\text{Wt. sample}}$$

This formula is a very useful one; together with the formula $(ml._1)(N_1) = (ml._2)(N_2)$ it can be used to solve practically all problems in volumetric analysis. There are five factors involved in this formula; in any volumetric analysis problem there will be four known quantities and one unknown. Most often the unknown will be the per cent of A, but it may be any of the others.

In the standardization of a solution against a primary standard material, the per cent purity is 100 and the unknown term the normality. Thus, a sample of primary-standard potassium acid phthalate weighing 0.6000 g. required 40.0 ml. of a certain sodium hydroxide solution for titration. The normality of the sodium hydroxide was calculated as follows:

$$\text{Per cent } KHC_8H_4O_4 = \frac{(ml._{NaOH})(N_{NaOH})(m.\ e.\ wt._{KHC_8H_4O_4})100}{\text{Wt. sample}}$$

$$100 = \frac{(40.0)(N_{NaOH})(0.2042)100}{0.6000}$$

$$N_{NaOH} = 0.0735$$

The standardization of a solution by a gravimetric method is handled in the same way. A volume of 50.0 ml. of a solution of sulfuric acid gave on precipitation 0.4660 g. of barium sulfate. The normality of the sulfuric acid solution was calculated using barium sulfate as substance A and assuming it to be 100 per cent pure.

$$\text{Per cent } BaSO_4 = \frac{(ml._{H_2SO_4})(N_{H_2SO_4})(m.\ e.\ wt._{BaSO_4})100}{\text{Wt. } BaSO_4}$$

$$100 = \frac{(50.0)(N_{H_2SO_4})(\frac{233}{2000})100}{0.4660}$$

$$N_{H_2SO_4} = 0.0800$$

In other problems it may be required to calculate the number of milliliters of a standard solution needed to react with a given amount of material, or it may be required to calculate the milliequivalent weight of an acid after the titration of a pure specimen of it. These problems can be handled in the same general way. Look for four known quantities and solve for the fifth.

Titer. In routine work where a great many analyses for the same material are being made the calculations are somewhat simplified by combining the normality and the milliequivalent weight. The product is called the *titer* for a given material. The sulfuric acid titer of sodium hydroxide solution would thus be

$$\text{Titer}_{H_2SO_4} = (N_{NaOH}) \left(\frac{\text{Mol. wt.}_{H_2SO_4}}{2000} \right)$$

The general equation developed above becomes in terms of titer

$$\text{Per cent } A = \frac{(\text{ml.}_B)(\text{Titer for } A)(100)}{\text{Wt. sample}}$$

In certain cases where a pure sample containing A can be used as a primary standard the titer for A is calculated directly and the normality need not be computed at all.

When a standard solution is to be used for the determination of some other material than that for which the titer is given, a new titer must be calculated. The titer for A may be converted to titer for B simply by multiplying by the ratio of the equivalent weights of B to A. Thus, given the sulfuric acid titer of a sodium hydroxide solution, the titer for hydrochloric acid is

$$\text{Titer}_{HCl} = \text{Titer}_{H_2SO_4} \left[\frac{\text{Mol. wt.}_{HCl}/1}{\text{Mol. wt.}_{H_2SO_4}/2} \right]$$

$$= (N_{NaOH}) \left(\frac{\text{Mol. wt.}_{H_2SO_4}}{2000} \right) \left[\frac{\text{Mol. wt.}_{HCl}/1}{\text{Mol. wt.}_{H_2SO_4}/2} \right]$$

$$= (N_{NaOH}) \left(\frac{\text{Mol. wt.}_{HCl}}{1000} \right)$$

Inasmuch as industrial work often requires a great many analyses for the same material, the titer system is widely used in commercial analytical laboratories.

PROBLEMS

1. Determine the milliequivalent weight of each of the underlined materials in the following reactions:

(a) $\underline{HCl} + NaOH = NaCl + H_2O$

(b) $\underline{H_2SO_4} + 2KOH = K_2SO_4 + 2H_2O$

(c) $\underline{Na_2CO_3} + \underline{HCl} = NaHCO_3 + NaCl$

(d) $\underline{NaHCO_3} + \underline{HCl} = H_2CO_3 + NaCl$

(e) $\underline{Na_2CO_3} + 2\underline{HCl} = H_2CO_3 + 2NaCl$

(f) $\underline{H_2SO_4} + BaCl_2 = BaSO_4 + 2HCl$

(g) $2\underline{H_2C_2O_4} + Ba(OH)_2 = Ba(HC_2O_4)_2 + 2H_2O$

(h) $\underline{NH_4Cl} + \underline{NaOH} = \underline{NH_4OH} + NaCl$

H_2SO_4 always goes two

2. Calculate the weight of each of the following required for 1 l. of 0.1000 N solution: (a) H_2SO_4, (b) NaOH, (c) Ca(OH)$_2$, (d) H_3PO_4 for conversion to KH_2PO_4, (?) $HKC_4H_4O_6$ (one replaceable hydrogen).

3. Calculate the weight of potassium hydroxide in 35.0 ml. of a 0.1300 N solution.

4. Calculate the volume of 0.015 N sodium hydroxide which would contain the same weight of sodium hydroxide as 10.0 ml. of a 0.200 N solution.

5. Calculate the volume of 0.1250 N hydrochloric acid needed to neutralize 50.0 ml. of 0.2000 N sodium hydroxide.

6. A sample of vinegar weighing 10.000 g. was diluted with water, phenolphthalein indicator added, and the acid in it titrated with 0.0955 N sodium hydroxide of which 41.5 ml. was required. Assuming that the acid present was all acetic acid, $HC_2H_3O_2$ (one replaceable hydrogen), calculate the per cent of acetic acid in the sample.

7. A sample of hydrobromic acid weighing 1.0500 g. required 35.0 ml. of 0.1110 N barium hydroxide for titration. Calculate the per cent of hydrobromic acid in the sample.

8. A sample of solid sodium hydroxide weighing 0.2000 g. was titrated with 0.1250 N nitric acid of which 39.5 ml. was required. Calculate the purity of the sodium hydroxide.

9. A 0.5420-g. sample containing phosphoric acid was titrated with 0.1500 N sodium hydroxide to the methyl red end-point corresponding to the conversion of the phosphoric acid to sodium dihydrogen phosphate. A volume of 30.0 ml. was required. Calculate the per cent of phosphoric acid in the sample.

10. A solution of sodium hydroxide was standardized against primary standard sulfamic acid, HSO_3NH_2. To titrate 0.2880 g. of sulfamic acid required 45.0 ml. of the alkali. Calculate the normality of the sodium hydroxide solution.

11. A volume of 25.00 ml. of a solution of sulfuric acid yielded 0.6010 g. of barium sulfate on treatment with excess barium chloride. Calculate the normality of the sulfuric acid solution.

12. Calculate the normality of a hydrochloric acid solution 25.0 ml. of which yielded 0.5620 g. of silver chloride.

13. A new organic acid was highly purified, and a sample weighing 0.4000 g. was titrated with 0.1000 N sodium hydroxide of which 48.0 ml. was required. Calculate the equivalent weight of the acid. What further information is required to obtain the molecular weight?

14. Calculate the volume of 0.1250 N barium hydroxide required to titrate 0.7500 g. of formic acid, $HCHO_2$ (one replaceable hydrogen).

15. Calculate the weight of monochloroacetic acid ($ClCH_2CO_2H$, one replaceable hydrogen) required to neutralize 50.0 ml. of 0.0800 N ammonium hydroxide.

16. The nitrogen in 50.0 ml. of a solution of nitric acid was reduced completely to ammonia which required for neutralization 35.0 ml. of 0.1000 N hydrochloric acid. Calculate the normality of the nitric acid solution.

17. A volume of 25.0 ml. of a hydrochloric acid solution required 30.0 ml. of 0.1250 N sodium hydroxide for titration. Calculate the normality of the hydrochloric acid solution.

18. Calculate the normality of concentrated sulfuric acid, sp. gr. 1.84, 95 per cent H_2SO_4.

19. Calculate the normality of concentrated ammonium hydroxide, sp. gr. 0.90, 28 per cent NH_3.

20. Calculate the volume of concentrated hydrochloric acid, sp. gr. 1.18, 35.5 per cent HCl, required to make 5 l. of 0.200 N hydrochloric acid.

21. Calculate the titer of a 0.1250 N potassium hydroxide solution for each of the following: (a) sulfuric acid; (b) hydrochloric acid; (c) phosphoric acid for the conversion to dipotassium hydrogen phosphate; (d) ammonium chloride for the conversion to ammonium hydroxide; (e) oxalic acid, $H_2C_2O_4$ (two replaceable hydrogen atoms).

22. A solution of sodium hydroxide was standardized against primary standard sulfamic acid; 0.3000 g. of the acid required 35.0 ml. of sodium hydroxide. Calculate the sulfamic acid titer of the sodium hydroxide solution.

23. The nitric acid titer of a potassium hydroxide solution was 0.007,875. Calculate the titer of this solution for perchloric acid.

24. A 0.8000-g. sample containing sulfuric acid and nitric acid required 65.0 ml. of 0.1000 N sodium hydroxide for neutralization. A second sample weighing 1.0000 g. yielded 0.1800 g. of barium sulfate on precipitation with excess barium chloride. Calculate the per cent of each acid in the mixture.

THE MECHANICS OF VOLUMETRIC ANALYSIS

The apparatus used in volumetric analysis consists principally of the buret, pipet, and volumetric flask. Most of the volumetric glassware being manufactured can be used directly for ordinary analytical work. For more accurate work, anything more accurate than 1 part in 500, the glassware should be calibrated as described in the latter part of this chapter.

Cleanliness. Volumetric glassware must be scrupulously clean; and the test is simple: does it drain without leaving drops clinging to the walls of the vessel? If it does, the apparatus may be used. If it does not, cleaning is in order.

A favorite for cleaning glassware is *cleaning solution,* prepared by dissolving 20 g. or so of sodium dichromate or potassium dichromate in a mixture of 80 ml. of technical, concentrated sulfuric acid and 20 ml. of water. Red chromic oxide separates from this mixture, particularly if it is heated, but this does no harm. The action of cleaning solution is rather slow, especially on greasy materials; warming the solution helps, but if time permits it is best to leave the mixture in the vessel overnight. A convenient way to handle cleaning solution if a considerable quantity of glassware is to be washed is to place the cleaning solution in a duriron [1] pot or evaporating dish so that it can be heated directly with a burner. Cleaning solution is a hazardous mixture, and care should be exercised in handling it. It is well not to allow cleaning solution to stand in contact with the stopcock grease in burets;

---

[1] Duriron is an iron-silicon alloy which is highly resistant to acids; it is manufactured by the Duriron Co., Inc., Dayton, Ohio.

one trick is to invert the buret in a bottle of cleaning solution and to draw the cleaning solution up into the buret just short of the stopcock by suction from an aspirator.

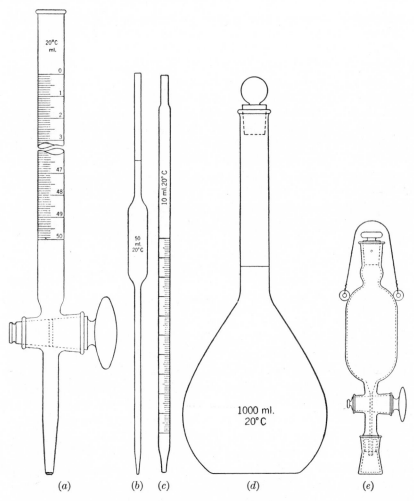

Fig. 39. Volumetric glassware. *a*, Buret; *b*, transfer pipet; *c*, measuring pipet; *d*, volumetric flask; *e*, weight buret.

A quite satisfactory job of cleaning glassware can be done with the alkaline detergents, trisodium phosphate mixtures, and similar preparations. Brushes with long wire handles which reach down the whole length of a buret are available from the laboratory supply houses.

After treatment with the cleaning mixture the glassware is rinsed thoroughly with tap water, two or three times with distilled water, and then inverted on a cloth or wire rack to drain dry. No attempt is made to dry chemical ware by wiping with a cloth.

The Buret. The buret is used to deliver and measure variable volumes. Its principal use is in titration, and it is designed to be operated with the left hand, leaving the right hand free to swirl the flask in which the titration is carried out. The handle of the stopcock is placed on the right so that the hand and fingers of the left hand can surround the barrel of the stopcock and operate the key with the fingers and thumb. The stopcock should work freely and have sufficient lubricant to prevent any leakage. Satisfactory stopcock greases are available from the laboratory supply houses: the silicone type of lubricant is positively not recommended for burets. In lubricating a stopcock, remove the plug and wipe the old grease from the key and barrel with a rag. Make sure that no particles of grease remain in the bore of the key or in the openings into the barrel. Spread a thin layer of lubricant over the key, spreading it out very thinly in the neighborhood of the bore. Insert the key and rotate it with moderate pressure. A properly lubricated stopcock will be uniformly transparent with no streaks; no particles of lubricant should appear in the bore.

After cleaning no attempt is made to dry the buret. Rinse it several times with water and then several times with small portions of the standard solution to be used. Burets of small size are most expediently filled by sucking the solution up into them. Bubbles of air should not be allowed to remain in the tip of the buret as they may pass out with the solution delivered and count as volume of liquid.

The surface of the liquid in the buret is concave up (aqueous solutions) and is referred to as the meniscus (from the Greek word meniskos, little moon). The bottom of the shaded portion of the meniscus is selected for reading (Fig. 40). The shaded portion of the meniscus can be made sharper by placing in back of the buret a piece of paper the bottom half of which is blackened. In reading the buret the eye should be in the same plane as the meniscus, to avoid parallax error.

The tip of the buret sometimes becomes plugged with a slug of grease from the stopcock. This grease can usually be removed by opening the stopcock, inclining the buret, and softening the grease by warming with the flame from a match; the pressure of the solution will force the grease plug out as soon as it softens.

Alkaline solutions should not be allowed to stand in a buret; the glass is attacked by the alkali, causing the stopcock to stick.

In routine work in which repeated titrations are made the operation of filling the buret can become a major factor in the time taken. Burets are available with two-way stopcocks. One opening is attached directly to a siphon from the storage bottle containing the standard solution, and the refilling is accomplished merely by opening the stopcock properly. Burets with automatic zeroing devices are also available.

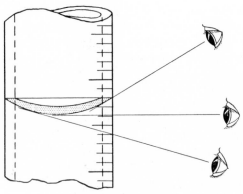

Fig. 40.   Meniscus.

The Pipet.   *Transfer pipets* have only one mark and are used to deliver an exact volume of solution. The mark is placed on the upper stem, which has a small diameter. The pipet is inherently more accurate than the buret for the measurement of a definite volume, for only one setting of the meniscus is made and that in a narrow tube where a variation in position corresponds to less volume. The pipet is allowed to drain naturally in such a manner that the liquid delivered does not spatter. After as much of the liquid has run out as will, the tip of the pipet is held for several seconds against the inner wall of the vessel receiving the liquid with the pipet in a nearly vertical position. The last portion of the liquid remains in the tip of the pipet and is not blown out. Pipets are both calibrated and used in this manner.

In most work the solution is drawn up into the pipet by mouth. Obnoxious and hazardous liquids are drawn in gently by suction from a water aspirator, the rubber tubing being placed over the top of the pipet so that it can be quickly withdrawn and the top closed by the dry finger.

The tips of pipets are easily damaged, and such damage can easily be concealed by fire polishing. In general, then, the analyst should adopt an especially critical attitude toward any pipet not taken directly from the manufacturer's wrapping or not calibrated by himself.

The *measuring pipet*, Fig. 39c, is in effect a small buret and is convenient for delivering, more or less precisely, volumes of solutions of reagents. It is not used for the exact measurement of volumes in volumetric work.

The Volumetric Flask. Some of the older volumetric flasks bear two marks, the lower mark calibrated to the nominal volume contained, the upper mark to the nominal volume delivered. This practice was abandoned, and all volumetric flasks currently being manufactured are calibrated only to contain the volume stated.

In the preparation of standard solutions by weighing a solid directly into a volumetric flask, all the solid should be dissolved before the final dilution to the mark on the neck of the flask is made. An appreciable volume change occurs on the dissolution of many solids, and this should take place before the volume of the solution is finally adjusted.

It is unwise to subject volumetric flasks to any heat treatment such as boiling water in them. The flask may not return to its original volume because of a hysteresis effect.

The best volumetric flasks are equipped with ground-glass stoppers. Rubber stoppers are used to close flasks not so equipped; cork stoppers absorb solutions and definitely should not be used.

Standard solutions must be thoroughly mixed; this can be done in a stoppered, volumetric flask by repeatedly inverting the flask and by vigorously shaking it so that the air and liquid are well dispersed. Four or five minutes of such activity are enough.

The Weight Buret. For highly precise volumetric work, the temperature must be controlled carefully or corrections applied as described under the calibration of volumetric glassware later in this chapter. Calibration and temperature corrections can be avoided by the use of the weight buret, Fig. 39e. The buret and standard solution are weighed before and after the titration. The solution is standardized in the same way, and the concentration expressed as normality by weight, N^w, that is, equivalent weights per 1000.0 g. of solution.

The weight buret is kept closed and capped at all times to prevent evaporation, and the cap is removed only for the actual titration. Just before weighing, the upper, ground-glass plug is opened briefly to adjust the pressure inside the weight buret to atmospheric pressure. In weighing the weight buret a second weight buret is used as counterpoise to counteract the effect of the adsorption of moisture on the large surface area of the buret.

Only if high precision is demanded and only if a precise method of locating the equivalence-point is available, is there justification for the extra time required for titration with a weight buret.

The weight buret is a convenient method of weighing out accurately a very small quantity of material when a microbalance (one sensitive to 0.01 or 0.001 mg.) is not available. A large quantity, say 0.1 g., is weighed out accurately on the ordinary balance, the material is dissolved, the solution is mixed well, and is then delivered in the neces-

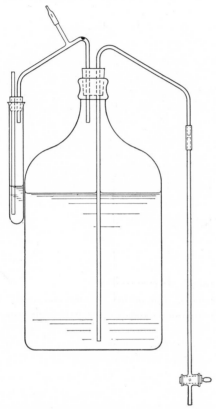

Fig. 41. Storage of large volumes of standard solutions.

sary volume from the weight buret. By weighing the larger amount of solution the small amount of dissolved material is weighed out equally accurately.

Aliquot Samples. Occasions arise in analytical work when it is desired to reduce the size of the sample for a titration or to make material available for several determinations by taking only a part of a solution. This is done by diluting the solution to a definite volume in a volumetric flask, mixing well, and then measuring out a portion of the solution with a delivery pipet. This process is known as taking an *aliquot*. This technique is sometimes used when the sample is rather inhomogeneous and can be put into solution readily. A large sample can be weighed, dissolved, diluted to a definite volume, well mixed, and an aliquot sample taken for the actual analysis. This process is often more convenient than grinding and mixing the solid

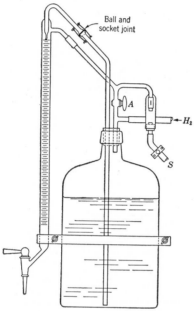

Fig. 42. Storage vessel and buret for strong reducing agents which must be protected from air. Apply suction at *S* with stopcock *A* closed to fill buret. Hydrogen is supplied by Kipp generator connected at H_2.

Fig. 43. Titration thief.

sample, but it should be remembered that any error in pipeting the aliquot will be multiplied by the ratio of the total volume to the volume of the aliquot.

Storage of Standard Solutions. Large volumes of standard solutions are stored in large bottles and removed through a siphon. The air entering the bottle will normally be only partially saturated with moisture and will cause evaporation of water from the solution. This is more serious than might first appear because the daily changes of temperature in the laboratory, cooling at night and warming up during the day, produce a continual movement of air in and out of the bottle. The effects of this breathing can be eliminated by an arrangement such as that shown in Fig. 41. Some of the same solution being stored is placed in the side-arm vessel. The air entering the bottle bubbles through this solution, its moisture content becomes the same as that above the main solution, and evaporation of the main solution is prevented. A piece of rubber tubing closed at one end and slit lengthwise for the distance of 5 mm. acts as a one-way valve (Bunsen valve), allowing the air to escape when the bottle warms up.

Fig. 44.   Titration in an inert atmosphere.

Standard solutions are altered by contact with air; the carbon dioxide is absorbed by alkalies, and powerful reducing agents are oxidized by oxygen. Carbon dioxide will be absorbed by an alkali solution in the side-arm vessel of Fig. 41. The removal of the 20 per cent oxygen in the air, however, is not so easy, and strong reducing agents are best stored under an atmosphere of inert gas, nitrogen, or hydrogen. In Fig. 42 is shown a convenient apparatus for the storage of such a solution; the apparatus pictured has a buret conveniently attached so that the solution may be transferred to the buret and delivered without exposure to air.

Miscellaneous Apparatus for Volumetric Analysis. In most titrations, the indicator gives adequate warning of the approach to the end-point. Where the drop of standard solution strikes the solution there is a high concentration of the standard solution which is

more than sufficient to react with the material in the immediate neigl ·
borhood of the drop.   In this local region the indicator therefoi e
changes color.   As the solution is mixed the indicator reverts to its
former color, the speed with which it does so becoming less as the end-
point is approached.   Some indicators, however, particularly those
which are slow in changing or are not readily reversible, do not give
such warning, and it is easy to overstep the end-point.   One way to
avoid overstepping such an end-point is to place in the solution a titration thief such as the one shown in Fig. 43.   This is a stirring rod made
of 8-mm. tubing with a small, funnel-shaped top and a 1-ml. bulb
near the bottom.   The lower end of the tube is constricted, the opening
being approximately 2 mm. in diameter.   When the stirring-rod thief
is placed in the beaker, it traps part of the liquid and keeps it isolated
from the main body of the solution during the titration.   The titration
is carried out rapidly, and when the end-point is overstepped, the thief
is withdrawn, which returns the untitrated portion to the main solution
and causes the indicator to revert to its first color.   The thief should
be rinsed out by raising and lowering it once or twice in the solution.
The titration can then be continued more slowly and the end-point
located accurately.

Occasionally it becomes necessary to carry out a titration in an
atmosphere of carbon dioxide, nitrogen, or hydrogen in order to keep
oxygen of the air from coming in contact with the solution.   The problem of passing the gas into the flask and of affording access to the buret
is solved neatly by the flask shown in Fig. 44, which has a side arm
attached by a ground-glass joint.   The use of the magnetic stirrer (see
page 42) makes it unnecessary to shake the flask.

In routine analytical work, that is, the analysis of a large number of
similar samples, it is frequently necessary to add a certain volume of
liquid to each of a number of beakers.   This operation is greatly facili-
tated by the device shown in Fig. 45.   When the dispensing flask is
tipped to the right the upper chamber fills, and when it is tipped to the
left the excess liquid is returned to the flask and a measured volume
(10 ml. in this case) is delivered through the nozzle.

THE CALIBRATION OF VOLUMETRIC APPARATUS

Definition of the Unit of Volume.   When first proposed the
units of mass and volume in the metric system were to be derived from
the unit of length.   Thus, the meter was first established and the kilogram derived from the weight of a cubic decimeter of water, the liter
then being defined as the cubic decimeter.

The problem of obtaining the exact mass of a cubic decimeter is simple in principle. By weighing a solid in air and in water the mass of the water displaced is obtained by difference. If the solid is so chosen that its volume can be obtained from its linear measurement then the volume of the water displaced becomes known. Knowing mass and volume, then, the mass of a cubic decimeter can be deter-

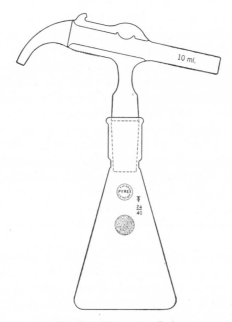

Fig. 45. Dispensing flask.

mined. The operation is not so easy as pictured, however, for a little calculation will show that an error of 0.001 mm. in the measurement of the distance between one pair of faces of a decimeter cube will introduce an error of 10 mg. into the mass of the kilogram.

The standard kilogram, the Kilogramme des Archives, was prepared by Lefevre-Gineau and Fabbroni in 1799. Modern repetitions of this work have shown the Kilogramme des Archives to be less than 30 mg. from the theoretical value, which is truly remarkable considering the time at which it was made.

The redetermination of the mass of the kilogram thus created the problem of either changing the standard of mass or of changing the definition of the kilogram. In 1872 the Commission International du Metre decided on changing the definition, and the original definition of the kilogram was abandoned and redefined as the mass of the Kilogramme des Archives in "its actual state."

Although units of volume are obtained easily from linear units, the determination of the volume of a vessel from its linear dimensions is attended with great difficulties. In practice the volume of a vessel is always determined by measuring the weight of a liquid, usually water, necessary to fill it. Practically, then, the unit of volume should be based on weight, and this is the case of the gallon and the liter.

The redefinition of the kilogram left the status of the liter in some doubt, but in 1901 the Comité International des Poids et Mesures defined the liter on the basis of weight. The liter is, then, the volume occupied by a mass of 1 kg. of pure water at its maximum density and under normal atmospheric pressure. Several precise determinations have shown 1 liter = 1000.028 cubic centimeters.

The difference of 0.028 c.c. between the liter and the cubic decimeter is negligible in ordinary analytical work, but in extremely accurate work it must be taken into consideration. As volumetric apparatus is calibrated on a weight basis the terms *liter* and *milliliter* should be employed in preference to *cubic decimeter* or *cubic centimeter*.

Standard Temperature and Factors Involved in the Calibration of Volumetric Apparatus. As the calibration of volumetric apparatus is always made on the basis of weight, all the errors affecting the determination of mass must be considered, the situation being aggravated by the large volumes involved. The correction to weight in vacuum is the great factor here; a liter of water, for example, being buoyed up by the weight of the liter of air displaced, about 1.2 g., makes a sizable correction which cannot be ignored.

Temperature affects the problem in two ways: the capacity of the apparatus itself changes because of the expansion of glass, and liquids contained or used in calibration change density. The expansion of the liquid is roughly ten times greater than that of the glassware, being of the order of 1 part per thousand per 5° temperature change around 20°.

Since a vessel calibrated at one temperature to contain a certain volume will not hold that volume at another temperature, it is necessary to specify the temperature of calibration, and for the sake of uniformity the National Bureau of Standards has chosen 20° C. as the standard temperature for the calibration of volumetric apparatus. This temperature was chosen as a convenient one to attain in laboratories in the United States, but in other countries other standard temperatures are used.

It is inconvenient and unnecessary to actually make the calibrations at exactly 20°, however, and in practice calibrations are made at room temperature in such a manner that if the temperature were changed to 20° the vessel would hold just the volume indicated, the so-called nominal value.

These factors involved in the calibration will be discussed separately but, as will be seen, the factors are most conveniently combined in the form of tables.

Correction to Weight in Vacuum. By the term "apparent weight" is meant the weight of an object in air as shown by brass weights. Assuming an average value of 0.001,20 g. for the mass of 1 ml. of air and applying the usual formula for correction to weight in vacuum on an apparent weight of 1 g. of water

$$W_{Vac.} = W_{App.} + W_{App.} \left[\frac{0.001,20}{d_{H_2O}} - \frac{0.001,20}{d_{Wt.}} \right]$$

$$= 1 + 1 \left[\frac{0.001,20}{1.0} - \frac{0.001,20}{8.4} \right]$$

$$= 1 + 0.001,06$$

The correction to weight in vacuum is seen to be 1.06 mg., and it is obvious that the introduction of a more accurate value for the density of the water into that part of the formula within the brackets will not influence the results significantly, the change in density of water being less than 5 in the third decimal up to 30°. The same value, 0.001,06, may then be applied over the entire temperature range used in calibration, usually only 10° to 30°.

Density Change. The density of water at various temperatures has been determined with great precision and may be found in handbooks and critical tables. The density may be given either as grams per milliliter, which is the one employed in the calibration of volumetric apparatus, or as grams per cubic centimeter. The density of water between 10° and 32° in grams per milliliter is given in Table 10.

For convenience, tables have been prepared giving the apparent weight of 1 ml. of water (see Table 10, column 3); this is simply the density (weight in vacuum of 1 ml. of water) minus the correction due to the difference of the buoyant effects of the air displaced by the water and the brass weights.

Tables have also been prepared giving the volume of an apparent weight of 1 g. of water (see Table 10, column 4); these values are obtained by the simple relation $d = m/v$, where d is the density at the given temperature and m is the weight in vacuum, 1.001,06 g., of an apparent weight of 1 g. of water.

TABLE 10.   DENSITY OF WATER AND RELATED VALUES FOR
WATER WEIGHED IN AIR [a]

Temperature (°C.)	Density (grams/milliliter)	Apparent Weight of 1 ml. Water (Brass Weights) [b] (grams)	Volume of an Apparent Weight of 1 g. Water (Brass Weights) [c] (milliliters)
10	0.999,727	0.998,67	1.001,33
11	0.999,633	0.998,57	1.001,43
12	0.999,525	0.998,47	1.001,53
13	0.999,404	0.998,34	1.001,66
14	0.999,271	0.998,21	1.001,79
15	0.999,127	0.998,07	1.001,93
16	0.998,970	0.997,91	1.002,09
17	0.998,802	0.997,74	1.002,26
18	0.998,623	0.997,56	1.002,43
19	0.998,433	0.997,37	1.002,63
20	0.998,232	0.997,17	1.002,83
21	0.998,021	0.996,96	1.003,05
22	0.997,799	0.996,74	1.003,27
23	0.997,567	0.996,51	1.003,50
24	0.997,325	0.996,26	1.003,74
25	0.997,074	0.996,01	1.004,00
26	0.996,813	0.995,75	1.004,26
27	0.996,542	0.995,48	1.004,53
28	0.996,262	0.995,20	1.004,82
29	0.995,974	0.994,91	1.005,11
30	0.995,676	0.994,62	1.005,40
31	0.995,369	0.994,31	1.005,72
32	0.995,054	0.993,99	1.006,04

[a] Average value of 0.001,20 taken for density of air.

[b] For stainless-steel weights, density 7.84, the numbers in this column are increased 1 in the fifth decimal place.

[c] For stainless-steel weights, density 7.84, the numbers in this column are decreased 1 in the fifth decimal place.

Change in Volume of Apparatus with Temperature.   This volume change can be calculated by the formula $V' = V[1 + Y(T' - T)]$, in which V is the volume at temperature T, and V' is the volume at temperature T'.   The term Y is the cubical coefficient of expansion of glass, which is generally taken as three times the linear coefficient. The cubical coefficient of expansion of soft glass is 0.000,025, of Pyrex 0.000,009,9.   The size of this volume change of a liter flask may be conveniently seen in Table 11.

TABLE 11. THE EXPANSION OF SOFT GLASS AND PYREX
VESSELS (MILLILITERS)

	Temperature				
	10°	15°	20°	25°	30°
Soft glass	999.75	999.88	1000.00	1000.12	1000.25
Pyrex	999.90	999.95	1000.00	1000.05	1000.10

TABLE 12. RELATED VALUES FOR WATER WEIGHED IN AIR [a]
WITH CORRECTION FOR CHANGES IN GLASSWARE FROM 20°

Temper- ature (°C.)	Apparent Weight of 1 ml. Water with Correction for Changes in Glassware from 20° (Brass Weights) [b] (grams)		Volume of an Apparent Weight of 1 g. Water with Correction for Changes in Glassware from 20° (Brass Weights) [c] (milliliters)	
	Soft Glass	*Pyrex*	*Soft Glass*	*Pyrex*
10	0.998,42	0.998,57	1.001,58	1.001,43
11	0.998,34	0.998,48	1.001,66	1.001,52
12	0.998,27	0.998,39	1.001,73	1.001,61
13	0.998,16	0.998,27	1.001,84	1.001,73
14	0.998,06	0.998,15	1.001,94	1.001,85
15	0.997,94	0.998,02	1.002,06	1.001,98
16	0.997,81	0.997,87	1.002,19	1.002,13
17	0.997,68	0.997,71	1.002,34	1.002,29
18	0.997,51	0.997,54	1.002,48	1.002,45
19	0.997,34	0.997,36	1.002,66	1.002,64
20	0.997,17	0.997,17	1.002,83	1.002,83
21	0.996,99	0.996,97	1.003,02	1.003,04
22	0.996,79	0.996,76	1.003,22	1.003,25
23	0.996,59	0.996,54	1.003,42	1.003,47
24	0.996,36	0.996,30	1.003,65	1.003,70
25	0.996,14	0.996,06	1.003,87	1.003,95
26	0.995,90	0.995,81	1.004,11	1.004,20
27	0.995,66	0.995,55	1.004,35	1.004,46
28	0.995,40	0.995,18	1.004,62	1.004,74
29	0.995,14	0.995,00	1.004,88	1.005,02
30	0.994,86	0.994,71	1.005,15	1.005,30
31	0.994,59	0.994,44	1.005,44	1.005,61
32	0.994,29	0.994,11	1.005,74	1.005,92

[a] Average value of 0.001,20 taken for density of air.

[b] For stainless-steel weights, density 7.84, increase the numbers in these columns by 1 in the fifth decimal place.

[c] For stainless-steel weights, density 7.84, decrease the numbers in these columns by 1 in the fifth decimal place.

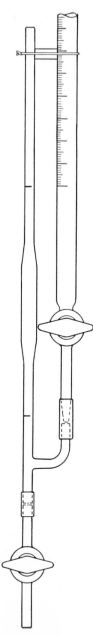

When flasks are calibrated directly by weighing the flask empty and filled with water, the problem is simplified by the use of tables giving the apparent weight of 1 ml. of water and the volume of an apparent weight of 1 g. of water in which the volume change of the glass apparatus with temperature is already included (see Table 12).

Thus, for example, assume that a flask is to be calibrated to hold 1 l. at 20°, the standard practice, but the calibration is actually made at 25°. The density of water at 25° is 0.997,07; the vacuum weight of 1 l. of water at 25° is, therefore, 997.07 g. and the apparent weight 996.01 g. If this weight of water were placed in the flask and the flask marked at the meniscus, the flask would hold 1 l. at 25°, but on cooling to 20° the flask would contract and hold less than 1 l.; therefore a further amount of water must be added to the flask at 25° equal to the apparent weight of a volume of water equal to the volume that the flask contracts, 0.125 ml. in this case. The apparent weight of 0.125 ml. of water is 0.1245 g. The weight of water which should be placed in the flask is, therefore, 996.01 + 0.1245 = 996.14 g. This value can be obtained directly from Table 12.

Calibration of Buret. A buret may be calibrated by weighing the water which it delivers over any given interval. As this involves a considerable number of weighings for the complete calibration of a buret, it is more rapid to compare the volume delivered by the buret over a certain interval with the volume of a small glass vessel the volume of which is either known or can be determined. The so-called Ostwald calibrating pipet, Fig. 46, is designed for this purpose. To be worthy of calibration a buret should conform to the specifications of the U. S. Bureau of Standards for minimum and maximum outflow time; these specifications are given in Table 13.

The error in the indicated capacity of any ten consecutive subdivisions must not exceed one-fourth the capacity of the smallest subdivision, and

Fig. 46. Ostwald calibrating pipet.

TABLE 13. MINIMUM OUTFLOW TIME FOR BURETS

Length Graduated (centimeters)	Outflow Time (seconds)	Length Graduated (centimeters)	Outflow Time (seconds)
70	160	40	70
65	140	35	60
60	120	30	50
55	105	25	40
50	90	20	35
45	80	15	30

The maximum outflow time for any length of graduation is 3 minutes.

the error in the total volume of a 50-ml. buret should not exceed 0.05 ml.

Procedure for the Calibration of a Buret. Determine the delivery time of the buret, and if it is not satisfactory exchange the buret for another. Clean the buret with cleaning solution and grease the stopcock properly.

Attach the Ostwald calibrating pipet to the buret, joining the upturned side arm of the pipet to the tip of the buret by means of a piece of rubber tubing, making glass-to-glass contact. If the calibrating pipet does not carry a stopcock it should be equipped with a piece of rubber tubing, a glass wash-bottle tip, and a screw clamp. Fill the buret and pipet completely with distilled water at room temperature and make certain that no air bubbles are entrapped. Withdraw water until the buret reads zero and the level of the liquid in the pipet stands at the lower mark. By opening the stopcock on the buret allow water to flow into the pipet until the level reaches the upper mark. Record the reading of the buret. Drain the calibrating pipet to the lower mark and again refill from the buret. Repeat this until a reading on the buret can no longer be obtained. Note the temperature of the water.

Disconnect the buret and refill with distilled water. Run the total volume of water, indicated by the last reading of the pipet, into a glass-stoppered weighing bottle, previously weighed with an accuracy of 1 mg. Stopper the bottle immediately and weigh. Divide the weight of the water by the number of times the pipet was filled; this gives the weight of water contained in the pipet. From Table 12 obtain the volume of the pipet at 20° from the apparent weight of the water. Calculate the volume corresponding to each buret reading and the correction to be applied to each reading. Plot a curve using the corrections as the ordinate and the buret readings as the abscissa, joining the observed readings by straight lines.

Calibration of Pipet. As only a single mark is employed in using a transfer pipet, it is convenient when calibrating a pipet to reestablish the mark so that the pipet will deliver exactly the nominal value at 20°. Pipets should meet the specifications established by the National Bureau of Standards, Table 14.

TABLE 14.　SPECIFICATIONS FOR PIPETS

Capacity (ml.), up to and including		5	10	50	100	200
Outflow time less than 60 seconds and more than			15	20	30	40	50

Capacity (ml.) up to and including	2	5	10	30	50	100
Limit of error (ml.)	0.005	0.01	0.02	0.03	0.05	0.08

Procedure for the Calibration of a Pipet. Clean the pipet with cleaning solution so that it is free from grease and leaves a continuous film of water on the inner surface on draining. Determine the time of drainage of the pipet and, if it does not fall within the limits specified, adjust the tip.

Fasten a narrow strip of millimeter graph paper 5 to 6 cm. long, along the suction tube of the pipet, placing it so that the mark on the pipet falls approximately in the middle of the strip, and secure the strip to the pipet by means of strips of gummed paper wrapped around the tube at each end of the strip. Make two marks on the graph paper, one at each end, and count the number of divisions between them.

Rinse the pipet several times with distilled water at room temperature to bring pipet and water to the same temperature. Fill the pipet to the lower mark and allow the water to flow into a previously weighed, glass-stoppered weighing bottle. Allow the liquid to run out freely and remove the excess by touching the tip to the inner surface of the bottle for 15 seconds; do not blow out the liquid remaining in the pipet. Stopper the bottle immediately and weigh. Repeat, using the upper mark. From the apparent weight of the water and using Table 12, calculate the volume at 20° at the lower and upper marks; the difference in these volumes divided by the number of divisions between the upper and lower marks gives the volume corresponding to each division. Using this and either the volume at the upper or at the lower mark, calculate the position of the mark which will indicate exactly the volume marked on the pipet. Paste a strip of paper around the tube with its upper edge at this mark. Check the position of the mark by weighing the water delivered from it just as above.

Calibration of Volumetric Flask. Ordinarily volumetric flasks are graduated to contain but occasionally may be calibrated both to contain and to deliver. If calibrated for both, the intention should be

TABLE 15. TOLERANCE LIMITS FOR VOLUMETRIC FLASKS

Capacity less than and including (milliliters)	Limit of Error (milliliters)	Capacity less than and including (milliliters)	Limit of Error (milliliters)
25	0.03	300	0.12
50	0.05	500	0.15
100	0.08	1000	0.30
200	0.10	2000	0.50

clearly indicated. The tolerances of the various sizes of volumetric flasks graduated to contain are given in Table 15.

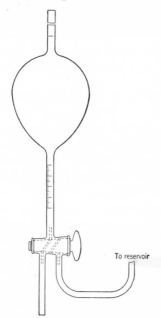

To reservoir

Fig. 47. Calibrating bulb.

Flasks may be calibrated by weighing them empty and again filled with water, or by filling them from a standard calibrating bulb, Fig. 47, which must be calibrated by weighing the water it delivers. It is then convenient to leave the calibrating bulb permanently set up.

Such calibrating bulbs are frequently designed with two bulbs, 50 ml. and 200 ml. in capacity, with a single mark on the upper stem and calibrated portions on the lower stem and on the stem between the bulbs. Other calibrating bulbs have only one bulb and one calibrated portion on the lower stem. Calibrating bulbs are usually fitted with a two-way stopcock at the bottom so that the bulb may be conveniently filled from a water reservoir.

Procedure for the Calibration of a Volumetric Flask. Fill the calibrating bulb with distilled water and weigh separately the water delivered by the bulb and by the graduated portion of the stem (by each bulb and each graduated stem if the calibrating bulb is of the type having two bulbs). Note the temperature and run two determinations to secure checks. Leave the calibrating bulb filled with water.

Calculate the volume of the bulb and of the calibrated portion of the stem at 20° using Table 12, column 4 or 5. Then calculate the number of scale divisions on the stem to which the water must be drawn to deliver exactly the volume of water desired, that is, the nominal value of the flask to be calibrated. The temperature of the water at this time need not be known since the bulb and the flask are of the same material and expand or contract alike for the same change in temperature. If the bulb is to be frequently used paste a strip of paper around the stem so that the upper edge of the paper marks the meniscus at this point.

Clean and dry the volumetric flask to be calibrated. Run the desired volume of water into the flask, shaking slightly to establish a normal meniscus. Complete the filling with the tip of the calibrating bulb in contact with the wall of the flask 1 or 2 cm. above the mark. Allow the water in the volumetric flask to drain and then paste a strip of gummed paper around the stem marking the meniscus with the upper edge of the paper.

Temperature Corrections in Practice. Inasmuch as the mass of material in solution does not change with temperature but the volume of the solution does change, the concentration must necessarily change, and in work accurate to 1 part in 1000 variation in temperature must be taken into consideration.

In using a volumetric flask calibrated to hold a certain volume at 20° in preparing a standard solution at some other temperature, it is apparent that the normality obtained will only be the true normality at 20°. The normality at the working temperature can be calculated by the formula

$$\text{Normality} = \left(\frac{\text{Weight taken}}{\text{Gram equivalent weight}}\right)\left(\frac{1000}{\text{Actual volume}}\right)$$

The actual volume at the working temperature can be calculated using the formula given above for the volume expansion of glass.

If the standard solution is used at a temperature other than that at which it was prepared, two factors enter: the density change of the solution and the volume change of the apparatus, the pipets and burets suffering the same relative volume changes as flasks. This correction is the difference between the two effects, the volume of the solution expanding or contracting at a greater rate than the volume of the glassware. Thus, assuming an exactly normal solution and apparatus holding exactly 1 l. at 20°, at 25° the apparatus will deliver 1000.12 ml. and the solution will occupy a volume of 1001.2 ml. If the solution is still assumed to be 1 N then a volume measured out must be decreased by 1.1 ml. per l. inasmuch as a greater volume must be measured out for a given quantity of dissolved material. However, the correction would be plus for temperatures below 20°.

The change in density of solutions with temperature is different from that of water and varies with the concentration of the solution. Fortunately the change is about the same for all electrolytes of the same concentration at the concentrations usually used in analytical work, 0.10 N or less, so that the values for 0.10 N hydrochloric acid may be taken as typical.

	15°	20°	25°	30°
Water	999.10	1000.00	1001.16	1002.56
0.10 N HCl	999.11	1000.00	1001.37	1002.86

Using 0.10 N HCl the temperature correction is then

	15°	20°	25°	30°
Volume of glassware (soft glass)	999.88	1000.00	1000.12	1000.25
Volume of 0.1 N HCl	999.11	1000.00	1001.37	1002.86
Difference	0.77	....	1.25	2.61

Thus, if a standard solution were prepared at 25° in a flask calibrated to hold 1000.0 ml. at 20°, the normality would be calculated using the volume 1000.12. If the solution were subsequently used at 15°, a correction of 1.25 + 0.77, or 2.02 ml., would be added per liter measured out.

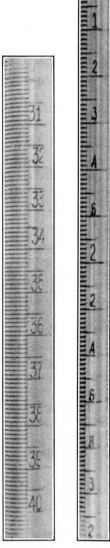

Problem 13.   Problem 14.

PROBLEMS

1. Calculate the weight in vacuum of 500 g. of water weighed in air with brass weights of density 8.4. Use as density of air the average value of 0.001,20 g. per ml.

2. Repeat the calculation of Problem 1 for stainless-steel weights of density 7.84.

3. Calculate the volume of the water in Problem 1 if its temperature is 26°. The density of water at 26° is 0.996,81. Check with Table 10.

4. Calculate the increase in the volume of a liter of water on warming it from 20° to 30°. Obtain the values for the densities at these temperatures from Table 10.

5. Calculate the increase in the capacity of a liter volumetric flask of soft glass on warming it from 20° to 30°. Compare this value with the value for the expansion of the same volume of water over the same temperature interval.

6. From Problem 5 it is apparent that, if a flask is to be calibrated at 30° so that at 20° the mark put on the flask will indicate exactly a liter, a volume of 1000.25 ml. must be placed in a soft-glass flask. Calculate the volume which should be placed in a Pyrex flask.

7. Calculate the weight in air of a liter of water at 30° weighed with brass weights. The density of water at 30° is 0.995,67. Check with Table 10.

8. Using the information secured in Problems 5 and 7 calculate the weight of water weighed in air with brass weights which must be placed in a soft-glass flask at 30° so that the mark placed at the meniscus at 30° will indicate exactly 1 l. when the empty flask is later cooled to 20°. Make the same calculation using Table 12.

9. Calculate the weight of water weighed in air with brass weights which should be placed in a 250-ml. Pyrex flask at 26° so that the flask will hold exactly 250 ml. at 20°.

10. A buret when drained to the 40.00-ml. mark delivers 39.90 g. of water weighed in air with brass weights at 26°. Calculate the correction when used at 26° and decide if the correction is plus or minus.

11. A liter flask of soft glass filled to exactly the 1000.0-ml. mark at 20° is warmed (flask and water both) to 30°. Explain what happens to the meniscus and calculate its movement, assuming the cross-sectional area of the neck to be 1 sq. cm.

12. A solution of hydrochloric acid is exactly 0.1000 N at 20°. Calculate its normality at 30°.

13. The accompanying illustration shows a part of a freak buret actually employed for several weeks before the errors in its markings were discovered. From a close examination of the buret decide how the error would show up during the calibration of the buret using, first, a calibrating pipet of 2-ml. volume, and second, one of 5-ml. volume.

14. Locate the flaws in the calibration of the measuring pipet shown in the accompanying illustration. Decide whether the lower portion of the pipet would give correct readings.

CHAPTER 8

Theory of
Neutralization Reactions

Le nombre d'atomes-grammes d'ions hydrogène par litre est plus petit que 1 et peut être posé égal à 10^{-p}, où pour le nombre p je propose le nom d'exposant des ions hydrogène et la désignation p_{H}^+. Par exposant des ions hydrogène (p_{H}^+) d'une solution, nous entendons donc le logarithme Brigg de la valeur réciproque du facteur de normalité de la solution relativement aux ions hydrogène—S. P. L. Sørensen.[1]

Practically all analytical chemistry is carried out in water solution. As the almost universal medium for the reactions of analytical chemistry, much of inorganic and organic chemistry, and all of biochemistry, water is the dominating substance, and its chemistry, particularly that of the neutralization process, is of enormous importance.

The fundamental reaction in the chemistry of water is its dissociation into hydrogen ions and hydroxyl ions:

$$H_2O = H^+ + OH^-$$

This reaction proceeds to the right to only a very slight extent; that is, water is an essentially non-ionized compound. It is because of this that acids neutralize bases.

The principle of mass action can be applied to the dissociation of water just as to any reversible reaction:

$$K = \frac{[H^+][OH^-]}{[H_2O]}$$

that is, the molar concentrations of the products divided by the molar concentrations of the reactants, each raised to a power equal to the number of molecules involved in the reaction, is a constant. In this particular case, the molar concentration (designated by brackets) of

---

[1] From the paper in which the term pH is first defined, *Compt. rend. Lab. Carlsberg,* **8,** 28 (1909). Sørensen's initial symbol, p_{H}^+, has been superseded by the simpler designation, pH.

the water is a very large number ($[H_2O] = 1000/18 = 55.5$) and remains practically constant at all times; for convenience, then, a new term K_W is defined as $(55.5)K$:

$$K_W = K[H_2O] = [H^+][OH^-]$$

K_W is called the dissociation (or ionization) constant of water. At room temperature it has a numerical value of 1.0×10^{-14}.

In pure water the hydrogen-ion concentration must equal the hydroxyl-ion concentration since the ions are formed simultaneously and in equivalent amounts

$$[H^+] = [OH^-]$$

and therefore

$$[H^+]^2 = 10^{-14}$$

$$[H^+] = [OH^-] = 10^{-7}$$

that is, the concentration of hydrogen ions in water is 0.000,000,1 M. In acid solutions the hydrogen-ion concentration is greater than this and the hydroxyl-ion concentration is less, but the product of the two is always constant and equal to 1.0×10^{-14}. Thus, in a solution 0.1 M in hydrogen ions,

$$[OH^-] = \frac{K_W}{[H^+]} = \frac{1 \times 10^{-14}}{0.1} = 1 \times 10^{-13}$$

or in a solution 0.001 M in hydroxyl ions

$$[H^+] = \frac{K_W}{[OH^-]} = \frac{1 \times 10^{-14}}{0.001} = 1.0 \times 10^{-11}$$

Hydrogen-Ion Concentration and pH. For convenience in handling such small concentrations of hydrogen ions as those just mentioned, a simplified exponential notation has been adopted and a new term, pH, is used as a measure of the hydrogen-ion concentration.

$$pH = -\log [H^+]$$

$$pH = \log \frac{1}{[H^+]}$$

$$[H^+] = 10^{-pH}$$

All three of these equations say the same thing mathematically, owing to the properties of logarithms. Thus, if $[H^+] = 10^{-8}$ the pH is equal to 8. The conversion of $[H^+] = 2 \times 10^{-8}$ to pH is a bit more complicated. By the definition of logarithms, however, $2 = 10^{+0.301}$, the 0.301 being the logarithm of 2. Therefore, $[H^+] = 2 \times 10^{-8}$ $= 10^{+0.301} \times 10^{-8} = 10^{-7.699}$. The pH is 7.699, or, better, from a practical standpoint, 7.70. It should always be remembered in making these transformations that the mantissa, that part of the logarithm which is found in the tables, is always positive. The characteristic, the number which locates the decimal point, may be positive or negative.

To convert pH to hydrogen-ion concentration the manipulations are reversed. Thus pH $= 3.85$ means

$$[H^+] = 10^{-3.85} = 10^{+0.15} \times 10^{-4}$$

$$= 1.4 \times 10^{-4}$$

$$= 0.000,14$$

In a similar manner the term pOH is defined by

$$p\text{OH} = -\log [\text{OH}^-] = \log \frac{1}{[\text{OH}^-]}$$

$$[\text{OH}^-] = 10^{-p\text{OH}}$$

and also $pK_W = -\log K_W$ and $K_W = 10^{-pK_W}$

That is to say, the p system of designation can be applied to any quantity.

A new relation of considerable importance can be derived from these definitions:

$$K_W = [H^+][\text{OH}^-]$$

$$-\log K_W = -\log [H^+] - \log [\text{OH}^-]$$

$$pK_W = p\text{H} + p\text{OH}$$

that is, pH $+ p$OH $= 14$.

The various relationships and magnitudes are perhaps more readily grasped from Table 16. The pH of a neutral solution or of pure water is 7.0; acid solutions have a lower pH, basic solutions a greater pH, than 7. It is important to note that each change in pH of 1 unit represents a tenfold change in hydrogen-ion concentration; thus in a solution of pH 3.0 the hydrogen-ion concentration is 100 times greater than in one of pH 5.

The hydrogen ion plays a part in the great majority of reactions taking place in water. In many cases it is the controlling factor determining the direction in which a reaction will proceed and deciding the

TABLE 16. RELATIONSHIP OF [H$^+$], [OH$^-$], pH, AND pOH

	[H$^+$]	[H$^+$]	pH	pOH	[OH$^-$]	[OH$^-$]	
Increasing Acidity	1.0	1×10^0	0	14	1×10^{-14}	0.000,000,000,000.01	
	0.1	10^{-1}	1	13	10^{-13}	.000,000,000,000,1	0.1 N HCl
	.01	10^{-2}	2	12	10^{-12}	.000,000,000,001	
	.001	10^{-3}	3	11	10^{-11}	.000,000,000,01	
	.000,1	10^{-4}	4	10	10^{-10}	.000,000,000,1	
	.000,01	10^{-5}	5	9	10^{-9}	.000,000,001	
	.000,001	10^{-6}	6	8	10^{-8}	.000,000,01	
Neutral	.000,000,1	10^{-7}	7	7	10^{-7}	.000,000,1	Distilled water
Increasing Basicity	.000,000,01	10^{-8}	8	6	10^{-6}	.000,001	
	.000,000,001	10^{-9}	9	5	10^{-5}	.000,01	
	.000,000,000,1	10^{-10}	10	4	10^{-4}	.000,1	
	.000,000,000,01	10^{-11}	11	3	10^{-3}	.001	
	.000,000,000,001	10^{-12}	12	2	10^{-2}	.01	
	.000,000,000,000,1	10^{-13}	13	1	10^{-1}	.1	0.1 N NaOH
	.000,000,000,000,01	10^{-14}	14	0	10^0	1.0	

$$[H^+] = 10^{-pH} \qquad [OH^-] = 10^{-pOH} \qquad K_W = [H^+][OH^-] = 1.0 \times 10^{-14} \qquad pH + pOH = pK_W = 14$$

equilibrium position. As a measure of hydrogen-ion concentration pH is involved in a great variety of chemical reactions, in fact, in almost every reaction in which water is present: the neutralization of acids and bases, the acidity of solutions of salts, the precipitation of hydroxides and basic salts, the dissolution of oxides and of carbonate and silicate rocks, the corrosion of metals, the growth of plants, the proper functioning of the blood, and in many other cases too numerous to list.

Strong Acids, Weak Acids, and Very Weak Acids. *The Ionization Constant, K_A.* Acids and bases vary considerably in the degree to which they dissociate or ionize when dissolved in water. The terms *strong* and *weak* are used to designate roughly the extent of this ionization. By *strong acid* is meant an acid which is more or less completely ionized when dissolved in water. The number of strong acids is quite limited: hydrochloric, sulfuric, nitric, perchloric, hydrobromic, and hydriodic acid. Thus, the terms *strong* and *weak* refer to the extent to which the acid is ionized and not to the amount of the acid in solution. A 0.0001 N solution of hydrochloric acid is a dilute solution of a strong acid.

For the purpose of this book, it is assumed that the strong acids mentioned above are 100 per cent ionized. This is not quite true, for at certain concentrations some of these acids may be as little as 10 per cent ionized. This makes no difference in the determination of these acids or in the theory of the neutralization process as developed in the next few pages. Methods of finding and expressing the actual extent of ionization of strong acids (and strong electrolytes, in general) are known but will not be discussed here.[1]

Those acids which ionize only partially are called *weak acids*. The mass-action law can be applied to the ionization of these acids and provides a quantitative measure of the extent of their ionization. Thus, for the weak acid HA,

$$HA = H^+ + A^-$$

the equilibrium constant is called the *dissociation constant* or *ionization constant* and is defined by the expression

$$K_A = \frac{[H^+][A^-]}{[HA]} \tag{1}$$

in which the brackets designate the molar concentration of the substance enclosed. Like any mass-action constant this constant is the product of the molar concentrations of the substances produced in the reaction, divided by the molar concentrations of the reacting materials each raised to a power equal to the number of times it occurs in the balanced equation.

Values of the dissociation constants of various acids are given in the Appendix, Table A3. Acids having dissociation constants between 10^{-3} and 10^{-8} are considered weak acids. Those with ionization constants smaller than 10^{-8} are classed as very weak acids; these cannot be determined by titration with standard alkali. Thus, formic acid and acetic acid are weak acids, but hydrocyanic acid is a very weak acid.

In a similar manner the bases which are highly ionized are called *strong bases*. Sodium hydroxide, potassium hydroxide, tetramethyl-ammonium hydroxide, and possibly a few others fall in this group. The bases which are only partly ionized are spoken of as *weak bases*; ammonium hydroxide is a typical example. The ionization of weak bases can be handled in quantitative fashion by the mass-action law, just as was done for the weak acids. For the weak base BOH, ionizing according to the equation $BOH = B^+ + OH^-$, the equilibrium is expressed by the equation

$$K_B = \frac{[B^+][OH^-]}{[BOH]}$$

[1] A discussion of the so-called activity of electrolytes will be found in textbooks on physical chemistry and is properly a subject for the junior course in physical chemistry.

K_B being the ionization constant. The numerical value of the dissociation constant of ammonium hydroxide is 1.75×10^{-5}. Values for other bases will be found in the Appendix, Table A3. Just as with acids, bases with dissociation constants 10^{-3} to 10^{-8} are classed as weak; those with constants less than 10^{-8} are classed as very weak.

Acids are determined volumetrically by titration with a standard base, and vice versa. As a matter of principle the standard solutions are made of strong acids and strong bases. The titration of a strong acid with a strong base, or vice versa, offers no difficulties. The situation is not so favorable, however, when weak acids or weak bases are being titrated. The indicators must be chosen with care and certain other precautions observed. Weak acids cannot be titrated with weak bases at all, at least if visual indicators are relied on to detect the end-point. These various cases will be taken up in detail.

The organic dyestuffs which act as indicators are themselves weak acids or bases, the colors of their salts differing from the colors of the free acids or bases. An important characteristic of such indicators, which will be readily understood after the discussion of the titration of weak acids and bases later in this chapter, is that the pH range over which they change from the acid color to the basic color varies from one indicator to another: methyl orange, pH 3.2 to 4.5; methyl red, pH 4.2 to 6.4; bromthymol blue, pH 6.0 to 7.6; phenolphthalein, pH 8.1 to 9.8. This is a fortunate circumstance, for it turns out in the titration of certain acids with a strong base that an indicator must be selected which changes color in the pH range 8 to 10 rather than at 7.

Titration of a Strong Acid with a Strong Base. In the titration of a strong acid with a strong base the pH at the equivalence-point changes abruptly. The course of the pH during the titration of perchloric acid with sodium hydroxide is shown in Fig. 48. From this so-called titration curve [1] it will be seen that at the equivalence-point the addition of a very small amount of the standard sodium hydroxide solution causes a change in pH of 7 or 8 units. The vertical portion of the curve passes through the bands of pH over which methyl red and phenolphthalein change color. Either of these indicators, then, may be used to mark the end-point; other indicators which change color at pH values between 4 and 9 could also be used, for example, bromthymol blue (6.0 to 7.6), phenol red (6.4 to 8.0), or chlorphenol red (4.8 to 6.4).

[1] This curve was obtained by measuring the pH after the addition of various amounts of standard sodium hydroxide, using a potentiometric method for the measurement. The potentiometric method of measuring pH is discussed in Chapter 18 after a suitable background in the theory of electrochemistry has been developed.

Similar titration curves are obtained with other strong acids.

The pH at various stages of the titration of a strong acid with a strong base can be calculated approximately, assuming that the acid remaining untitrated is 100 per cent ionized. For example, in the titration of

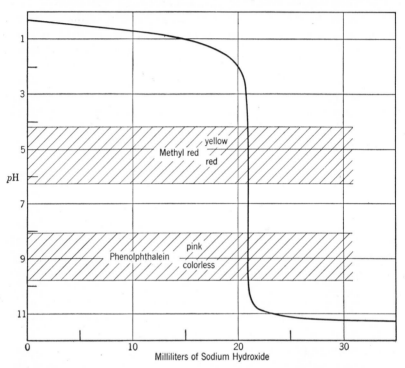

Fig. 48. Titration of perchloric acid with sodium hydroxide. Taken: 25.0 ml. of 0.3520 N perchloric acid; titrated with: 0.4193 N sodium hydroxide. The perchloric acid taken was diluted with water before the titration was begun.

perchloric acid shown in Fig. 48, 25.0 ml. of 0.3520 N perchloric acid was taken; after 10.0 ml. of 0.4193 N sodium hydroxide had been added, the total volume of the solution was 35.0 ml. The amount of acid is figured in terms of milliequivalent weights (ml. of 1 N):

Originally taken: $(25.0)(0.3520) = 8.80$ m. e. wt. $HClO_4$
Neutralized: $(10.0)(0.4193) = 4.19$ m. e. wt. $HClO_4$
Remaining: 4.61 m. e. wt. $HClO_4$

from which the normality of the solution can be calculated:

$$4.61/35.0 = 0.131 \ N \ HClO_4$$

Assuming complete ionization, the pH corresponding to this normality is 0.88. The pH actually observed was 0.76. This method of calculating the pH is used up to the end-point; beyond the end-point the same general method is used, calculating the hydroxyl ion introduced by the excess of sodium hydroxide added. The difference between the pH value just calculated and the pH observed is due probably to a combination of several factors: an error in the calibration of the potentiometric system used to follow the titration; the presence of dissolved carbon dioxide in the solution; and incorrectness of the assumption that the acid is completely ionized and that the salt present has no effect.

Titration of a Strong Base with a Strong Acid. In the titration of a strong base with a strong acid the change in pH at the endpoint is very abrupt. A typical titration curve is shown in Fig. 49.

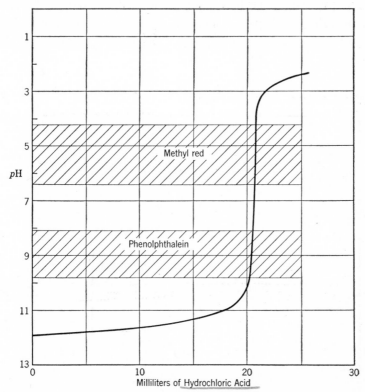

Fig. 49. Titration of sodium hydroxide with hydrochloric acid. Taken: 20.0 ml. of 0.1020 N sodium hydroxide; titrated with 0.0988 N hydrochloric acid. The sodium hydroxide was diluted with water before the titration was begun.

The vertical portion of the curve passes through the pH band of both phenolphthalein and methyl red, and either indicator may be used to mark the end-point.

Titration of a Weak Acid with a Strong Base. The titration of a weak acid with a strong base is complicated by the fact that the reaction does not go to completion. The reason for this is that slightly ionized substances both enter and are produced by the reaction and an equilibrium is set up:

$$\text{HA} \quad + \quad \text{NaOH} \quad \xrightleftharpoons[\text{Hydrolysis}]{\text{Neutralization}} \quad \text{NaA} \quad + \quad \text{H}_2\text{O}$$

$$\text{H}^+ \quad + \quad \text{A}^- \qquad\qquad\qquad \text{H}^+ \quad + \quad \text{OH}^-$$

The position of the equilibrium is governed by the relative degrees of dissociation of the weak acid and of the water. The sodium hydroxide and the salt are completely ionized. Expressed in another way, the

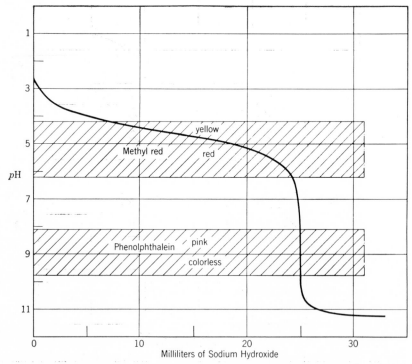

Fig. 50. Titration of acetic acid with sodium hydroxide. Taken: 25.0 ml. of 0.4209 N acetic acid; titrated with 0.4193 N sodium hydroxide.

salt produced by the neutralization of a weak acid with a strong base is hydrolyzed. Hydrolysis is the reverse of neutralization. At the equivalence-point, because of this hydrolysis, there is present a slightly ionized acid and a highly ionized base. The solution is therefore alkaline, and an indicator must be chosen which changes color in the alkaline region. Phenolphthalein is commonly used.

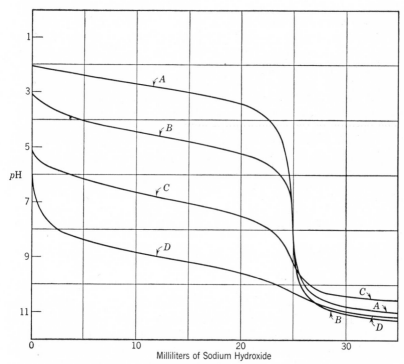

Fig. 51. Titration of weak acids of various strengths with sodium hydroxide. *A*, Chloroacetic acid, $K_A = 1.4 \times 10^{-3}$; *B*, acetic acid, $K_A = 1.75 \times 10^{-5}$; *C*, cyanuric acid, $K_A = 2.0 \times 10^{-7}$; *D*, boric acid, $K_A = 5.8 \times 10^{-10}$. Each acid 0.05 *N* and titrated with 0.05 *N* sodium hydroxide.

The titration curve of acetic acid, a typical weak acid, $K_A = 1.75 \times 10^{-5}$, with sodium hydroxide is shown in Fig. 50. The change in *p*H in the neighborhood of the equivalence-point is neither so great nor so abrupt as in the titration of the strong acid shown in Fig. 48, and it occurs in the alkaline range, *p*H 7 to 10.

As might be expected, acids which are weaker than acetic acid give poorer end-points on titration. In Fig. 51 are given the titration curves of four acids, chloroacetic acid, acetic acid, cyanuric acid, and boric acid, which are progressively weaker in the order named. For the weaker acids the break in the titration curve covers a smaller interval of pH, the change is less sharp, and the equivalence-point occurs at progressively higher values of pH where more standard solution is required to change the indicator. In the case of boric acid no satisfactory end-point can be obtained with visual indicators, and even the potentiometric method by which the data for Fig. 51 were obtained does not yield a precise determination of the end-point.

It is possible to calculate the pH at the various stages of the titration of a weak acid with a strong base, using the dissociation constant of the weak acid and the dissociation constant of water. No single, simple mathematical treatment will cover the entire titration, but if the problem is broken up into four parts it can be handled fairly simply: pH at the beginning of the titration; pH during the titration; pH at the end-point; and pH after the end-point. Each of these four steps will now be considered.

1. *pH of a Solution of a Weak Acid.* When a weak acid having the general formula HA ionizes,

$$HA = H^+ + A^-$$

1 hydrogen ion and 1 anion are formed simultaneously, and if the solution contains only this weak acid it is evident that the concentration of the two will be equal: $[H^+] = [A^-]$. It follows, then, that $K_A = [H^+][H^+]/[HA]$, and therefore that

$$[H^+]^2 = K_A[HA] \qquad (2)$$

Usually only the overall or gross concentration of the acid is known, that is, the amount of acid added. This is designated as C_{HA}. The term $[HA]$ represents the concentration of nonionized acid present at any time. Thus, if a solution is made $0.1\ M$ in the weak acid, $[HA]$ is smaller than 0.1 by the amount of acid which ionizes. Since 1 hydrogen ion is formed from each molecule of acid which ionizes

therefore

$$[HA] = C_{HA} - [H^+]$$
$$[H^+]^2 = K_A(C_{HA} - [H^+]) \qquad (3)$$

This is a quadratic equation which may be solved by use of the quadratic formula to give an exact value for $[H^+]$. If $[H^+]$ is small compared to C_{HA}, as is usually the case, the $[H^+]$ term on the right may be dropped

$$[H^+] = \sqrt{K_A C_{HA}} \qquad (4)$$

and an answer is obtained only slightly different from that obtained by the quadratic formula.

Another way of writing equation 4 is to take the negative logarithm of both sides of the equation

$$- \log [\mathrm{H^+}] = -\tfrac{1}{2} \log K_A - \tfrac{1}{2} \log C_{HA}$$

$$pH = \tfrac{1}{2}pK_A - \tfrac{1}{2} \log C_{HA} \tag{4'}$$

As an example, we calculate the pH of a 0.100 M solution of acetic acid for which $K_A = 1.75 \times 10^{-5}$. Using equation 3, the quadratic solution is

$$[\mathrm{H^+}]^2 = 1.75 \times 10^{-5}(0.100 - [\mathrm{H^+}])$$

$$[\mathrm{H^+}]^2 = 1.75 \times 10^{-5}[\mathrm{H^+}] - 1.75 \times 10^{-6} = 0$$

Solving this equation by the quadratic formula (see Appendix, Table A7) yields $[\mathrm{H^+}] = 0.001,31$, for which the corresponding pH is 2.88. Using the approximate equation 4

$$[\mathrm{H^+}] = \sqrt{1.75 \times 10^{-5} \times 0.1} = 0.001,32$$

a result less than 1 per cent different from that obtained by the use of the quadratic formula and so close that the extra work of the quadratic formula is hardly justified. The use of the equivalent equation 4′ leads to the same result.

$$pH = \tfrac{1}{2} \times 4.76 - \tfrac{1}{2} \log 0.1 = 2.38 - \tfrac{1}{2}(-1) = 2.88$$

It is evident from equations 4 and 4′ that the hydrogen-ion concentration decreases (pH increases) for a given acid as its concentration decreases. Also, for a series of acids all at the same concentration, the hydrogen-ion concentration decreases as the ionization constant decreases. In both cases the decrease is proportional to the square root of the ionization constant.

Once the hydrogen-ion concentration is known, the per cent ionization of a weak acid at a specified concentration may be calculated, remembering that $[\mathrm{H^+}] = [\mathrm{A^-}] = [\mathrm{HA\ ionized}]$

$$\frac{[\mathrm{H^+}]}{C_{HA}} 100 = \text{Per cent ionization} \tag{5}$$

Thus, in the 0.1 M acetic acid solution above, the hydrogen-ion concentration was calculated to be 0.001,31. The per cent ionization is then

$$\frac{1.31 \times 10^{-3}}{1.0 \times 10^{-1}} 100 = 1.3$$

2. *pH of Mixtures of a Weak Acid and Its Salt. pH at Various Stages of a Titration.* To illustrate the method of calculating the pH at various points in the course of the titration of a weak acid with a strong base, consider the neutralization of acetic acid with sodium hydroxide. To 100 ml. of 0.100 M acetic acid (represented as HA) add 25 ml. of 0.100 M sodium hydroxide. The total volume is now 125 ml. The untitrated acid corresponds to 75 ml. of 0.100 M acid, but the solution is not 0.100 M because the volume has been increased to 125 ml., or

$$C_{\text{HA}} = \tfrac{75}{125}(0.1)$$

The salt formed is equal to the titrated acid (1 molecule of salt from each molecule of acid), and since the salt is completely ionized

$$C_{A^-} = \tfrac{25}{125}(0.1)$$

The mathematical expression for the ionization constant may be rearranged to

$$[\text{H}^+] = K_\text{A} \frac{[\text{HA}]}{[\text{A}^-]}$$

Strictly, $[\text{HA}] = C_{\text{HA}} - [\text{H}^+]$ and $[\text{A}^-] = C_{A^-} + [\text{H}^+]$, owing to the fact that the untitrated acid ionizes to a slight extent, producing 1 hydrogen ion and 1 A^- ion for each molecule of acid ionizing. Usually $[\text{H}^+]$ is small compared to C_{HA}, and C_A, and may be neglected:

$$[\text{H}^+] = K_\text{A} \frac{C_{\text{HA}}}{C_{A^-}}$$

or in this case

$$[\text{H}^+] = K_\text{A} \frac{\tfrac{75}{125}(0.1)}{\tfrac{25}{125}(0.1)}$$

the total volume and the initial concentration cancel, and

$$[\text{H}^+] = K_\text{A}[\tfrac{75}{25}]$$

Inserting the numerical value of K_A, taking acetic acid as an example,

$$[\text{H}^+] = (1.75 \times 10^{-5})\tfrac{75}{25}$$
$$= 10^{+0.24} \times 10^{-5} \times 10^{+0.48} = 10^{-4.28}$$

$$pH = 4.28$$

This same method may be applied to other volumes of sodium hydroxide added, and in general

$$[\text{H}^+] = K_\text{A} \left[\frac{\text{Fraction untitrated}}{\text{Fraction titrated}} \right] \tag{6}$$

This equation may also be expressed in logarithmic form

$$- \log [H^+] = - \log K_A - \log \left[\frac{\text{Fraction untitrated}}{\text{Fraction titrated}} \right]$$

$$pH = pK_A + \log \left[\frac{\text{Fraction titrated}}{\text{Fraction untitrated}} \right] \tag{6'}$$

Equation 6 (or 6') can be used to calculate the pH of the solution throughout the titration but not at the end-point, for at this stage of a titration the salt formed is appreciably hydrolyzed, an effect which was not considered in deriving this formula.

When the concentration of the acid and its salt are equal, that is, at the half-way point of the titration, the ratio of untitrated to titrated acid becomes equal to 1 and $[H^+] = K_A$, or $pH = pK_A$. Use is made of this relation in determining the K_A of an acid. The pH at the half-titration point is measured, or equivalent amounts of the acid and its salt may be dissolved in the same solution and the pH measured. This is a quite satisfactory procedure, for the solution has its maximum buffering capacity at this point and is not greatly subject to the effect of impurities such as carbon dioxide.

3. *pH of a Solution of the Salt of a Weak Acid and a Strong Base. pH at the Equivalence-Point of the Titration of a Weak Acid with a Strong Base.* For the neutralization of a weak acid with a strong base

$$HA + NaOH = NaA + H_2O$$

a mass-action constant may be written

$$K_N = \frac{[Na^+][A^-]}{[HA][Na^+][OH^-]} \tag{7}$$

where K_N is the neutralization constant. The sodium hydroxide and salt are completely ionized and enter the expression as the molar concentration of the various ions; the concentration of the water is a constant quantity and is lumped in with the constant. The $[Na^+]$ terms cancel, and the constant K_N is evaluated by multiplying the numerator and denominator of the right side by $[H^+]$ and regrouping

$$K_N = \frac{[A^-][H^+]}{[HA][OH^-][H^+]} = \frac{[H^+][A^-]}{[HA]} \cdot \frac{1}{[OH^-][H^+]}$$

By definition $\quad K_A = \dfrac{[H^+][A^-]}{[HA]} \quad$ and $\quad K_W = [H^+][OH^-]$

It follows that
$$K_N = \frac{K_A}{K_W}$$

and
$$K_N = \frac{[A^-]}{[HA][OH^-]} = \frac{K_A}{K_W} \tag{8}$$

When the salt present at the equivalence-point hydrolyzes, the weak acid and sodium hydroxide are formed simultaneously, and $[HA] = [OH^-]$; therefore, equation 8 becomes

$$\frac{[A^-]}{[OH^-]^2} = \frac{K_A}{K_W}$$

and
$$[OH^-] = \sqrt{\frac{K_W}{K_A}[A^-]}$$

This can be obtained in terms of the hydrogen-ion concentration by the use of $K_W = [H^+][OH^-]$

$$[OH^-] = \frac{K_W}{[H^+]} = \sqrt{\frac{K_W}{K_A}[A^-]}$$

$$[H^+] = \sqrt{\frac{K_W K_A}{[A^-]}} \tag{9}$$

or
$$pH = \tfrac{1}{2}pK_W + \tfrac{1}{2}pK_A + \tfrac{1}{2}\log[A^-] \tag{9'}$$

If C_{A^-} is the total salt concentration, $[A^-]$ is strictly C_{A^-} minus the amount hydrolyzed and plus the amount formed by ionization of the weak acid, or $[A^-] = C_{A^-} - [OH^-] + [H^+]$. This leads to a quadratic equation in $[H^+]$ which will give a more exact answer, but in most practical problems it is sufficiently accurate to neglect $[OH^-]$ and $[H^+]$ since both are much smaller than C_{A^-}. The formula for calculating the pH at the equivalence-point of the titration of a weak acid with a strong base is, then,

$$[H^+] = \sqrt{\frac{K_W K_A}{C_{A^-}}} \tag{10}$$

$$pH = \tfrac{1}{2}pK_W + \tfrac{1}{2}pK_A + \tfrac{1}{2}\log C_{A^-} \tag{10'}$$

For an example, we again examine acetic acid. If to 25.0 ml. of 0.1000 N acetic acid has been added 25.0 ml. of 0.1000 N sodium hydroxide, the concentration of sodium acetate is 0.05 M, owing to the dilution to 50.0 ml. Application of equation 10 gives

$$[H^+] = \sqrt{\frac{1.0 \times 10^{-14} \times 1.75 \times 10^{-5}}{5 \times 10^{-2}}} = 1.87 \times 10^{-9}$$

corresponding to a pH of 8.73.

From the nature of equation 10 it will be observed that for smaller values of K_A the hydrogen-ion concentration at the equivalence-point is lower, that is, the pH at the equivalence-point becomes higher. This is in accord with the actual titration of weak acids of various strengths as shown in Fig. 51.

The extent to which the hydrolysis takes place can be obtained also for $[HA] = [OH^-]$. In the example above, the pH at the equivalence-point was found to be 8.73; this corresponds to $pOH = 5.27$ and $[OH^-] = 5.37 \times 10^{-6}$. The concentration of weak acid formed by hydrolysis and of the salt hydrolyzed is thus 5.37×10^{-6}; the fraction of salt hydrolyzed is therefore

$$= \frac{5.37 \times 10^{-6}}{5 \times 10^{-2}} = 1.07 \times 10^{-4}$$

or

$$= (1.07 \times 10^{-4})(100) = 0.01 \text{ per cent}$$

The value of $[OH^-]$ could have been obtained more directly using one of the equations in the development above

$$[OH^-] = \sqrt{\frac{K_W}{K_A}[A^-]}$$

This gives the same value, $[OH^-] = 5.37 \times 10^{-6}$. It is apparent from this equation that the amount of hydrolysis (as measured by $[OH^-]$ which is equal to $[HA]$ formed and to $[A^-]$ hydrolyzed) is inversely proportional to the square root of the ionization constant.

4. *pH Beyond the Equivalence-Point.* After the equivalence-point has been passed in the titration of a weak acid with a strong base, the hydroxyl ion present in the solution is derived from two sources. That produced by the hydrolysis of the salt is equal in concentration to the weak acid formed at the same time, and that from the excess base added is calculated from the volume of base added, its strength, and the total volume, $[OH^-] = [HA] + C_{NaOH}$, in which C_{NaOH} denotes the molar concentration of the excess base added. The base added represses the hydrolysis by mass-action effect so that the con-

tribution to $[OH^-]$ by hydrolysis rapidly becomes negligible as the titration is continued beyond the equivalence-point. The equation developed above to calculate the extent of hydrolysis can be used to show this.

$$K_N = \frac{[A^-]}{[HA][OH^-]} = \frac{K_A}{K_W}$$

Thus, considering the titration of 25.0 ml. of 0.1000 N acetic acid with 0.1000 N sodium hydroxide, the pH at the equivalence-point was calculated above as 8.73 and the total volume at the end-point as 50.0 ml. If an excess of 0.1 ml. of 0.1000 N sodium hydroxide is added, the concentration of the excess alkali will be

$$C_{NaOH} = 0.1 \frac{0.1}{50.1} = 0.000,200$$

Using the equations above

$$\frac{[A^-]}{([HA] + C_{NaOH})[HA]} = \frac{K_A}{K_W}$$

$$\frac{5 \times 10^{-2}}{[HA]^2 + 2.0 \times 10^{-4}[HA]} = \frac{1.75 \times 10^{-5}}{1.0 \times 10^{-14}}$$

Solving this by the quadratic formula [1] gives $[HA] = 0.000,000,14$. This is so little different from the result obtained by the simpler method of neglecting $[HA]$ in comparison with C_{NaOH}

$$[HA] = \frac{[A^-]K_W}{C_{NaOH}K_A}$$

$$= \frac{5 \times 10^{-2} \times 1 \times 1.0 \times 10^{-14}}{2 \times 10^{-4} \times 1.75 \times 10^{-5}} = 1.43 \times 10^{-7}$$

that it is apparent that the hydrolysis is negligible.

The titration curve beyond the equivalence-point, therefore, can be calculated simply from the excess alkali added; in the above example for 0.10 ml. of 0.100 N sodium hydroxide in excess

$$[OH^-] = 2.0 \times 10^{-4}$$

or pOH = 3.70   (pH = 10.30)

[1] In the course of the solution of the quadratic it becomes necessary to obtain the square root of 0.000,000,040,114 more accurately than can be done with five-place logarithms. This is best done by evaluating the quantity $(4 \times 10^{-8} + 11.4 \times 10^{-11})^{1/2}$ by the binomial expansion. Only the first two terms are necessary.

With weaker acids the contribution of hydrolysis to the total hydroxyl ion present is not negligible as it turned out to be in this case.

Titration of a Weak Base with a Strong Acid. The titration of a weak base with a strong acid is also complicated by the hydrolysis of the salt produced. Adopting for a typical weak base the symbol

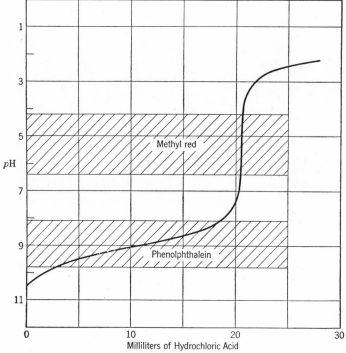

Fig. 52. Titration of ammonium hydroxide with hydrochloric acid. Taken: 20.0 ml. of 0.1015 N ammonium hydroxide; titrated with 0.0988 N hydrochloric acid.

BOH, the opposing reactions of neutralization and hydrolysis may be written

$$\text{BOH} + \text{HCl} \xrightleftharpoons[\text{Hydrolysis}]{\text{Neutralization}} \text{BCl} + \text{H}_2\text{O}$$

At the equivalence-point the salt hydrolyzes, giving a slightly ionized base and a highly ionized acid. The solution is acidic, and an indicator must be used which changes on the acid side of neutral. Methyl red is commonly used, for example, in the titration of ammonium hydroxide, Fig. 52.

As in the case of the titration of a weak acid with a strong base, the pH at the various stages of the titration of a weak base with a strong acid can be handled theoretically. As before, different methods are used for the various parts of the titration curve, and the method employed and the assumptions necessary to reduce the complexity of the mathematics are strictly parallel. The fundamental definition is

$$BOH = B^+ + OH^- \qquad K_B = \frac{[B^+][OH^-]}{[BOH]}$$

K_B being the dissociation constant of the weak base.

1. *pH of a Solution of a Weak Base. pH at the Beginning of a Titration.* A weak base alone in solution ionizes to produce equivalent quantities of B^+ and OH^-. Combining $[B^+] = [OH^-]$ and $K_W = [H^+][OH^-]$ with the equation defining K_B gives

$$[H^+] = \sqrt{\frac{K_W{}^2}{K_B[BOH]}} \tag{11}$$

If C_{BOH} is the total concentration of the weak base in the solution, the non-ionized portion, $[BOH]$, is given by $[BOH] = C_{BOH} - [OH^-]$. The use of this relation with equation 11 yields a quadratic which gives an exact solution. If the hydroxyl-ion concentration is small compared to the total concentration of the base, it may be neglected and the equation simplified.

2. *pH During the Titration of a Weak Base with a Strong Acid.* Rearrangement of the equation defining K_B gives

$$[OH^-] = K_B \frac{[BOH]}{[B^+]}$$

or, in terms of the hydrogen-ion concentration,

$$[H^+] = \frac{K_W[B^+]}{K_B[BOH]}$$

In evaluating $[B^+]$ and $[BOH]$ the volume of the solution drops out and the ratio of $[B^+]$ to $[BOH]$ may be simply replaced by the ratio of the fraction titrated to the fraction untitrated

$$[H^+] = \frac{K_W \text{ (Fraction titrated)}}{K_B \text{ (Fraction untitrated)}} \tag{12}$$

Actually two assumptions are made in doing this: (a) the salt produced is not hydrolyzed, and (b) the untitrated base is not dissociated. Inasmuch as the hydrolysis would produce hydrogen ions and the dissociation of the base hydroxyl ions, the effects counteract each other and equation 12 describes the titration curve fairly well in the region 10 to 90 per cent titrated.

3. *pH at the Equivalence-Point in the Titration of a Weak Base with a Strong Acid.* The neutralization constant for the reaction

$$BOH + HCl = BCl + H_2O$$

is defined by

$$K_N = \frac{[B^+][Cl^-]}{[BOH][H^+][Cl^-]} \tag{13}$$

and can be evaluated by multiplying above and below by $[OH^-]$

$$K_N = \frac{[B^+][OH^-]}{[BOH][H^+][OH^-]} = \frac{K_B}{K_W}$$

At the equivalence-point, $[BOH] = [H^+]$, for they are formed in equivalent amounts by the hydrolysis of the salt. Equation 13 then becomes

$$\frac{[B^+]}{[H^+]^2} = \frac{K_B}{K_W}$$

which gives

$$[H^+] = \sqrt{\frac{K_W}{K_B}[B^+]} \tag{14}$$

In evaluating the hydrogen-ion concentration at the equivalence-point, $[B^+]$ is equal to the total concentration of the salt present (calculated from the amounts of material added) minus the salt which has been hydrolyzed:

$$[B^+] = C_{BCl} - [H^+]$$

The exact solution of equation 14 is therefore a quadratic, but usually the hydrogen-ion concentration is small compared to the total concentration of the salt and may be neglected, and a satisfactory result may be obtained by the simpler, linear equation. For an example, consider 100 ml. of 0.1 N ammonium hydroxide to which has been added 200 ml. of 0.05 N hydrochloric acid. The total volume is 300 ml., and the total concentration of the salt is 0.033 N. The quadratic solution is

$$[H^+]^2 = \frac{1.0 \times 10^{-14}}{1.75 \times 10^{-5}}(3.33 \times 10^{-2} - [H^+])$$

$$[H^+]^2 + 5.7 \times 10^{-10}[H^+] - 1.9 \times 10^{-11} = 0$$

$$[H^+] = 4.36 \times 10^{-6} \quad (pH = 5.36)$$

The linear equation yields

$$[H^+] = \frac{1.0 \times 10^{-14}}{1.75 \times 10^{-5}} \, (3.33 \times 10^{-2})$$

$$[H^+] = 4.45 \times 10^{-6} \qquad (pH = 5.35)$$

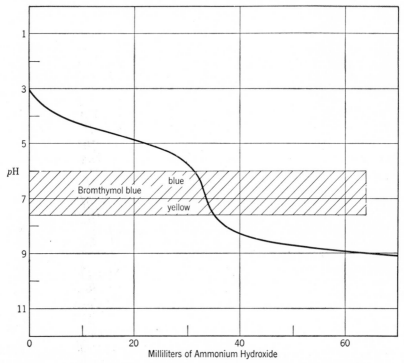

Fig. 53. Titration of acetic acid with ammonium hydroxide. Taken: 25.0 ml. of 0.0520 N acetic acid; titrated with 0.0360 N ammonium hydroxide.

Titration of a Weak Acid with a Weak Base. This is a titration normally considered to be impossible with visual indicators to detect the end-point. The reason for this is obvious from an inspection of Fig. 53, which shows the course of the pH in the titration of acetic acid with ammonia. This titration curve was determined potentiometrically by measuring the pH after each addition of ammonium hydroxide. The pH at the equivalence-point is theoretically about 7 because the dissociation constants of ammonium hydroxide and acetic acid happen to be equal, 1.75×10^{-5}. The range of pH over which bromthymol blue changes color is spaced almost equally on each side of 7, and theoretically this indicator could be used to locate the end-point. A close inspection of the titration curve of Fig. 53, however, shows that from the point where the color begins to change to the point where the change is complete corresponds to about 3 ml. This is an uncertainty of almost 10 per cent. The end-point can be determined somewhat more precisely by this indicator by preparing a suitable color standard and carrying out the titration until the colors match. For this an equal volume of a solution of *p*H 7 ("buffer" solution, see later in this chapter) is treated with the same amount of indicator. Even so, the precision of the determination will not approach that of the titration of acetic acid with a strong base such as sodium hydroxide.

The Titration of Two Acids of Different Strengths. If the ionization constants of two acids differ by 10^4 a satisfactory determination of both acids can usually be made. In Fig. 54 is shown the titration curve of a mixture of perchloric acid and acetic acid. The ionization constant of perchloric acid is greater than 0.1 (perchloric acid is practically 100 per cent ionized, and dissociation constants

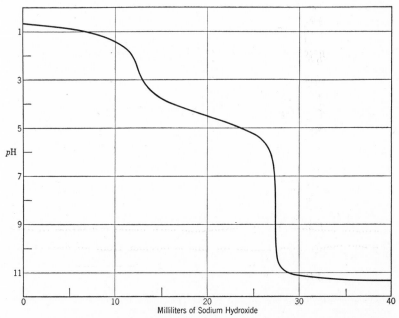

Fig. 54. The titration of a mixture of perchloric acid and acetic acid with sodium hydroxide. Taken: 15.0 ml. of 0.3520 N perchloric acid plus 15.0 ml. of 0.4209 N acetic acid; titrated with 0.4193 N sodium hydroxide.

of such acids are of little significance), and that of acetic acid is 1.75×10^{-5}. This difference is ample to afford a determination of both acids with considerable precision. Unfortunately the equivalence-point occurs in the very acid region (pH 2.6), where it takes a considerable volume of standard solution to change the pH of the solution, and although an indicator can be found for this region the end-point would be rather broad at best. A quite satisfactory end-point can be obtained by the potentiometric method used to obtain the data plotted in Fig. 54.

In general, the titration of a mixture of acids can be more precisely carried out potentiometrically than with visual indicators if one or the other end-point occurs at a high or low pH where the change of pH of the solution with the addition of the standard solution is not sharp. A satisfactory end-point can be obtained visually by preparing a solution having the pH at the end-point as calculated or as shown by a potentiometric titration, and carrying out the titration until the colors of the indicator in the buffer and titrating solutions match.

In the case of the titration of a very strong acid and a weak acid such as the perchloric acid-acetic acid mixture shown in Fig. 54, the pH at the first equivalence-point is simply the pH of a solution of the weak acid at the concentration of weak acid prevailing at the first end-point. In the example shown in Fig. 54, 15.0 ml. of 0.4209 N acetic acid was mixed with 15.0 ml. of 0.3520 N perchloric acid, and at the first equivalence-point 12.55 ml. of 0.4193 N sodium hydroxide was added. The concentration of acetic acid at this point was

$$C_{HC_2H_3O_2} = \frac{15.0}{42.55} \, 0.4209 = 0.1482$$

The pH of the solution can be calculated using equation 4

$$[H^+] = \sqrt{K_{HC_2H_3O_2}C_{HC_2H_3O_2}} = \sqrt{1.75 \times 10^{-5} \times 0.1482}$$

$$[H^+] = 1.62 \times 10^{-3} \quad (p\text{H} = 2.79)$$

The observed value at the equivalence-point was 2.60.

In the case of a mixture of two weak acids, the pH at the equivalence-point can be calculated from the dissociation constants of the acids involved. Thus, for two weak acids, HA_1 and HA_2,

$$K_{A_1} = \frac{[H^+][A_1^-]}{[HA_1]} \qquad K_{A_2} = \frac{[H^+][A_2^-]}{[HA_2]}$$

By solving each of these equations for $[H^+]$ and multiplying the two new equations by each other

$$[H^+] = \sqrt{K_{A_1}K_{A_2}\frac{[HA_1][HA_2]}{[A_1^-][A_2^-]}} \tag{15}$$

After alkali equivalent to the stronger acid HA_1 has been added the concentration of the salt formed should be equal to the original concentration of the acid decreased by the dilution resulting from the addition of the base. Actually, however, some of the stronger acid has perhaps not been titrated, and an equivalent amount of the weaker acid has been. Let b represent the equivalents per liter not titrated. Then

$$[HA_1] = b$$

$$[A_1^-] = C_{A_1^-} - b$$

$$[HA_2] = C'_{HA_2} - b$$

$$[A_2^-] = b$$

in which $C_{A_1^-}$ is the concentration of the salt produced by the neutralization of the stronger acid; it is equal to the concentration of the stronger acid corrected for the dilution caused by the addition of the alkali. Similarly, C'_{HA_2} is the initial volume of the second acid corrected for the dilution; therefore

$$[H^+] = \sqrt{K_1K_2\frac{b(C'_{HA_2} - b)}{(C_{A_1^-} - b)b}} \tag{16}$$

If b is small in comparison to C_{HA_1} and C_{HA_2} it may be neglected. The hydrogen-ion concentration at the equivalence-point may then be calculated using

$$[H^+] = \sqrt{K_1K_2\frac{C'_{HA_2}}{C_{A_1^-}}} \tag{17}$$

or in the special case where the original concentrations of the two acids are equal

$$[H^+] = \sqrt{K_1K_2} \tag{18}$$

This is so in the titration of a dibasic acid such as carbonic or oxalic.

The Titration of Dibasic and Tribasic Acids. In aqueous solutions of sulfuric acid, both replaceable hydrogen atoms of the sulfuric acid are more or less completely dissociated from the sulfate radical

$$H_2SO_4 = 2H^+ + SO_4^=$$

On titration with alkali the two are neutralized simultaneously, and the titration curve is identical with that for perchloric acid, Fig. 54, except that two equivalents of alkali are used. Some dibasic acids, however, dissociate stepwise, carbonic acid, H_2CO_3, for example. In

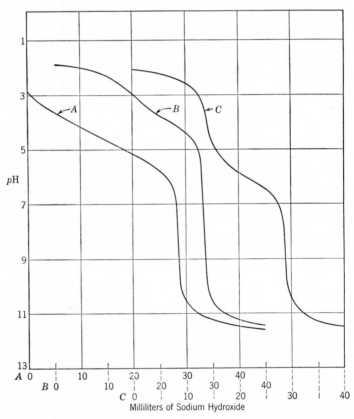

Fig. 55. Titration of dibasic acids with sodium hydroxide. Taken: 12.5 ml. of 0.1000 N acid in each case; titrated with 0.0870 N sodium hydroxide.

A, Succinic Acid	B, Oxalic Acid	C, Maleic Acid
$K_1 = 6.31 \times 10^{-5}$	$K_1 = 5.01 \times 10^{-2}$	$K_1 = 1.20 \times 10^{-2}$
$K_2 = 2.51 \times 10^{-6}$	$K_2 = 5.13 \times 10^{-5}$	$K_2 = 5.95 \times 10^{-7}$
$K_1/K_2 = 25$	$K_1/K_2 = 975$	$K_1/K_2 = 20,200$

the first step the bicarbonate ion is formed, which undergoes further ionization to give a second hydrogen ion and the carbonate ion. Dissociation constants are written for the two steps

$$H_2CO_3 = H^+ + HCO_3^- \qquad K_1 = \frac{[H^+][HCO_3^-]}{[H_2CO_3]}$$

$$HCO_3^- = H^+ + CO_3^= \qquad K_2 = \frac{[H^+][CO_3^=]}{[HCO_3^-]}$$

The numerical values of these constants are $K_1 = 4.47 \times 10^{-7}$ and $K_2 = 5.62 \times 10^{-11}$. The first replaceable hydrogen atom is a weak acid which can be satisfactorily titrated; the second is so weak that it cannot be. In the case of other dibasic acids both replaceable hydrogen atoms can be titrated (phthalic acid, oxalic acid). In still others one replaceable hydrogen atom is very highly ionized and the other only slightly ionized (chromic acid, sulfurous acid).

The shape of the titration curve obtained depends on the relative sizes of the two dissociation constants. In general, if the ratio of the two constants is greater than 10,000 (and if the second is sufficiently large), it is possible to locate both equivalence-points with visual indicators. If the ratio is greater than 1000 it is possible to locate the first equivalence-point (as well as the second) potentiometrically. If the ratio is smaller than 1000 the second hydrogen atom is neutralized in part before the first is completely neutralized and the first equivalence-point cannot be distinguished. All three cases are shown in Fig. 55. The ionization constants of succinic acid are so much alike in size that both hydrogen atoms are neutralized at the same time; for oxalic acid, the constants are sufficiently separated that the first equivalence-point can be found potentiometrically; maleic acid, however, gives two distinct equivalence-points on titration with a strong base.

Equation 18 developed above can be used to determine the pH at the equivalence-point of the titration of the first replaceable hydrogen. In the case of carbonic acid

$$[H^+] = \sqrt{4.47 \times 10^{-7} \times 5.62 \times 10^{-11}}$$

$$= 5.0 \times 10^{-9} \qquad (p\text{H} = 8.3)$$

This is the pH of a solution of sodium bicarbonate. Phenolphthalein is obviously the indicator for this titration.

Phosphoric acid is interesting, for it is a tribasic acid having three dissociation constants all quite widely different in value:

$$H_3PO_4 = H^+ + H_2PO_4^- \qquad K_1 = \frac{[H^+][H_2PO_4^-]}{[H_3PO_4]} = 7.54 \times 10^{-3}$$

$$H_2PO_4^- = H^+ + HPO_4^= \qquad K_2 = \frac{[H^+][HPO_4^=]}{[H_2PO_4^-]} = 6.23 \times 10^{-8}$$

$$HPO_4^= = H^+ + PO_4^\equiv \qquad K_3 = \frac{[H^+][PO_4^\equiv]}{[HPO_4^=]} = 4.79 \times 10^{-13}$$

When titrated with sodium hydroxide, phosphoric acid is neutralized in steps because of the great differences in the values of the dissociation constants

$$H_3PO_4 + NaOH = NaH_2PO_4 + H_2O$$

$$NaH_2PO_4 + NaOH = Na_2HPO_4 + H_2O$$

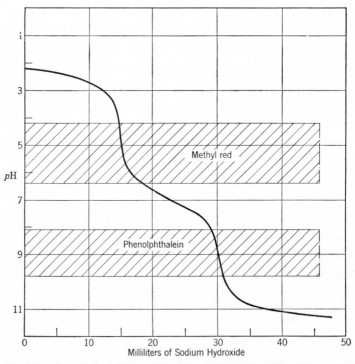

Fig. 56. Titration of phosphoric acid with sodium hydroxide. Taken: 15.0 ml. of 0.1000 N phosphoric acid; titrated with 0.1000 N sodium hydroxide.

Equation 18 may be applied to K_1 and K_2 and again to K_2 and K_3 to find the pH at the equivalence-points of the first and second stages respectively. The third hydrogen of phosphoric acid is so weak that it cannot be titrated. The titration curve of phosphoric acid is shown in Fig. 56. It is apparent that methyl red and phenolphthalein would be used to locate the first and second end-points respectively.

In the two cases just cited the difference between successive values of K is greater than 10^4, which makes it possible to titrate the first replaceable hydrogen atom completely before the second is neutralized. In the case of dibasic acids having values of K lying closer together, the neutralization of the second hydrogen begins before the neutralization of the first is complete, and the overlapping obliterates the first end-point.

BUFFER MIXTURES

A buffer is a solution of a mixture of materials which resists a change in pH on the addition of strong acid or base. It usually consists of a mixture of a weak acid and one of its salts or a weak base and one of its salts. Thus, a solution containing acetic acid and sodium acetate constitutes a buffer. The addition of sodium hydroxide to the solution does not raise the pH appreciably, for the hydroxide is neutralized by the acetic acid. The addition of hydrochloric acid does not lower the pH appreciably either, for the acid reacts with the sodium acetate to introduce an equivalent quantity of acetic acid which is only weakly ionized. A buffer, then, has a double action:

$$HA + NaOH = NaA + H_2O$$

$$NaA + HCl = HA + NaCl$$

A mixture of a weak base and one of its salts has a similar double-barreled action.

A mixture of a weak acid and its salt is present during the titration of a weak acid with a strong base. During such a titration, therefore, the solution is buffered and there is relatively little change in pH over a long portion of the titration curve; for example, in the titration of acetic acid with sodium hydroxide (Fig. 50) that is between 10 and 90 per cent neutralized the pH changes only from 3.7 to 5.8. Similarly, relatively horizontal portions in the titration curves of Figs. 51, 52, 53, and 56 indicate the presence of buffer mixtures.

It is possible by selecting the proper weak acid or base to obtain a buffer mixture of any desired pH value. Buffers of ammonium hydroxide and ammonium chloride, for example, cover the range 8.2 to

9.8; of chloroacetic acid and sodium chloroacetate, 2.3 to 3.8; and of boric acid and sodium borate, 8.2 to 10. The case of sodium bicarbonate is a curious one, for, in being at once a salt and a weak acid, it constitutes a buffer by itself, pH 8.3.

From a quantitative standpoint buffer mixtures can be handled by the same general treatment which was previously used to calculate the pH during the titration of a weak acid with a strong base or a weak base with a strong acid. This is simply a rearrangement of the equation defining K_A or K_B, for a buffer consists of a weak acid and its salt

$$[H^+] = K_A \frac{[HA]}{[A^-]}$$

Neglecting the ionization of the weak acid and the hydrolysis of the salt, the concentrations of the acid and salt present may be substituted for [HA] and [A$^-$] respectively. With this it is possible to calculate the pH of buffer mixtures and to predict what change in pH will occur on the addition of acid or base.

Because of the slight departure of the pH calculated by the above formula from the actual pH it is better in practice to prepare buffer solutions of definite pH by mixing certain materials and in the amounts specified by Clark and Lubs and by MacIlvaine in their buffer tables (see pages 454 and 455 for these). Such buffer mixtures find many uses, for example, in the colorimetric determination of pH.

The equilibrium of many reactions in aqueous solution is governed by the hydrogen-ion concentration of the solution. The principle of buffering provides a way of maintaining more or less constant hydrogen-ion concentration and thus of regulating a reaction. For example, in the precipitation of zinc as zinc ammonium phosphate, $ZnNH_4PO_4$, a buffer consisting of ammonium dihydrogen phosphate, $NH_4H_2PO_4$, and diammonium hydrogen phosphate, $(NH_4)_2HPO_4$, is used to hold the hydrogen-ion concentration in the pH range of 7 to 8; in this range the precipitate has a minimum solubility; at higher and lower pH values it dissolves so appreciably that it cannot then be used for the determination of zinc.

PROBLEMS

1. Convert $[H^+]$ = 0.0058 to pH; convert pH = 9.80 to $[H^+]$.
2. Convert $[OH^-]$ = 0.022 to pOH; convert pOH = 5.3 into $[OH^-]$.
3. From the expression defining K_W derive the relation $pH + pOH = pK_W$ = 14.
4. For pH = 9.80 find the corresponding $[OH^-]$.

5. Compute the quantity $(\log n) - 1$ for $n = 1.00$, 1.5, 2.0, 2.5, $\cdots$ 9.5, 10.0. On graph paper plot $(\log n) - 1$ (as ordinate) against n (as abscissa). Hydrogen-ion concentration can be rewritten in an exponential form to take advantage of this plot in converting $[H^+]$ to pH. For example,

$$[H^+] = 0.0058 = 5.8 \times 10^{-3}$$

$$= 10^{+0.76} \times 10^{-1} \times 10^{-2} = 10^{-2.24}$$

The value of $10^{+0.76} \times 10^{-1}$ can be obtained from the plot by looking up the ordinate corresponding to 5.8. Check this and then convert $[H^+] = 0.000,006,4$ to pH. Write a concise sentence to serve as a legend to the graph telling how the graph is used.

6. Explain the statement: A solution of pH 3 is 100 times more acid than one of pH 5.

7. From Table A3 of dissociation constants in the Appendix pick out the bases which are classed as weak and those which are classed as very weak. Explain why this differentiation is made.

8. Arrange a list of weak and very weak acids in which the acid strength decreases by a factor of approximately 10 from one acid to the next.

9. Calculate the hydrogen-ion concentration of a solution 0.100 M in formic acid. Calculate this first making the assumption that the hydrogen-ion concentration is small compared to C_{HA} and may be neglected. Then calculate the exact result using the quadratic formula (see Appendix, Table A7, for quadratic formula).

10. Calculate the per cent to which 0.100 M formic acid is ionized, using the information obtained in Problem 9.

11. Calculate the pH of a series of acids, all 0.1 M, having dissociation constants 1×10^{-3}, 1×10^{-5}, 1×10^{-7}, 1×10^{-9}, 1×10^{-11}, 1×10^{-13}.

12. Calculate the pH of solutions of acetic acid, $K_A = 1.75 \times 10^{-5}$, having the following strengths: 1.0 M, 0.1 M, 0.01 M, 0.0001 M, 0.000,001 M.

13. Calculate the change in pH of a solution of acetic acid having a pH of 3.5 when diluted with an equal volume of water. $K_A = 1.75 \times 10^{-5}$.

14. Calculate the pH of 100 ml. of 0.100 N formic acid to which has been added 10.0 ml. of 0.100 N sodium hydroxide. Repeat the calculation for 20.0, 40.0, 50.0, 70.0, 90.0, 95.0, and 99.0 ml. of 0.100 N sodium hydroxide added.

15. Calculate the pH of 80.0 ml. of 0.200 N acetic acid to which has been added 30.0 ml. of 0.150 N potassium hydroxide.

16. The pH of a solution 0.05 M in a certain weak acid and 0.05 M in the sodium salt of the acid was found to be 6.50. Calculate the ionization constant of the acid.

17. Calculate the pH at the equivalence-point of the titration of 100 ml. of 0.100 N formic acid with 0.100 N sodium hydroxide.

18. Calculate the pH of a solution containing 25.0 g. of sodium propionate per liter. See Appendix, Table A3, for the dissociation constant of propionic acid, $CH_3CH_2CO_2H$.

19. Using the data of Problems 9, 14, and 17 prepare a titration curve for the neutralization of 100 ml. of 0.100 N formic acid with 0.100 N sodium hydroxide. Plot carefully on graph paper. Draw in bands indicating the pH ranges over which the following indicators change color: methyl orange, methyl red, bromthymol blue, phenolphthalein.

20. Derive the equation which is used for calculating the pH of a solution of a weak base (equation 11, page 186). Show that the difference in the pH values

obtained using the exact, quadratic solution and the approximate solution is negligible for a 0.1 M solution of a weak base having a dissociation constant 1×10^{-4}.

21. Calculate the pH of a 0.01 M solution of ammonium hydroxide.

22. Show that, at the midpoint in the titration of a weak base with a strong acid, $pK_B = p$OH.

23. Calculate the pH of an equimolecular mixture of pyridine and pyridinium chloride.

24. Explain why a solution of methylammonium chloride reacts acid to litmus. Calculate the pH of a 0.05 M solution of methylammonium chloride.

25. Calculate the pH at the equivalence-point of the first stage of the titration of sulfurous acid. (See Table A3 in Appendix for the dissociation constants of sulfurous acid.)

26. Calculate the pH of an equimolecular mixture of sodium dihydrogen phosphate and disodium hydrogen phosphate.

27. The pH at the equivalence-point in the titration of 0.2 N phosphoric acid with 0.2 N sodium hydroxide according to the equation $H_3PO_4 + NaOH = NaH_2PO_4 + H_2O$ is calculated by equation 18 to be 4.66. Check this value. Then calculate the fraction of the phosphoric acid not converted to sodium dihydrogen phosphate at the equivalence-point. *Hint:* solve the equations defining K_{A_1} and K_{A_2} for $[H^+]$ and equate; use the definitions of b and other terms in the development preceding equation 16; note that 2 molecules of the salt produced are involved in the failure of all of the H_3PO_4 to be neutralized:

$$2NaH_2PO_4 = H_3PO_4 + Na_2HPO_4$$

Solve for b using the assumption that b is small compared to the concentration of the salt, and finally calculate $100b/C_{H_3PO_4}$. *Ans.:* 0.29 per cent.

28. Assuming that equivalent quantities of two monobasic weak acids are present in solution, that sufficient alkali has been added to be just equivalent to one of them, and that the solution at this point is 0.1 N in the sodium salt of the stronger acid and 0.1 N in the second acid, calculate the per cent of the stronger acid not titrated if: (a) $K_1/K_2 = 10^4$, and (b) $K_1/K_2 = 10^2$. See Problem 27 for hint. *Ans.:* (a) 1.0 per cent on first approximation (b neglected in comparison with 0.10), 0.99 per cent on second approximation; (b) 10 per cent on first approximation, 9.1 per cent on second approximation.

29. In the titration curve shown in Fig. 49, page 175, 20.0 ml. of 0.1020 N sodium hydroxide was taken for titration but the pH at the start did not correspond to that of a 0.1020 N solution of a strong base. Calculate the volume to which the solution was diluted with water before the titration was begun.

CHAPTER 9

The Practice

of Neutralization Reactions

For the reasons discussed in detail in Chapter 8, acids and bases are placed in three classes: strong, weak, and very weak, depending on the degree to which they are ionized when dissolved in water. The strong acids can be titrated with standard solutions of strong bases, and any one of several indicators may be used to mark the equivalence-point. The weak acids and bases are those having dissociation constants of the order of 10^{-3} to 10^{-8}. Their salts are appreciably hydrolyzed in solution, and the indicator chosen to mark the end-point must be one that changes color on the alkaline side of neutral. The very weak acids, those having dissociation constants smaller than 10^{-8}, cannot be titrated satisfactorily for there is no abrupt change in hydrogen-ion concentration (pH) at the equivalence-point.

Similar relations hold for the bases, which also are classed as strong, weak, and very weak, depending on the extent to which they are ionized in aqueous solution. The strong bases are titrated with strong acids, and any indicator changing in the pH range 4 to 10 may be used to locate the end-point. Weak bases, those having dissociation constants in the range 10^{-3} to 10^{-8}, can be determined by titration only with strong acids, and an indicator changing in the acid range, pH 4 to 7, must be used. Again, the very weak bases cannot be determined satisfactorily by titration.

Although the very weak acids and very weak bases cannot be determined by titration, their salts can be determined by so-called displacement titrations in which the free, very weak acid or base is displaced from its salt by a strong acid or base. Such titrations are an important branch of volumetric analysis.

The theory of these various types of neutralization titrations is discussed in Chapter 8. The following material is concerned primarily with the practical aspects and working details of volumetric analyses employing these reactions. The subject of equivalent weight in neutralization reactions was discussed in the general chapter on volumetric analysis, Chapter 7, in connection with the explanation of the normal system. The various concepts associated with equivalent weight and the normal system and the methods of making the calculations of volumetric analysis should be understood before proceeding.

STANDARD SOLUTIONS OF ACIDS AND BASES; PRIMARY-STANDARD ACIDS AND BASES

A number of highly satisfactory primary-standard acids are available for the standardization of solutions of hydroxides: sulfamic acid, potassium acid phthalate, potassium acid iodate, 2,4,6-trinitrobenzoic acid, benzoic acid, furoic acid, constant-boiling hydrochloric acid, and constant-boiling perchloric acid. Of these, sulfamic acid is probably the best, being a solid which is convenient to handle and a strong acid which yields a sharp end-point on titration. Only two, constant-boiling hydrochloric acid and constant-boiling perchloric acid, can be weighed out and diluted to a definite volume to produce stable, strong acid solutions of known strength. Unfortunately both constant-boiling hydrochloric acid and constant-boiling perchloric acid are not available commercially, are difficult to prepare, and must be handled with great care; for these reasons they are of no importance in practical analysis. Standard solutions of acid are made up approximately from the reagent-grade commercial concentrated acids, and the solutions are standardized in an appropriate manner.

In the case of the bases there is no hydroxide which meets the requirements of a primary standard. The strong alkalies are hygroscopic and are usually contaminated with carbon dioxide absorbed from the atmosphere. Various carbonates have been proposed as primary standards. Of these, sodium carbonate is the only one which has found much use. Like the standard solutions of strong acids, then, the standard solutions of the strong bases must be made up approximately and standardized.

Once the solutions of strong acid and strong base have been made up approximately, there are three ways of proceeding with the standardization. (1) The strong acid may be standardized by titrating a weighed sample of primary standard sodium carbonate, and the strong base may be standardized by titrating a weighed sample of a primary standard acid, either sulfamic acid, potassium acid phthalate, potassium acid iodate, or 2,4,6-trinitrobenzoic acid. (2) The strong acid may be standardized gravimetrically; for example, the chloride in a measured volume of hydrochloric acid may be converted to silver chloride and the silver chloride filtered off, dried, and weighed. (3) A measured volume of the strong acid may be titrated with a strong base, and vice versa; if the concentration of either one is known, the concentration of the other can be calculated.

In acid-base titrations it is convenient to have on hand solutions of both strong acid and strong base. If the end-point is overstepped with one, a measured volume of the other can be added and the end-point approached again.

Sulfamic Acid. HSO_3NH_2. Equiv. wt. 97.09. Sulfamic acid is a white, crystalline solid which can be readily obtained in high purity by recrystallization from water. The solid is anhydrous and non-hygroscopic. It is stable at temperatures up to 130°. It dissolves readily in water. In solution it hydrolyzes slowly, yielding ammonium acid sulfate, but the total replaceable hydrogen is not changed in the process. It is a strong monobasic acid, so that either methyl red or phenolphthalein can be used as indicator when it is titrated with a strong base. It is available commercially and is the best of the primary standard acids.

Potassium Acid Phthalate. $KHC_8H_4O_4$. Equiv. wt. 204.22. Potassium acid phthalate is a white, crystalline solid which can be readily obtained in pure form. It is anhydrous, non-hygroscopic, and stable on drying at 110°. The second replaceable hydrogen atom of phthalic acid is a weak acid ($K_1 = 1.26 \times 10^{-3}$; $K_2 = 3.1 \times 10^{-6}$) so that it can only be titrated with strong bases; phenolphthalein must be used as indicator.

2,4,6-Trinitrobenzoic Acid. $HC_7H_2O_8N_3$. Equiv. wt. 257.12. Trinitrobenzoic acid is a white crystalline solid. It is anhydrous and non-hygroscopic. It is a strong acid ($pK_A = 2.38$) and is ideal for the standardization of solutions of alkalies. Trinitrobenzoic acid serves as its own indicator, changing from colorless to red at the equivalence-point. Material of primary-standard quality is available on the market. The commercial-grade material can easily be purified; it is first converted to the sodium salt by titration with sodium hydroxide until the solution turns red, the solution is then filtered, and the free acid is precipitated by the addition of sulfuric acid. The pure acid is filtered off, washed with water, and air dried.

Potassium Acid Iodate. $KH(IO_3)_2$. Equiv. wt. 389.94. Potassium acid iodate is a white, crystalline solid. It is stable at 110°, is anhydrous and non-hygroscopic. It is a strong acid; when it is titrated with a strong base any indicator changing in the pH range 4 to 10 can be used; methyl red, bromthymol blue, or phenolphthalein, for example. Potassium acid iodate may be purchased in a purity satisfactory for use as a primary standard. The rate of solution of the material is greatly speeded if the material is first ground to reduce the size of the crystals. A saturated solution of potassium acid iodate at room temperature is approximately 0.1 N. Potassium acid iodate is practically a universal primary standard for it can be used in acidimetry and iodometry and to prepare a standard iodate solution.

Sodium Carbonate. Na_2CO_3. Equiv. wt. 106.00 or 53.00. Sodium carbonate can be used for the standardization of strong acids by virtue of the very slight ionization of carbonic acid which causes the displacement reaction

$$Na_2CO_3 + 2HCl = H_2CO_3 + 2NaCl$$

to go completely to the right. This reaction is discussed in detail later in this chapter in the section dealing with the determination of carbonate. Sodium carbonate (known in commerce as "soda ash") is produced in large quantity in highly pure form except for the presence of sodium bicarbonate. Fortunately the bicarbonate can be converted to sodium carbonate by heating: $2NaHCO_3 = Na_2CO_3 + H_2CO_3$. The temperature for effecting this conversion completely is 300°. When sodium carbonate is to be used as a primary standard this heat treatment should not be neglected, as even reagent-grade sodium carbonate contains an appreciable amount of bicarbonate. When sodium carbonate is titrated with a strong acid to the sodium bicarbonate (phenolphthalein) end-point the equivalent weight is the molecular weight divided by 1, 106.00; when it is titrated to the free carbonic acid (methyl orange) end-point the equivalent weight is the molecular weight divided by 2, 53.00. The details of this titration are given later under the determination of carbonate.

Gravimetric Standardization. The precipitation of silver chloride is one of the best of the known gravimetric processes and can be carried out with almost any desired degree of accuracy if the techniques used in atomic-weight determinations are employed.[1] It is apparent that any other acids present will vitiate the results. Reagent-grade

---

[1] The most precise chemical analysis ever carried out is the determination of the atomic weight of silver, a determination made by several independent methods with an accuracy of 1 in 100,000. The importance of the atomic weight of silver arises from the very satisfactory character of the silver chloride precipitation process. The atomic weights of most of the metals are determined by analysis of the chlorides of the metals; the chlorides can be obtained pure and their chloride content determined by precipitation as silver chloride. Knowing the atomic weight of silver, the atomic weight of the metal can be calculated. It can almost be said that silver is the basis of the atomic-weight table rather than oxygen. Because this is so, most primary-standard acids are tested by check against hydrochloric acid standardized gravimetrically.

hydrochloric acid meeting the A.C.S. specifications has less than 0.0002 per cent sulfuric acid present and is satisfactory for practically all work; if uncertainty exists, the hydrochloric acid can be first distilled and then used to prepare the standard solution.

Sulfuric acid can be standardized by precipitation of barium sulfate, and results satisfactory for practically all work obtained, but the unsatisfactory character of the barium sulfate precipitation procedure makes this method inherently less accurate than the silver chloride standardization of hydrochloric acid.

There are no good gravimetric methods for standardizing solutions of nitric acid or perchloric acid.

The Preparation of Standard Solutions of Strong Acids. In practice, the standard solutions of strong acids which are used are solutions of hydrochloric acid, sulfuric acid, nitric acid, and perchloric acid. The solutions are made up to have approximately the concentration desired and then standardized. The necessary volume of reagent-grade (A.C.S. specifications) concentrated acid is measured out and diluted with water. Table A1 in the Appendix gives the specific gravity and concentration of the concentrated acids as marketed.

All of the four acids mentioned, hydrochloric, sulfuric, nitric, and perchloric, are strong acids which react quickly and completely with strong bases, all are stable, all about the same price in reagent-grade quality, so that there is little advantage of one over the other.

Hydrochloric acid forms insoluble salts with silver, lead, and the mercurous ion, and sulfuric acid forms insoluble salts with barium, strontium, and lead. This is usually not a matter for concern anyway because the titration of hydroxides in the presence of metals (lead as plumbate, zinc as zincate, aluminum as aluminate) is confused by the precipitation of the metal hydroxide or basic salt in neutral solution. Barium and strontium hydroxides, which can be titrated with standard acids, yield insoluble sulfates with sulfuric acid; these precipitates adsorb the indicator so that the use of one of the other acids is better. All the metal nitrates and perchlorates are soluble, although potassium and ammonium perchlorate may precipitate from very concentrated solutions when formed during a titration.

Hydrochloric acid is not appreciably volatile from the concentrations of acids used in analytical work; solutions 0.1 N in hydrochloric acid can be boiled for some time without losing acid.

The oxidizing power of nitric acid may make its use as a standard acid objectionable under some circumstances.

In most analytical work standard solutions having concentrations about 0.1 N are used. This is the concentration that works out about right for samples of reasonable size (0.3 to 1.5 g.) and for the ordinary 50-ml. buret. Titrations with strong acids can be carried out well with visual indicators if the concentration of the strong acid is greater than 0.01 N. Titrations with 0.001 N acid can be made, but the equivalence-point is best determined potentiometrically (see Chapter 18).

Solutions of strong acids can be standardized by titration with a solution of sodium hydroxide of known strength or by titrating a weighed sample of sodium carbonate. The details of the sodium carbonate titration are discussed under the determination of carbonate.

Procedure for the Preparation of Approximately 0.1 N *Hydrochloric Acid.* The equivalent weight of hydrochloric acid is 36.465, so that 3.645 g. of hydrogen chloride are required for 1 l. of 0.1 N acid. Concentrated hydrochloric acid as marketed has a specific gravity of about 1.19 and contains 37 per cent of hydrogen chloride by weight. The weight of concentrated acid required for 1 l. of 0.1 N acid is $3.645/0.37 = 9.85$ g.; volume of acid required is $9.85/1.19 = 8.3$ ml.

In a clean, glass-stoppered, 1-l. bottle place approximately 1 l. of water. Add 8.2 ml. of reagent-grade concentrated hydrochloric acid measured with a graduated cylinder of suitable size or a measuring pipet fitted with a rubber bulb. Stopper the bottle and mix thoroughly by shaking vigorously for several minutes. Label the bottle. Standardize the solution by one of the following procedures: (1) Gravimetrically, procedure given immediately below; (2) by titration with standard sodium hydroxide, procedure given on page 207; (3) by titration of a weighed sample of sodium carbonate, procedure given on page 216.

It is recommended that students approaching this problem for the first time standardize the hydrochloric acid solution both gravimetrically and by titration with standard sodium hydroxide. The sodium hydroxide is in turn standardized by titrating a weighed sample of a primary standard acid; see below. The two values obtained in this way for the concentration of the standard acid should check within at least 1 part in 200, that is, for a solution approximately 0.1 N, to within ±0.0005. If they do not check the work should be repeated.

Procedure for the Gravimetric Standardization of Solutions of Hydrochloric Acid. Using the approximate strength of the solution to be standardized, choose a volume which will give 0.5 to 1.0 g. of silver chloride; for example, 50 ml. of 0.1 N hydrochloric acid contains 0.182 g. of hydrogen chloride, which is equivalent to 0.725 g. of silver chloride. If the acid is approximately 0.1 N, carefully pipet exactly 50.00 ml. of the solution into a 400-ml. beaker; if the solution is approximately 0.2 N pipet 25.00 ml. Rinse the pipet two or three times with small portions of the acid before measuring out the sample. Do not blow through the pipet but touch it to the side of the beaker as it empties; leave a drop of liquid in the tip of the pipet. Dilute to 150 ml. with distilled water and add 1 ml. of nitric acid. Heat the solution to boiling, and with constant stirring add 30 ml. of 0.25 M silver nitrate. Continue the heating for a few minutes and when the precipitate has coagulated sufficiently test for completeness of precipitation by the addition of a little silver nitrate solution. Cool the solution to room temperature before filtering.

Filter the silver chloride on a porous-bottom filtering crucible which has been previously dried at 110° and weighed. See page 27 for the technique of filtering with these crucibles. Decant off the supernatant liquid and wash the precipitate several times in the beaker, beating the precipitate up vigorously with the wash water. As wash water use distilled water containing 0.5 ml. of concentrated nitric acid per 200 ml. Finally, transfer the precipitate to the filtering crucible and wash it five or six times further. Place the crucible in a beaker, cover the beaker with a disk of filter paper or a cover glass, and place the beaker in a drying oven at 120° for 2 hours or more. After cooling to room temperature weigh the crucible and silver chloride. From the weight of silver chloride obtained calculate the normality of the hydrochloric acid solution.

The Preparation of Standard Solutions of Strong Bases. The strong bases which are available and commonly used as standard solutions are sodium hydroxide, potassium hydroxide, and barium hydroxide. Sodium hydroxide is most often used because it is somewhat cheaper than the others. Being strong alkalies, these materials absorb carbon dioxide from the atmosphere, and as purchased from the chemical companies contain carbonate, at least as a surface coating. These bases are also hygroscopic, absorbing water with great avidity, and thus contain water in varying amounts. The presence of carbon dioxide and water renders them unfit as primary standards and complicates their use as standard solutions under some circumstances.

If the strong base is to be used for the titration of a strong acid and if the concentration of the base is 0.1 N or greater the presence of a little carbonate in the standard solution usually has a negligible effect; the solution then can be prepared by simply dissolving the solid base in water. If carbonate must be absent, as is necessary when titrating with standard solutions 0.05 N or less and preferably when a weak acid is being titrated, two procedures are available: (1) Barium chloride may be added to solutions of sodium hydroxide or of potassium hydroxide to precipitate out the carbonate; (2) advantage may be taken of the fact that sodium carbonate is insoluble in concentrated sodium hydroxide solutions. The first of these methods cannot be used if sulfuric acid is to be titrated, for the barium sulfate precipitated adsorbs the indicator and thus interferes with the end-point. The second method is applicable only to sodium hydroxide, for potassium carbonate is soluble in concentrated potassium hydroxide solutions. In diluting carbonate-free solutions of hydroxides and when titrating weak acids or strong acids less than 0.05 N in concentration, water free of carbon dioxide should be used. Such water is most easily prepared by boiling distilled water for a few minutes and cooling in such a manner that it is not exposed to the atmosphere.

Solutions of the strong bases may be standardized against any of the primary-standard acids mentioned previously. Sulfamic acid and potassium acid phthalate are recommended as best and are about equally good. A sample of the primary standard is weighed out and titrated, phenolphthalein being used as indicator.

An instructive procedure and one recommended to students, particularly if a standard solution of a strong acid is needed later for the carbonate or Kjeldahl determinations, is to standardize the sodium hydroxide in two ways: against a standard solution of a strong acid and against a weighed sample of a primary-standard acid. The standard, strong-acid solution is prepared approximately as described previously and standardized gravimetrically, or by titrating a weighed sample of sodium carbonate. In this manner, checks by independent methods may be obtained for the normality of the standard sodium hydroxide, and the composition of an unknown acid is then subsequently determined with greater assurance.

The maximum accuracy in the titration will be obtained when the number of milliliters of standard solution used is nearly the maximum capacity of the buret, for then the errors in the two buret readings cause a minimum relative error in the volume measured. The size of the sample of primary-standard material weighed should be chosen to make the volume used in the titration 40 to 50 ml., near the full capacity of the burets commonly used. The error in each reading of the buret will be about 0.02 ml., the smallest division on the buret corresponding to 0.05 ml. The errors in the two buret readings to determine a volume may add so that the error in the volume may be 0.04 in 40, which is 4 parts in 4000, or 1 part in 1000. The maximum accuracy that can be expected will thus be about 1 part in 1000. In the standardization of a 0.1 N solution this corresponds to an error in the normality of 0.0001. In good work the values for the normality obtained by two successive titrations of a primary standard should check within 2 or 3 in the fourth decimal. The normality obtained by the two different methods suggested above for standardizing the sodium hydroxide solution should check within 3 to 5 parts in 1000 also. If they do not the work should be repeated before proceeding to the analysis of an unknown replaceable hydrogen sample.

Procedure for the Preparation of Approximately 0.1 N Sodium Hydroxide. The equivalent weight of sodium hydroxide is 40.0, so that 4.0 g. are required for 1 l. of 0.1 N solution. If the sodium hydroxide solution is to be used subsequently for the titration of a strong acid or if the error due to the presence of carbonate may be ignored, weigh on the side-shelf balance 4.0 g. of stick, flake, or pellet sodium hydroxide. Place this in a beaker, add 75 ml. of water, and stir vigorously for a few seconds. The sodium hydroxide will dissolve quickly with the evolution of heat. Dilute the solution somewhat and transfer to a 1-l. bottle. Dilute to approximately 1 l., stopper the bottle with a rubber stopper, and shake it vigorously for a few minutes.

Bottles with ground-glass stoppers are not recommended for the storage of alkali solutions unless the solutions are used frequently. The alkali attacks the glass, and the stoppers ultimately freeze to the bottles.

Procedure for the Preparation of Carbonate-Free Sodium Hydroxide Solutions. Barium Chloride Method. Dissolve 4.2 g. of sodium hydroxide sticks or pellets in 500 ml. of water. Add 10 ml. of 0.25 M barium chloride solution, mix well, and allow to stand overnight. Decant the clear liquid into a 1-l. bottle without stirring up the precipitate. Dilute the solution to 1 l. with water previously boiled and cooled, and shake vigorously.

Concentrated Sodium Hydroxide Method. Dissolve 50 g. of sodium hydroxide in 75 ml. of water and allow the mixture to stand in a rubber-stoppered flask or preferably in a silver or nickel dish in an empty desiccator. When the precipitate of sodium carbonate has separated, pipet out 7 ml. of the clear liquid, being careful to avoid drawing any of the solid sodium carbonate into the pipet. Transfer this sodium hydroxide solution to a bottle containing approximately 1 l. of distilled water previously boiled and cooled. Stopper and shake vigorously for several minutes. Standardize the solution as described below.

Procedure for the Standardization of Sodium Hydroxide Against Standard Hydrochloric Acid. Fill a 50-ml. buret with standard hydrochloric acid, approximately 0.1 N, prepared and standardized as previously described. Rinse the buret several times with small portions of the solution before making the final filling. Place the sodium hydroxide solution in a second buret, rinsing the buret in the same fashion before filling. Run 40.0 ml. of hydrochloric acid into a 250-ml. conical flask. Add 3 drops of phenolphthalein solution and 40 or 50 ml. of water. Titrate with the sodium hydroxide to the first permanent pink color. Swirl the flask with the right hand and operate the stopcock of the buret with the fingers of the left hand, the handle of the stopcock being to the right and the stopcock surrounded by palm, fingers, and thumb. If the stopcock is properly greased the key will operate easily with slight pressure from thumb and fingers. Toward the end of the titration wash down the sides of the flask with a stream of water from the wash bottle. Fractions of a drop can be taken from the buret by touching the flask to the tip of the buret and washing the liquid removed into the solution with water from the wash bottle. The pink color of the phenolphthalein at the end-point fades on standing because of the absorption of carbon dioxide from the air. Calculate the normality of the alkali using the relation $(N_{NaOH})(ml._{NaOH}) = (N_{HCl})(ml._{HCl})$.

Procedure for the Standardization of Sodium Hydroxide Against a Primary-Standard Acid. Dry the primary-standard material selected for 2 hours at 100°; this can be done conveniently by placing the material in a weighing bottle and placing the weighing bottle, unstoppered, in a beaker which can then be covered and placed in the oven. Neither sulfamic acid nor potassium acid phthalate is hygroscopic; the surface moisture on them is usually only a few hundredths of 1 per cent; and if time is short the drying operation may be omitted. A sample should be chosen of a size that will require about 45 ml. of sodium hydroxide solution. If 0.1 N sodium hydroxide is being standardized this represents about $(45)(0.1)$ or 4.5 milliequivalent weights. The milliequivalent weight of sulfamic acid is 0.097,09, so that a weight of approximately $(4.5)(0.097,09) = 0.44$ g. of sulfamic acid should be taken for each sample; the corresponding figures for potassium acid phthalate are: 0.204,22 and 0.91 g.; for 2,4,6-trinitrobenzoic acid: 0.257,12 and 1.15 g.; and for potassium acid iodate: 0.389,94 and 1.75 g. Weigh exactly about the calculated amount of the primary-standard acid selected. Dissolve the acid in about 100 ml. of water and add a few drops of phenolphthalein solution. Titrate with the sodium hydroxide solution to the first permanent pink color. Add the sodium hydroxide dropwise toward the end of the reaction, swirling the mixture constantly. The pink color of the phenolphthalein fades on standing because of the absorption of carbon dioxide from the air.

The milliequivalent weights of the various primary standards are given in the preceding paragraph. The values for the normality obtained for the sodium hydroxide on two successive standardizations should agree with each other to within 2 or 4 parts in 1000, or about 0.0004 in the normality of 0.1 N solutions.

THE DETERMINATION OF REPLACEABLE HYDROGEN

The most common volumetric analysis is the determination of replaceable hydrogen, that is, the hydrogen in acidic compounds which can be replaced by metals to form salts. The reaction of an acid with a base proceeds to form a salt and water because of the very slight extent to which water is ionized. The reaction of acids with bases is, however, not complete in all cases. The acid itself may be so slightly ionized that it competes with water for the hydrogen ion and in effect causes a reversal of the neutralization reaction:

$$HA + NaOH \underset{\text{Hydrolysis}}{\overset{\text{Neutralization}}{\rightleftarrows}} NaA + H_2O$$

It becomes necessary, therefore, to differentiate acids on the extent to which they are ionized in solution: strong, weak, and very weak.

The strong acids are more or less completely ionized in solution. Included in this group are hydrochloric acid, nitric acid, sulfuric acid, perchloric acid, hydrobromic acid, and hydriodic acid. When any of these acids is titrated with a strong base, the change in pH at the equivalence-point is large and sharp, the salts produced are not hydrolyzed so that the pH at the equivalence-point is about 7, and any indicator changing color in the pH range 4 to 10 can be used to mark the end-point.

The weak acids are those having dissociation constants in the range 10^{-3} to 10^{-8}; included in this group are many of the common acids such as oxalic acid, formic acid, acetic acid, benzoic acid, and chloroacetic acid. These acids can only be determined by titration with a strong base. The salt produced hydrolyzes, and at the equivalence-point there are present in the solution appreciable amounts of the slightly ionized acid and an equivalent amount of a highly ionized base; the solution, therefore, reacts alkaline, and an indicator must be chosen which changes color on the alkaline side. Phenolphthalein is the most usual indicator. The pH at the equivalence-point can be calculated since the value of the dissociation constant of the acid and the concentration of the salt are known:

$$[H^+] = \sqrt{\frac{K_W K_A}{C_{A^-}}}$$

In the case of acetic acid, $K_A = 1.75 \times 10^{-5}$, and for a salt concentration at the equivalence-point of 0.05 M, $[H^+] = 1.87 \times 10^{-9}$, corresponding to a pH of 8.72. Phenolphthalein, which changes color over the pH range 8.1 to 9.8, is an ideal indicator for this titration.

The very weak acids, those having dissociation constants less than 10^{-8}, cannot be titrated at all; in this group are hydrocyanic acid, phenol, carbonic acid, and boric acid. The pH change is so gradual around the equivalence-point that no indicator functions to mark the end-point.

Procedure for the Determination of Replaceable Hydrogen. If the material for analysis is a solid, place it in a weighing bottle and dry it for 2 hours in the oven at 110°. Weigh exactly three samples of 1.0 to 1.3 g. into 250-ml. conical flasks. Dissolve each sample in about 100 ml. of water and add 2 or 3 drops of phenolphthalein solution. Titrate with a standard sodium hydroxide solution to the first pink color. Wash down the walls of the flask with a stream of water from the wash bottle toward the end of the titration. The color of the indicator will fade as the solution stands, owing to the absorption of carbon dioxide from the atmosphere. Calculate the per cent hydrogen in the sample; the milliequivalent weight is 0.001,008.

If the material for analysis is a liquid, weigh the sample in the following manner: Weigh a clean, dry, glass-stoppered weighing bottle with the stopper in place. Place in the weighing bottle 1 to 5 ml. or a suitable volume of the liquid for analysis. Weigh the weighing bottle again. Transfer the sample from the weighing bottle to a 250-ml. conical flask using a stream of water from the wash bottle to effect the transfer quantitatively. Dilute the solution to about 100 ml. with distilled water, add phenolphthalein, and titrate with a standard sodium hydroxide solution as described in the preceding paragraph. Some information as to the approximate content of replaceable hydrogen is required in advance to determine the size of the sample to be taken. If no such information is known a preliminary titration with a small sample is necessary. If the acid is quite concentrated it may be necessary to take an aliquot of the first sample for the actual titration. Weigh a sample of 1 to 5 ml. in the manner described. Transfer the liquid from the weighing bottle to a 250-ml. volumetric flask. Dilute to the mark on the flask with distilled water and mix the solution thoroughly by shaking and inverting the flask. Pipet 25.0 ml. of this solution into a 250-ml. conical flask. Dilute the solution to about 100 ml. with water, add phenolphthalein, and titrate with standard sodium hydroxide as described in the preceding paragraph. In calculating the per cent of replaceable hydrogen in the sample, multiply by 10 the number of milliliters of the standard sodium hydroxide solution used, or by some other factor if the volume to which the sample was diluted or the volume of final sample taken are not the volumes specified above.

THE TITRATION OF HYDROXIDES

As with the acids, it is necessary to differentiate the alkalies into three groups: strong, weak, and very weak. The strong bases, such as sodium hydroxide, potassium hydroxide, and tetramethylammonium hydroxide, are highly ionized. The salts produced by neutralizing these bases with strong acids are not hydrolyzed, and either phenolphthalein or methyl red may be used as indicator when such bases are titrated with strong acids.

The weak bases must be titrated with a strong acid, and because of the hydrolysis of the salt at the equivalence-point an indicator must be chosen which changes color in the acid region; methyl red is commonly used. In Chapter 8 on the theory of neutralization reactions a formula was developed for calculating the pH at the equivalence-point in the titration of a weak base with a strong acid:

$$[H^+] = \sqrt{\frac{K_W}{K_B}\,C_{B^+}}$$

Applied to ammonium hydroxide, $K_B = 1.75 \times 10^{-5}$, in a case where the salt concentration at the equivalence-point is 0.05 M, this gives a pH value of 5.27. Ammonium hydroxide is a typical weak base, and its determination is a matter of considerable importance.

The organic bases, the so-called *amines*, are an important class of compounds containing the amino group —NH_2. These bases are derivatives of ammonia in which 1 or more hydrogen atoms of the ammonia have been replaced by organic groups; for example,

H_3C-NH_2	$(C_2H_5)_2NH$	$C_6H_5-NH_2$
Methylamine	Diethylamine	Aniline

Like ammonia, the amines add on water to form hydroxides

H_3C-NH_3OH	$(C_2H_5)_2NH_2OH$	$C_6H_5-NH_3OH$
Methylammcnium hydroxide	Diethylammonium hydroxide	Phenylammonium hydroxide

The salts formed on neutralization are analogous to ammonium salts, thus:

H_3CNH_3Cl	$(C_2H_5)_2NH_2Cl$	$C_6H_5NH_3Cl$
Methylammonium chloride	Diethylammonium chloride	Phenylammonium chloride

These salts are referred to in the older literature as amine hydrochlorides: methylamine hydrochloride, diethylamine hydrochloride, aniline hydrochloride. As will be observed from the values of the dissociation constants given in Table A3 in the Appendix, many of these amines are stronger bases than ammonia.

The very weak bases, those having dissociation constants smaller than 10^{-8}, such as aniline and pyridine, cannot be determined by titration because there is no abrupt change in pH at the equivalence-point.

Most alkalies, solids, or solutions will contain some carbonate picked up by contact with the atmosphere. This introduces some error the magnitude of which depends on the indicator used in the titration. The nature of this error will be more easily understood after one reads the following section dealing with the titration of sodium carbonate with hydrochloric acid.

PROBLEMS

1. A solution of hydrochloric acid was standardized gravimetrically, a volume of 50.00 ml. yielding 0.8500 g. of silver chloride. Calculate the normality of the acid.

2. Calculate the volume of concentrated sulfuric acid, sp. gr. 1.83, 94 per cent H_2SO_4, which is needed to make 5 l. of 0.2000 N sulfuric acid.

3. A solution of sulfuric acid was standardized by precipitating the sulfate as barium sulfate. A volume of 25.0 ml. of the solution gave 0.4668 g. of barium sulfate. Calculate the normality of the solution.

4. A mixture containing only potassium acid sulfate and sodium chloride was titrated with 0.1250 N sodium hydroxide to the phenolphthalein end-point. A sample weighing 0.7500 g. required 35.0 ml. Calculate the per cent of potassium acid sulfate in the mixture.

5. A solution of phosphoric acid was standardized by precipitating magnesium ammonium phosphate and igniting to the pyrophosphate. A volume of 40.0 ml. of the solution gave 0.2226 g. of magnesium pyrophosphate. Calculate the normality of the solution for the reaction $H_3PO_4 + 2NaOH = Na_2HPO_4 + 2H_2O$.

6. A sample of a pure organic acid weighing 0.5000 g. required for titration 50.0 ml. of 0.2000 N sodium hydroxide. Calculate the equivalent weight of the acid. Tell what further information would be needed to learn the molecular weight.

7. A brine tank in a refrigeration plant contained 40,000 gal. of concentrated calcium chloride solution. The refrigeration coils sprang a leak, and ammonia gas passed into the brine. A 10.0-ml. sample of the brine required 83.3 ml. of 0.1000 N hydrochloric acid for neutralization to the methyl red end-point. Calculate (a) the grams of ammonia (NH_3) per liter, and (b) the number of gal. of concentrated hydrochloric acid, sp. gr. 1.19, 37 per cent HCl, required to neutralize the ammonia; 3.785 l. = 1 gal. Suggest a practical way to eliminate the ammonia and save the brine and the cost of acid for neutralizing the ammonia.

8. Water was saturated with barium hydroxide, the excess solid barium hydroxide was filtered off, and a sample of the clear filtrate weighing 18.523 g. was titrated to the methyl red end-point with 0.1000 N hydrochloric acid, 92.7 ml. being required. Calculate the solubility of barium hydroxide in grams per 100 g. of solution.

9. Two pure compounds having different properties were isolated from a solution containing potassium iodate and iodic acid. The compounds were both undoubtedly acid salts of the general formula $KH_y(IO_3)_{y+1}$. Samples of each weighing 1.000 g. were titrated with 0.1500 N sodium hydroxide. The compound designated A required 17.1 ml. Compound B required 23.5 ml. Decide the value of y in each compound.

10. The replaceable hydrogen in a sample weighing 1.2000 g. was determined by titration with sodium hydroxide, a volume of 46.0 ml. of the sodium hydroxide being required. The sodium hydroxide solution was standardized against primary-standard sulfamic acid, a sample of which weighing 0.3000 g. required 40.0 ml. for titration. Afterward it was discovered that the buret, which was used in both titrations, was defective, the number 35 having been omitted and an extra number 42 being inserted between 42 and 43. Calculate the error in the per cent of hydrogen which resulted from using this faulty buret in the manner described.

11. From a knowledge of the chemistry of the Solvay process explain why commercial sodium carbonate contains sodium bicarbonate.

12. Devise a scheme for determining the sulfuric acid, the chromic acid, and the iron present in a solution containing sulfuric acid, chromic acid, and ferric sulfate. Give formulas for calculating the results for each.

13. A volumetric analysis can be conducted without a set of weights if a buret and a balance are available. Show how this can be done, illustrating with the analysis of a solid acid for the per cent of replaceable hydrogen. It is assumed also that primary-standard acids are available.

14. Potassium tetraoxalate, $KH_3(C_2O_4)_2 \cdot 2H_2O$, was used as a primary standard for determining the strength of a potassium hydroxide solution. A sample weighing 0.9000 g. required 45.0 ml. for titration to the phenolphthalein end-point. Calculate the normality of the potassium hydroxide solution.

15. Fuming sulfuric acid (oleum) is concentrated sulfuric acid in which sulfur trioxide has been dissolved. The total SO_3 in such an acid is determined by diluting a weighed sample with water and titrating with standard alkali. In one such analysis the following data was obtained: weight of sample, 1.0000 g.; volume of 0.5000 N sodium hydroxide required, 42.65 ml. Calculate the per cent of the SO_3 in the acid.

16. One of the disadvantages of oxalic acid, $H_2C_2O_4 \cdot 2H_2O$, as a primary standard is that it contains water of crystallization which is lost or gained depending on the water content of the air to which it is exposed. For example, a specimen of oxalic acid from a bottle of reagent-grade material weighing 1.2250 g. required 80.0 ml. of 0.2500 N sodium hydroxide for titration, phenolphthalein being used as indicator. Calculate the apparent number of molecules of water of crystallization in the acid assuming it to be otherwise pure. The theoretical value is 2 molecules of water of crystallization. Decide if the normality of a potassium hydroxide solution would be high or low if standardized with this material on the assumption that it consisted of $H_2C_2O_4 \cdot 2H_2O$.

17. A sample of a pure organic acid weighing 0.5310 g. on a porcelain boat was placed in a tube, and dry ammonia gas was passed over it. The material gained 0.0415 g. in weight. Calculate the equivalent weight of the acid.

DISPLACEMENT TITRATIONS; THE TITRATION OF SODIUM CARBONATE

Strong acids react with the salts of very weak acids to liberate the weak acid. The reaction goes to completion because a very slightly ionized compound (the weak acid) is formed. Such reactions are called displacement reactions; they can be carried out as quantitative titrations if an indicator is available which is not converted to its acid color by the very weak acid but is converted by the first excess of the standard strong acid. In a similar manner the salts of very weak bases can be titrated with a strong base. Displacement titrations of this type constitute an important phase of volumetric analysis.

Carbonic acid is a typical very weak acid, and its salts can be determined by a displacement titration with hydrochloric acid. In fact, both replaceable hydrogen atoms of carbonic acid are so weakly ionized that both the normal and acid salts can be so titrated, $K_1 = 4.47 \times 10^{-7}$ and $K_2 = 5.62 \times 10^{-11}$. This is especially useful because sodium carbonate and sodium bicarbonate are important items of commerce and because sodium carbonate can be obtained in sufficient purity for use as a primary standard in determining the strength of standard solutions of strong acids.

The titration of sodium carbonate with hydrochloric acid actually takes place in two stages, owing to the great difference in the values of the two ionization constants of carbonic acid:

$$Na_2CO_3 + HCl = NaHCO_3 + NaCl$$

$$NaHCO_3 + HCl = H_2CO_3 + NaCl$$

At the end of the first step sodium bicarbonate is present and the pH of the solution is about 8.3. The sodium chloride present is strictly neutral, being the salt of a strong acid and a strong base. Sodium bicarbonate, however, is the salt of a strong base and a weak acid and hydrolyzes giving the solution an alkaline reaction. As the titration is continued the bicarbonate is converted to carbonic acid, and at the close of the second stage of the titration the solution contains only sodium chloride and carbonic acid. During the latter part of the titration the carbonic acid begins to break down into water and carbon dioxide. The entire picture can perhaps be understood more readily from the titration curve given in Fig. 57.

As will be seen from the titration curve phenolphthalein functions as a suitable indicator for the first stage of the titration. The endpoint is none too sharp, as might be expected for an acid as weak as

10^{-7}. At the equivalence-point of the second stage the solution is saturated with carbon dioxide; the pH of such a solution is 3.8. This falls in the pH region in which methyl orange changes color. The color change is not very sharp. The titration curve at the end-point is not perfectly vertical but slopes through the methyl orange band,

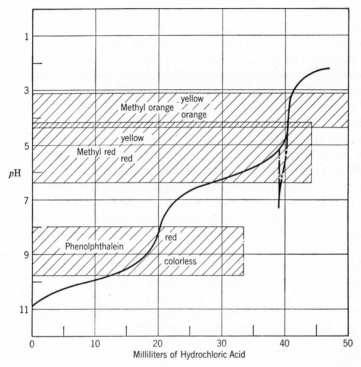

Fig. 57. Titration of sodium carbonate with hydrochloric acid. Taken: 20.0 ml. of 0.1000 N sodium carbonate; titrated with 0.0988 N hydrochloric acid.

which means that an appreciable volume of acid must be added to change the pH from the point where the color begins to change to the pH at which the indicator has been converted to the other color. In a case like this it is best to prepare a buffer solution having a pH corresponding to the equivalence-point, to add the same amount of indicator to it, and to titrate the solution until the colors match. A solution having a pH of about 4.0 can be prepared by dissolving 1.0 g. of potassium acid phthalate in 100 ml. of water.

An inspection of the titration curve of sodium carbonate with hydrochloric acid shows that methyl red cannot be used as indicator in the titration; indeed, methyl red is completely converted to its acid form before the end-point is reached. A satisfactory end-point with methyl red can be obtained by removing the carbon dioxide from the solution. The titration is stopped when the methyl red has turned to the red, acid form and the titration is just short of the equivalence-point; the carbon dioxide is removed from the solution either by boiling or by vigorous shaking,[1] and the titration is continued. On removal of the carbon dioxide the pH rises as shown by the dotted line in Fig. 57 and the indicator changes back to the alkaline form, a small amount of bicarbonate still being present. The buffering action of the carbon dioxide having been removed, the pH drops sharply on continuing the titration, giving a good end-point with methyl red.

Procedure for the Determination of Sodium Oxide in Sodium Carbonate. Methyl Orange Method. Dry the material for analysis in the oven for at least 2 hours at 110°. Weigh accurately three samples of 0.25 to 0.35 g., transferring the samples to 250-ml. conical flasks. Dissolve each sample in 150 ml. of water. Add 2 to 3 drops of methyl orange solution. Prepare a comparison buffer of pH 4 by dissolving 1.0 g. of potassium acid phthalate, $KHC_8H_4O_4$, in 100 ml. of water; add to it the same volume of indicator solution. Titrate with 0.1 N hydrochloric acid until the color of the indicator matches that of the comparison buffer.

The hydrochloric acid solution may be standardized in a similar manner by titrating a sample of primary-standard sodium carbonate. The weight taken for each sample should be between 0.20 and 0.25 g.

The results of the sodium carbonate titration are usually reported as per cent sodium oxide. The milliequivalent weight is 0.031,00, that is, $Na_2O/2000$, since 2 replaceable hydrogen atoms are involved in the titration.

Procedure for the Determination of Sodium Oxide in Sodium Carbonate. Methyl Red Method. Dry the material for analysis in the oven at 110° for at least 2 hours. Weigh exactly into 250-ml. conical flasks three samples of 0.25 to 0.35 g. Dissolve each sample in about 125 ml. of water. Add 2 or 3 drops of methyl red, and titrate with 0.1 N hydro-

---

[1] Equilibrium in the reaction $H_2CO_3 \rightleftharpoons H_2O + CO_2$ is obtained rather slowly. Shaking or boiling the solution hastens the process by removing the carbon dioxide formed. This same problem arises in the animal body, efficiency demanding that the carbonic acid liberated from the hemoglobin of the blood be broken down rapidly so that the carbon dioxide can be released in the lungs and carried away by the exhaled air. There is present in the blood a zinc-protein material called *carbonic acid anhydrase* which greatly catalyzes the reaction. The expulsion of carbon dioxide is thus brought about in the animal body without boiling or even vigorous agitation.

chloric acid. The indicator changes color gradually. When it has a pronounced red color, add 1 ml. more of hydrochloric acid. Discontinue the titration and remove the carbon dioxide from the solution by one of the following two methods.

a. Heat the solution to boiling and continue to boil gently for 3 or 4 minutes. The indicator will turn back to the yellow, alkaline form as the pH rises. Cool the solution to room temperature.

b. Swirl the flask vigorously for about three rotations in one direction, then sharply reverse the direction for three swirls. Continue this reverse swirling for 2 minutes, making the swirling as vigorous as possible without spattering any of the solution from the flask. There is relatively little carbon dioxide in the atmosphere, and vigorous agitation rapidly brings the carbon dioxide out of the solution. The indicator should turn to its yellow form during this operation.

After expelling the carbon dioxide from the solution, continue the titration with 0.1 N hydrochloric acid until the acid color is restored. The color change should now be very sharp. If more than 4 or 5 drops are needed, repeat the treatment to expel carbon dioxide and then complete the titration.

Report the per cent of sodium oxide in the sample; the milliequivalent weight is $Na_2O/2000$ or 0.031,00.

Analysis of Mixtures of Carbonate and Hydroxide. A simple method for the analysis of a mixture of sodium carbonate and sodium hydroxide is possible because of the great difference in the values of the first and second ionization constants of carbonic acid. As shown in Fig. 57, the titration of carbonate proceeds in two steps, the first being practically complete at a pH of 9 without the second reaction having occurred to a significant extent. If a mixture of sodium hydroxide and sodium carbonate is titrated to the phenolphthalein end-point, the carbonate is converted to bicarbonate and the hydroxide neutralized completely

$$Na_2CO_3 + HCl = NaHCO_3 + NaCl$$

$$NaOH + HCl = NaCl + H_2O$$

Because the phenolphthalein is colorless on the acid side a second indicator may now be added and the titration continued, converting the bicarbonate formed in the first titration to carbonic acid. The end-point may be determined with either methyl orange or methyl red (removal of carbon dioxide) as described in the preceding section.

The amount of sodium carbonate in the sample may be calculated from the number of milliliters of standard acid used in the second titration, the equivalent weight being equal to the molecular weight since only 1 hydrogen atom was involved in converting the bicarbonate to carbonic acid. An equal volume of standard acid was used in the first titration to convert the carbonate to bicarbonate. The volume actually used minus this volume, then, is the volume required to neutralize the sodium hydroxide in the sample.

Procedure for the Determination of Carbonate and Hydroxide in a Mixture. Weigh a sample of such size that it will require about 40 ml. of 0.1 N hydrochloric acid. This requires a preliminary guess as to the total alkaline materials present. For example, if the sodium hydroxide plus the sodium carbonate are estimated to be 80 per cent, all the material may be assumed to be sodium hydroxide; then 40 ml. of 0.1 N HCl is equivalent to $(40)(0.1)(0.040)$, or 0.16 g. of sodium hydroxide; a sample $0.16/0.8 = 0.20$ g. would then be taken. Dissolve the sample in 125 ml. of water, add a few drops of phenolphthalein solution, and titrate with standard hydrochloric acid until the pink color of the indicator just fades. Read the buret. Add methyl orange or methyl red and continue the titration as described under the determination of sodium carbonate, methyl orange method, page 216, or methyl red method, page 216. Calculate the sodium carbonate in the sample, using the number of milliliters taken between the first and second end-points. The equivalent weight is equal to the molecular weight, Na_2CO_3. Subtract this volume from the total volume taken to reach the first end-point and use the difference to calculate the amount of sodium hydroxide in the sample.

Analysis of Mixtures of Carbonate and Bicarbonate. A solution containing both sodium carbonate and sodium bicarbonate will react alkaline and have a pH above 8.3, the pH of a solution of bicarbonate alone. On the titration of such a mixture with hydrochloric acid, the carbonate is first converted to bicarbonate, phenolphthalein being used as indicator. Thus, at the phenolphthalein end-point bicarbonate from two sources is present: that originally present and that derived from the carbonate. On continuing the titration with standard acid, using methyl orange as indicator or carbon dioxide removal and methyl red indicator, all the bicarbonate is converted to carbonic acid. The volume used in the second titration is greater than that used in the first by an amount equivalent to the bicarbonate originally present in the sample; that is, the same amount of standard acid is required to convert the bicarbonate formed to carbonic acid as is required to convert the carbonate to the bicarbonate. Thus, two titrations on one sample give the carbonate and the bicarbonate content.

Procedure for the Determination of Carbonate and Bicarbonate in a Mixture. Weigh a sample of approximately 0.4 g. Dissolve the material in about 125 ml. of water, add 2 or 3 drops of phenolphthalein solution, and titrate the mixture with standard hydrochloric acid to the point where the pink color of the indicator just fades. Continue the titration using methyl orange or methyl red as indicator and employing a buffer and color comparison with methyl orange, as described on page 216, or the carbon dioxide removal technique with methyl red, page 216. Calculate the amount of sodium carbonate in the sample from the volume of acid used in reaching the first end-point; the milliequivalent weight is 0.1060. Calculate the amount of bicarbonate in the sample, using the volume obtained by subtracting the volume to the phenolphthalein (first) end-point from the volume required to pass from the first to the second end-point. The milliequivalent weight is $NaHCO_3/1000$, 0.084,00.

PROBLEMS

1. Determine which pairs of the four chemicals carbonic acid, sodium hydroxide, sodium carbonate, and sodium bicarbonate could exist in solution. Tell why the other pairs are impossible. Give the pH range in which each of the possible pairs would fall.

2. Sketch the titration curve of a mixture of sodium carbonate and sodium bicarbonate with hydrochloric acid, showing (*a*) what is present at each point or region of the curve; (*b*) where buffer mixtures are present during the titration; (*c*) end-points, and the pH bands of indicators used; (*d*) the volumes of hydrochloric acid used for the various steps; and (*e*) formulas for calculating the results.

3. A solution was known to contain two of the following chemicals: sodium carbonate, sodium hydroxide, and sodium bicarbonate. A 10.000-g. sample was titrated with 0.1000 N hydrochloric acid, 25.0 ml. being required to reach the phenolphthalein end-point and 15.0 ml. being required to pass from the phenolphthalein end-point to the methyl orange end-point. Tell what mixture was present and calculate the per cent of each component.

4. Calculate the per cent of sodium carbonate and sodium bicarbonate present in a mixture of the two that also contains inert material. A sample weighing 0.4000 g. required 30.0 ml. of 0.1000 N acid for titration to the phenolphthalein end-point and 40.0 ml. more for titration to the methyl orange end-point.

5. A sample weighing 1.0000 g. containing sodium hydroxide, sodium carbonate, and inert material was titrated with 0.1000 N acid to the phenolphthalein end-point, 100 ml. being required. The titration was then continued, using methyl orange as indicator, 20.0 ml. more being required. Calculate the per cent of sodium hydroxide and of sodium carbonate in the sample.

6. A mixture of 1.000 g. of sodium hydroxide and 1.000 g. of sodium bicarbonate was dissolved in water. Calculate the amount of 0.1000 N acid or 0.1000 N base required to bring the solution to the phenolphthalein end-point.

7. A 100-ml. sample of well water was titrated with 0.02 N sulfuric acid to the methyl orange end-point, 45.0 ml. being required. Calculate (*a*) the per cent of

calcium bicarbonate in the water, and (b) the milligrams per liter (parts per million) of calcium bicarbonate in the water.

8. A modified method of analyzing a sodium hydroxide-sodium carbonate mixture consists in precipitating the carbonate by the addition of barium chloride; barium carbonate is very insoluble, and the hydroxide remaining in the solution may be titrated directly. The total alkalinity is determined on a second sample by titrating directly to the methyl orange end-point. In such an analysis two 1.0000-g. samples were taken. After the addition of barium chloride the first sample required 35.0 ml. of 0.2500 N hydrochloric acid for titration to the phenolphthalein end-point. The second titration required 62.0 ml. of 0.2500 N acid for titration to the methyl orange end-point. Calculate the per cent of sodium hydroxide and of sodium carbonate in the sample.

9. Calculate the loss in weight of 1.0000 g. of pure sodium bicarbonate on conversion to sodium carbonate at 300°, the reaction being $2NaHCO_3 = Na_2CO_3 + H_2O + CO_2$. Calculate the volume of 1.000 N sodium hydroxide which will accomplish the same purpose.

10. Commercial sodium carbonate is sold on the basis of its sodium oxide content as determined by titration. Calculate the theoretical percentage of sodium oxide in (a) soda ash (anhydrous sodium carbonate), (b) crystalline sodium carbonate ($Na_2CO_3 \cdot H_2O$), (c) washing soda ($Na_2CO_3 \cdot 10H_2O$), and (d) sodium bicarbonate.

11. In September of 1949 a gusher was struck 34 miles north of Rock Springs in southwestern Wyoming at a depth of 467 ft. It delivers a 5 per cent solution of nearly pure trona, a mixture of sodium carbonate and sodium bicarbonate, at the rate of 10,000 bbl. per day (Chem. Eng. News, 27, 2938, Oct. 10, 1949). Tell how to determine the exact amount of each salt in the solution. State what size samples to take, what concentration of standard solutions to use, and what indicators to employ. Tell what additional information is needed in order to calculate the pounds of each material delivered per day.

THE DETERMINATION OF NITROGEN BY THE KJELDAHL METHOD

One of the important chemical constituents of plant and animal life is protein, a complex organic material containing carbon, nitrogen, oxygen, hydrogen, and sometimes other elements such as sulfur, phosphorus, and certain metals. Most, but not all, of the nitrogen in protein is present as the amino group $—NH_2$, in which the nitrogen is

attached to the carbon atom, $—\overset{|}{\underset{|}{C}}—NH_2$. This may be considered as

ammonia with 1 hydrogen replaced by carbon. The nitrogen is thus in its lowest valence state, -3. When such material is heated with concentrated sulfuric acid, the organic material is destroyed, the carbon being oxidized to carbon dioxide and the amino nitrogen being converted to ammonium acid sulfate. When hot and concentrated, sulfuric acid acts as an oxidizing agent:

$$H_2SO_4 = SO_2 + H_2O + [O]$$

$$\overset{\displaystyle |}{\underset{\displaystyle |}{-C}}-NH_2 + H_2SO_4 = CO_2 + (NH_4)_2SO_4 + SO_2$$

The oxidation is accompanied by extensive dehydration and consequent carbonization of the organic material. In the Kjeldahl method advantage is taken of this to eliminate the organic material and to fix the nitrogen as ammonium sufate, thus converting it to a form in which it can be readily determined. The determination itself consists in making the residue from the sulfuric acid digestion highly alkaline with sodium hydroxide (a "fixed" or non-volatile alkali) and distilling off the ammonia so liberated $(NH_4)_2SO_4 + 2NaOH = 2NH_3 + Na_2SO_4 + 2H_2O$ into a measured excess of standard hydrochloric acid. The excess of hydrochloric acid is then back-titrated with standard sodium hydroxide:

$$NH_3 + HCl = NH_4Cl$$

$$HCl + NaOH = NaCl + H_2O$$

Although the back titration consists of the neutralization of a strong acid with a strong base, the ammonium chloride present hydrolyzes, making the solution acid, or in effect making the titration one of a strong acid being neutralized by a weak base, ammonia. At the end-point, therefore, the solution is not neutral but acid and an indicator changing color on the acid side must be used; methyl red, changing over the pH range of 4.2 to 6.4, is very suitable for the purpose.

The decomposition of organic matter by sulfuric acid is often very slow. The addition of a considerable quantity (10 g.) of potassium sulfate or sodium sulfate to the digestion mixture helps speed the process by raising the boiling point of the sulfuric acid. Various catalysts have also been proposed to accelerate the digestion; of these, copper sulfate, various compounds of mercury, and selenium have been commonly used. One of the most effective catalysts is copper selenite, $CuSeO_3 \cdot 2H_2O$; only a small amount, 0.3 g., is required, and for most nitrogenous materials it is so effective that the addition of potassium sulfate is not necessary, which is a good thing as its absence makes the subsequent distillation much smoother. When mercury is used as the catalyst it is necessary to add sodium sulfide or sodium thiosulfate before the distillation to precipitate the mercury and to decompose mercury compounds which do not yield their ammonia during the distillation.

The nitrogen in ammonium salts can be determined by this procedure, but obviously the digestion with sulfuric acid is not necessary in this case. Nitrogen in its higher valence forms (for example, in hydrazine, N_2H_4 (valence -2); hydroxylamine, NH_2OH (valence -1); nitrite, NO_2^- (valence -3); and NO_3^- (valence -5)) will not yield an ammonium salt to which the distillation procedure can be applied unless the nitrogen is first reduced to its lowest valence. In the case of nitrate this reduction can be effected by heating the material in a basic solution with Devarda's alloy, an alloy having the composition 5 per cent zinc, 45 per cent aluminum, and 50 per cent copper; the ammonia is distilled off during the reduction, collected in standard acid, and determined as described above.

Inorganic nitrates and some organic compounds can be handled by a modified digestion procedure in which sulfuric acid containing salicylic acid is used for the digestion and sodium thiosulfate is added after the digestion has proceeded for a time. Other organic compounds require more strenuous reduction, for example, with metallic zinc or stannous chloride in hydrochloric acid.

In many types of organic compounds, even in certain types of protein, the nitrogen is not present as amino nitrogen but in a more complex union with carbon or in a higher plex union with carbon or in a higher valence form which does not yield ammonium sulfate on digestion with sulfuric acid. In some cases reduction with Devarda's alloy is effective but in others the procedure must be quite extensively modified; treatises on physiological chemistry discuss many of these unusual cases.

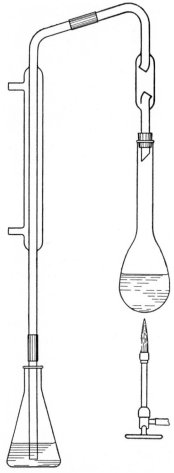

Fig. 58. Distillation apparatus for the Kjeldahl determination of nitrogen.

The digestion and distillation are usually carried out in a flask with an elongated neck. This serves to separate the sodium hydroxide which is carried along in the spray during the distillation. A distillation trap, such as that shown in Fig. 58, is also employed to further remove the fixed alkali from the gas stream. The condenser used may be an ordinary straight-tube glass condenser with jacket for the passage of cooling water. Commercial Kjeldahl distillation racks on which a large number of distillations can be carried out simultaneously have condensers made of tin or stainless steel. During the distillation, the alkaline mixture has a great tendency to bump, particularly if potassium sulfate was added to the digestion mixture. The addition of two or three pieces of mossy zinc, which dissolve in the sodium hydroxide liberating a stream of bubbles of hydrogen, promotes smooth boiling and minimizes this bumping.

More consistent results are obtained starting the digestion with the dilute sulfuric acid (1:1) mixture recommended below than by the more common procedure of starting the digestion with concentrated sulfuric acid.

Procedure for the Determination of Nitrogen by the Kjeldahl Method. Weigh samples of 0.5 to 0.7 g. of the material on pieces of filter paper, fold the paper neatly into a ball, and drop the folded paper and sample into a 500-ml. Kjeldahl flask. The use of the filter paper makes it possible to get the entire sample to the bottom of the flask without the troublesome adherence of a portion of the sample to the upper walls of the long neck of the flask. Add 50 ml. of dilute sulfuric acid (1:1) and 0.3 g. of cupric selenite. Heat the mixture to a gentle boil. Carry this out on the Kjeldahl digestion rack where provision is made for the removal of fumes, or, if a rack is not available, in a good hood. Continue the digestion until the black carbonaceous deposit first formed has been oxidized and the solution is a clear light blue owing to the copper present. If the mixture froths badly during the early part of the digestion it may be necessary to turn the burner down for a time. Cool the mixture and dilute it with 100 ml. of water, adding the water gradually with shaking.

While the mixture is cooling to room temperature rinse out the distillation apparatus, the trap, the condenser, and the lower delivery tube. Place exactly 50.0 ml. of standard 0.1 N hydrochloric acid in the receiving flask and place in position so that the lower delivery tube extends just below the surface of the acid solution. With great care, add 100 ml. of a 40 per cent solution of sodium hydroxide to the Kjeldahl flask while holding the flask in an inclined position so that the thick alkali solution slowly runs down to the bottom and forms a separate layer without mixing. Drop in a piece of litmus paper and two or three pieces of mossy zinc. Connect the flask to the distillation trap, and cause the two layers in the Kjeldahl flask to mix by gently shaking the flask. Do not allow this mixing to take place too rapidly as the heat evolved may generate sufficient steam to blow out the stopper and project the mixture out of the flask. Immediately after the mixing has been completed light the burner and heat the mixture to boiling. Watch that hydrochloric acid is not sucked from the receiving flask up into the condenser during the mixing and heating. Boil the mixture at such a rate that water (and the ammonia) distills over but not so fast that condensed water accumulates in the trap.

Continue the distillation until about two-thirds of the liquid in the flask has been distilled over and a dark gray sludge of copper hydroxide and sodium sulfate has settled out. Disconnect the delivery tube, leaving it in the flask, and turn off the burner. After the mixture has cooled somewhat but while it is still hot pour the contents of the distillation flask into a bowl full of water in the sink. If the residue from the distillation is allowed to cool in the flask it will solidify and may crack the flask. Finally, rinse and remove the delivery tube and back-titrate the excess hydrochloric acid with standard 0.1 N sodium hydroxide using methyl red as indicator. The milliequivalent weight of nitrogen in this analysis is 0.0140.

PROBLEMS

1. A sample of feed weighing 1.0000 g. was analyzed for nitrogen by the Kjeldahl method. A volume of 50.0 ml. of 0.1000 N hydrochloric acid was placed in the receiver; the excess required for back titration 25.0 ml. of 0.1550 N sodium hydroxide. Calculate the per cent of nitrogen in the sample.

2. A solution containing both sodium and ammonium hydroxides was analyzed as follows: A 10.000-g. sample was titrated to the methyl red end-point, a volume of 45.0 ml. of 0.1500 N hydrochloric acid being required. A second sample weighing 15.000 g. was treated with an excess of sodium hydroxide and the ammonia distilled over into a receiver containing 50.0 ml. of 0.1500 N hydrochloric acid; the excess acid required 25.0 ml. of 0.1250 N sodium hydroxide for back titration to the methyl red end-point. Calculate the per cent of sodium hydroxide and of ammonia (NH_3) in the sample.

3. The nitrate in a sample of crude sodium nitrate weighing 1.000 g. was reduced to ammonia with metallic zinc and distilled from a strong sodium hydroxide solution into 100 ml. of 0.1000 N acid. The excess acid required 10.0 ml. of 0.1000 N sodium hydroxide for back titration to the methyl red end-point. Calculate the per cent of sodium nitrate in the sample.

4. Given a buret which is calibrated from 50.0 ml. at the top to 0 ml. at the bottom, devise a factor weight-factor normality scheme for the Kjeldahl method such that the buret reading multiplied by 0.1 gives the per cent of nitrogen in the sample. *Suggestion:* use a 1.4000-g. sample.

5. Calculate the number of milliliters of 0.2000 N hydrochloric acid equivalent to the nitrogen in 1.000 g. of glycine, $H_2NCH_2CO_2H$, as determined in the Kjeldahl method.

6. A 10.000-g. sample of a solution containing sulfuric acid and nitric acid was neutralized to the phenolphthalein end-point by the addition of 40.0 ml. of 0.1000 N sodium hydroxide. The nitrate in another 10.000-g. sample was reduced to ammonia and the ammonia distilled into 50.0 ml. of 0.1000 N hydrochloric acid; 45.0 ml. of 0.1000 N sodium hydroxide was required for the back titration. Calculate the per cent of each acid in the sample.

CHAPTER 10

The Theory of Oxidation-Reduction Reactions

The term *oxidation* was originally used to cover the reactions in which substances combined with oxygen. As the concept of valence was worked out the term became more generally used to include all reactions in which the valence state of a material is raised irrespective of whether or not oxygen is involved. The term *reduction* is similarly used to cover those reactions in which the valence is lowered. Thus, the conversion of ferric iron to ferrous iron by trivalent titanium

$$Fe^{+3} + Ti^{+3} = Fe^{++} + Ti^{+4}$$

is an oxidation-reduction reaction, the ferric iron being reduced and the trivalent titanium ion oxidized. Whenever oxidation occurs reduction must also occur in an equivalent amount. This is the basic principle in balancing oxidation-reduction equations.

OXIDATION NUMBER AND BALANCING OXIDATION-REDUCTION EQUATIONS

For most work the valences of the substances involved provide sufficient information for balancing oxidation-reduction equations. In a few cases the apparent valence comes out a fractional number rather than a whole number and it appears sounder to speak of this as *oxidation number* rather than valence, for it is difficult to conceive of a valence as anything but a whole number. The oxidation number of an element which occurs twice in a formula is twice the valence; for example, in $K_2Cr_2O_7$ the valence of chromium is 6 but the oxidation number is 12. A few simple rules suffice for determining oxidation number:

The oxidation number of elements in the free or elemental state is 0, for example, in the gases: H_2, O_2, Cl_2, N_2, and in the metals: Na^0, Cu^0, Fe^0.

The oxidation number of hydrogen and the alkali metals, Li^+, Na^+, K^+, in compounds is always $+1$.

The oxidation number of oxygen in compounds is always -2, except in hydrogen peroxide in which it is -1.

The sum of all of the oxidation numbers in a compound must equal 0, or, if the substance is an ion, the total must equal the charge on the ion. For example:

H_2O	KCl	K_2SO_4	$Na_2S_2O_3$
$2H = +2$	$K = +1$	$2K = +2$	$2Na = +2$
$O = -2$	$Cl = -1$	$S = +6$	$2S = +4$
		$4O = -8$	$3O = -6$

$SO_4^=$	NH_4^+	$(NH_4)_2SO_4$	
$S = +6$	$N = -3$	$2N = -6$	$S = +6$
$4O = -8$	$4H = +4$	$8H = +8$	$4O = -8$

In balancing oxidation-reduction reactions the fundamental rule is that the total increase in oxidation number must equal the total decrease. Often the change in oxidation number of the material being oxidized will not equal the change in oxidation number of the material being reduced. By simply multiplying one by the other the total increase can be made to equal the total decrease. Thus, to balance the equation $FeCl_3 + SnCl_2 = FeCl_2 + SnCl_4$ the changes in oxidation number are: Fe (3 to 2) change -1; Sn (2 to 4) change $+2$. By multiplying the number of iron atoms by two, the total decrease in oxidation number will equal the increase: $2FeCl_3 + SnCl_2 = 2FeCl_2 + SnCl_4$. In the balanced equation the number of atoms of each kind on each side of the equation must be equal, 2 Fe, 1 Sn, and 8 Cl in this case.

When oxygen-containing acids are involved in the reduction, water and acid are also included in the reaction, as in the oxidation of ferrous iron by dichromate in a sulfuric acid solution

$$FeSO_4 + K_2Cr_2O_7 = Fe_2(SO_4)_3 + K_2SO_4 + Cr_2(SO_4)_3$$

The changes in oxidation number are Fe (2 to 3) $+1$, 2 Cr (12 to 6) -6. Six molecules of ferrous sulfate must be taken so that the total increase in oxidation number will equal the decrease. The next step in balancing the equation is then to write all the products using the ratio $6:1$:

$$6FeSO_4 + K_2Cr_2O_7 = 3Fe_2(SO_4)_3 + K_2SO_4 + Cr_2(SO_4)_3$$

Thirteen sulfate ions appear on the right, only 6 on the left, so that

7 molecules of sulfuric acid must be added. The hydrogen atoms form water:

$$6FeSO_4 + K_2Cr_2O_7 + 7H_2SO_4 = 3Fe_2(SO_4)_3 + K_2SO_4$$

$$+ Cr_2(SO_4)_3 + 7H_2O$$

As a final check the numbers of oxygen atoms on both sides should be the same, and they are, as written.

A few special cases arise, particularly with sulfur and carbon, the elements which combine with themselves. The oxidation numbers of these elements in some of their compounds often turn out to be rather surprising numbers, for example:

Sodium Oxalate $Na_2C_2O_4$		Sodium Formate $NaCHO_2$		Sodium Thio-sulfate $Na_2S_2O_3$		Sodium Acetate $NaC_2H_3O_2$		Ethyl Alcohol C_2H_5OH		Sodium Tetra-thionate $Na_2S_4O_6$	
2Na	+2	Na	+1	2Na	+2	Na	+1	6H	+6	2Na	+ 2
4O	−8	H	+1	3O	−6	3H	+3	O	−2	6O	−12
2C	+6	2O	−4	2S	+4	2O	−4	2C	−4	4S	+10
		C	+2			2C	0				

By using the total change in oxidation number, the equations can always be balanced. For example, on treatment with potassium permanganate in acid solution, oxalic acid is oxidized to carbon dioxide in which the oxidation number of the carbon is 4 and the total change per molecule of oxalic acid is from 6 to 8, or 2; the manganese is reduced from oxidation number 7 to 2; and therefore the equation is balanced using the ratio 5:2:

$$5Na_2C_2O_4 + 2KMnO_4 + 8H_2SO_4 = 5Na_2SO_4 + K_2SO_4 + 2MnSO_4$$

$$+10CO_2 + 8H_2O$$

When both carbon and sulfur are present in the compound the change in oxidation number can be thrown entirely on one element or the other. In the oxidation of carbon disulfide to carbon dioxide and sulfuric acid $CS_2 \rightarrow CO_2 + H_2SO_4$ there is a change of 16 in the oxidation number and it is immaterial which way the oxidation number is determined. The final oxidation number of the carbon is +4, the final oxidation number of the sulfur is 12, and the total is 16. The oxidation numbers in the carbon disulfide may be considered

$$
\begin{array}{lllll}
CS_2 & & & CO_2 + 2H_2SO_4 & \\
C & +4 & \text{giving} & C & +4 & \\
S & -4 & & S & +12 & \text{change} = 16
\end{array}
$$

or as

$$
\begin{array}{lllll}
CS_2 & & & CO_2 + 2H_2SO_4 & \\
C & -12 & \text{giving} & C & +4 & \\
S & +12 & & S & +12 & \text{change} = 16
\end{array}
$$

If the oxidizing agent used is potassium bromate the oxidation number of which changes from $+5$ to -1, or by 6, the final equation is balanced by taking 6 molecules of carbon disulfide and 16 of potassium bromate.

$$6CS_2 + 16KBrO_3 + 12H_2O = 6CO_2 + 12H_2SO_4 + 16KBr$$

Occasionally a reaction is encountered in which two elements in the same molecule are oxidized, or even one oxidized and one reduced. The total or net change is then computed with due regard to the ratios in which the elements occur in the compound. In potassium cobalti-nitrite, $K_3Co(NO_2)_6$, the cobalt and each nitrogen have an oxidation number of $+3$; on treatment with potassium permanganate in an acid solution the cobalt is reduced to the bivalent state and the nitrogen is oxidized to nitrate, in which the nitrogen has an oxidation number of $+5$. The net effect is $-1 + 6(5 - 3) = +11$, and the equation is balanced using 5 molecules of potassium cobaltinitrite and 11 molecules of potassium permanganate:

$$5K_3Co(NO_2)_6 + 11KMnO_4 + 29H_2SO_4 = 13K_2SO_4 + 5CoSO_4$$

$$+11MnSO_4 + 30HNO_3 + 14H_2O$$

In the balanced equation the numbers of oxygen atoms on each side of the equation are equal.

ELECTROCHEMICAL THEORY

Whenever two different substances come into contact an electrical potential is set up. In the case of two metals this phenomenon is known as the Seebeck effect, and in the form of wires of two different metals is known as a thermocouple and is extensively used to measure temperature. When two different liquids touch each other or a liquid comes in contact with a solid, an electrical potential is set up at the surface of contact, but here it is not as easy to measure the potential as in the case of two metals touching each other, where the metals may be made into wires and these wires led off to a voltmeter.

The potential set up where a metal comes in contact with a solution can only be measured by making a second electrical contact with the solution, that is, by introducing a second metal. A second potential is created at the surface of contact of the second metal and the solution. A voltmeter attached to the two metals will then read the difference of the two potentials. No way exists of measuring one alone, and therefore it becomes necessary to establish an arbitrary zero to which to refer all others. The normal hydrogen electrode is chosen for this purpose.

By the term *single electrode potential* is meant the electrical potential set up at the surface of a metal in contact with a liquid. Two single electrode potentials set up in the same solution constitute an electrolytic cell. The origin of the single electrode potential is the tendency of the metal to dissolve in the liquid to form the ion of the metal and to free an electron. Thus, metallic zinc dissolves, forming Zn^{++} and liberating 2 electrons. The electrons collect on the metallic zinc, giving it a negative charge, but the process soon stops because there is no way for the charge to be carried away. This tendency for the metal to dissolve and impart a charge to the metal differs from one metal to another and is measured quantitatively by so-called *standard reduction potential*, E^0, which determines the position of the metal in the electromotive series.

Thus, wherever a single electrode potential is developed, two forms of an element are present: the oxidized form and the reduced form, and these are related by a more or less simple reaction involving electrons; thus

$$Ag^+ + e^- = Ag^0$$
$$Fe^{+3} + e^- = Fe^{++}$$
$$Cu^{++} + 2e^- = Cu^0$$
$$H^+ + e^- = \tfrac{1}{2}H_2$$
$$Zn^{++} + 2e^- = Zn^0$$
$$Na^+ + e^- = Na^0$$
$$AsO_4^{-3} + 2H^+ + 2e^- = AsO_3^{-3} + H_2O$$
$$CuCl_3^{=} + e^- = Cu^0 + 3Cl^-$$

Such pairs are referred to as *oxidation-reduction couples*. Half-cell reactions of the kind just written, that is, reactions involving the electron, e^-, must balance both chemically and electrically, the electron having a negligible mass but carrying a single, negative charge.

For the arbitrary zero which must be set up in order to have a point to which to refer the various single electrode potentials, the normal hydrogen electrode is used. Hydrogen gas has the remarkable property of dissolving in platinum, and a considerable quantity of hydrogen is taken up by a platinum foil covered with finely divided, spongy, metallic platinum (so-called *platinum black*, easily made by depositing the platinum electrolytically). Platinum itself is quite inert, and when charged with hydrogen acts essentially as a metallic hydrogen electrode. The potential of such an electrode dipping into a solution 1.000 N in hydrogen ions is taken as the arbitrary zero of the electromotive series. The hydrogen electrode is usually made up in the form shown in Fig. 59.

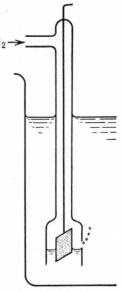

Fig. 59. Hydrogen electrode.

The potentials of all other electrodes or oxidation-reduction couples are referred to the hydrogen electrode taken arbitrarily as zero. The values of E^0, the standard reduction potential, for a few couples are given in Table 2 on page 20 and many more in the more extensive table, on page 236, Table 17.

The sign given the electrode potential of a given oxidation-reduction couple depends on which side of the arbitrary zero (normal hydrogen electrode) the system lies and also on the way in which the electrode reaction is written. Thus, for the zinc ion-metallic zinc couple, written as a reduction, the electrode potential is negative (reduction potential),

$$Zn^{++} + 2e^- = Zn^0 \qquad E^0_{Zn^{++}, Zn^0} = -0.762 \text{ volt}$$

but if written as an oxidation reaction the electrode potential is positive (oxidation potential),

$$Zn^0 = Zn^{++} + 2e^- \qquad E^0_{Zn^0, Zn^{++}} = +0.762 \text{ volt}$$

These are two entirely equivalent ways of expressing the same thing. It is perhaps more convenient to think in terms of reduction potentials, for the sign given zinc is negative, corresponding to the actual electric charge zinc acquires when used in electrolytic cells with other common metals such as copper or mercury.

Any combination of two single electrode potentials produces a potential which can be measured or made to supply useful electrical work. Thus, the Daniell cell, Fig. 60, consists of metallic zinc dipping into a solution of zinc sulfate and metallic copper dipping into a solution of copper sulfate; the solutions must be in contact with each other, but for practical purposes they are kept from mixing by a porous membrane or by a difference in specific gravity.

In the Daniell cell the zinc electrode is negative. Should current be drawn from the cell by connecting the electrodes by a wire, reactions

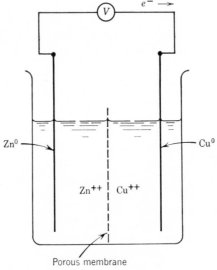

Fig. 60.   The Daniell cell.

take place at the electrodes, zinc passing into solution and copper being plated out. The electrons leave the zinc electrode, travel the external circuit, and enter the cell by way of the copper electrode. The reactions occurring at the electrodes and the electrode potentials written to conform with the order in which the reactions are written are

$$Zn^0 = Zn^{++} + 2e^- \qquad E^0_{Zn^0,Zn^{++}} = +0.762 \text{ volt}$$

(written as an
oxidation potential)

$$Cu^{++} + 2e^- = Cu^0 \qquad E^0_{Cu^{++},Cu^0} = +0.345 \text{ volt}$$

(written as a
reduction potential)

Simple addition of these equations and of the electrode potentials gives the overall reaction of the cell and the potential developed by the cell, V (assuming for the moment that the concentrations of zinc and cupric ions are both 1 M):

$$Zn^0 + Cu^{++} = Zn^{++} + Cu^0 \qquad V = +0.762 + 0.345$$

$$= 1.107 \text{ volts}$$

If the arbitrary convention is adopted that such electrolytic cells are always written so that the electrons leave the left electrode, a

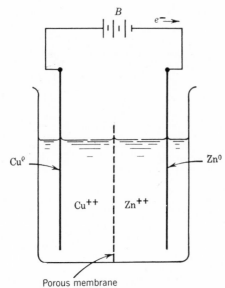

Fig. 61. Daniell cell with greater, external potential imposed.

positive value of the potential V of the cell indicates that the reaction will occur spontaneously as written. On the other hand, if V is negative the reaction must be forced by the application of a greater external potential; thus, had the Daniell cell been written, as shown in Fig. 61, and sufficient voltage impressed by the battery B to make the electrons leave the left electrode, then

$$Cu^0 = Cu^{++} + 2e^- \qquad E^0 = -0.345 \text{ volt}$$
$$\text{(oxidation potential)}$$

$$Zn^{++} + 2e^- = Zn^0 \qquad E^0 = -0.762 \text{ volt}$$
$$\text{(reduction potential)}$$

$$\overline{Cu^0 + Zn^{++} = Cu^{++} + Zn^0} \qquad V = -1.107 \text{ volts}$$

the negative sign indicating that the reaction is not spontaneous as written.

In a similar manner the potential of any cell can be calculated if the single electrode potentials are known and provided the conventions just outlined are observed in setting up the cell, a positive sign for the potential of the cell indicating that the reaction will take place spontaneously.[1]

So far in this discussion the concentration of the metal ions in the solution has been assumed to be 1 M. Actually, the single electrode potential varies with the concentration. For the reduction to the metal of an ion carrying n positive charges

$$M^{n+} + ne^- = M^0$$

the single electrode potential, E, varies with the logarithm of the concentration of the ion

$$E = E^0_{M^{n+},M^0} + RT/nF \ln [M^{n+}]$$

in which E^0 is the standard reduction potential, R is a constant [2] having the value 8.314 joules per mole per degree, T is the absolute temperature, n is the number of electrons involved in the reduction, F is the faraday (96,500 coulombs, the amount of electricity associated with 1 gram electrochemical equivalent weight), and the brackets indicate molar concentration of the ions M^{n+}. At a temperature of 25° this equation becomes

$$E = E^0_{M^{n+},M^0} + \frac{(8.314)(273 + 25)}{n(96,500)} \; 2.3 \log_{10} [M^{n+}]$$

$$E = E^0_{M^{n+},M^0} + (0.059/n) \log [M^{n+}]$$

When the molar concentration of the metal ions is 1, the log term drops out, since the logarithm of 1 is 0. This is the reason we were able to add values of E^0 in the foregoing discussion of the potential of the Daniell cell where all the concentrations were taken as 1 M.

[1] The potential of an electrolytic cell is related to another quantity, the change in free energy, which is studied in the course on physical chemistry. The relation between the change in free energy (ΔF) and V,

$$\Delta F = -nFV$$

is very useful because it makes possible a calculation of the heat of reaction from the potentials observed for a cell at two temperatures.

[2] This is the same constant which appears in the equation of the state for an ideal gas $PV = nRT$. This constant is one of the important natural constants, like π, e (the base of natural logarithms), and Planck's constant h. The units in which R is expressed vary with the setting in which it is used, milliliter-atmospheres per mole per degree or liter-pounds per mole per degree, for example, in the gas law, or the equivalent joules per mole per degree in the single-electrode-potential equation.

A decrease in the concentration of the metal ions shifts the single electrode potential in the negative direction. Each tenfold change in concentration effects a change of $0.059/n$ volt in the single electrode potential. This change of potential with concentration is important in that it gives a convenient way of following the change in concentration of materials in solution, for example, during the course of a titration or an electrodeposition. Returning to the Daniell cell: the course of the potential of the cell as current is drawn from it can be predicted. As the zinc passes into solution the concentration of zinc ion increases, shifting the single electrode potential of the zinc in the positive direction; conversely, the decreasing concentration of the copper ions shifts the potential of the copper electrode in the negative direction. The difference between the two single electrode potentials thus decreases, which, of course, is what happens when current is drawn from a battery.

Generalized Electromotive Series. It is not necessary that the electrode reaction be the reduction of an ion to the metal. Both the oxidized and the reduced forms of the couple may be soluble, for example, ferric and ferrous iron, permanganate and manganous ion. Such systems find their place in the series along with the metal ion-metal couples, and the series thus becomes a general measure of oxidizing and reducing power. The single electrode equation for a system in which both forms of the couple are soluble has the form [1]

$$E = E^0{}_{\text{Ox.,Red.}} + \frac{0.059}{n} \log \frac{[\text{Ox.}]}{[\text{Red.}]}$$

When the molar concentrations of the oxidized and reduced forms are equal (midpoint of a titration) the logarithm term drops out and $E = E^0$. The standard reduction potentials of many couples in which both forms are soluble are given in the more extensive electromotive series given in Table 17.

[1] This equation is a more general form of the electrode potential equation given earlier for a metal ion-metal electrode. The earlier equation is a special case in which the term in the denominator has been separated and combined with the constant

$$E = E' + (0.059/n) \log [\text{Ox.}] - (0.059/n) \log [\text{Red.}]$$
$$= E^\circ + (0.059/n) \log [\text{Ox.}]$$

on the assumption that the concentration of the dissolved metal in solution is constant and independent of the concentration of the metal ions in solution. In the texts on physical chemistry it is often stated that the metal is in its standard state with an activity (molar concentration for such dilute solutions) of 1; this is equivalent to the assumption made above about the constance of the concentration of the dissolved metal and the mathematical operation used of separating the log term and combining the constant terms of the equation.

TABLE 17.   ELECTROMOTIVE SERIES.   STANDARD REDUCTION
POTENTIALS, 25°

See also Table 2, page 20.   Conditions: $[H^+] = 1$ unless otherwise stated.

Oxidized Form	Reduced Form	E^0	Reaction
F_2	F^-	$+2.85$	$F_2 + 2e^- = 2F^-$
$K_2S_2O_8$	SO_4^-	2.05	$S_2O_8^- + 2e^- = 2SO_4^-$
Co^{++}	Co^{++}	1.84	$Co^{+3} + e^- = Co^{++}$
H_5IO_6	IO_3^-	1.71	$H_5IO_6 + H^+ + 2e^- = IO_3^- + 3H_2O$
$Ce^{IV}(HClO_4)$	Ce^{+3}	1.71	$Ce^{IV}(HClO_4) + e^- = Ce^{+3}$
$KMnO_4$	MnO_2	1.67	$MnO_4^- + 4H^+ + 3e^- = MnO_2 + 2H_2O$ (Neutral or alkaline solution)
$NaBiO_3$	Bi^{+3}	1.6	
$KMnO_4$	Mn^{++}	1.52	$MnO_4^- + 8H^+ + 5e^- = Mn^{++} + 4H_2O$
$KBrO_3$	Br^-	1.52	$BrO_3^- + 6H^+ + 6e^- = Br^- + 3H_2O$
$Ce^{IV}(H_2SO_4)$	Ce^{+3}	1.44	$Ce^{IV}(H_2SO_4) + e^- = Ce^{+3}$
$K_2Cr_2O_7$	Cr^{+3}	1.36	$Cr_2O_7^- + 14H^+ + 6e^- = 2Cr^{+3} + 7H_2O$
Cl_2	Cl^-	1.36	$Cl_2 + e^- = 2Cl^-$
MnO_2	Mn^{++}	1.28	$MnO_2 + 4H^+ + 2e^- = Mn^{++} + 2H_2O$
O_2	H_2O	1.229	$O_2 + 4H^+ + 4e^- = 2H_2O$ $([H^+] = 1)$
Br_2	Br^-	1.09	$Br_2 + 2e^- = 2Br^-$
KIO_3	KI	1.085	$IO_3^- + 6H^+ + 6e^- = I^- + 3H_2O$
HVO_3	$VOSO_4$	1.000	$H_3VO_3 + H^+ + e^- = VO^{++} + 2H_2O$
O_2	H_2O	0.815	$O_2 + 4H^+ + 4e^- = 2H_2O$ (Pure water, $[H^+] = 10^{-7})$
Ag^+	Ag^0	0.7995	$Ag^+ + e^- = Ag^0$
Fe^{+3}	Fe^{++}	0.771	$Fe^{+3} + e^- = Fe^{++}$
H_3AsO_4	H_3AsO_3 or $HAsO_2$	0.559	$H_3AsO_4 + 2H^+ + 2e^- = HAsO_2 + 2H_2O$
$I_2(KI_3)$	I^-	0.5345	$I_2 + 2e^- = 2I^-$
Cu^{++}	$CuCl_3^-$	0.51	$Cu^{++} + 3Cl^- + e^- = CuCl_3^-$ (1 M HCl)
O_2	H_2O	0.401	$O_2 + 2H_2O + 4e^- = 4OH^-$ $([OH^-] = 1)$
$K_3Fe(CN)_6$	$K_4Fe(CN)_6$	0.36	$Fe(CN)_6^{-3} + e^- = Fe(CN)_6^{-4}$
Cu^{++}	Cu^0	0.3448	$Cu^{++} + 2e^- = Cu^0$ (1 M H_2SO_4)
Saturated Calomel Electrode		0.2458	$Hg_2Cl_2 + 2e^- = 2Hg^0 + 2Cl^-$ (Saturated KCl)
$CuCl_3^-$	Cu^0	0.178	$CuCl_3^- + e^- = Cu^0 + 3Cl^-$ (1 M HCl)
$Na_2S_4O_6$	$Na_2S_2O_3$	0.17	$S_4O_6^- + 2e^- = 2S_2O_3^-$
Sn^{+4}	Sn^{++}	0.154	$Sn^{+4} + 2e^- = Sn^{++}$ (1 M HCl)
S^0	H_2S	0.141	$S^0 + 2H^+ + 2e^- = H_2S$
Ti^{+4}	Ti^{+3}	0.1	$TiO^{++} + 2H^+ + e^- = Ti^{+3} + H_2O$
H^+	$\frac{1}{2}H_2$	0.0000	$H^+ + e^- = \frac{1}{2}H_2$ $([H^+] = 1)$
Sn^{++}	Sn^0	-0.136	$Sn^{++} + 2e^- = Sn^0$ (1 M H_2SO_4)
V^{+3}	V^{++}	-0.20	$V^{+3} + e^- = V^{++}$
Cr^{+3}	Cr^{++}	-0.41	$Cr^{+3} + e^- = Cr^{++}$
H^+	$\frac{1}{2}H_2$	-0.414	$H^+ + e^- = \frac{1}{2}H_2$ (Pure water, $[H^+] = 10^{-7})$
H_3PO_3	H_3PO_2	-0.59	$H_3PO_3 + 2H^+ + 2e^- = H_3PO_2 + H_2O$
Zn^{++}	Zn^0	-0.762	$Zn^{++} + 2e^- = Zn^0$
H^+	$\frac{1}{2}H_2$	-0.828	$H^+ + e^- = \frac{1}{2}H_2$ $([OH^-] = 1)$

From the position of oxidation-reduction couples in the table it is
possible to predict whether and how completely a reaction should occur.
The oxidized form of a couple will oxidize the reduced form of a second
couple provided the E^0 of the first couple is more positive than the E^0

of the second. The greater the difference in the E^0 valves the more completely the reaction will proceed. The quantitative treatment of this is discussed below where it is shown how the equilibrium constant for the reaction can be calculated from the values of E^0.

Reference Electrodes. As pointed out above, the hydrogen electrode dipping into a solution 1 M in hydrogen ions has been adopted as the arbitrary zero of the electromotive series. When used as a reference electrode in the measurement of the potential of some other

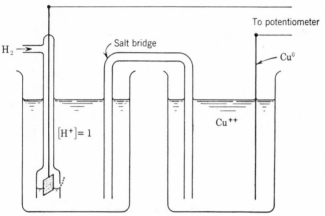

Fig. 62. Use of the hydrogen electrode as a reference electrode.

oxidation-reduction couple, electrical contact between the solutions is usually established through a so-called *salt bridge* of potassium chloride. Thus, the potential of the copper electrode dipping in a solution containing cupric ions is measured by the cell shown in Fig. 62. An accurate measurement of the potential between the two electrodes gives the potential of the copper electrode because the single electrode potential of the hydrogen electrode dipping into a solution 1 M in hydrogen ions has the arbitrary value of 0.

The salt bridge is usually an inverted U-tube filled with a saturated solution of potassium chloride containing 3 per cent agar; such a solution is liquid when hot but becomes a jelly when cold, preventing diffusion but still having a low electrical resistance. In this form the hydrogen electrode is inconvenient to use since it requires a source of hydrogen and is sensitive to variations in atmospheric pressure.

Other more convenient reference electrodes have been devised which have been carefully related to the hydrogen electrode. Of these the so-called calomel electrodes are the most popular; see Fig. 63. Electrical contact is made to metallic mercury which is in contact with mercurous chloride (calomel). The logarithm term of the expression

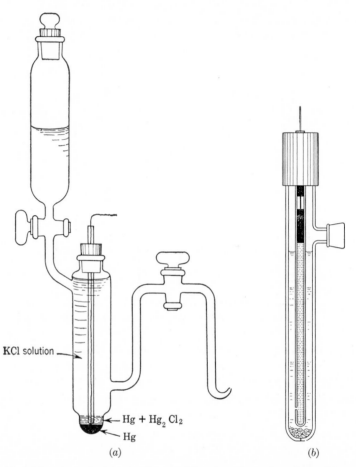

KCl solution

Hg + Hg$_2$Cl$_2$
Hg
(a)

(b)

Fig. 63. Calomel electrode. *a*, Classical laboratory type; *b*, commercial type; contact made through asbestos fiber sealed in bottom. The value of the calomel electrode depends on the strength of the potassium chloride solution; saturated KCl +0.246 volt; 1.0 *M* KCl +0.281 volt; 0.1 *M* KCl +0.333 volt.

for single electrode potential is fixed because the solution is saturated with mercurous chloride. The solubility of mercurous chloride depends in turn on the strength of the potassium chloride solution which is used as the salt bridge. Usually a saturated solution of potassium chloride is used. The saturated calomel electrode has the value

+0.246 volt when referred to the 1 M hydrogen electrode. This value being known, potentials measured against the saturated calomel electrode can be easily corrected to the hydrogen scale

$$E_{vs.\ \text{Sat. cal. elec.}} + 0.246 = E_{vs.\ \text{H elec.}}$$

No source of hydrogen gas is needed for the calomel electrode, a standard acid solution is not needed, and the calomel electrode is therefore more simple to use than the hydrogen electrode. Commercial models of the saturated calomel electrode are compact, rugged, and suitable for use in both the laboratory and the industrial plant.

Indicator Electrodes. In a preceding section the use of the hydrogen electrode as a reference electrode was discussed and it was pointed out that other electrodes were more convenient to use than the hydrogen electrode, notably the saturated calomel reference electrode. The purpose of the *reference electrode* is to make electrical contact with the solution in such a manner that the single electrode potential so developed is constant and has a known, reproducible value. The second electrode of the cell is called the *indicator electrode*. Its potential is a function of the composition of the solution, and it is used to follow changes in the concentration of some ion in the solution, the potential developed being a logarithmic function of the concentration according to the electrode potential equation given earlier.

Several indicator electrodes are available for measuring the concentration of hydrogen ions; these are discussed in detail in Chapter 18 dealing with the potentiometric determination of pH. Of the various indicator electrodes for the hydrogen ion, the hydrogen electrode is the fundamental one but the others are more convenient to use, particularly the glass electrode. In a few cases metal electrodes can be used to measure the concentration of the ion of the metal of the electrode; these are rather unusual, however, for the metals more negative than silver in the reduction-potential series (and this includes most of the common metals) are attacked by acids and their potentials vary unpredictably. The noble metals such as platinum and gold are inert and have no tendency to dissolve ($E^0_{Pt^{++},Pt^0} = +1.2$ volts; $E^0_{Au^{+++},Au^0}$ + 1.4 volts) and become charged like metals more negative in the electromotive series. When dipped into solutions containing oxidizing and reducing agents they act as collectors of electrons and thus register the oxidation-reduction level of the solution; that is, they function as indicator electrodes for oxidation-reduction couples of which both forms are soluble. The usual indicator electrode for oxidation-reduction reactions is simply a bright platinum foil or wire.

For following the course of an oxidation-reduction reaction, then, the electrode system used is simply a platinum wire or foil (the indicator electrode) and a saturated calomel electrode (the reference electrode). The platinum electrode is cleaned before use by dipping it into a mixture of sulfuric acid and potassium dichromate and then washing it well with water.

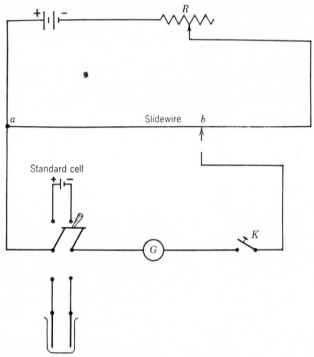

Fig. 64.   The potentiometer.

The Measurement of Potential.   The potential of a cell cannot be accurately measured directly with a voltmeter.   Although voltmeters are spoken of as high-resistance instruments, they still draw sufficient current from the cell to cause chemical changes in the immediate neighborhood of the electrodes which alter the potential of the cell.   This is spoken of as *polarization*.

The potential of a cell can be measured without drawing current, however, by means of a potentiometer, Fig. 64.   Essentially the potentiometer is a device for balancing a second, variable potential against the potential being measured, using a sensitive galvanometer to indicate when the two potentials have been made equal.   A slidewire is used to supply the variable potential.   The so-called working circuit of the potentiometer consists of a battery, a variable resistance, R, and a slidewire. By Ohm's law, $E = IR$, a current passing through a resistance (slidewire in this case) creates a potential. The potential to be measured is connected so as to oppose the potential of the slide-wire, that is, plus to plus. A tapping key and a galvanometer are placed in series with the potential being measured. When the potential drop from a to b on the slidewire equals the potential being measured, the galvanometer G shows no deflection on closing the key K. For convenience the slidewire is calibrated directly in volts by use of a standard cell whose voltage is accurately known. The double pole-double throw switch is closed to connect the standard cell, the slide-wire is set at the voltage of the standard cell (1.018 volts for the Weston standard cell), and the resistance R is varied until the galvanometer shows no deflection on closing the circuit with the key. With the slide-wire thus adjusted to read directly in volts the switch is thrown to the potential being measured and the balancing is repeated moving the slidewire.

Potentiometric Titrations Involving Oxidation-Reduction Reactions. As indicated in the foregoing sections two electrodes are required in order to follow the course of a titration, an indicator electrode, consisting of a bright platinum foil, and a reference electrode, usually a saturated calomel electrode. The potential of the cell is measured with a potentiometer. The solution must be well stirred; a mechanical stirrer is best. After each addition of the standard solution from the buret the potential is read on the potentiometer. A plot of the data obtained in this manner in the titration of ferrous sulfate with sulfatoceric acid is shown in Fig. 65. The rise in potential marks the equivalence-point. Over the lower portion of the curve the potential is determined by the ferric-ferrous system. At the equiva-lence-point, when all the ferrous iron has been oxidized the potential rises abruptly to that of the ceric-cerous system.

In titrations of powerful oxidizing and reducing agents the vertical portion of the curve is great, equal in some titrations to a change in potential of more than 1 volt. With weaker oxidizing and reducing agents the break may not be so great, and the point of inflection of the curve must be determined carefully to ascertain the equivalence-point. The size of the vertical portion of the curve depends on the difference of the E^0 values of the two oxidation-reduction systems involved.

At the midpoint of a titration, half of the reducing agent will have been oxidized and the concentrations of the oxidized and reduced forms will be equal. The logarithm term of the electrode potential equation then becomes 0

$$E = E^0 + \frac{0.059}{n} \log \frac{[\text{Ox.}]}{[\text{Red.}]}$$

and $\qquad\qquad E = E^0$ (at midpoint)

Thus, in Fig. 65, at the midpoint $E = +0.690$ volt (on the hydrogen

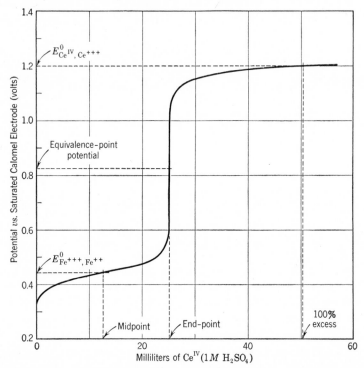

Fig. 65. Potentiometric titration of ferrous sulfate with sulfatoceric acid. Taken: 25.0 ml. of 0.1000 N ferrous ethylenediammonium sulfate; titrated with 0.1013 N sulfatoceric acid. Both solutions 1.00 M in sulfuric acid. Add 0.246 volt to potentials on calomel scale shown to obtain potentials on hydrogen scale.

scale), the E^0 value of the ferric-ferrous couple in a 1 M sulfuric acid solution. At 100 per cent past the end-point, the concentrations of the oxidized and reduced forms of the standard solution are also equal and the potential is equal to the E^0 of the standard solution. In the titration of ferrous sulfate with ceric sulfate just shown, the E^0 of the ceric-cerous system is $+1.44$ volts.

The potential at the equivalence-point can be determined from the E^0 values of the two oxidation-reduction couples involved. A fraction of a second after the addition of ceric sulfate to the ferrous sulfate the reaction will have taken place and equilibrium will have been established. The single electrode potentials of the two systems are then equal, and addition of the equations for the two single electrode potentials gives

$$E_{Fe} = E^0_{Fe^{+3},Fe^{++}} + 0.059 \log \frac{[Fe^{+3}]}{[Fe^{++}]}$$

$$E_{Ce} = E^0_{Ce^{+4},Ce^{+3}} + 0.059 \log \frac{[Ce^{+4}]}{[Ce^{+3}]}$$

$$2E = E_{Fe} + E_{Ce} = E^0_{Fe^{+3},Fe^{++}} + E^0_{Ce^{+4},Ce^{+3}} + 0.059 \log \frac{[Fe^{+3}][Ce^{+4}]}{[Fe^{++}][Ce^{+3}]}$$

At the equivalence-point, equivalent quantities of ceric and ferrous will have been mixed. There will be a slight amount of ferrous iron not oxidized and an equivalent amount of ceric not reduced, that is, $[Fe^{++}] = [Ce^{+4}]$. The concentrations of ferric and cerous formed in the reaction must also be equal, $[Fe^{+3}] = [Ce^{+3}]$. This being so, all the factors in the logarithm term cancel, the log of 1 is 0, and

$$E_{Equiv.} = \frac{E^0_{Fe^{+3},Fe^{++}} + E^0_{Ce^{+4},Ce^{+3}}}{2}$$

that is, in this case the potential at the equivalence-point is simply the average of the two E^0 values.[1]

Calculation of Equilibrium Constants from E^0 Values. As indicated in the preceding section the greater the difference between the values of E^0 of the two oxidation-reduction couples involved in the reaction the greater the rise in potential at the equivalence-point. The greater this rise in potential the more complete the reaction. The matter can even be handled quantitatively, for the equilibrium constant of the reaction can be calculated from the values of E^0.

---

[1] For reactions involving oxidation-reduction couples in which the number of electrons involved are different, the potential is calculated by the formula

$$E_{Equiv.} = \frac{aE^0_A + bE^0_B}{a + b}$$

in which a and b are the number of electrons involved in the oxidation-reduction couples

$$A_{Ox.} + ae^- = A_{Red.}$$

$$B_{Ox.} + be^- = B_{Red.}$$

the reaction being

$$bA_{Red.} + aB_{Ox.} = bA_{Ox.} + aB_{Red.}$$

Thus the equilibrium constant of the reaction $Fe^{++} + Ce^{+4} = Fe^{+3} + Ce^{+3}$ is defined as

$$K = \frac{[Fe^{+3}][Ce^{+3}]}{[Fe^{++}][Ce^{+4}]}$$

K has a constant value, and the expression holds for any mixture of these components after equilibrium has been established (a matter of a fraction of a second). The single electrode potentials of the two oxidation-reduction couples involved are equal after equilibrium is established

$$E_{Fe} = E_{Ce}$$

$$E^0_{Fe^{+3},Fe^{++}} + \frac{0.059}{1} \log \frac{[Fe^{+3}]}{[Fe^{++}]} = E^0_{Ce^{+4},Ce^{+3}} + \frac{0.059}{1} \log \frac{[Ce^{+4}]}{[Ce^{+3}]}$$

which on rearrangement gives

$$E^0_{Ce^{+4},Ce^{+3}} - E^0_{Fe^{+3},Fe^{++}} = \frac{0.059}{1} \log \frac{[Fe^{+3}][Ce^{+3}]}{[Fe^{++}][Ce^{+4}]}$$

$$= 0.059 \log K$$

Using the values of E^0 of Table 17,

$$\log K = \frac{1.44 - 0.77}{0.059}$$

$$= 11.3$$

$$K = 10^{11.3} = 2.0 \times 10^{11}$$

The large value of K means that the reaction proceeds completely to the right.

It is even possible to calculate the extent to which the reaction takes place. Thus if equal volumes of 0.1 N ferrous sulfate and ceric sulfate were mixed (essentially the situation at the equivalence-point) it is apparent that the concentration of the ferrous ion, that is, the iron not oxidized, will be equal to the concentration of the unreacted ceric ion. The concentrations of ferric ion and cerous ion will also be equal since they were formed at the same time. Thus

$$[Fe^{++}] = [Ce^{+4}] \qquad \text{and} \qquad [Fe^{+3}] = [Ce^{+3}]$$

so that
$$K = \frac{[Fe^{+3}][Ce^{+3}]}{[Fe^{++}][Ce^{+4}]}$$

$$= \frac{[Fe^{+3}]^2}{[Fe^{++}]^2} = 10^{11.3}$$

and
$$[Fe^{+3}] = 10^{5.7}[Fe^{++}]$$

In other words, the concentration of the ferric ion is so vastly greater than that of the ferrous that it is essentially 0.05 N, and the ferrous ion concentration is therefore

$$[Fe^{++}] = \frac{5 \times 10^{-2}}{10^{5.7}} = \frac{10^{-1.30}}{10^{5.7}} = 10^{-7.0} = 1 \times 10^{-7}$$

or about 10^{-7} M. For the purposes of a titration this reaction may be regarded as complete. Similar calculations can, of course, be made at any stage of the titration, for equilibrium is established quickly in this reaction; it is only necessary to calculate the concentrations of three of the components to obtain the fourth, and in a titration the problem is relatively simple because in the process only two of the components are being added.

When one of the couples involves more than one electron the problem is only slightly more complicated. For example, if to 50 ml. of 0.1 N stannous chloride is added 100 ml. of 0.1 N ferric chloride:

$$SnCl_2 + 2FeCl_3 = SnCl_4 + 2FeCl_2$$

The values of E^0 are quite widely separated

$$E^0{}_{Sn^{+4},Sn^{++}} = +0.15 \text{ volt} \qquad E^0{}_{Fe^{+3},Fe^{++}} = +0.77 \text{ volt}$$

so that it is evident that the reaction will proceed far to the right, and after equilibrium has been established, the concentrations of the stannic tin will be $^{50}\!\!/_{150}(0.1) = 0.033$ M and that of the ferrous iron $^{100}\!\!/_{150}(0.1) = 0.066$ M, except for the very small amounts of stannous ion not oxidized and ferric reduced. After equilibrium is established

$$E^0{}_{Sn^{+4},Sn^{++}} + \frac{0.059}{2} \log \frac{[Sn^{+4}]}{[Sn^{++}]} = E^0{}_{Fe^{+3},Fe^{++}} + \frac{0.059}{1} \log \frac{[Fe^{+3}]}{[Fe^{++}]}$$

which on rearrangement yields

$$E^0{}_{Fe^{+3},Fe^{++}} - E^0{}_{Sn^{+4},Sn^{++}} = \frac{0.059}{2} \log \frac{[Sn^{+4}]}{[Sn^{++}]} - \frac{0.059}{1} \log \frac{[Fe^{+3}]}{[Fe^{++}]}$$

The log term involving the concentrations of the iron ions may be multiplied above and below by 2, giving

$$E^0{}_{Fe^{+3},Fe^{++}} - E^0{}_{Sn^{+4},Sn^{++}} = \frac{0.059}{2} \log \frac{[Sn^{+4}][Fe^{++}]^2}{[Sn^{++}][Fe^{+3}]^2}$$

or $\qquad E^0{}_{Fe^{+3},Fe^{++}} - E^0{}_{Sn^{+4},Sn^{++}} = \frac{0.059}{2} \log K$

$$\log K = (0.77 - 0.15)(2/0.059) = 21.0$$

$$K = 10^{21.0} = 1.0 \times 10^{21}$$

As before, a large, positive value for K indicates that the equilibrium lies far to the right.

The Rate at which Oxidation-Reduction Reactions Occur. The calculations outlined in the foregoing sections have to do only with the conditions prevailing after the reaction has occurred, that is, with the final, equilibrium conditions. They have nothing to do with the speed with which the reaction may take place. Unfortunately some oxidation-reduction reactions which should occur according to the E^0 values for the couples involved will not take place. For example, arsenite ($E^0 = +0.56$ volt) and dichromate ($E^0 = +1.36$ volts) on mixing simply do not react. Often a catalyst may be found which will initiate the reaction, after which it proceeds to completion according to theory. A trace of potassium iodide or of osmium tetroxide added to the arsenite-dichromate mixture causes the reaction to take place quickly.

Variation of Standard Reduction Potential with Acid Concentration. The standard reduction potential of oxidation-reduction systems which involve only a simple electron transfer are not influenced by hydrogen-ion concentration, theoretically. Thus the couples

$$Fe^{+3} + e^- = Fe^{++}$$

$$Ti^{+4} + e^- = Ti^{+3}$$

involve only the simple ions and an electron and are roughly independent of the acidity of the solution.

On the other hand, in systems in which oxygen-containing acids are involved

$$AsO_4^{-3} + 2H^+ + 2e^- = AsO_3^{-3} + H_2O$$

the reduction potential depends on the acid concentration and the hydrogen-ion concentration appears in the electrode potential equation

$$E = E^0_{AsO_4^{-3}, AsO_3^{-3}} + \frac{0.059}{2} \log \frac{[AsO_4^{-3}][H^+]^2}{[AsO_3^{-3}]}$$

The standard reduction potential is the electrode potential when all the components are in the standard state (molar concentration of 1); that is, E^0 in such cases refer to solutions 1 M in hydrogen ions. It is evident that in the arsenate-arsenite system an increase in the acid concentration shifts the potential in the positive direction, that is, increases the oxidizing strength of the arsenate. This is a very striking example, for this reaction can be used quantitatively in both directions merely by changing the acid concentration.

The standard reduction potential of many oxidation-reduction couples varies with the hydrogen-ion concentration even though oxygen-containing acids are not involved. The ferric-ferrous couple, for example, is not completely independent of the acidity, $E^0_{Fe^{+3},Fe^{++}}$ shifting from 0.68 volt in 1 M to 0.65 volt in 4 M hydrochloric acid. Moreover, the nature of the anion often has a great effect. This is especially true in the ceric-cerous system, $E^0_{Ce^{IV},Ce^{III}(1\ M\ HCl)} = +1.28$ volts; $E^0_{Ce^{IV},Ce^{III}(1\ M\ H_2SO_4)} = +1.44$ volts; $E^0_{Ce^{IV},Ce^{III}(1\ M\ HNO_3)} = +1.61$ volts; $E^0_{Ce^{IV},Ce^{III}(1\ M\ HClO_4)} = +1.71$ volts. The change of E^0 with the strength of the acid is appreciable here also. These effects are generally ascribed to the formation of complex ions, for example, $CeCl_6^=$ and $Ce(SO_4)_3^=$; the stabilities of these complexes are rather low, and the extent to which they are formed depends on the strength of the acid. The value of E^0, of course, depends on the nature of the ions involved.

Formal Reduction Potentials. Standard reduction potentials, such as those given in Table 17, are determined under very specific and unusual conditions which are not at all the conditions under which the reactions of analytical chemistry are normally carried out. Standard reduction potentials are determined in solutions in which all the reactants are 1 M [1] in concentration and in which all the materials are present as their simple ions; that is, none of the material is tied up as a complex ion. In practice this limits the measurements to salts and to perchlorates and nitrates which rarely form complex ions with the metals. The standard reduction potentials are often unreliable when applied to the conditions met in chemical analysis where the acid and salt concentrations employed are often much greater than 1 M and where the anions can hardly be limited to perchlorate or nitrate. Practical, working reduction potentials, determined under the conditions employed in common analytical work, are known as *formal reduction potentials*. Formal concentration is the same as molar concentration, and formal reduction potentials are simply those determined potentiometrically in an acid solution of the stated formal concentration. The formal reduction potentials of the ferric-ferrous and dichromate-chromic couples have been determined in various acids of different concentrations; the values in hydrochloric acid solutions,

---

[1] Strictly, the standard potentials are on a molal basis, that is, 1 gram molecular weight of material dissolved in 1000 g. of water. The difference between molar and molal concentration is so small that no effort has been made previously in this text to differentiate them.

TABLE 18. FORMAL REDUCTION POTENTIALS OF THE FERRIC-
FERROUS AND DICHROMATE-CHROMIC COUPLES IN
HYDROCHLORIC ACID

Concentration (formal)	Ferric-Ferrous (volt)	Dichromate-Chromic (volt)
0.10	+0.73	+0.93
0.25	0.73	0.96
0.50	0.72	0.97
0.75	0.71	0.99
1.00	0.70	1.00
1.50	0.70	1.02
2.00	0.69	1.05
3.00	0.68	1.08
4.00	0.66	1.10

given in Table 18, are considerably different from the standard reduction potentials, $E^0_{Fe^{+3},Fe^{++}} = +0.77$ volt and $E^0_{Cr_2O_7^=,Cr^{+3}} = +1.36$ volts. This is a matter of considerable significance in the dichromate determination of iron for on the basis of the standard reduction potential a far greater break at the equivalence-point is predicted than is actually obtained. The standard reduction potential may lead also to the choice of a wholly inappropriate indicator for marking the end-point.

The values of many oxidation-reduction couples show comparable differences in their standard and formal reduction potentials; the cupric-cuprous couple in hydrochloric acid, for example, is much different from the +0.345 volt given in Table 17, and the same is true for the ferricyanide-ferrocyanide couple, the thallic-thallous couple, and others.

Tables of the formal potentials of the ceric-cerous couple, dichromate-chromic couple, and ferric-ferrous couple are given in Chapter 11 in the sections dealing with ceric salts and potassium dichromate as standard oxidizing agents.

The changes in the reduction potential of a couple on passing from one acid to another are largely caused by the formation of complex ions, the extent of which varies with the nature of the anion and the concentrations of acid and salt. The nature of some of these complex ions has been established. Phosphate, for example, combines with ferric ions to form $Fe(PO_4)_2^{-3}$. This reduces the concentration of ferric ions in the solution, and thus the numerator of the logarithm term of the electrode potential equation, shifting the potential of the couple in the negative direction. If the reduced form of the couple forms a complex ion, the electrode potential is shifted in the positive direction. This happens in the formation of the iron-1,10-phenanthroline complex, for the ferrous ion forms a more stable complex ion with 1,10-phenan-throline than the ferric ion does; the E^0 of the couple as measured potentiometrically is $+1.06$ volts.

Oxidation-Reduction Indicators. Many organic materials have the property of changing color when treated with oxidizing agents. Some of these revert to their original color when further treated with an excess of a reducing agent. Such compounds can be used as indicators in oxidation-reduction titrations. Of the oxidation-reduction indicators listed in Table 19, diphenylaminesulfonic acid and ferrous 1,10-phenanthroline sulfate have proved to be the most useful.

Oxidation-reduction indicators are oxidation-reduction systems just like any other oxidation-reduction couple and can be treated in the same way. In Table 19, E^0 values are given for the various indicators.

TABLE 19. OXIDATION-REDUCTION INDICATORS

| | Color | | |
Compound	Oxidized Form	Reduced Form	E^0 (volts)
Ferrous 5-nitro-1,10-phenan-throline sulfate (nitro-fer-roin)	Blue	Red	$+1.25$
Phenylanthranilic acid	Pink	Colorless	1.08
Ferrous 1,10-phenanthroline sulfate (ferroin)	Blue	Red	1.06
Ferrous 5-methyl-1,10-phe-nanthroline sulfate	Blue	Red	1.02
Eriogreen	Rose	Red-yellow	0.99
Ferrous 2,2'-bipyridyl sulfate	Blue	Red	0.97
Ferrous 4,7-dimethyl-1,10-phenanthroline sulfate	Blue	Red	0.87
Ferrous 3,4,7,8-tetramethyl-1,10-phenanthroline sulfate	Blue	Red	0.81
Diphenylaminesulfonic acid	Purple	Colorless (green)	0.84
Diphenylamine	Violet	Colorless	0.76
Starch-iodine-iodide	Blue	Colorless	0.54
Methylene blue	Colorless	Blue	0.53 (pH = 2.86)
Indigo sulfonates	Blue	Colorless	0.26–0.38

The indicator chosen for a given oxidation-reduction titration should be selected so that the color change occurs as close as possible to the equivalence-point. If the intensity of the colors of the oxidized and reduced forms of the indicator are about the same the color change of the indicator will occur at a potential about equal to the E^0 value of the indicator. An indicator can then be selected whose reduction potential is as close as possible to the potential at the equivalence-point. Thus, for the titration of ferrous sulfate with sulfatoceric acid, the potential at the equivalence-point is 1.08 volts on the hydrogen scale, and inspection of Table 19 indicates that ferrous 1,10-phenan-throline sulfate, $E^0 = +1.06$ volts, would be the correct indicator. The red color of the reduced form of ferrous 1,10-phenanthroline indi-cator, however, is about ten times as intense as the blue color of the oxidized form and is only obscured by the blue color when the oxidized form has a concentration ten times as great as the reduced form. Application of the electrode potential gives

$$E = 1.06 + 0.059 \log (10/1) = +1.12 \text{ volts}$$

so that $+1.12$ volts is a more appropriate value to use in selecting an application of ferrous 1,10-phenanthroline sulfate than the standard reduction potential of $+1.06$ volts.

   Ferrous 1,10-*Phenanthroline Sulfate* (*Ferroin*). 1,10-phenanthroline (*o*-phenanthroline) is a heterocyclic organic compound having two ring

$C_{12}H_8N_2$

nitrogen atoms. This substance forms a compound with the ferrous ion in which three molecules of 1,10-phenanthroline are attached to the iron atom in covalent (non-ionic) fashion. On oxidation this red ferrous compound is converted to a blue ferric compound, the reaction being reversible:

$$\text{Fe(1,10-phenanthroline)}_3{}^{+++} + e^- = \text{Fe(1,10-phenanthroline)}_3{}^{++}$$

Ferriin   Ferroin
(faint blue)   (red)

It requires a strong oxidizing agent to convert ferroin to the oxidized form, ferriin, the value of E^0 being $+1.06$ volts. Ferroin has been found to be especially useful in titrations with cerate salts. Although the standard reduction potential of ferrous 1,10-phenanthroline is $+1.06$ volts, in practice the color change occurs at a higher potential because the color of the reduced form is so much more intense than that of the oxidized blue form, about $+1.12$ volts.

A 0.01 N solution of ferrous 1,10-phenanthroline sulfate is generally prepared for use as indicator solution. One or two drops of this solution in a volume of 200 ml. is usually sufficient. Ferrous 1,10-phenanthroline perchlorate is only sparingly soluble; a saturated solution of it is easy to prepare and makes an ideal indicator solution, about 2 ml. being required per determination.

Substituted Ferroin Indicators. The introduction of various groups into the 1,10-phenanthroline molecule shifts the reduction potential of the ferric phenenthroline-ferrous phenanthroline systems. Substitu-

tion in the 2 or 9 positions destroys the property of phenanthroline of combining with iron. The introduction of a nitro group elsewhere in the molecule raises the reduction potential; methyl groups lower the reduction potential. A number of such substituted phenanthroline indicators have been prepared, so that indicators are available having E^0 values separated by only small intervals over the range 0.8 to 1.25 volts. Several of these are listed in Table 19.

Diphenylaminesulfonic Acid. Diphenylamine behaves as an oxidation-reduction indicator, but the compound is quite insoluble in water and its reactions with oxidizing and reducing agents are rather slow. The sulfonic acid derivative of diphenylamine is soluble in water, and its reactions with oxidizing and reducing agents are rapid and completely reversible. Both diphenylamine and diphenylaminesulfonic acid are colorless and become purple on oxidation. A green intermediate compound forms in this oxidation, and the reversible oxidation-reduction reaction is really only between the green intermediate and the purple forms.

Diphenylaminesulfonic acid is particularly useful as an indicator in titrations with dichromate. A 0.01 M solution of diphenylaminesulfonic acid is used. If the material is obtained as its barium salt, the barium is precipitated by the addition of sodium sulfate, and the barium sulfate is filtered off; the solution of the sodium salt is then used as indicator. The reduction potentials of diphenylamine and diphenylaminesulfonic acid are $+0.76$ and $+0.84$ volt, respectively.

Phenylanthranilic Acid.   Phenylanthranilic acid is the carboxylic acid derivative of diphenylamine

$C_{13}H_{11}O_2N$
Mol. wt. 213

It is colorless and on oxidation becomes red. The color change is reversible. The standard reduction potential of phenylanthranilic acid is $+1.08$ volts. This value does not change with the concentration of acid in the solution in which it is used, and may be employed in solutions as strong as 8 N in acid. Phenylanthranilic acid has been found useful in titration with dichromate and vanadate in strongly acid solutions and in titration with sulfatoceric acid.

A 0.005 M solution of phenylanthranilic acid is used as indicator; this is made up by dissolving 1.07 g. of the acid in 20 ml. of 5 per cent sodium carbonate solution and diluting with water to 1000 ml. A volume of 0.15 ml. of the solution is sufficient for a titration, the indicator correction being negligible.

Irreversible Oxidation-Reduction Indicators.   Some use is made of organic dyestuff materials which change color on oxidation but with which the original color is not restored on further treatment with a reducing agent. Among such irreversible indicators are methyl orange, methyl red, and naphthol blue black used in the bromate titration of arsenite.

Such irreversible indicators are also used in titrations with iodate in 4 to 6 M hydrochloric acid solutions. The principal ones are naphthol blue black (green to pink to colorless), brilliant ponceaux 5 R (orange to colorless) and amaranth (red to colorless). Irreversible indicators should be added toward the end of the titration, or, if added at the start, additional indicator must be added before reaching the end-point; this is not a particularly undesirable procedure as the indicator requires only a negligible amount of oxidizing agent for its oxidation.

PROBLEMS

1. Balance the following equations:
   (a) $FeCl_3 + TiCl_3 = FeCl_2 + TiCl_4$
   (b) $CuCl_2 + Cu^0 + HCl = H_2CuCl_3$
   (c) $H_3AsO_4 + KI + HCl = H_3AsO_3 + I^0 + KCl$
   (d) $H_2S + I^0 = S^0 + HI$

2. Balance the following equations:

    (a) $FeSO_4 + KMnO_4 + H_2SO_4 = Fe_2(SO_4)_3 + MnSO_4 + K_2SO_4$

    (b) $MnSO_4 + KMnO_4 + KOH = MnO_2 + K_2SO_4$

    (c) $KIO_3 + KI + HCl = I^0 + KCl$

    (d) $Sb_2S_3 + HNO_3 = Sb(NO_3)_5 + NO + H_2SO_4$

3. From an examination of the electromotive series, Table 17, compose an electrolytic cell which will develop the greatest voltage possible. State which electrode is negative and which is positive, and calculate the voltage of the cell. Point out the practical difficulties in making such a cell.

4. Calculate the potential developed by a cell consisting of a strip of metallic silver dipping into a solution 1 M in silver ions and a strip of metallic nickel dipping into a solution 1 M in nickel ions, the two solutions being separated by a porous membrane. Decide which electrode is negative. Write an equation for the reaction that will occur at the silver electrode and another for that at the nickel electrode if the two electrodes are connected outside the cell by a wire. Indicate the direction of flow of electrons in the wire.

5. Calculate the change in the single-electrode potential on decreasing the concentration of the metal ion from 1.0 M to 0.1 M in each of the following cases:

$$Ag^+ + e^- = Ag^0 \qquad E^0{}_{Ag^+,Ag^0} = +0.7995 \text{ volt}$$
$$Cu^{++} + 2e^- = Cu^0 \qquad E^0{}_{Cu^{++},Cu^0} = +0.3448 \text{ volt}$$
$$Cr^{+3} + 3e^- = Cr^0 \qquad E^0{}_{Cr^{+3},Cr^0} = -0.71 \text{ volt}$$

6. Show that any tenfold change in the molar concentration of the metal ion causes the same change in single-electrode potential calculated in Problem 5.

7. Calculate the potential of a Daniell cell in which the concentration of the zinc ions is 0.001 M and that of the cupric ions is 0.1 M.

8. From an inspection of the standard reduction potentials, Table 17, decide if dichromate could be expected to oxidize (a) bromide to bromine, (b) ferrocyanide to ferricyanide, (c) bromide to bromate, (d) fluoride to free fluorine.

9. From an inspection of Table 17, the standard reduction potentials, pick out (a) the most powerful oxidizing agent known, (b) the most powerful oxidizing agent which exists in solution in ionic form, (c) the strongest water-soluble reducing agent.

10. From a close inspection of Table 17, standard reduction potentials, decide if hydrogen gas is a stronger reducing agent in solutions having pH equal to 1, 7, or 14.

11. Oxygen is a stronger oxidizing agent in acid solution than in neutral or basic solution. Show that this is to be expected, from the values of the standard reduction potentials given in Table 17 and also from the nature of the chemical reaction involved.

12. Determine if metallic zinc can be expected to reduce (a) quadrivalent titanium to the trivalent form; (b) Cr^{+3} to Cr^{++}, and Al^{+3} to Al^0.

13. Calculate the value of $2.3RT/F$ at $30°$.

14. Calculate the potential which would be developed between a saturated calomel electrode and a 0.1 N calomel electrode if both were dipped into the same solution. See legend of Fig. 63 for values. State which electrode would be positive.

15. Calculate the potential at the equivalence-point in the oxidation of titanous sulfate with ferric sulfate. Choose an oxidation-reduction indicator which would be suitable for the reaction. See Tables 17 and 19 for numerical values.

16. Calculate the equilibrium constant for the reaction of ferric sulfate with titanous sulfate.

17. To a volume of 100 ml. of exactly 0.1 N ferric sulfate was added 100 ml. of exactly 0.1 N titanous sulfate. Calculate the concentration of ferric ion remaining in the solution.

CHAPTER 11

The Practice of

Oxidation-Reduction Titrations

The general meanings of the terms *oxidation* and *reduction* were covered in the preceding chapter together with the methods of balancing oxidation-reduction equations and the electrochemical principles, which furnish a beautiful theoretical background for oxidation-reduction chemistry. The present chapter is devoted to the uses made of oxidation-reduction reactions in volumetric analysis. From a practical standpoint the theory developed in the preceding chapter is useful in predicting whether reactions are possible, in predicting the effects of hydrogen-ion concentration on the equilibrium, and in aiding in the selection of suitable indicators for specific titrations. The theory has two principal limitations. Even though theory may indicate that a reaction should take place, the rate at which it occurs may be so slow that no practical use can be made of the reaction unless a catalyst can be found. Secondly, the potential at the end-point may not agree in practice with that calculated because the values of the standard reduction potentials are determined under conditions quite different from those prevailing in volumetric analyses.

In practice, then, the analytical chemist is forced to find the answer to any specific problem by resort to experiment on known materials. Once a method has been proved on a primary-standard material and any disturbing effects of foreign substances has been made known, a method may be applied with some degree of assurance to the analysis of unknown materials.

Before proceeding to detailed discussions of specific methods involving oxidation-reduction titrations, we pause for a review of certain general aspects of the subject: the matter of equivalent weight, the primary standards available, the standard solutions commonly used, and the methods of making the necessary preliminary adjustments of oxidation state before titration.

DEFINITION OF EQUIVALENT WEIGHT

It has been stated on several occasions in previous chapters that the equivalent weight of a material is not constant but depends on the reaction in which the material is involved. The definition of equivalent weight changes with the type of reaction. In each of the three classes of volumetric reactions the definition of equivalent weight is different. The equivalent weight of a material in an oxidation-reduction reaction is the molecular weight of the material divided by the change in its oxidation number in the reaction in which it takes part. For example, the oxidation number of tin in stannous chloride is 2, in stannic chloride 4; on oxidation the change is 2 and the equivalent weight is therefore the molecular weight of stannous chloride divided by 2.

Potassium permanganate has several equivalent weights, for the extent to which it is reduced depends on the conditions

$KMnO_4 \rightarrow Mn^{++}$	Sulfuric acid solution	$KMnO_4/5$
$KMnO_4 \rightarrow K_2MnF_5$	Hydrofluoric acid solution	$KMnO_4/4$
$KMnO_4 \rightarrow MnO_2$	Neutral or sodium hydroxide solution	$KMnO_4/3$
$KMnO_4 \rightarrow BaMnO_4$	Barium hydroxide solution	$KMnO_4/1$

A solution of potassium permanganate may be standardized using one type of reaction and later used in a titration involving another type, so that it becomes necessary on occasion to convert normality on one basis to normality on another. For a given solution the normality is calculated from the weight of potassium permanganate in 1 l. of solution by

$$N = \frac{\text{Grams } KMnO_4 \text{ per liter}}{\text{Equivalent weight}}$$

Thus, if the permanganate is found to be 0.1000 N by standardization against sodium oxalate in a sulfuric acid solution,

$$\text{Grams } KMnO_4 \text{ per liter} = N_{KMnO_4(H_2SO_4)} [KMnO_4/5]$$

If used in a neutral or sodium hydroxide solution,

$$\text{Grams } KMnO_4 \text{ per liter} = N_{KMnO_4(NaOH)} [KMnO_4/3]$$

The weight of potassium permanganate in the solution remains constant, so that

$$N_{KMnO_4(H_2SO_4)} [KMnO_4/5] = N_{KMnO_4(NaOH)} [KMnO_4/3]$$

that is, the normality when used in neutral or sodium hydroxide solution is

$$N_{KMnO_4(NaOH)} = N_{KMnO_4(H_2SO_4)}\left(\tfrac{3}{5}\right)$$

In general, for a given solution the normalities for use under different conditions are inversely proportional to the equivalent weights.

GENERAL SURVEY OF OXIDATION-REDUCTION TITRATIONS

The standard oxidizing agents which are commonly used are potassium permanganate, potassium dichromate, quadrivalent cerium salts, iodine, and potassium bromate. Separate sections will be devoted to the applications of each of these reagents. Although a variety of materials may be determined by titration with permanganate and cerate, the indirect iodometric method has the greatest number of applications of any of the oxidation-reduction methods. By the indirect iodometric method any oxidizing agent which will oxidize potassium iodide to iodine can be determined, and this means most of the materials thought of as oxidizing agents; the iodine liberated is titrated with sodium thiosulfate.

The standard reducing agents used in volumetric work are sodium thiosulfate (for titrating iodine only), sodium arsenite, ferrous sulfate, titanous chloride, and chromous sulfate. Titanous chloride and chromous sulfate are powerful reducing agents and find use in the titration of certain types of organic materials as well as inorganic materials.

Fortunately a number of highly satisfactory primary-standard oxidizing and reducing materials are available. These are discussed separately in the next section.

PRIMARY-STANDARD OXIDIZING AND REDUCING MATERIALS

Of the three strong, standard oxidizing agents, permanganate, cerate, and dichromate, only cerate and dichromate solutions can be made up by weight. Ammonium hexanitratocerate, $(NH_4)_2Ce(NO_3)_6$, and potassium dichromate, $K_2Cr_2O_7$, are primary-standard materials which can be dried and weighed out either for direct titration or for the preparation of a standard solution by dilution to a known volume. Permanganate solutions must be prepared approximately and standardized.

Several primary-standard reducing agents are available: sodium oxalate, arsenious oxide, ferrous ethylenediammonium sulfate, and electrolytic iron.

Sodium Oxalate.[1] $Na_2C_2O_4$. Mol. wt. 134.014. Equiv. wt. 67.007. Sodium oxalate is a stable, anhydrous salt which reacts stoichiometrically and rapidly with permanganate and cerate under the proper conditions. It is oxidized to carbon dioxide by these agents. The change in oxidation number is 2 in this reaction (from 6 to 8 for 2-carbon atoms), so that the equivalent weight is the molecular weight divided by 2, $Na_2C_2O_4/2$.

Arsenious Oxide.[1] As_2O_3. Mol. wt. 197.82. Equiv. wt. 49.46. Arsenious oxide is sublimed during its manufacture, and the reagent-grade material is highly pure and satisfactory for use as a primary standard. Arsenious oxide is used for the standardization of iodine solutions and also for the standardization of permanganate and cerate solutions provided suitable catalysts are added. Arsenious oxide will not dissolve in acid solutions but must first be dissolved in a sodium carbonate solution and then acidified to form arsenious acid.

Ferrous Ethylenediammonium Sulfate (Oesper's Salt). $Fe(C_2H_4\text{-}(NH_3)_2(SO_4)_2 \cdot 4H_2O$. Mol. wt. 382.2. Equiv. wt. 382.2. Ferrous ethylenediammonium sulfate is a stable compound which is very satisfactory for standardizing permanganate, cerate, or dichromate solutions. It is simply dissolved in water, the solution acidified with sulfuric acid, and the ferrous iron titrated. The corresponding ammonium salt, $Fe(NH_4)_2(SO_4)_2 \cdot 6H_2O$ (Mohr's Salt), is not sufficiently stable to be acceptable as a primary standard.

Metallic Iron. Fe^0. At. wt. 55.85. Equiv. wt. 55.85. Iron of sufficiently high purity for use as a primary standard is available, usually in the form of wire. An iron of unusually high purity is also available in pieces 1 to 2 mm. in size; this material is prepared electrolytically and ignited in a stream of moist hydrogen which removes any film of oxide and reduces the content of carbon and phosphorus. Iron wire if rusty should be sandpapered and wiped clean before use.

[1] Certain primary-standard materials can be purchased from the National Bureau of Standards. These have been carefully analyzed and can be used in crucial work in which all possibility of doubt as to the quality of the primary standard must be eliminated.

Bureau of Standards Number	Chemical	Purity
40e	Sodium oxalate	99.96
83a	Arsenious oxide	99.99
136	Potassium dichromate	100.00

The metallic iron is dissolved in hydrochloric acid, the iron then reduced to the ferrous state with zinc, and the ferrous iron titrated with the solution of the oxidizing agent being standardized. The procedure is given under the volumetric determination of iron.

Iodine. I^0. At. wt. 126.92. Equiv. wt. 126.92. Iodine is readily sublimed and obtained in pure form. The reagent-grade material is quite satisfactory as a primary-standard material, and standard solutions of iodine can be prepared by weight. Owing to its volatility and corrosive properties it must not be weighed on an open dish in the analytical balance and must be handled so that no loss results during the interval between weighing and dissolution. Iodine is not appreciably soluble in water but does dissolve in a solution of potassium iodide, owing to the formation of potassium triiodide, KI_3.

Potassium Iodate. KIO_3. Mol. wt. 214.02. Equiv. wt. 35.67. Potassium iodate is anhydrous, non-hygroscopic, and excellent for the standardization of sodium thiosulfate solutions, for it reacts with potassium iodide in the presence of acids to liberate 6 equivalents of iodine:

$$KIO_3 + 5KI + 6HCl = 6I^0 + 6KCl + 3H_2O$$

The iodine set free is titrated with sodium thiosulfate. The equivalent weight of potassium iodate when so used is one-sixth the molecular weight.

Potassium Acid Iodate. $KH(IO_3)_2$. Mol. wt. 389.94. The equivalent weight of potassium acid iodate depends on nature of reaction; a typical use is

$$KH(IO_3)_2 + 10KI + 11HCl = 12I^0 + 11KCl + 6H_2O$$

in which the equivalent weight is one-twelfth the molecular weight. Potassium acid iodate is available commercially in highly pure form. It can also be used as a primary standard in neutralization reactions.

Potassium Dichromate. $K_2Cr_2O_7$. Mol. wt. 294.21. Equiv. wt. 49.035. Potassium dichromate is an excellent primary standard. It is anhydrous, non-hygroscopic, and may be dried at a temperature of 150° or higher. For the standardization of solutions of reducing agents such as ferrous sulfate and titanous chloride, small samples of potassium dichromate may be weighed out and titrated. Standard solutions of potassium dichromate may be prepared by dissolving an accurately weighed amount of the salt and diluting exactly to known volume. When hot, potassium dichromate has a somewhat different color than when cold; this does not indicate decomposition. The reagent-grade potassium dichromate obtained from the chemical companies is usually sufficiently good for primary-standard use.

Ammonium Hexanitratocerate. $(NH_4)_2Ce(NO_3)_6$.   Mol. wt. 548.26.
Equiv. wt. 548.26.   The use of ammonium hexanitratocerate as a primary standard has been carefully checked; it is as satisfactory a primary standard as potassium dichromate, sodium oxalate, or arsenious oxide.   The salt is anhydrous and non-hygroscopic.   It keeps indefinitely but may not be dried at over 85°.   Some care must be exercised in preparing a standard solution of sulfatoceric acid from it; detailed directions are given on page 274.   Ammonium hexanitratocerate is available commercially.

TABLE 20.   REAGENTS FOR EFFECTING PRELIMINARY
OXIDATIONS AND REDUCTIONS

Oxidizing Agents	Approximate Reduction Potential (volts)	Method of Removing Excess
Perchloric acid, $HClO_4 \cdot 2H_2O$, hot and concentrated	+2.0	Dilution with water and boiling to remove trace of free chlorine
Potassium persulfate, $K_2S_2O_8$	2.0	Usually used with Ag^+ as catalyst; excess destroyed by boiling
Ozone, O_3	2.0	Boiling
Hydrogen peroxide, H_2O_2	1.8	Boiling
Potassium periodate, KIO_4	1.7	Precipitation as $Hg_5(IO_6)_2$
Lead dioxide, PbO_2	1.7	Filtration
Sodium bismuthate, $NaBiO_3$	1.6	Filtration
Potassium chlorate, $KClO_3$	1.5	Boiling in acid solution
Potassium permanganate, $KMnO_4$	1.5	Boiling, with a little HCl if permissible; also by warming with $NaNO_2$ or NaN_3
Reducing Agents		
Bismuth amalgam, Bi^0Hg^0	+0.3	Liquid-liquid separation
Silver, Ag^0, HCl solution	0.2	Filtration
Hydrogen sulfide, H_2S	0.2	Boiling
Hydroxylammonium chloride, NH_3OHCl	—	——
Stannous chloride, $SnCl_2$	0.1	Oxidation by mercuric chloride
Sulfurous acid, SO_2, H_2SO_3	0.1	Boiling
Sodium hyposulfite (sodium hydrosulfite), $Na_2S_2O_4$,		Boiling acid solution
Acid solution	0.0	
Alkaline solution	−1.4	
Lead amalgam, Pb^0Hg^0	−0.1	Liquid-liquid separation
Cadmium amalgam, Cd^0Hg^0	−0.4	Liquid-liquid separation
Zinc, Zn^0	−0.76	Filtration

PRELIMINARY OXIDATIONS AND REDUCTIONS

Usually in any oxidation-reduction titration some preliminary steps are necessary to adjust properly the valence state of the material being determined before the titrations can actually be made. The excess of the oxidizing or reducing agent used to make this preliminary adjustment must be removed. For metallic reducing agents, such as zinc and silver, simple filtration serves. Sometimes the excess reagent can be destroyed by boiling, or removed by precipitation; occasionally still another oxidizing or reducing agent is added to remove the first reagent. For the purpose of this preliminary oxidation or reduction many reagents can be employed which cannot be used as standard solutions: they may be insoluble, or their solutions unstable, or their reactions not stoichiometric or rapid. Some of these agents are listed in Table 20.

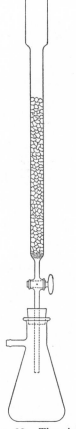

Reduction by metallic zinc or by metallic silver is of quite general utility and is carried out by passing the solution through a tall column of the finely granulated metal. These columns are known as reductors.

The Zinc Reductor. Metallic zinc is a powerful reducing agent and is used in the determination of several elements to reduce these elements to their lower valences before they are titrated with a standard oxidizing agent. The common form of the zinc reductor is a glass tube approximately 2.5 cm. in diameter and 30 cm. long, charged with granulated zinc which has been amalgamated (alloyed with mercury); Fig. 66. A perforated porous plate covered with a bit of glass wool is used to support the zinc. The solution to be reduced is

Fig. 66. The zinc reductor.

simply poured through the column and is followed by a wash of dilute sulfuric acid.

The reduction may also be carried out by inserting a spiral of zinc wire directly into the solution, Fig. 71. About 60 g. of zinc wire, 3.5 to 4 mm. in diameter and wound into a spiral which will pass through the neck of the flask used, will last for many determinations. The wire spiral is somewhat slower in action than the zinc column but requires less attention. The zinc wire is also amalgamated before use.

Zinc is less readily attacked by acids, with the liberation of hydrogen, if its surface has been amalgamated with mercury. The amalgamation is effected by shaking the zinc with a slightly acid solution of mercuric chloride; the mercury is reduced by the zinc and alloys with it. The acid brightens the surface of the zinc to promote the reaction.

The zinc reductor can be used with sulfuric acid solutions only; hydrochloric acid solutions react so rapidly with the zinc that the hydrogen liberated interferes with the use of the reductor.

The most frequent uses of the zinc reductor are in the determination of iron and of molybdenum. The behavior of some of the common elements on passage through the reductor is given in Table 21.

TABLE 21. ACTION OF ZINC AND SILVER REDUCTORS

Amalgamated Zinc Reductor, Sulfuric Acid Solution	Silver Reductor, Hydrochloric Acid Solution
$Fe^{+3} = Fe^{++}$	$Fe^{+3} = Fe^{++}$
$Ti^{+4} = Ti^{+3}$	$Ti^{+4} = $ No reduction
$CrO_4^{=} = Cr^{++}$	$CrO_4^{=} = Cr^{+3}$
$MnO_4^{-} = Mn^{++}$	$MnO_4^{-} = Mn^{++}$
$MoO_4^{=} = Mo^{+3}$	$MoO_4^{=} = Mo^{+5}$ (2 M HCl)
$HVO_3 = V^{++}$	$HVO_3 = VO^{++}$
$UO_2^{++} = U^{+3} + U^{+4}$	$UO_2^{++} = U^{+4}$
$Cu^{++} = Cu^{0}$	$Cu^{++} = CuCl_3^{=}$
$Ag^{+} = Ag^{0}$	
$Al^{+3} = $ No reduction	

When properly activated, amalgamated zinc will reduce oxygen to hydrogen peroxide: $O_2 + 2H^{+} + Zn^{0} = H_2O_2 + Zn^{++}$. Contact of air with the amalgamated zinc in a reductor then may lead to the formation of hydrogen peroxide. Hydrogen peroxide is a reducing agent (as well as an oxidizing agent) and is oxidized by strong oxidizing agents to oxygen and water; thus with permanganate:

$$5H_2O_2 + 2KMnO_4 + 3H_2SO_4 = K_2SO_4 + 2MnSO_4 + 8H_2O + 5O_2$$

Obviously, such reduction may lead to a serious error if it occurs simultaneously with the reduction of some element being determined by reduction on the zinc and subsequent titration with an oxidizing agent. It can be avoided by never allowing the liquid level to fall below the top of the zinc column.

Preparation of the Zinc Reductor. Weigh enough granulated zinc, 20 to 30 mesh, to fill the reductor with a column about 2.5 cm. in diameter and 25 to 30 cm. high. Place the zinc in a large conical flask.

Add a solution of mercuric chloride containing sufficient salt to give an amount of mercury equal to 1 per cent of the weight of the zinc. Add 1 ml. of concentrated hydrochloric acid. Close the flask with a rubber stopper and shake the mixture for several minutes, stopping now and then to release any pressure developed. Decant the liquid from the amalgamated zinc and wash the zinc several times with water. Place a plug of glass wool at the bottom of the reductor and transfer the amalgamated zinc to the reductor. Wash the reductor several times with dilute sulfuric acid (2:100). Do not allow the level of the liquid to fall below the top of the zinc. Rinse the receiver and then draw through the reductor 150 ml. of dilute sulfuric acid. Titrate the solution with 0.1 N potassium permanganate. Not more than 0.1 ml. of the permanganate solution should be required for this titration. If this blank titration is greater than 0.1 ml., continue the washing, being careful not to draw the level of the liquid below the metal, and repeat the blank titration. When work with the reductor is over, fill the reductor with dilute sulfuric acid and cover it with an inverted beaker.

The Silver Reductor. Metallic silver is a convenient agent for effecting the reduction of certain materials before their titration with standard oxidizing agents. The material being reduced must be present in a hydrochloric acid solution, silver chloride being formed in the reaction; thus

$$FeCl_3 + Ag^0 = FeCl_2 + AgCl$$

$$CuCl_2 + Ag^0 + 2HCl = H_2CuCl_3 + AgCl$$

The standard reduction potential of the silver chloride-silver couple is

$$AgCl + e^- = Ag^0 + Cl^- \qquad E^0 = +0.2245 \text{ volt}$$

Metallic silver is thus only a mild reducing agent. Although it reduces ferric iron to ferrous it does not reduce titanic salts to the trivalent state or chromic salts to chromous. The reducing actions of the zinc and silver reductors are summarized in Table 21.

The only contamination introduced into a solution on passage through the silver reductor is the very small amount of silver chloride necessary to saturate the solution. A vertical tube similar to that used for the zinc reductor, Fig. 66, is also used for the silver reductor. Usually it is not necessary to use suction. The metallic silver for the reductor is very easily prepared by reducing silver nitrate with metallic copper or by electroreduction. When hydrochloric acid solutions of reducible substances are passed through the silver reductor, the silver on the surface is converted to silver chloride; this limits the amount of material which may be reduced at one time to about 250 ml.

of 0.1 N solution (iron, copper, and so on), but the silver chloride coating is readily dissolved away by treatment with ammonia and the reductor thus regenerated. Very little silver is lost when working with hydrochloric acid solutions, and one charge lasts for a great many determinations.

Preparation of the Silver Reductor. Metallic silver prepared by electrolytic reduction of silver nitrate and having a particle size of 20 to 40 mesh is best for the purpose. The column of silver should be about 2 cm. in diameter and 20 to 25 cm. long; the tube used for the zinc reductor, Fig. 66, is about the right size for the purpose. Place a plug of glass wool in the tube above the stopcock and transfer the metallic silver to the reductor; about 120 to 150 g. of silver is needed. Wash the reductor once or twice with 1 M hydrochloric acid. If electrolytically deposited silver is used, liquid will run through the reductor freely and suction will not be required.

In use, allow the solution to run through the reductor at the rate of about 20 ml. per minute. Do not allow the level of the liquid to fall below the top of the silver column. Use 1 M hydrochloric acid for washing the solution being reduced through the reductor, using 20 to 25-ml. portions.

When the silver has become black over 75 per cent of its length, indicating that it is spent, regenerate the silver in the following manner: Pass water through the reductor to wash out the hydrochloric acid. Fill the reductor with dilute ammonia (1:1) and allow the ammonia to stand in contact with the silver for 10 minutes. Wash the reductor once with the same dilute ammonia and then five or six times with water. Finally, fill the reductor with 1 M hydrochloric acid. The reductor is then ready again for use. The regeneration may be repeated a great number of times.

THE POTENTIOMETRIC DETERMINATION OF THE EQUIVALENCE-POINT IN OXIDATION-REDUCTION REACTIONS

In those oxidation-reduction titrations for which no suitable oxidation-reduction indicator is known, the equivalence-point may often be determined potentiometrically. A potentiometric titration is necessarily slower than a titration using a visual indicator, for the potential of the electrodes dipping into the solution must be measured after each addition of the standard solution, at least in the neighborhood of the equivalence-point, and a plot must be made of the potential against volume of solution added to locate precisely the center of the vertical portion, or break, in the curve. A potentiometric titration gives more information about the nature of the reaction, for from it the standard reduction potentials of the couples involved and the potential at the equivalence-point can be found, and from these data the equilibrium constant for the reaction can be calculated. All this is explained in Chapter 10. In routine analytical work, the potentiometric method is used only when a visual indicator

Fig. 67. Potentiometric titration.

is lacking. When a new reaction is under investigation, the quickest way to find a suitable visual indicator is to run a potentiometric titration first and then select an oxidation-reduction indicator which has a standard reduction potential close to the equivalence-potential found for the titration; obviously this is a lot shorter than trying to select an indicator by trying out one after another until one is found which gives the correct result.

The electrode system used for the potentiometric titration of oxidation-reduction reactions consists of a reference electrode (usually the saturated calomel electrode) and a bright platinum foil or wire as indicator electrode. The saturated calomel reference electrode used may be the conventional laboratory model or one of the more compact, commercial types shown in Fig. 63.

Mechanical stirring is essential in a potentiometric titration, for the presence of the electrodes practically precludes shaking or hand stirring.   Mechanical stirring is usually accomplished by a motor-driven glass stirring rod, but magnetic stirring is more convenient because it leaves more room at the top of the vessel for the electrodes, the buret, and an inlet tube for inert gas if it is necessary to maintain an atmosphere free of oxygen.

The Potentiometer.   The potentiometer actually used for the measurement of the potential of a cell is somewhat more complicated

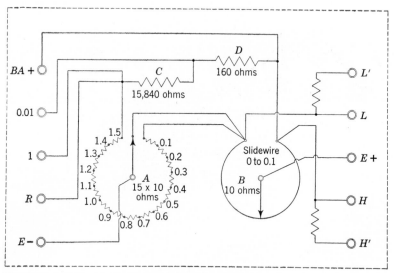

Fig. 68.   Leeds and Northrup students' potentiometer.   Internal connections.
(Diagram by permission.)

than the simple potentiometer discussed on page 240, although the basic principle is the same.   In order to obtain a sufficiently high accuracy the slidewire must be made very long; this is most conveniently accomplished by combining a relatively short slidewire with a series of fixed resistors each exactly equal to the total resistance of the slidewire.   The potential drop over the slidewire, and each of the resistors can be made exactly 0.1 volt and they can be arranged so that any potential from zero to the capacity of the instrument can be used to balance the voltage being measured.   The Leeds and Northrup students' potentiometer has fifteen such fixed resistors in series with the slidewire and measures potentials up to 1.6 volts.   The working circuit thus consists of a battery, a variable resistor, the series of fixed resistors (each 10 ohms), and the slidewire (10 ohms), all connected in series; see Fig. 68.   By adjusting the variable resistor the current in the working circuit can be made the exact value that will give a potential drop of exactly 0.1000 volt over the slidewire and over each resistance. The potential taken from the working circuit to oppose the potential being measured is taken between the slidewire contact and the selector switch contact.

The instrument is provided with two ranges: 0 to 1.6 volts, and 0 to 0.016 volt. Either may be selected by connecting to the proper binding post. The upper range is used for the measurement of the potential

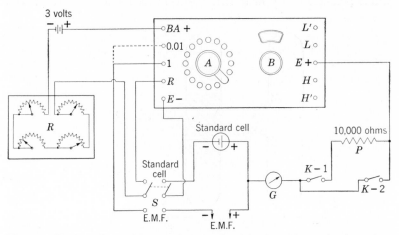

Fig. 69. Leeds and Northrup students' potentiometer. External connections. (*Diagram by permission.*)

of an electrolytic cell, the lower range for the measurement of temperature with a thermocouple. The range is changed by two shunt coils C (15,840 ohms) and D (160 ohms), so proportioned that, when the connection is made to binding post 1, the current through A and B is one hundred times that through C and D. When connection is made to post 0.01, coil C is in series with A and B and the current through this circuit is reduced to one-hundredth of that through D. The total current remains the same.

The five binding posts on the left of the instrument and the one in the central position on the right are the six used for potentiometer measurement. The other four binding posts, L', L, H, H', at the right of the instrument are provided for making independent connections to the slidewire, either with or without end coils, so that the instrument may be used as part of a Wheatstone bridge circuit.

Operation of the Students' Potentiometer. Make the connections exactly as shown in Fig. 69, paying strict attention to the polarities.

Be sure to include the 10,000-ohm resistance P to protect the galva-nometer. Use two 1.5-volt dry cells for the working battery. The total resistance in the fixed resistors and coils is about 160 ohms, and about 140 ohms more are needed in the variable resistor R. When using the 1.6-volt range, connection should be made to 1 as shown; when using the 16-mv. range this connection should be transferred to 0.01.

First adjust the working current in the potentiometer. Throw the double pole-double throw switch S to connect the standard cell. Set

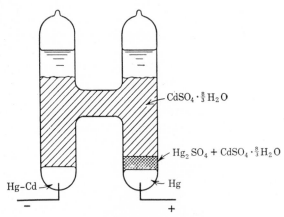

Fig. 70. Weston cell.

the dial and slidewire to the voltage of the standard cell. The Weston standard cell, Fig. 70, is usually employed; its potential is 1.018 volts at 20°. Adjust the variable resistance R until on closing the key K-1 there is only a small deflection of the galvanometer. Continue the adjustment, tapping key K-2 until there is no deflection of the galva-nometer. The potentiometer then reads directly in volts and is ready for the measurement.

Throw the double pole-double throw switch to connect the potential to be measured. Tap key K-1 and note the galvanometer deflection. Adjust the dial and slidewire to reduce the deflection of the galva-nometer. Make the final adjustment using key K-2. The sum of the readings on the dial and slidewire gives the potential being meas-ured on the 1.6-volt range. On the 16-mv. range, the sum of the two readings multiplied by 0.01 gives the potential measured.

To make sure the current through the potentiometer has not changed, again connect the standard cell, set the dial switch and the slidewire to the voltage of the standard cell, and close key K-2. If there is no deflection the current has not changed; if there is a small deflection adjust R until no deflection occurs.

If it is necessary to measure a potential greater than 1.6 volts, recalibrate the potentiometer, setting the slidewire at one-half the voltage of the standard cell. Readings made subsequently must then be multiplied by 2, and the range covered is 3.2 volts. It is usually necessary to place a third 1.5-volt dry cell in the working circuit.

Carrying out the Titration. Arrange to stir the solution either with a motor-driven stirring rod or with a magnetic stirrer. Clean the platinum electrode by immersing it for a while in cleaning solution, a mixture of sulfuric acid and sodium dichromate. Suspend the platinum electrode and the calomel electrode within the vessel in such a way that they are not struck by the stirrer. If the titration must be carried out in an inert atmosphere, a wide-neck flask of suitable size is much better for the purpose than a beaker. A side arm may be sealed into the flask, and extending it almost to the inside bottom provides a good way to introduce the inert gas. If a magnetic stirrer is used, the room at the top of the vessel is ample for the two electrodes, the buret tip, and a gas outlet tube; all these can pass through or be carried by a rubber stopper.

After placing the solution in the titration vessel, make certain the electrodes are immersed in the solution, start the stirring, and adjust the potentiometer to read directly in volts. Add the standard solution in large increments at first and then dropwise as the end-point is approached. Measure the potential after each addition until a large sudden change occurs, marking the end-point. Take a few additional readings beyond the end-point.

Plot the data, using the potential as ordinate and the volume of the standard solution as abscissa. The end-point lies at the steepest part of the curve where the rate of change is greatest.

Applications of Potentiometric Titrations. Both neutralization and oxidation-reduction reactions may be followed potentiometrically. The indicator electrodes for the hydrogen ion which are used in potentiometric titrations involving acids and bases are discussed in Chapter 18. In general the potentiometric method is used in titrations of colored solutions or for titrations for which no suitable indicator is available. It has been applied most extensively to oxidation-reduction titrations, for oxidation-reduction indicators are a fairly recent development.

The potentiometric methods work well with titrations involving permanganate, cerate, dichromate, bromate, and with most of the iodometric methods. The size of the vertical portion of the titration curve, that is, the curve in the neighborhood of the equivalence-point, depends largely on the difference between the standard reduction potentials of the two couples involved. This vertical portion may be as much as 1.2 volts, as in the titration of chromous sulfate with cerate; or there may be almost no vertical portion at all if the difference in the values of E^0 is small, but even here there will always be a point of inflection in the curve, at the steepest part of the curve, which corresponds to the equivalence-point. Titrations can thus be made potentiometrically which could not possibly be made with a visual indicator; an analogous situation in neutralization reactions is the titration of acetic acid with ammonia and of perchloric acid in the presence of acetic, which can be accurately done potentiometrically but not at all with indicators.

In general, potentiometric titrations are most satisfactory with solutions about 0.1 N in concentration. Although they can be carried out successfully with solutions as dilute as 0.001 N, the time required to reach equilibrium after each addition of standard solution may be so long that titrations with such dilute solutions are often impractical.

TITRATIONS WITH CERATE SALTS

The salts of quadrivalent cerium are the most versatile of the strong oxidizing agents which may be used as standard solutions. Quadrivalent cerium salts are light yellow and on reduction form trivalent, colorless cerous salts. Titrations with cerate salts may be carried out in hydrochloric acid solutions as strong as 1 N and in sulfuric acid, nitric acid, and perchloric acid solutions of any strength. The titration in hydrochloric acid solution is of particular advantage in the determination of iron in iron ores for these ores are soluble only in hydrochloric acid. The oxidizing power of cerate salts in hydrochloric acid is not as great as in solutions of the other acids; the values of the formal reduction potentials given in Table 22 show this clearly.

TABLE 22. FORMAL REDUCTION POTENTIALS OF THE
CERATE-CEROUS COUPLE IN VARIOUS MEDIA

Acid Concentration (molar)	HCl (volts)	HNO$_3$ (volts)	H$_2$SO$_4$ (volts)	HClO$_4$ (volts)
1	1.28	1.61	1.44	1.71
2	—	1.62	1.44	1.71
4	—	1.61	1.43	1.75
6	—	—	1.43	1.82
8	—	1.56	1.42	1.87

The nature of ceric compounds in solution is not clearly understood, and for this reason different names are applied to solutions of quadrivalent cerium salts. The standard reduction potential of the ceratecerous system changes greatly with the nature of the acid present in the solution; this fact indicates that it is not likely that the cerium is present as the ceric ion, Ce^{+4}, but more probably exists as an anion in combination with a varying number of acid and hydroxyl groups. Thus, it has become customary in the last few years to speak of *cerate oxidimetry*, of *sulfatoceric acid, nitratoceric acid*, and of *perchloratoceric acid*, rather than of *ceric sulfate, ceric nitrate*, and *ceric perchlorate*. Possible formulas for these acids are, respectively, $H_2Ce(SO_4)_3$, $H_2Ce(NO_3)_6$, and $H_2Ce(ClO_4)_6$. Salts of the first two acids are well known.

On reduction, quadrivalent cerium compounds pass to colorless, trivalent cerium salts, the cerous ion being simply Ce^{+3}, probably carrying a number of molecules of water as a surrounding shell. In the titration of otherwise colorless solutions, then, a cerate solution can act as its own indicator. However, the various ferrous 1,10-phenanthroline indicators, which have color transitions at high reduction potentials, are ideally adapted to use with cerate solutions and give a more vivid color change than that obtained with cerate salts alone.

The formal reduction potentials of the cerate-cerous couple under different conditions are given in Table 22. Except in the perchloric acid solutions, there is not a great deal of change in the value of the reduction potential with change in the acid concentration, although there is a major change on passing from one acid to another. Perchloric acid solutions of quadrivalent cerium have the greatest oxidizing power of all of the various cerate solutions studied, the 8 N perchloric acid solution having the exceptionally high value of $+1.87$ volts.

Cerate solutions are usually made up to approximately the concentration desired and then standardized, although the compound ammonium hexanitratocerate, $(NH_4)_2Ce(NO_3)_6$, has been shown to be an excellent primary standard. Various cerate compounds are available as starting materials: sulfatoceric acid ($H_2Ce(SO_4)_3$), ammonium sulfatocerate ($(NH_4)_4Ce(SO_4)_4 \cdot 2H_2O$), and hydrated ceric oxide ($CeO_2 \cdot xH_2O$). These materials are dissolved in fairly strong acid as a considerable amount of free acid must be present to prevent the hydrolysis of the compounds and the formation of insoluble basic substances. Solutions of cerate salts in sulfuric acid are stable indefinitely; such solutions can even be boiled for extended periods. Solutions of nitratoceric acid and perchloratoceric acid decompose, but only at a very slow rate. Solutions of quadrivalent cerium in hydrochloric acid stronger than 1 N, however, are not stable, the quadrivalent cerium oxidizing the chloride to free chlorine.

The presence of moderate concentrations of hydrochloric acid in the solutions being titrated is permissible, for the reduction potential of cerate in hydrochloric acid is so low that the oxidation of chloride to free chlorine takes place slowly.

Cerate solutions may be standardized with arsenious oxide, sodium oxalate, ferrous ethylenediammonium sulfate, and electrolytic iron. The reaction of arsenious acid with sulfatoceric acid is very slow unless osmium tetroxide is added as catalyst. The oxidation of oxalic acid by cerate proceeds rapidly at room temperature in a 2 N perchloric acid solution, and 2 N perchloric acid is the best solvent for sodium oxalate, therefore, when sodium oxalate is used as primary standard. For this titration perchloratoceric acid in 2 N $HClO_4$ is used as the oxidizing agent. The titration of oxalic acid in a sulfuric acid solution can only be made in a hot solution and is best done by adding an excess of cerate solution and later back-titrating the excess with standard ferrous sulfate. Either sodium oxalate or arsenious acid may be titrated in hydrochloric acid with a cerate solution if iodine chloride is added as catalyst; the titrations must be made at a temperature of 45–50° if ferroin is to be employed as indicator. The most convenient way of all to standardize cerate solutions is against ferrous ethylenediammonium sulfate, which only needs to be weighed out, dissolved in dilute sulfuric acid, and titrated. The standardization of cerate solutions against electrolytic iron is carried out using the same procedure employed for the determination of iron.

Applications of Cerate Oxidimetry. Iron is oxidized from the ferrous to the ferric state by cerate solutions, and the titration may be carried out in hydrochloric acid solution in which the oxide ores of iron are almost invariably soluble. The ferric chloride formed is reduced with stannous chloride or metallic silver prior to titration. The details of this determination are discussed in a separate section below.

Cupric copper in hydrochloric acid solution is reduced to chlorocuprous acid, H_2CuCl_3, on passage through the silver reductor, and can be determined by titrating the chlorocuprous acid back to cupric copper with sulfatoceric acid. The chlorocuprous ion is a powerful reducing agent and is easily oxidized by air so that it is best to place an excess of ferric sulfate in the receiver beneath the silver reductor. Ferrous iron equivalent to the univalent copper is formed and is titrated with the cerate, using ferrous 1,10-phenanthroline sulfate as indicator. Nitric acid, zinc, stannic tin, arsenate, bismuth, and cadmium do not interfere in this determination, but iron, molybdenum, uranium, and vanadium must be absent.

Ferrocyanide can be determined by titration in hydrochloric acid or sulfuric acid solution

$$Fe(CN)_6{}^{-4} + Ce(SO_4)_3{}^= = Ce^{+3} + Fe(CN)_6{}^{-3} + 3SO_4{}^=$$

Ferrous 1,10-phenanthroline sulfate is used to mark the equivalence-point.

Any of the elements reduced on passage through the zinc reductor can be titrated back to their higher valence states by cerate.

$$Ti^{+3} \text{ to } Ti^{+4} \qquad V^{++} \text{ or } VO^{++} \text{ to } HVO_3$$

$$Cr^{++} \text{ to } Cr^{+3} \qquad U^{+3} \text{ or } U^{+4} \text{ to } UO_2{}^{++}$$

$$Mo^{+3} \text{ to } H_2MoO_4$$

The titration of molybdenum is used indirectly for the determination of phosphorus after precipitation of ammonium molybdiphosphate, $(NH_4)_3P(Mo_3O_{10})_4$. The uranyl ion, $UO_2{}^{++}$, on passage through the zinc reductor, is reduced to a mixture of tri- and quadrivalent uranium. The trivalent uranium is converted to quadrivalent uranium by bubbling air through the solution, after which the uranium can be titrated from 4 to 6 with sulfatoceric acid. This titration has been used indirectly for the determination of sodium after precipitation as sodium magnesium uranyl acetate, $NaMg(UO_2)(C_2H_3O_2)_9 \cdot 6.5H_2O$.

The titration of arsenious acid must be catalyzed by osmic acid; the procedure is given later under the standardization of sulfatoceric acid with arsenious oxide. Antimony can be determined in a similar fashion. Thallium may be determined by oxidation from the univalent to the trivalent state.

Oxalic acid is oxidized by perchloratoceric acid to carbon dioxide and water, making possible a direct determination of oxalic acid and an indirect determination of a variety of metals, such as calcium and zinc, which form insoluble oxalates. Other organic materials are not oxidized by cerate salts to carbon dioxide and water. Rather the reaction often stops at the formation of formic acid, HCO_2H. This is the case with formaldehyde, glycolic acid, and glycerol. The further oxidation of formic acid to carbon dioxide and water is very slow.

Preparation of 0.1 *N Sulfatoceric Acid. A, Using Ceric Hydroxide.* Cautiously and with continuous stirring, add 78.2 ml. of concentrated sulfuric acid to 300 ml. of water in a 600-ml. beaker. Weigh on the side-shelf balance 20.8 g. of ceric hydroxide and transfer it to a 1500-ml.

beaker. Add the hot, diluted sulfuric acid with vigorous stirring and stir until all the ceric hydroxide has dissolved. Dilute the solution to 1 l. by adding water. Cool, and transfer to a glass-stoppered bottle. Mix thoroughly. Cover the bottle with an inverted beaker. The solution is approximately 1 M in sulfuric acid. Standardize the solution as described below.

B, *Using Ammonium Hexanitratocerate.* If primary-standard material is used the solution may be made up by weight. Weigh exactly 54.826 g. of the primary-standard-grade salt and place it in a 1-l. beaker. If the ammonium hexanitratocerate is the ordinary, reagent-grade material, the solution must be made up approximately 0.1 N and standardized. Weigh on the side-shelf balance 56 g. of the salt and place it in a 1-l. beaker. To the salt in either case add 56 ml. of concentrated sulfuric acid and stir the acid and salt thoroughly together for 2 minutes. Add 50 to 100 ml. of water and stir for 2 minutes. Add 100 ml. of water and stir again for 2 minutes. Continue the addition of 100-ml. portions of water with intervening stirring periods until a clear orange solution is obtained and the volume is 500 to 600 ml. If the solution is being made up approximately for later standardization, dilute the solution to 1 l., cool, and transfer to a glass-stoppered bottle. If primary-standard material had been weighed exactly, cool the solution and transfer it quantitatively to a 1-l. volumetric flask. Dilute with water, mixing well after each addition. Cool to room temperature before making the final dilution to exactly 1000 ml.

The procedure just described must be followed closely. If the ammonium hexanitratocerate is dissolved in 900 ml. of water to which 56 ml. of concentrated sulfuric acid has been added, a clear solution will result. Upon standing 12 to 24 hours an insoluble precipitate forms in every case. The addition of the concentrated sulfuric acid to the crystalline cerate followed by gradual dilution generates heat and converts the nitratocerate ion to the sulfatocerate ion with the liberation of nitric acid. The solution prepared as described is permanently stable on storage. It may be heated to boiling without decomposition and may be standardized by the methods described in the following paragraphs.

Standardization of 0.1 N Sulfatoceric Acid with Arsenious Oxide. Dry primary-standard-grade arsenious oxide at 110° for 1 to 2 hours. Weigh accurately a sample of 0.20 to 0.30 g. into a 400-ml. beaker. Rinse down the walls of the beaker with 10 ml. or so of water from the wash bottle. Add 2 g. of sodium hydroxide and swirl the solution gently to dissolve the arsenious oxide. When all the arsenious oxide has dissolved, dilute the solution to 100 ml. Acidify the solution by adding 30 ml. of dilute sulfuric acid (1:10). Add 1 or 2 drops of osmic acid solution (0.125 g. of osmic acid in 50 ml. of water containing a drop of sulfuric acid). Add 2 drops of 0.01 N ferrous 1,10-phenanthroline sulfate (or 2 ml. of a saturated solution of ferrous 1,10-phenanthroline perchlorate). Titrate with the 0.1 N sulfatocerate solution. The pink color of the indicator fades somewhat during the early part of the titration, then intensifies, and with the first drop of cerate solution in excess changes from pink to colorless. The blue color of the oxidized form of the indicator is very faint.

No warning of the approach to the end-point in the reaction of arsenite with sulfatoceric acid is given by the transitory, reversible oxidation of the indicator; this is a good titration in which to use the titration thief described on page 152, Fig. 43.

Calculate the normality of the solution by dividing the weight of arsenious oxide taken by the milliequivalent weight of arsenious oxide, 0.049,455, and by the volume of sulfatoceric acid used.

Standardization of 0.1 N *Sulfatoceric Acid with Ferrous Ethylenediammonium Sulfate.* Weigh accurately samples of 1.5 to 1.8 g. of ferrous ethylenediammonium sulfate. Transfer a sample to a 400-ml. beaker. Dissolve the salt in 150 ml. of water containing 10 ml. of concentrated sulfuric acid. Add 2 drops of 0.01 N ferrous 1,10-phenanthroline sulfate (or 2 ml. of a saturated solution of ferrous 1,10-phenanthroline perchlorate). Titrate without undue delay with the sulfatocerate solution to the point where the pink color changes sharply from pink to colorless. Calculate the normality of the sulfatoceric acid solution; the milliequivalent weight of the ferrous ethylenediammonium sulfate is 0.3822.

Preparation of 0.1 N *Perchloratoceric Acid.* If the solution is to be made up exactly 0.1 N by weight, weigh accurately 54.826 g. of primary-standard ammonium hexanitratocerate, $(NH_4)_2Ce(NO_3)_6$; if the solution is to be made up approximately and later standardized, weigh on the side-shelf balance 55 g. of ordinary, reagent-grade ammonium hexanitratocerate. In either case proceed as follows, using vessels which have been carefully cleaned and avoiding all contact of the solution with dust and organic matter. Transfer the salt to a 1500-ml. beaker. Add 167 ml. of 72 per cent perchloric acid and warm the mixture to 50 to 60°, stirring continuously. Only a little of the orange, crystalline ammonium hexanitratocerate dissolves in this strength of acid, but nitric acid is liberated, as evidenced by the odor. Add 100 ml. of water and stir vigorously for 2 minutes. Repeat the addition of 100 ml. of water with 2-minute intervals of stirring until all the cerate salt is in solution; this will occur when the volume has reached 500 to 600 ml. If the solution is being made up by weight from primary-standard material, dilute the solution to 800 to 900 ml., transfer it quantitatively to a 1-l. volumetric flask, dilute to the mark, and mix thoroughly. If the solution is being made up approximately, simply dilute to 1 l., transfer to a storage bottle, and mix well.

The procedure given must be followed exactly or a precipitate will form as the solution stands.

Perchloratoceric acid has a very high reduction potential $(+1.75$ volts) and decomposes slowly on standing; in 72 hours a detectable loss can be observed. Store the solution in a cool, dark place to minimize such loss.

Standardization of 0.1 N Perchloratoceric Acid with Sodium Oxalate. Weigh accurately a sample of 0.2 to 0.25 g. of primary-standard sodium oxalate. Dissolve the sample in 150 ml. of 2 M perchloric acid (167 ml. of 72 per cent perchloric acid diluted to 1 l. with water). Add 1 drop of 0.025 M nitro-ferroin indicator (5-nitro-1,10-phenanthroline ferrous sulfate). Titrate the solution with approximately 0.1 N perchloratoceric acid until the oxalate is oxidized and the first drop in excess decolorizes the solution. No catalyst is required, and the reaction is carried out at room temperature.

DETERMINATION OF IRON BY TITRATION WITH SULFATOCERIC ACID OR WITH PERCHLORATOCERIC ACID

The chief ore of iron is hematite, Fe_2O_3, which constitutes the great ore deposits at the west end of Lake Superior. Magnetite, Fe_3O_4, and limonite, a hydrated ferric oxide, $Fe_2O_3 \cdot xH_2O$, are of some importance as ore minerals. All three minerals can be dissolved in hydrochloric acid; magnetite forms a mixture of ferrous chloride and ferric chloride, corresponding to the apparent valences of iron in the mineral:

$$Fe_2O_3 + 6HCl = 2FeCl_3 + 3H_2O$$

$$Fe_3O_4 + 8HCl = FeCl_2 + 2FeCl_3 + 4H_2O$$

The principal impurities in iron ore are silica and silicate rock. Certain other elements are also always present: manganese, phosphorus (as phosphate), sulfur, aluminum, calcium, magnesium, titanium, sodium, and potassium; ores from certain regions contain considerable titanium and others appreciable amounts of chromium. Practically all iron ores will dissolve in hydrochloric acid, leaving a white or slightly colored residue which can be ignored in the remainder of the determination. Occasionally a dark residue of an iron-containing silicate remains, which must be given special treatment.

Unlike the permanganate titration, the sulfatocerate or perchloratocerate titration may be carried out in a hydrochloric acid solution. The reduction of the iron to the ferrous state can be made with the silver reductor

$$FeCl_3 + Ag^0 = FeCl_2 + AgCl$$

or by means of stannous chloride. If stannous chloride is used, the excess is disposed of by the addition of mercuric chloride; the mercurous chloride which forms is insoluble and does not react with the cerate solution during the titration.

$$2FeCl_3 + SnCl_2 = 2FeCl_2 + SnCl_4$$

$$SnCl_2 + 2HgCl_2 = SnCl_4 + Hg_2Cl_2$$

If a large excess of stannous chloride is added the reduction may proceed to dark gray metallic mercury

$$SnCl_2 + HgCl_2 = SnCl_4 + Hg^0$$

and the results for iron are then inaccurate.

As indicator either diphenylaminesulfonic acid or ferrous 1,10-phenanthroline sulfate may be used.

In the silver reductor, titanium, chromium, vanadium, and molybdenum are not reduced to their lower valence forms and hence do not interfere in the determination of iron. This is in sharp contrast to the reduction in the zinc reductor where these metals are reduced and later titrated with iron.

Procedure for the Determination of Iron by Titration with Sulfatoceric Acid or with Perchloratoceric Acid. Dry the iron ore to be analyzed for 2 hours at 110°. Weigh accurately a sample of approximately 1 g. into a 400-ml. beaker. Cover the beaker and add 20 ml. of dilute hydrochloric acid (1:1). Heat the mixture in the hood and hold it near the boiling point until all the ore has dissolved except a small amount of flocculent silica. Discontinue the heating, rinse the cover glass, and wash down the sides of the beaker with a stream of water from the wash bottle. The iron content of the silica-silicate residue is usually small and may be disregarded in most cases; however, if the residue is dark and is suspected to be a silicate-containing iron, decompose it by the procedure given in the footnote, page 286.

After the dissolution of the ore, the iron may be reduced in either of two ways: by the silver reductor (*A*) or by stannous chloride (*B*).

A, *Reduction of Ferric Chloride by the Silver Reductor.* Dilute the solution to 100 ml. and transfer the solution to the silver reductor, rinsing the contents of the beaker into the upper reservoir of the reductor quantitatively. Use a 400-ml. beaker as receiver. Open the stopcock to allow the solution to run through. When the level of the liquid in the reductor has reached the upper surface of the silver column, close the stopcock. Wash the reductor with six 20-ml. portions of dilute hydrochloric acid (1:15), completing the washing of the original beaker by pouring the wash liquid first into it and then into the reductor. Allow the liquid to drain to the level of the silver before making the next addition. Proceed immediately with the titration.

B, *Reduction of Ferric Chloride by Stannous Chloride.* Evaporate the solution containing the ferric chloride to a volume of 15 to 20 ml.; the evaporation will be speeded by raising the cover glass off the beaker by glass hooks. From this point on work one sample at a time. To the hot solution add a 10 per cent solution of stannous chloride in dilute hydrochloric acid (1:10). Make the addition dropwise with constant stirring until the yellow color is almost gone. Continue the reduction by the dropwise addition of a 1 per cent solution of stannous chloride until 1 drop just causes the color to change from yellow to pale green. Add 1 or 2 drops in excess but no more. This is a critical part of the process, for the excess stannous chloride must not amount to more than 1 or 2 drops. The addition of the stannous chloride can be conveniently made from a pipet or a dropping bottle. After the reduction is complete dilute the solution to 150 ml. with water and add at once 10 ml. of a 10 per cent solution of mercuric chloride. A light, white precipitate of mercurous chloride should form within 1 or 2 minutes, indicating that an excess of stannous chloride has been added; if no precipitate appears it is probable that the reduction of iron was incomplete. If more than a slight amount of mercurous chloride precipitates, too much stannous chloride was added and the sample must be discarded. Proceed immediately to the titration.

Titration. Add 2 drops of 0.01 N ferrous 1,10-phenanthroline sulfate (or 2 ml. of a saturated solution of ferrous 1,10-phenanthroline perchlorate) and titrate with 0.1 N sulfatoceric acid solution. The color of the ferrous chloride solution before the indicator is added is faint green or colorless. After the indicator is added the color is reddish orange. As the ferrous chloride is oxidized it adds yellow to the solution, and the color is gradually converted from reddish orange to orange. At the equivalence-point there is a sharp color change from orange to pale yellow.

Standardize the sulfatoceric acid solution by carrying out the identical procedure on electrolytic iron, or standardize it against arsenious oxide or ferrous ethylenediammonium sulfate as described earlier.

Calculate the per cent of iron in the sample. The milliequivalent weight of iron is 0.055,85.

DETERMINATION OF COPPER IN BRASS

On passage through a silver reductor in a hydrochloric acid solution cupric chloride is reduced to chlorocuprous acid, H_2CuCl_3.

$$CuCl_2 + Ag^0 + 3HCl = H_2CuCl_3 + AgCl$$

The chlorocuprous ion may then be titrated back to cupric chloride with sulfatoceric acid, using ferrous 1,10-phenanthroline sulfate as indicator.

This is a convenient method for the direct determination of copper in brass and bronze. The nitric acid used to dissolve the alloy has no effect on the reduction and titration, but the small amount of iron always present in a copper-base alloy is also reduced and titrated so that it counts as copper. This iron can be removed by precipitation with ammonia, and since it is small in amount one reprecipitation reduces the copper coprecipitated to a negligible amount.

Procedure for the Determination of Copper in Brass. Weigh accurately a sample of brass of about 0.3 g. Transfer to a 400-ml. beaker. Cover the beaker and add 1 ml. of concentrated nitric acid and 4 ml. of concentrated hydrochloric acid. Heat until the brass is completely dissolved. Dilute the solution to 150 ml. and neutralize with ammonia. Add sufficient ammonia in excess to convert all the copper to the deep blue cupric-ammonia compound. Filter on a medium-texture paper and wash with dilute ammonia (1:100). Place the original beaker under the funnel and dissolve the iron by pouring over the filter 20 ml. of hot, dilute hydrochloric acid (1:10). Wash the filter a few times with water. To the hydrochloric acid solution of the iron add a few drops of methyl red and reprecipitate the ferric hydroxide, adding enough ammonia to change the indicator and a very slight excess. Filter through the same paper. Combine the filtrates. Neutralize the solution with hydrochloric acid, adding just enough acid to dissolve the cupric hydroxide. Evaporate the solution to a volume of 50 ml. Add 23 ml. of concentrated hydrochloric acid. Pass the solution through the silver reductor, page 263, at the rate of 25 ml. per minute, receiving the filtrate in a 400-ml. beaker holding 20 ml. of a solution containing 48.2 g. of ferric alum and 2.5 ml. of concentrated sulfuric acid per 100 ml. Wash the reductor column with 100 ml. of dilute hydrochloric acid (1:4). Add 1 drop of 0.025 M ferrous 1,10-phenanthroline indicator solution. Titrate with sulfatoceric acid. The color of the cupric ion does not interfere, and the end-point is quite sharp.

Standardize the sulfatoceric acid in a similar manner, using pure copper.

Calculate the per cent of copper in the sample.

PROBLEMS

1. Complete and balance the following equations:
   - (a) $CuCl_2 + Ag^0 + HCl =$
     $H_2CuCl_3 + H_2Ce(SO_4)_3 =$
   - (b) $Ti_2(SO_4)_3 + H_2Ce(SO_4)_3 =$
   - (c) $Mo_2(SO_4)_3 + H_2Ce(SO_4)_3 =$
   - (d) $H_3AsO_3 + H_2Ce(SO_4)_3 + H_2SO_4 =$
   - (e) $Na_2C_2O_4 + H_2Ce(ClO_4)_6 + HClO_4 =$

2. Calculate the equivalent weight of copper, titanium, molybdenum, arsenic, and sodium oxalate in the oxidation-reduction reactions of Problem 1.

3. Calculate the weight of anhydrous ceric sulfate, 80 per cent $Ce(SO_4)_2$, required for the preparation of 500 ml. of 0.1500 N sulfatoceric acid solution.

4. A sample of pure ferrous ethylenediammonium sulfate weighing 1.500 g. required 42.0 ml. of a solution of sulfatoceric acid for titration in sulfuric acid solution. Calculate the normality of the cerate solution.

5. The iron in a sample of ore weighing 0.4852 g. required for titration from the ferrous to the ferric state 42.15 ml. of a 0.093,45 N cerate solution. Calculate the per cent of iron in the sample.

6. Decide which oxide of iron has the greater iron content: Fe_3O_4, FeO, or Fe_2O_3.

7. A sample of a pure uranium oxide weighing 0.4910 g. was dissolved, and a sulfuric acid solution of the uranium was passed through the zinc reductor. The trivalent uranium was oxidized to quadrivalent uranium by blowing air through the solution and the quadrivalent uranium was titrated to uranyl sulfate, UO_2SO_4. A volume of 35.0 ml. of 0.1000 N sulfatoceric acid was required. Find the formula of the oxide. This was a pure material, and the analysis was carefully made. Consult a handbook for the possible oxides of uranium if necessary.

8. Devise a scheme for the determination of the copper in both valence forms in a hydrochloric acid solution containing dissolved cuprous chloride and cupric chloride, the solution being stored in a bottle under an atmosphere of nitrogen because the chlorocuprous acid, H_2CuCl_3, present is an excellent absorbent for oxygen.

9. Calculate the volume of 0.750 N perchloratoceric acid required to oxidize 0.5000 g. of formaldehyde, CH_2O, to formic acid.

10. Decide how closely it is necessary to weigh (a) ferrous ethylenediammonium sulfate, (b) arsenious oxide, and (c) metallic iron to achieve an accuracy of 1 part in 1000 in the standardization of 0.1 N sulfatoceric acid. Assume that a sample of such size is taken that 50.0 ml. of the cerate solution will be used.

11. Calculate the error in the per cent of iron in a sample containing 0.10 per cent titanium when the reduction before the titration is made with the zinc reductor.

12. Determine the number of milliliters of 0.1000 N cerate solution required to completely oxidize 2 ml. of 0.01 N ferrous 1,10-phenanthroline sulfate.

13. A sample of pure potassium ferrocyanide, $K_4Fe(CN)_6 \cdot xH_2O$, weighing 1.000 g. required for titration 18.9 ml. of 0.1250 N cerate solution. Calculate the number of molecules of water of crystallization in the compound.

14. A solution containing 0.1500 g. of sodium nitrate dissolved in dilute sulfuric acid was run through the zinc reductor, and after the reductor was well washed with water, the solution was titrated with 0.1500 N standard cerate solution. A volume of 70.6 ml. was required to reach the end-point with ferrous 1,10-phenanthroline sulfate. Determine the oxidation state to which the nitrogen was reduced and name the compound probably produced.

TITRATIONS WITH POTASSIUM PERMANGANATE

Potassium permanganate, $KMnO_4$, and quadrivalent cerium salts are the two strongest oxidizing agents that can be used as standard solutions. In sulfuric acid solution potassium permanganate is reduced to manganous sulfate, the standard reduction potential for this reaction being $+1.52$ volts. In neutral or alkaline solutions potassium permanganate is reduced to manganese dioxide, MnO_2, the standard reduction potential for the reaction being $+1.67$ volts; potassium permanganate is thus a stronger oxidizing agent in neutral or alkaline solutions than in acid solution. In neutral or alkaline solutions permanganate effects the oxidation of several materials which it will not oxidize in acid solution.

Potassium permanganate is not a primary standard. Although it can be easily prepared pure it decomposes slowly on storage, forming manganese dioxide. A standard solution of potassium permanganate cannot therefore be made up directly by weight but must be made up approximately and standardized against some primary-standard reducing agent. The presence of manganese dioxide in the solution catalyzes the decomposition of potassium permanganate and for this reason should be filtered off during the preparation of the permanganate solution. If properly prepared and stored, permanganate solutions will keep for some time without change in normality. In careful work, however, the permanganate should be standardized the same day it is used.

Potassium permanganate acts as its own indicator in colorless or slightly colored solutions; a fraction of a drop of 0.1 N solution is sufficient to impart a distinct pink color to 200 ml. of colorless solution.

The principal uses of permanganate are in the determination of iron (Fe^{++} to Fe^{+3}), arsenic (H_3AsO_3 to H_3AsO_4), antimony (SbO^+ to

H_3SbO_4), molybdenum (Mo^{+3} to H_2MoO_4), chromium (Cr^{++} to Cr^{+3}), vanadium (VO^{++} to HVO_3), titanium (Ti^{+3} to Ti^{+4}), ferrocyanide ($Fe(CN)_6^{-4}$ to $Fe(CN)_6^{-3}$), oxalic acid ($H_2C_2O_4$ to CO_2 + H_2O), nitrite (NO_2^- to NO_3^-), and hydrogen peroxide (H_2O_2 to $O_2 + H_2O$). All these determinations are made in acid solution. In addition, a few determinations can be made which are carried out in alkaline or neutral solution: manganese (Mn^{++} to MnO_2), and iodide (I^- to IO_3^-). The problem of changing the normality on going from one type of reaction to another is discussed on page 256.

The titration of oxalate is rather important, because sodium oxalate is good as a primary standard and because it furnishes an indirect method for the determination of a number of metals, notably calcium, zinc, and thorium, which form insoluble oxalates. The oxalates of all the metals but the alkalies are insoluble in neutral solution but soluble in strong acids. The metal can thus be precipitated as the oxalate, then dissolved in sulfuric acid, and the oxalic acid titrated with permanganate. The reaction of oxalic acid with permanganate is quite complicated and gives exactly correct results only when the reaction is carried out in a certain manner. The method, detailed directions for which are given later, consists in titrating the major portion of the oxalate at 27 to 30° and in completing the titration at 50°. The initial reaction of permanganate with oxalic acid is very slow; the reaction is catalyzed by manganous salts, and once the reaction has started it proceeds rapidly.

The reaction of permanganate with arsenite is not clean cut but stops with the manganese in the valence of 3 or 4; a trace of iodide catalyzes the reaction so that it proceeds stoichiometrically to form manganous ion. The procedure for carrying out this titration is also given below under the standardization of permanganate with arsenious oxide.

Oxidations with permanganate are not carried out in hydrochloric acid solutions because permanganate is a sufficiently powerful oxidizing agent to convert chloride to free chlorine. This reaction is rather slow in acid solution but fast enough to make a determination of the end-point indefinite. In the determination of iron with permanganate described below, the hydrochloric acid used to put the iron into solution is eliminated by evaporation with sulfuric acid before the titration is made. There is a technique of carrying out the titration of ferrous iron with permanganate in hydrochloric acid solution (the so-called Zimmerman-Reinhardt method) which minimizes the oxidation of the chloride by adding to the solution a quantity of manganous sulfate. The addition of the manganous ion, the product of the reaction, decreases the oxidizing power of the permanganate, as might be expected on the basis of mass action; in terms of the reduction potential

$$E = +1.52 + \frac{0.059}{5} \log \frac{[MnO_4^-][H^+]^8}{[Mn^{++}]}$$

an increase in the denominator makes the log term smaller, shifting the reduction potential toward the negative end of the reduction-potential series. The reduction potential of the chlorine-chloride couple is $+1.36$, and the reduction potential is sufficiently low to reduce greatly the amount of free chlorine formed during a titration. Some oxidation may still occur because of the local, high concentration of permanganate at the point where the drop strikes the solution. There is hardly any excuse for carrying out the determination of iron in the presence of hydrochloric acid, however; the hydrochloric acid needed to dissolve the ore can be eliminated by evaporation with sulfuric acid, and if in routine work this time cannot be taken, then one of the other methods which can be carried out in hydrochloric acid solutions should be employed, using potassium dichromate or cerate.

Procedure for the Preparation and Standardization of Approximately 0.1 *N Potassium Permanganate.* The equivalent weight of potassium permanganate is one-fifth the molecular weight, or $158.03/5 = 31.61$ g. Weigh on the side-shelf balance 3.2 g. of potassium permanganate and place it in a beaker. Add 50 ml. of water and stir the mixture vigorously. Decant the colored solution into another container. Add another 50 ml. of water, stir, and decant as before. Repeat this until all the crystals of potassium permanganate are dissolved. Filter the solution, using a porous-bottom filtering crucible and mild suction. Transfer the solution to a clean glass-stoppered bottle and dilute the solution to 1 l. with distilled water. Shake the solution vigorously for several minutes. Do not allow the permanganate solution to come in contact with filter paper or other organic matter. Standardize the solution by one of the following methods within a day or two of the time the solution is to be used. In order to clean the manganese dioxide out of the filtering crucible pour onto it a little concentrated hydrochloric acid or dilute sulfuric acid containing some sodium sulfite, and then wash with water.

If a large volume of permanganate solution is to be prepared for use over a considerable period of time, it must be protected from dust. This can be done by washing the air entering the bottle. The device shown in Fig. 41, Chapter 7, works very well. It has been stated that permanganate solutions keep longer if the bottles are covered to keep light away from the solutions.

Standardization with Sodium Oxalate. Dry the sodium oxalate at 110°. Weigh accurately samples of approximately 0.3 g. into 600-ml. beakers. Add 250 ml. of dilute sulfuric acid (5:100). Stir until the sodium oxalate is dissolved. Adjust the temperature to 24 to 30° by warming the solution, or by cooling it by immersing it in a pan of cold water, as necessary. From the weight of the sample taken calculate approximately the volume of 0.1 N permanganate which will be required; each milliliter of 0.1 N solution corresponds to 0.0067 g. of sodium oxalate. Add about 90 per cent of this volume of 0.1 N permanganate at a rate of 25 to 35 ml. per minute while stirring slowly. Allow the solution to stand until the pink color disappears, about 45 seconds. If the pink color does not disappear because the permanganate solution was too strong and an excess was added, discard the sample and begin again, adding a few less milliliters of permanganate solution. Heat the solution to 55 to 60° and complete the titration by adding permanganate until a faint pink color persists for 30 seconds. Add the last 0.5 to 1 ml. dropwise with particular care to allow each drop to become decolorized before the next drop is added. Calculate the normality of the permanganate solution by dividing the weight of the sample of sodium oxalate by the milliequivalent weight of sodium oxalate, 0.067,00, and by the number of milliliters of potassium permanganate required.

Standardization with Arsenious Oxide. Weigh accurately a sample of approximately 0.25 g. of dried arsenious oxide into a 400-ml. beaker. Add 10 ml. of a cool, 20 per cent solution of sodium hydroxide. Allow the solution to stand for 8 to 10 minutes, stirring it occasionally. When solution is complete add 100 ml. of water, 10 ml. of concentrated hydrochloric acid, and 1 drop of 0.0025 M potassium iodide. Titrate with the permanganate solution until a faint pink color persists for 30 seconds. Add the last 1 to 1.5 ml. dropwise, allowing each drop to become decolorized before the next is introduced. Calculate the normality of the permanganate solution by dividing the weight of the sample by the milliequivalent weight of arsenious oxide, 0.049,46, and by the number of milliliters of permanganate solution required.

Standardization with Ferrous Ethylenediammonium Sulfate. Weigh accurately a sample of 1.5 to 1.8 g. of ferrous ethylenediammonium sulfate. Transfer the sample to a 400-ml. beaker. Dissolve the salt in 150 ml. of water containing 10 ml. of concentrated sulfuric acid and 5 ml. of concentrated phosphoric acid. Without undue delay titrate with the permanganate solution until a faint pink color persists for 30 seconds. Calculate the normality of the permanganate solution by dividing the weight of the sample by the milliequivalent weight of ferrous ethylenediammonium sulfate, 0.3822, and by the number of milliliters of permanganate solution required.

THE PERMANGANATE TITRATION OF IRON

The chief ore of iron is hematite, Fe_2O_3, which constitutes the great ore deposits at the west end of Lake Superior. Magnetite, Fe_3O_4, and limonite, a hydrated ferric oxide $Fe_2O_3 \cdot xH_2O$, are of some importance as ore minerals. All three minerals can be dissolved in hydrochloric acid; magnetite forms a mixture of ferrous and ferric chlorides, corresponding to the apparent valences of iron in the mineral.

The principal impurities in iron ore are silica and silicate rock. Certain impurities are always present: manganese, phosphorus (as phosphate), sulfur,. aluminum, calcium, magnesium, titanium, sodium, and potassium; ores from certain regions contain considerable titanium and others appreciable amounts of chromium. Practically all iron ores will dissolve in hydrochloric acid, leaving a white or slightly colored residue which can be ignored in the remainder of the determination. Occasionally a dark residue of an iron-containing silicate remains which must be given special treatment.

As explained earlier, permanganate titrations are not normally made in hydrochloric acid solutions because of the oxidation of chloride to free chlorine by the permanganate. The hydrochloric acid must therefore be removed following the dissolution of the sample in hydrochloric acid; this is best done by evaporating the solution with sulfuric acid. It is possible by certain artifices to carry out the titration of iron in a hydrochloric acid solution, but the scheme does not give good results in the hands of beginners.

There are several ways of reducing the iron to the ferrous state before the titration with permanganate. The zinc reductor is one of the most convenient. Any titanium and chromium in the sample are reduced to lower valence forms and later reoxidized by the permanganate. Using the zinc reductor, then, the sum of the iron, titanium, and chromium present is obtained.

Procedure for the Determination of Iron. Dry the finely ground sample of iron ore at 110° for at least 2 hours. Weigh exactly a sample of approximately 0.4 g. into a 600-ml. beaker or 500-ml. conical flask. Add 5 ml. of water and 10 ml. of concentrated hydrochloric acid.

Place the flask on a gauze in a hood and heat the mixture gently until all the ore has dissolved except for a white residue of silica. A black insoluble residue at this point may be an iron silicate which requires special treatment;[1] all the samples given out for analysis dissolve, leaving only a colorless residue of silica. Add 15 ml. of concentrated sulfuric acid and evaporate the solution to heavy fumes of sulfuric acid to expel the hydrochloric acid. The evaporation should be made in a hood and can be carried out by leaving the solution overnight on the steam plate (135°) if time permits; raise the cover glass off the beaker with glass hooks so as to allow the steam and acid fumes to escape. Cool and dilute to 75 ml. Reduce the ferric sulfate, using either the zinc reductor as described in the next paragraph or using a zinc wire spiral as described in the second paragraph below.

Prepare the zinc reductor as described previously, page 261, and test it by passing through it 150 ml. of dilute sulfuric acid (2:100) and titrating with 0.1 N potassium permanganate. The blank should be less than 0.1 ml. of 0.1 N permanganate. Rinse the receiver and pour the solution containing the ferric sulfate through the reductor. It should take 2 to 3 minutes for the solution to pass through the reductor; if the time required is greater than this apply a gentle suction from an aspirator. Do not allow the level of the liquid to fall below the surface of the zinc. Wash the beaker and the reductor with six 20-ml. portions of dilute sulfuric acid. Disconnect the receiving flask and rinse the tip of the reductor in it. Add 5 ml. of concentrated phosphoric acid and titrate the ferrous sulfate with 0.1 N potassium permanganate until the permanganate color persists in the solution, marking the end-point.

The ferric sulfate may also be reduced by means of a spiral of amalgamated zinc wire; see Fig. 71. Bend the end of the wire into a hook so that the spiral may be later withdrawn with a hooked glass rod. Wash the zinc spiral with water and place it in the solution. Cover

[1] If a dark residue is present decompose it according to the following procedure: Filter the solution, washing the filter well with dilute hydrochloric acid (1:100) until all traces of ferric iron have been removed and then a few times more. Finally, wash the filter a few times with water. Transfer to a platinum crucible and burn away the paper. Add about 0.05 g. of sodium carbonate and heat the crucible over a Meker burner to melt the carbonate. With the tongs rotate the crucible so that the melted sodium carbonate covers the lower portions of the crucible and touches all of the residue present. Cool the crucible and place it in a 250-ml. beaker. Add 20 ml. of water and 5 ml. of concentrated hydrochloric acid. Stir gently until the melt has dissolved. Remove the platinum crucible with a hooked stirring rod, rinsing the rod with a stream of water as it is withdrawn. Pour the solution into the main solution and continue the analysis as directed above.

the beaker with a cover glass or if the solution is in a flask cover the flask with an inverted crucible cover. Heat the solution just to boiling and digest at a gentle boil until the solution is colorless, and then 5 minutes longer. A total of 15 minutes is usually required. Cool the solution to room temperature and withdraw the spiral, rinsing it with a stream of water from the wash bottle. Add 5 ml. of concen-

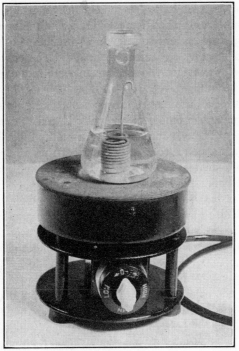

Fig. 71. Amalgamated zinc wire spiral for reduction of ferric sulfate.

trated phosphoric acid and titrate the ferrous sulfate with 0.1 N potassium permanganate until a permanent permanganate color is formed, marking the end-point.

Standardize the permanganate solution in a similar manner, using a pure iron, preferably an electrolytically prepared iron ignited in hydrogen. Alternatively, the permanganate may be standardized against sodium oxalate, arsenious oxide, or ferrous ethylenediammonium sulfate, as described in the section dealing with the preparation and standardization of permanganate solutions. Report the per cent of iron in the sample. The milliequivalent weight of iron is 0.055,85.

INDIRECT DETERMINATION OF CALCIUM BY PERMANGANATE TITRATION

Calcium may be determined volumetrically by an indirect method involving calcium oxalate. The calcium is first precipitated as calcium oxalate, the calcium oxalate is then filtered off and dissolved in sulfuric acid, and the oxalic acid formed is then titrated with permanganate. Calcium is frequently determined in this manner, for there is no direct volumetric method for calcium. The method is applicable to soluble calcium salts and to calcium carbonate or oxide, which can be put into solution by treatment with acid. The only other cations which may be present are those of magnesium, ammonium, and the alkali metals.

The oxalates of all the metals except the alkali metals, ammonium, and magnesium are insoluble in neutral solution, but all are soluble in strong acids. There is thus provided a method for the determination of many metals once they are separated from other metals which form insoluble oxalates. Zinc and thorium, as well as calcium, are commonly determined in this way.

Procedure for the Determination of Calcium. Weigh accurately a sample of such size that it will contain about 0.08 g. of calcium. Dissolve the sample in 20 ml. of dilute hydrochloric acid (1:1). Dilute the solution to about 175 ml. Add a solution of 1.1 g. of ammonium oxalate, $(NH_4)_2C_2O_4 \cdot H_2O$, or 1.0 g. of oxalic acid, $H_2C_2O_4 \cdot 2H_2O$, dissolved in about 25 ml. of water. A part of the calcium may precipitate when the calcium oxalate is added. Add 2 drops of methyl red and heat the solution to boiling. Add filtered, dilute ammonia (1:3) dropwise with stirring until the indicator becomes yellow, and add a few drops in excess. Digest the mixture for 1.5 hours, keeping the solution hot but not necessarily boiling. Cool to room temperature. Filter the calcium oxalate on a porous-bottom filtering crucible. Transfer and wash the precipitate with water, washing until the water running through is chloride free. Use small portions of wash water and as small a total volume of water as permissible.

Heat a solution of 10 ml. of concentrated sulfuric acid in 100 ml. of water to 80°. Place a clean receiver under the filtering crucible and dissolve the calcium oxalate by pouring the sulfuric acid solution over the precipitate in the filter. Before drawing the solution into the receiving flask stir up the acid and precipitate with a short glass stirring rod. Wash the filtering crucible well with hot, dilute sulfuric acid to make certain that all the calcium oxalate has dissolved.

Adjust the temperature of the solution to 24 to 30° by warming the solution or by cooling it by immersing it in a pan of cold water as necessary. From the weight of the sample taken and the approximate per cent of calcium in it, calculate approximately the volume of 0.1 N permanganate which will be required; each milliliter of 0.1 N permanganate corresponds to 0.0020 g. of calcium. Add about 90 per cent of this volume (on the first sample it is best to take only 70 per cent to avoid overstepping the end-point) of standard permanganate solution at a rate of 25 to 35 ml. per minute while stirring slowly. Allow the solution to stand until the pink color disappears, about 45 seconds. Heat the solution to 55 to 60° and complete the titration by adding permanganate until a faint pink color persists for 30 seconds. Add the last 0.5 to 1 ml. dropwise with particular care to allow each drop to become decolorized before the next drop is added. Using the normality of the permanganate solution (best obtained by titration of primary-standard sodium oxalate) and the volume of permanganate solution used, calculate the per cent of calcium in the sample. The equivalent weight of calcium is one-half its atomic weight, or 20.04, in this determination because 1 calcium is equivalent to 1 oxalate and the oxalate undergoes a change in oxidation number of 2 during the titration.

PROBLEMS

1. Complete and balance the following equations:
   - (a) $KMnO_4 + FeSO_4 + H_2SO_4 =$
   - (b) $KMnO_4 + CrSO_4 + H_2SO_4 =$
   - (c) $KMnO_4 + VOSO_4 + H_2SO_4 =$
   - (d) $KMnO_4 + NaNO_2 + H_2SO_4 =$
   - (e) $KMnO_4 + Mn^{++} + KOH =$

2. Calculate the equivalent weight of each of the oxidizing and reducing agents in the equations of Problem 1.

3. A sample of sodium oxalate known to be 99.70 per cent pure and weighing 0.3500 g. required 42.0 ml. of potassium permanganate solution for titration. Calculate the normality of the permanganate solution.

4. A sample of iron ore weighing 0.4000 g. required 35.40 ml. of a 0.1100 N solution of potassium permanganate for titration. Calculate the per cent of iron in the sample.

5. Pieces of pure, electrolytic iron weighing about 0.2 g. were placed on the right-hand pan of a balance, and sufficient iron ore was added to the left-hand pan to balance them exactly. Both iron and ore were transferred to beakers, and their iron content was determined. The ore required 26.0 ml., and the pure iron 46.0 ml., of a certain standard solution of potassium permanganate. Calculate the per cent of iron in the ore.

6. The zinc in a sample of ore weighing 1.500 g. was precipitated as zinc oxalate, and the zinc oxalate was subsequently filtered off, dissolved in dilute sulfuric acid, and titrated. A volume of 35.0 ml. of 0.0800 N potassium permanganate was required. Calculate the per cent of zinc oxide in the sample.

7. A solution of potassium permanganate was standardized against sodium oxalate in sulfuric acid solution and found to be 0.1250 N. What normality should be used to calculate the per cent of iodide titrated in neutral solution with this permanganate solution, manganese dioxide being the reduction product?

8. A sample of calcium molybdate weighing 0.3100 g. was dissolved in perchloric acid and the solution passed through the zinc reductor. The reduced molybdenum required 45.0 ml. of 0.1000 N potassium permanganate for titration. Calculate the per cent of calcium molybdate in the sample.

9. Calculate the number of milliliters of 0.1000 N potassium permanganate required to oxidize in acid solution 1.000 g. of sodium thiosulfate completely to sodium sulfate.

10. Devise a scheme for the determination of both sulfuric acid and oxalic acid in a mixture using only volumetric methods.

11. In running a blank determination on the zinc reductor the liquid was inadvertently drawn from the reductor and air was brought in contact with the zinc. The next washing with 200 ml. of 2 per cent sulfuric acid, passed through in several portions without allowing further contact of the zinc with air, required 1.50 ml. of 0.1000 N potassium permanganate for titration. Calculate (a) the weight in grams of hydrogen peroxide which was formed and (b) the volume of oxygen which was reduced. The equations for the formation and the titration are

$$O_2 + Zn^0 + H_2SO_4 = H_2O_2 + ZnSO_4$$

$$5H_2O_2 + 2KMnO_4 + 3H_2SO_4 = 5O_2 + K_2SO_4 + MnSO_4 + 8H_2O$$

12. Calculate the number of milliliters of 1.000 N potassium permanganate that would be required to generate 500 ml. of oxygen at 0° and 760 mm. Hg pressure by the action of the potassium permanganate on an excess of hydrogen peroxide in acid solution. See Problem 11 for equation for the reaction.

13. A volume of 46.0 ml. of a solution of sodium hydroxide 0.1200 N was used to titrate 40.0 ml. of a solution of oxalic acid. A volume of 32.0 ml. of potassium permanganate was used to titrate 40.0 ml. of the same oxalate solution. Calculate the normality of the permanganate solution.

14. A pure organic acid containing only carbon, hydrogen, and oxygen was found to consist of 32.5 per cent carbon and 2.70 per cent hydrogen. A sample of the material weighing 0.3330 g. required 45.0 ml. of 0.1000 N sodium hydroxide for titration. Another sample weighing 0.1480 g. required 80.0 ml. of 0.1000 N potassium permanganate for titration in acid solution to carbon dioxide and water. Decide if it is possible to determine the actual formula of the compound on the basis of the data given.

TITRATIONS WITH POTASSIUM DICHROMATE

Potassium dichromate, $K_2Cr_2O_7$, is a strong but somewhat less powerful oxidizing agent than potassium permanganate and quadrivalent cerium salts. The standard reduction potential for the dichromate-chromic couple is +1.36 volts.

Potassium dichromate is an anhydrous salt of definite composition; the reagent grade obtained from the chemical companies is suitable for primary-standard use after drying. A standard solution of potassium dichromate can thus be made by diluting a weighed amount of the salt to a known volume.

The chromic salts formed on the reduction of potassium chromate are deep green. Fortunately, the oxidized form of the indicator commonly used in dichromate titrations, diphenylaminesulfonic acid, is purple and so intensely colored that it is clearly visible over the green color of the chromic salts. In a titration, a small but significant excess of the standard dichromate solution is required to oxidize the indicator. Because of the rather large indicator blank, it is perhaps better in the determination of iron to standardize the dichromate solution against pure electrolytic iron. If the amount of iron in the sample and the blank are about the same the indicator correction cancels and need not be considered.

Ferrous 1,10-phenanthroline sulfate may also be used as the oxidation-reduction indicator in titrations with dichromate, the pink-to-blue color change being quite easily seen over the green color of the chromium. When ferrous 1,10-phenanthroline sulfate is used as indicator the acid concentration must be made quite high. The reason for this will be readily grasped from an inspection of the formal reduction potentials given in Table 23.

TABLE 23. FORMAL REDUCTION POTENTIALS OF THE DICHROMATE-CHROMIC SYSTEM AND OF THE FERRIC-FERROUS SYSTEM IN HYDROCHLORIC ACID AND SULFURIC ACID OF VARIOUS STRENGTHS

Acid Present	Dichromate-Chromic (E^0 in volts)	Ferric-Ferrous (E^0 in volts)
0.1 M Hydrochloric	+0.93	+0.73
1 M Hydrochloric	1.00	0.70
2 M Hydrochloric	1.05	0.69
3 M Hydrochloric	1.08	0.68
4 M Hydrochloric	1.10	0.66
1 M Sulfuric	1.03	0.69
2 M Sulfuric	1.11	0.688
4 M Sulfuric	1.15	0.687
6 M Sulfuric	1.30	0.681
8 M Sulfuric	1.35	0.658
1 M Perchloric	1.025	0.735
1 M Sulfuric + 0.5 M Phosphoric		0.61

The standard reduction potential given for the dichromate-chromic system, $+1.36$ volts, is misleading, for the value depends on the particular acid present in the solution and on its concentration. The values of E^0 under the practical conditions of an analysis are greatly less than $+1.36$ volts. From these values it is apparent that the dichromate will oxidize ferrous 1,10-phenanthroline sulfate sharply only in sulfuric acid solutions 4 M or greater in acid.

Titrations with potassium dichromate may be made in hydrochloric acid solution, for dichromate does not oxidize chloride to free chlorine. This is an advantage over potassium permanganate in the determination of iron in iron ore, for iron ores are soluble only in hydrochloric acid and the removal of hydrochloric acid by evaporation with sulfuric acid is time consuming. As indicated above the dichromate is a great deal weaker as an oxidizing agent in hydrochloric acid solution. This can be partially offset in the iron determination by the addition of phosphoric acid which ties up the ferric iron in a non-ionized compound and lowers the reduction potential of the ferric-ferrous system, that is, makes the ferrous ion a stronger reducing agent. The addition of phosphoric acid has the additional effect of removing the color of the ferric iron from the solution and thus of increasing the sharpness of the color change of the diphenylaminesulfonic acid at the end-point.

Preparation of 0.1 *N Potassium Dichromate.* The change in oxidation number on the reduction of potassium dichromate to chromic sulfate ($K_2Cr_2O_7$ to $2Cr^{+3}$) is 6, and the equivalent weight is therefore one-sixth the molecular weight, $K_2Cr_2O_7/6 = 294.21/6 = 49.035$. Place approximately 4.9 g. of reagent-grade potassium dichromate in a clean, dry weighing bottle and place it in the oven at 110° for at least 2 hours. When cool, weigh the bottle and salt accurately. Holding the weighing bottle over a 400-ml. beaker, remove the cap and empty the salt into the beaker, not attempting to transfer any crystals which cling to the bottle. Replace the cap on the weighing bottle and weigh cap and bottle again accurately. Dissolve the salt in 200 ml. of water and transfer it to a 1-l. flask. Wash out the beaker thoroughly in the process. Dilute the solution exactly to the mark and mix the solution well by inverting the flask forty or fifty times. Transfer the solution to a clean, dry bottle. Calculate the normality of the solution by dividing the weight of potassium dichromate taken by the equivalent weight of potassium dichromate, 49.035.

Procedure for the Determination of Iron by Titration with Potassium Dichromate. Dry the sample of iron ore for 2 hours at 110°. Weigh accurately a sample of approximately 1 g. into a 400-ml. beaker. Cover the beaker and add 20 ml. of dilute hydrochloric acid (1:1). Heat the mixture in the hood and hold it near the boiling point until all the ore has dissolved except for a small amount of flocculent silica. Discontinue the heating, rinse the cover glass, and wash down the sides of the beaker with a stream of water from the wash bottle. The iron content of the silica-silicate residue is usually small and may be disregarded in most cases; however, if the residue is dark and is suspected to be a silicate containing iron, decompose it by the procedure given in the footnote, page 286.

After the dissolution of the ore, the iron may be reduced in either of two ways: by the silver reductor (*A*) or by stannous chloride (*B*).

A, *Reduction of Ferric Chloride by the Silver Reductor*. Dilute the solution to 100 ml. and transfer the solution to the silver reductor, rinsing the contents of the beaker into the upper reservoir of the reductor quantitatively. Use a 400-ml. beaker as receiver. Open the stopcock to allow the solution to run through. When the level of the liquid in the reductor has reached the upper surface of the silver column, close the stopcock. Wash the reductor with six 20-ml. portions of dilute hydrochloric acid (1:15), completing the washing of the original beaker by pouring the wash liquid first into the beaker and then into the reductor. Allow the liquid to drain to the level of the silver before making the next addition. Proceed immediately to the titration.

B, *Reduction of Ferric Chloride by Stannous Chloride*. Evaporate the solution containing the ferric chloride to a volume of 15 to 20 ml.; the evaporation will be speeded by raising the cover glass off the beaker by glass hooks. From this point on work with one sample at a time. To the hot solution add a 10 per cent solution of stannous chloride in dilute hydrochloric acid (1:10). Make the addition dropwise with constant stirring until the yellow color is almost gone. Continue the reduction by the dropwise addition of a 1 per cent solution of stannous chloride until 1 drop just causes the color to change from yellow to pale green. Add 1 or 2 drops in excess but no more. This is a critical part of the process, for the excess stannous chloride must not amount to more than 1 or 2 drops. The addition of stannous chloride can conveniently be made from a pipet or a dropping bottle. After the reduction is complete dilute the solution to 150 ml. with water and add at once 10 ml. of a 10 per cent solution of mercuric chloride. A light, white precipitate of mercurous chloride should form within 1 or 2 minutes, indicating that an excess of stannous chloride has been added; if no precipitate appears it is probable that the reduction of the iron was incomplete. If more than a slight amount of mercurous chloride precipitates, too much stannous chloride was added and the sample must be discarded. Proceed immediately to the titration.

Titration with Potassium Dichromate. Add 10 ml. more of concentrated hydrochloric acid, 5 ml. of concentrated phosphoric acid, and 1.5 ml. of 0.01 M diphenylaminesulfonic acid solution. Titrate with 0.1 N potassium dichromate to the point where the indicator turns to a permanent blue color.

Standardize the solution of potassium dichromate by running samples of pure electrolytic iron in the same manner or by titrating a weighed sample of ferrous ethylenediammonium sulfate dissolved in 200 ml. of dilute sulfuric acid (1:10). If the normality obtained by making up the potassium dichromate solution by weight is used, subtract an indicator correction of 0.03 ml.

Calculate the per cent of iron in the sample; the milliequivalent weight of iron is 0.055,85.

PROBLEMS

1. Give equations for all the reactions involved in the determination of iron by the dichromate method, starting with a hematite ore.

2. Calculate the maximum weight of sample of an iron ore containing 50 per cent iron which may be taken for titration with 0.1000 N potassium dichromate without having to refill a 50-ml. buret.

3. A sample of iron ore weighing 0.7000 g. was dissolved in hydrochloric acid in an atmosphere of carbon dioxide. The solution was immediately titrated with 0.1000 N potassium dichromate, of which 29.5 ml. was required. Calculate (a) the per cent of ferrous oxide (FeO), and (b) the per cent of magnetite (Fe_3O_4) in the sample, assuming that all the ferrous iron in the sample was derived from magnetite.

4. Outline a procedure by which the iron and aluminum could both be determined in a solution containing aluminum chloride, ferric chloride, and hydrochloric acid.

5. A sample of primary-standard potassium dichromate weighing 0.5000 g. was dissolved in dilute sulfuric acid and run through the zinc reductor. Calculate the volume of 0.1000 N potassium permanganate required to oxidize the chromium to the trivalent state.

6. Through a mistake in packaging, a chemical company sent out ammonium dichromate for potassium dichromate. This material was used to make up a standard dichromate solution by weight, and on the assumption that the material was pure potassium dichromate the normality calculated was 0.1188. The solution was then used for the determination of iron in an ore and the result, 45.7 per cent iron, obtained. Calculate (a) the correct normal concentration of the dichromate solution, and (b) the correct per cent of iron.

7. On the basis of the formal reduction potentials for potassium dichromate shown in Table 23, pick out the conditions under which ferrous 1,10-phenanthroline sulfate can be used as indicator in the titration of ferrous iron with dichromate.

IODOMETRIC METHODS

Iodometric methods are classed as direct and indirect. In the direct method a reducing agent is titrated with a standard solution of iodine, for example,

$$SnCl_2 + 2I^0 + 2HCl = SnCl_4 + 2HI$$

In the indirect method an oxidizing agent is made to react with potassium iodide and the elemental iodine liberated is titrated with sodium thiosulfate with the formation of sodium tetrathionate:

$$KClO_3 + 6KI + 6HCl = 6I^0 + 7KCl + 3H_2O$$

$$2I^0 + 2Na_2S_2O_3 = 2NaI + Na_2S_4O_6$$

This rather unusual state of affairs, that is, the use of an oxidation-reduction couple quantitatively in two directions arises from the fact that the standard reduction potential of the iodine-iodide couple is +0.535 volt, a middle value that makes iodine only a mild oxidizing agent. Although the number of reducing agents which can be determined by the direct method is rather small, the number of oxidizing agents capable of oxidizing iodide to iodine and thus of being determined indirectly is quite great.

Iodine is not appreciably soluble in water but does dissolve in solutions containing potassium iodide. It is generally assumed that a compound KI_3 is formed, but the compound is not very stable because the solution behaves as if it were a solution of iodine. The numerical value of the constant for the reaction $I_3^- = I^- + 2I^0$ is 1.4×10^{-3}.

Iodine can readily be sublimed and obtained in high purity, so that it can be used as a primary standard, the only precaution needed being to insure that no iodine is lost by volatilization during the weighing and solution process. As a matter of fact, iodine is sublimed during its manufacture, and the reagent-grade material is satisfactory as a primary standard. A variety of other primary standards is also available for the standardization of solutions of iodine and of thiosulfate.

In colorless solutions iodine serves as its own indicator. A fraction of a drop of 0.1 N solution of iodine, for example, will impart a distinct yellow color to 200 ml. of water. The color of iodine is actually about as intense and as good a test for free iodine as the blue color of iodine with starch; most analysts, however, prefer the starch end-point.

Starch must be used, of course, if the solution has any color of its own. The reaction of starch with iodine is a rather complex one. The iodine is rather loosely bound to the starch, for it behaves essentially as free iodine. Potassium iodide must be present for the blue color to form, and starch itself is composed of two components, amylose and amylopectin, of which only the amylose gives the blue color with iodine and iodide. The origin of the starch and the treatment it has received have a good deal to do with the character of the color. A starch quite satisfactory as an indicator is marketed by the reagent-chemical companies as "Soluble Starch." The active principle, amylose, is also available.

In general, iodometric methods are carried out in acid or neutral solutions. In alkaline solution, above pH 11, iodine reacts with water (or hydroxyl) to form hypoiodite, $2I^0 + 2OH^- = IO^- + I^- + H_2O$, which is unstable and decomposes to give iodate and iodide: $3IO^- = IO_3^- + 2I^-$. Inasmuch as the iodate formed will not oxidize reducing materials at this pH, iodine is used up and the results of direct titrations will therefore be high and those of indirect titrations low. Care must be taken therefore in both direct and indirect iodometric methods not to allow the pH to be above 11.

DIRECT IODOMETRIC METHODS

As might be expected from its mild oxidizing strength, iodine can be used to titrate only quite strong reducing agents. The materials which are commonly determined by direct titration with iodine are: tin (Sn^{++} to Sn^{+4}, hydrochloric acid solution); hydrogen sulfide (H_2S to S^0, acid solution); thiosulfate ($S_2O_3^=$ to $S_4O_6^=$, acid solution); sulfite ($SO_3^=$ to $SO_4^=$, acid solution); arsenic (AsO_3^{-3} to AsO_4^{-3}, neutral solution); antimony (KSbO-tartrate to SbO_4^{-3}, neutral solution containing tartrate); ferrocyanide ($Fe(CN)_6^{-4}$ to $Fe(CN)_6^{-3}$, neutral solution). The stronger reducing agents can be titrated in acid solution, the weaker ones such as arsenious and antimonous acids can only be oxidized quantitatively in a strictly neutral solution.

The titration of trivalent arsenic is discussed in considerable detail in the next section. Arsenic trioxide is a very suitable primary standard for standardizing a solution of iodine.

Tin is commonly determined by direct titration with iodine. The tin is first reduced in a hydrochloric acid solution with metallic iron or lead, and the stannous chloride is titrated with iodine. The excess metallic iron is filtered off or if lead is used the solution is simply cooled below 5°, at which temperature the reduction of stannic chloride is very slow:

$$SnCl_4 + Pb^0 = SnCl_2 + PbCl_2$$

$$SnCl_2 + 2I^0 + 2HCl = SnCl_4 + 2HI$$

Small amounts of hydrogen sulfide are usually determined by titration with iodine:

$$H_2S + 2I^0 = S^0 + 2HI$$

In the determination of sulfur in steel, for example, the hydrogen sulfide evolved on dissolving the sample in hydrochloric acid is collected by bubbling the gases evolved through a solution of zinc sulfate in ammonia. The zinc sulfide which precipitates is later decomposed with hydrochloric acid, and the liberated hydrogen sulfide is titrated with standard iodine.

The oxidation of trivalent antimony by iodine is only complete in a neutral solution. By adding tartaric acid to the solution, the trivalent antimony is kept from precipitating as a basic salt when the solution is neutralized:

$$KSbOC_4H_4O_6 + 2I + 4NaHCO_3$$

$$= KH_2SbO_4 + 2NaI + Na_2C_4H_4O_6 + 4CO_2 + H_2O$$

Preparation of 0.1 N Iodine Solution. The solution may be made up by weight or prepared approximately and standardized. The student is encouraged to do both as a check on his work. The equivalent weight of iodine is equal to its atomic weight, 126.92, since the change in oxidation number is only 1 on its reduction to iodide.

To prepare a solution by weight, weigh a clean, dry, glass-stoppered weighing bottle. Add to it 12.7 g. of sublimed iodine weighed out approximately on the side-shelf balance. Do not attempt to weigh or transfer iodine crystals in the vicinity of an analytical balance as the vapors are corrosive. Stopper the bottle and weigh it again accurately. In a 600-ml. beaker place 200 ml. of water containing 30 g. of potassium iodide. Open the weighing bottle inside the beaker and allow the weighing bottle and cap to drop gently into the potassium iodide solution. Stir the solution gently until all the iodine has dissolved. Transfer the iodine solution to a 1-l. volumetric flask, holding back the weighing bottle and cap with a stirring rod. Wash all the iodine into the flask. If any iodine crystals remain add several large crystals of potassium iodide and a little water to aid their solution. Dilute the solution to exactly 1 l. and mix the solution by inverting the flask forty or fifty times. Calculate the normality of the solution by dividing the weight of iodine taken by 126.92.

If the solution is to be prepared approximately, weigh out 12.7 g. of iodine on a watch glass on the side-shelf balance. Transfer this and 30 g. of potassium iodide to a beaker. Add 50 ml. of distilled water and stir vigorously for several minutes. Decant the liquid into a clean 1-l. bottle. If any crystals remain in the beaker add a bit more potassium iodide and a small volume of water to aid their solution. Finally, dilute the solution to 1 l. and mix thoroughly. Standardize the iodine solution with arsenious oxide as described under the determination of iodine.

Preparation of Starch Indicator Solution. Heat to boiling 500 ml. of water. Add to this 5 g. of soluble starch which has been previously mixed with a little water to form a slurry. Cool the solution and add 15 g. of potassium iodide. Starch solutions will spoil after a week or two owing to the growth of microorganisms; this deterioration can be minimized by covering the solution with a thin layer of toluene.

Two to three milliliters of this starch solution should be used per determination. In indirect iodometric determinations the starch should not be added until close to the end-point in the titration with sodium thiosulfate; at high concentrations of iodine an irreversible starch-iodine compound is formed which is not decolorized at the end-point.

Potassium iodide must be present for the formation of the starch-iodine blue.

THE IODOMETRIC DETERMINATION OF ARSENIC

The standard reduction potentials of iodine-iodide ($E^0 = +0.535$) and the arsenate-arsenite couples ($E^0 = +0.559$) are so close together that in an acid solution the reaction between arsenious acid and iodine is far short of completion at the equivalence-point. However, the arsenate-arsenite couple involves the hydrogen ion

$$H_3AsO_4 + 2H^+ + 2e^- = H_3AsO_3 + H_2O$$

and as the concentration of the hydrogen ion is decreased the strength of the arsenious acid as a reducing agent rises. There is little change in the strength of iodine as an oxidizing agent with change in pH, and thus in neutral or alkaline solution the reaction between iodine and arsenious acid will take place with satisfactory completeness. If the solution is too alkaline, however, there may be a significant reaction between the hydroxyl ion and iodine, and considerably more iodine may be used to reach the starch end-point than is equivalent to the arsenious acid. In alkaline solution iodine reacts with water to form hypoiodite, $2I^0 + 2OH^- = IO^- + I^- + H_2O$, which disproportionates to give iodate and iodide, $3IO^- = IO_3^- + 2I^-$. Although hypoiodite is able to oxidize arsenite to arsenate, iodate will not. It has been shown experimentally that the highest pH at which the arsenite titration can be run is 11.0; at higher values extra iodine is used and the results are high. The lowest hydrogen-ion concentration at which the reaction is complete corresponds to a pH of about 5.

Arsenious oxide dissolves very slowly in water but rapidly in alkali. Sodium hydroxide or sodium carbonate is used therefore to dissolve the sample. In the usual procedure, after the sample is dissolved the solution is acidified with hydrochloric acid and the pH is then adjusted by the addition of a considerable quantity of sodium bicarbonate; the bicarbonate and the carbonic acid buffer the solution at a pH of 7 to 8. In the procedure given below the acidification step is eliminated and the titration carried out at the somewhat higher pH, around 10, obtained with a carbonate-bicarbonate buffer.

Procedure for the Direct Iodometric Determination of Arsenic. Carry out the standardization of the iodine solution and the analysis in identical fashion by the following procedure: Samples containing arsenious oxide should not be dried in the oven above 100° because of the possibility of volatilizing a portion of the arsenious oxide present and thus changing the composition of the sample. For the standardization, weigh exactly into 500-ml. conical flasks several samples of arsenious oxide, keeping the weight close to 0.23 g. to avoid using more than 50 ml. of the iodine solution; for the analysis, weigh samples of 0.3 to 0.35 g. Dissolve each sample in 20 ml. of water containing 3.0 g. of sodium carbonate, $Na_2CO_3 \cdot H_2O$. Heat to 60–70° and swirl gently until clear, rinsing down the walls of the flask to be sure all the arsenious oxide has dissolved. Dilute the solution to 100 ml., cool, and add 1.0 g. of sodium bicarbonate. By this procedure the pH will be approximately 10.4 at the start and 9.5 at the end. Add 2 ml. of 2 per cent starch solution. Titrate with approximately 0.1 N iodine solution, swirling the solution vigorously throughout the titration. Titrate until a faint blue (pink or lavender with some types of starch) tint persists for 30 seconds.

INDIRECT IODOMETRIC METHODS

Any oxidizing agent which will oxidize iodide to free iodine can be determined indirectly, for the liberated iodine is equivalent to the oxidizing agent and can be titrated with sodium thiosulfate, for example,

$$KMnO_4 + 5KI + 4H_2SO_4 = 5I^0 + 3K_2SO_4 + MnSO_4 + 4H_2O$$

$$2I^0 + 2Na_2S_2O_3 = 2NaI + Na_2S_4O_6$$

Two equations are thus necessary to describe indirect iodometric methods.

With strong oxidizing agents the first reaction proceeds completely in acid or neutral solution. With milder oxidizing agents the reaction must be forced. If the oxidizing agent contains oxygen this forcing can be done by increasing the hydrogen-ion concentration. In any such reaction the hydrogen ion enters the reaction and an increase in the hydrogen-ion concentration drives the reaction to the right:

$$KIO_3 + 5KI + 6HCl = 6I^0 + 6KCl + 3H_2O$$

The addition of a considerable amount of potassium iodide has the same effect. In some instances the iodine may be distilled from the reaction mixture or swept by a stream of air into a receiving solution of potassium iodide where it can later be titrated.

The reaction of iodine and thiosulfate to form sodium tetrathionate proceeds rapidly and completely in acid solution. The number of oxidizing agents which can be determined in this way is surprisingly large, and in general analytical work a standard thiosulfate solution is more often used than any other standard solution with the possible exception of standard solutions of a strong acid. The only use ever made of standard thiosulfate solutions, however, is in the titration of iodine; stronger oxidizing agents oxidize it in part to sulfite and sulfate.

Solutions of sodium thiosulfate are not stable and must be standardized at about the time they are used. Slow decomposition of thiosulfate is caused by strong acids, but even in neutral and alkaline solutions the concentration changes, apparently because of the growth in the thiosulfate solution of microorganisms.

Solutions of sodium thiosulfate may be standardized using the crystalline, primary-standard oxidizing agents iodine, potassium dichromate, potassium iodate, and metallic copper, or with standard solutions of potassium permanganate or of ceric salts. The standardization should be made about the time the solution is to be used. If a primary standard of the material being determined is available, its use is recommended in preference to other methods; for example, in the determination of copper by the indirect iodometric method, it is best to standardize the thiosulfate against pure metallic copper.

The end-point in the titration of iodine with sodium thiosulfate is determined by the disappearance of the blue color of starch and iodine. However, when starch is added to a strong solution of iodine an irreversible starch-iodine compound is formed which is not bleached subsequently when an excess of thiosulfate is added. For this reason the starch solution is not added until practically all the iodine has been titrated.

A serious error in indirect iodometric processes is the oxidation of potassium iodide to iodine by oxygen of the air: $4HI + O_2 = 4I^0 + 2H_2O$. This reaction does not take place in neutral solution but does in acid solution. Indirect procedures, then, especially those in which the acidity is high, should be carried out rapidly and if necessary in an inert atmosphere of nitrogen or carbon dioxide provided by bubbling the gas into the solution before and during the titration.

Applications of Indirect Iodometric Methods. Among the oxidizing agents which can be determined by the indirect iodometric method are a number of considerable commercial importance. The strong oxidizing agents potassium permanganate, potassium dichromate, potassium iodate, and quadrivalent cerium salts have already been mentioned. In addition there are the free halogens, chlorine and bromine, and the various oxygen-containing acids of the halogens and their salts: hypochlorous acid ($HClO$), chlorous acid ($HClO_2$), chloric acid ($HClO_3$), bromic acid ($HBrO_3$), hypoiodous acid (HIO), iodous acid (HIO_2), iodic acid (HIO_3), and periodic acid (HIO_4), but not perchloric acid ($HClO_4$) which has no oxidizing properties in dilute solution.

Several metals may be determined in this way. Cupric copper when treated with potassium iodide forms insoluble cuprous iodide and free iodine; this reaction is discussed in detail below, for the determination of copper is of great importance. The reaction of arsenic acid with iodide goes to completion in an acid solution. As mentioned in connection with direct iodometric methods, arsenious acid can be titrated with a standard iodine solution. This is a remarkable reaction, for it can be used quantitatively in both directions by a change in the hydrogen-ion concentration. Ferric iron also oxidizes iodide to iodine.

The oxidizing power of the oxides of the higher valences of certain metals can be determined iodometrically. Manganese dioxide (pyrolucite) and lead dioxide are two good examples. The oxide is dissolved in hot hydrochloric acid in a distilling flask so arranged that the gases leaving the flask are bubbled through a solution of potassium iodide. An equivalent amount of free iodine is liberated which is later titrated with sodium thiosulfate.

A method for determining the amount of oxygen dissolved in water is based on an indirect method. To a full bottle of the water being tested is added manganous chloride and then ammonia. In such an alkaline solution, manganous hydroxide is oxidized by the dissolved oxygen to manganese dioxide. The solution is then acidified with hydrochloric acid and potassium iodide is added. The manganese dioxide dissolves, liberating iodine which is then titrated with sodium thiosulfate.

Preparation of 0.1 *N Sodium Thiosulfate.* The equivalent weight of sodium thiosulfate is equal to its molecular weight. Sodium thio- sulfate solutions must be made up approximately and standardized, as crystalline sodium thiosulfate contains a varying amount of water of crystallization. Dissolve 25.0 g. of sodium thiosulfate, $Na_2S_2O_3 \cdot 5H_2O$, and 0.2 g. of sodium carbonate in 1 l. of water and mix well by shaking vigorously for several minutes. The thiosulfate will keep longer if the water used is first sterilized by boiling. If the solution is to be stored in a bottle which is to be frequently opened there is hardly any point in this sterilization. If the solution is stored in a bottle with a siphon and arranged so that the entering air is washed, sterilization may help. In any case the thiosulfate solution should be standardized the same day it is used.

Standardization of 0.1 *N Sodium Thiosulfate with Iodine.* Weigh a glass-stoppered, clean, dry weighing bottle. Add to the bottle 0.5 g. of iodine weighed on a watch glass on the side-shelf balance. Stopper the bottle and weigh it again accurately. In a 400-ml. beaker place 100 ml. of distilled water and 5 g. of potassium iodide. Unstopper the weighing bottle and immerse the bottle and iodine in the solution. Stir gently until the iodine has dissolved. The titration can be made with the weighing bottle left in the flask, or it can be removed with a hooked stirring rod, washing bottle and rod with a stream of water from the wash bottle as they are withdrawn. Add 5 ml. of dilute hydrochloric acid (1:10) and titrate with the thiosulfate solution. When the color of the iodine has almost all disappeared, add 2 ml. of starch solution and continue the titration to the disappearance of the blue color. Calculate the normality of the thiosulfate solution.

If the standardization is to be made against a solution of iodine whose normality is known, measure out 40.0 ml. of the iodine solution with a buret and dilute to about 100 ml. Titrate with the thiosulfate solution until the color of the iodine has almost disappeared. Add 2 ml. of starch solution and continue the titration to the disappearance of the blue color. Calculate the normality of the thiosulfate, using the relation $(ml._{I^0})(N_{I^0}) = (ml._{Na_2S_2O_3})(N_{Na_2S_2O_3})$.

Standardization of 0.1 *N Sodium Thiosulfate with Potassium Iodate.* Weigh accurately into a 500-ml. conical flask a sample of about 0.15 g.

Dissolve the salt in about 75 ml. of water. Add 3 g. of potassium iodide and 10 ml. of dilute hydrochloric acid (1:10). Titrate the iodine liberated with the thiosulfate solution to the point where the color of the iodine has almost disappeared. Add 2 ml. of starch solution and continue the titration to the disappearance of the blue color. Calculate the normality of the thiosulfate solution by dividing the weight of potassium iodate taken by the number of milliliters used and by the milliequivalent weight of potassium iodate, $KIO_3/6000$, or 0.035,67.

THE IODOMETRIC DETERMINATION OF COPPER

The determination of copper iodometrically is based on the reactions

$$CuSO_4 + 2KI = CuI + K_2SO_4 + I^0$$

$$2I^0 + 2Na_2S_2O_3 = 2NaI + Na_2S_4O_6$$

The first reaction proceeds to the right owing to the formation of insoluble cuprous iodide; the second reaction, the titration of the iodine liberated, is the standard one for concluding the determination of oxidizing agents by the indirect iodometric method. The iodometric method of determining copper is extensively used in the copper refining industry because it is rapid and the interfering substances commonly associated with copper in its sulfide ores, iron, arsenic, and antimony, can be rendered innocuous by suitably adjusting the conditions.

Ferric iron is a sufficiently strong oxidizing agent to liberate iodine from potassium iodide; this reaction, however, does not occur in the presence of fluoride which ties up ferric iron in a stable complex ion, probably FeF_6^{-3}. The reaction of pentavalent arsenic and antimony with potassium iodide to liberate iodine is greatly dependent on the pH of the solution. In acid solution the reactions proceed quantitatively to the right and can be used for the determination of arsenic and antimony in their higher valence states; in very slightly acid solutions the equilibrium is reversed and the reverse reaction can be used for the determination of trivalent arsenic and antimony by direct titration with standard iodine. In the process of dissolving the copper ore, the arsenic and antimony are oxidized to their higher valent forms, and in the determination of copper, therefore, if the pH is held about 3.5 (but not so high as to cause the precipitation of cupric hydroxide), the interference of pentavalent arsenic and antimony is avoided. An ideal buffer combination for this purpose is ammonium acid fluoride, NH_4HF_2, and hydrofluoric acid. The fluoride ties up the ferric iron so that it does not interfere in the determination and thus accomplishes two purposes at once. The usual starch indicator is used to mark the end-point in the titration of the iodine with the thiosulfate. The end-point, however, is somewhat obscured by the brownish color of the precipitate of cuprous iodide on which is adsorbed some free iodine. This adsorbed iodine can be displaced from the cuprous iodide by the addition of potassium thiocyanate which is more strongly adsorbed than the iodine. The cuprous iodide at the end-point is then white, and the end-point is sharp. Part of the action of the thiocyanate is to drive the reaction of the cupric and iodide ions further to the right, cuprous thiocyanate being less soluble than cuprous iodide. In any case the reaction is stoichiometric when the thiocyanate is used but not when it is omitted. The thiocyanate may not be added early in the titration.

The sodium thiosulfate solution may be standardized against pure copper or against iodine. If copper is used, the procedure in determining the unknown must be followed exactly, including the addition of the thiocyanate. If iodine is used as the primary standard, the solution of the iodine should be treated with ammonium acid fluoride as in the copper determination before titration with the thiosulfate.

Sulfide minerals must normally be dissolved in nitric acid. In this process some free sulfur is formed which must be removed by oxidation before the copper determination can be made. Most of the nitric acid must also be removed as appreciable concentrations of nitric acid oxidize potassium iodide to free iodine.

By using perchloric acid as the solvent for the sulfide ores much time and trouble can be eliminated. No sulfur bead forms, and nitric acid is not present to interfere. Arsenic and antimony are oxidized to the pentavalent forms at the same time that the sample is being dissolved. Some free chlorine is formed in the action of perchloric acid on the mineral and must be boiled off after the addition of water to the reaction mass. Dilute perchloric acid is not an oxidizing agent. Hot, concentrated perchloric acid is a powerful oxidizing agent, and care must be exercised in its use.

Procedure for the Determination of Copper. Dry the finely ground copper ore at 110° for 2 hours. In the meantime read over the section dealing with the precautions to be observed in the use of perchloric acid, page 43. Weigh accurately a sample of approximately 0.6 g. Transfer the sample to a small-mouth, 500-ml. conical, Vycor (see page 36) flask; the flask should be dry. Add about 15 ml. of 72 per cent perchloric acid; pour the acid down the wall of the flask while revolving the flask so that any particles on the walls will be washed to the bottom. Add one or two glass beads to promote smoother boiling and insert the special condenser head shown in Fig. 72. Heat the flask with a burner at medium heat. The acid should reflux [1] down the sides of the flask, but no pronounced heavy white perchloric acid fumes should leave the flask. The refluxing will serve to wash down the walls of the flask. The sample should have dissolved by the time the condensation ring has reached halfway up the walls of the flask; this should take about 5 minutes.

When the sample has dissolved, remove the flask from the burner and allow it to cool for about 3 minutes. Add 50 ml. of water through the condenser head, mix well, and heat to boiling. Swirl the solution during this stage and until the boiling is proceeding smoothly. Boil the solution gently for 5 minutes. Cool the solution to room temperature. Neutralize with dilute ammonium hydroxide (1:1) until the brown ferric hydroxide that first precipitates turns brownish green owing to the appearance of some cupric ammonium ion. If too much ammonium hydroxide is added so that a deep blue color is obtained add enough dilute sulfuric acid to restore the blue green color. At this point it is better to have the solution somewhat more basic (deep blue) than acid (brown). Cool, and add 2 g. of ammonium acid fluoride, NH_4HF_2, crystals. Mix, and wash down the walls of the flask. The color should change back to clear pale blue. The total volume should be about 150 ml. at this stage. Add 2 g. of potassium iodide and titrate immediately with 0.1 N thiosulfate solution, swirling the mixture constantly. Add the thiosulfate until the coffee-colored solution changes to a cream color. Then add 2 ml. of starch solution and continue to titrate until the color returns rather slowly after each drop of thiosulfate. At this point add 2 g. of potassium thiocyanate and titrate dropwise until the final disappearance of all blue color. No starch-iodine color should reappear as the solution stands for several minutes. Split drops near the end-point by allowing a bit of solution to emerge from the tip of the buret and transferring it to the

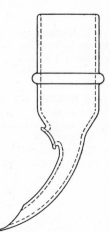

Fig. 72. Condenser head for conical flasks.

---

[1] The term *reflux* refers to the condensation of vapor to liquid on the walls of the flask and drainage back into the solution.

solution by touching the buret tip with the flask and washing the liquid into the solution being titrated.

Standardize the thiosulfate solution using copper wire that has been sandpapered and polished with a cloth. Weigh about 0.17 g., dissolve it in 15 ml. of concentrated perchloric acid. Add 5 ml. of a solution containing 10 g. of ferric chloride per l. and proceed as with the copper ore, as given above.

PROBLEMS

1. A commercial bleach solution was analyzed for sodium hypochlorite, NaOCl, by the indirect iodometric method. A sample weighing 3.725 g. required 42.5 ml. of 0.0800 N sodium thiosulfate solution to titrate the liberated iodine. Give equations for the reactions involved and calculate the per cent of sodium hypochlorite in the sample.

2. A sample of tartar emetic, $K(SbO)C_4H_4O_6$, weighing 1.000 g. was analyzed by direct iodometric titration. A volume of 40.0 ml. of 0.1000 N iodine was required for the titration. Calculate the purity of the sample.

3. A sample of pure potassium iodate weighing 0.4280 g. required 50.0 ml. of sodium thiosulfate solution to titrate the iodine liberated in the presence of excess potassium iodide and hydrochloric acid. Calculate the normality of the sodium thiosulfate solution.

4. The amount of manganese dioxide in a sample weighing 0.3500 g. was determined by heating it with hydrochloric acid. The free chlorine liberated was collected in a potassium iodide solution, setting free an equivalent amount of iodine. This iodine required 28.0 ml. of 0.1500 N sodium thiosulfate for titration. Write balanced equations for the reactions involved and calculate the per cent of manganese dioxide in the sample.

5. The lead in a sample of white lead weighing 0.5000 g. was precipitated as lead chromate, $PbCrO_4$, dissolved in hydrochloric acid and treated with potassium iodide. The iodine liberated required 42.0 ml. of 0.1100 N sodium thiosulfate for titration. Write balanced equations for the reactions involved. Calculate the per cent of lead in the sample.

6. Devise a scheme for determining the sodium chloride and sodium hypochlorite in a commercial bleaching solution.

7. Tell how to determine the amounts of both arsenious acid and arsenic acid in a solution containing the two.

8. Show how to decide positively whether a certain crystalline material is potassium iodate or potassium periodate.

9. A sample of steel weighing 1.000 g. was dissolved in hydrochloric acid, and the hydrogen sulfide evolved was collected in an ammoniacal zinc sulfate solution. Later the zinc solution was acidified with hydrochloric acid and the precipitated zinc sulfide dissolved. The hydrogen sulfide liberated required 15.0 ml. of 0.050 N iodine for titration. Write equations for the reactions involved and calculate the per cent of sulfur in the sample.

10. The air in a room in which an electrolysis cell was being operated was analyzed for chlorine by bubbling a large sample of air through a solution of potassium

iodide and titrating the iodine liberated with thiosulfate. The sample taken was 60.0 l.; the volume of 0.0900 N thiosulfate required was 25.2 ml. Calculate the volume per cent of chlorine gas in the atmosphere disregarding the volume change from standard conditions to room conditions.

11. Small amounts of carbon monoxide can be determined by the reaction $5CO + I_2O_5 = 2I^0 + 5CO_2$. The iodine is collected in a potassium iodide solution and titrated with sodium thiosulfate. Decide what the milliequivalent weight of carbon monoxide is in this reaction.

12. A solution of cupric sulfate was treated with excess potassium iodide, and the iodine liberated required 25.2 ml. of 0.1500 N sodium thiosulfate for titration. Calculate the weight of cuprous iodide formed.

13. The chromic acid in a plating bath was determined by treatment with potassium iodide and titration of the iodine formed with standard sodium thiosulfate. A sample of 10.00 ml. was taken; the volume of 0.0750 N sodium thiosulfate used was 43.0 ml. Calculate the grams per liter of chromic acid in the bath.

14. A neutral solution is known to contain potassium iodide and potassium iodate. Outline a procedure for determining both salts. Give equations for the reactions employed. Give also mathematical equations by which the results may be calculated.

15. An indirect volumetric method for the determination of sulfate consists in adding a measured volume of standard solution of barium chromate dissolved in hydrochloric acid. Barium sulfate is precipitated, and the excess barium is then precipitated as the chromate by neutralizing with ammonia. The chromate left in the solution is determined by the addition of potassium iodide and titration of the iodine liberated with sodium thiosulfate. The slight error caused by the solubility of the barium chromate is eliminated by running a blank. A boiler water was analyzed in this fashion. To 50.0 ml. of the water and also to 50.0 ml. of distilled water (blank) were added 50.0 ml. of the barium chromate solution. In the final titrations 0.10 ml. of 0.05 N sodium thiosulfate was required for the sample and 30.10 ml. for the blank. Calculate the $SO_4^=$ in the sample in parts per million (milligrams per liter).

TITRATIONS WITH POTASSIUM BROMATE

In strongly acid solutions, potassium bromate, or rather bromic acid, $HBrO_3$, is a powerful oxidizing agent, and standard solutions of bromate may be used for the determination of arsenic, antimony, iron, nitrite, oxalate, and various other materials. Unfortunately, the reduction of bromate may proceed in two ways, with the formation of free bromine, or with the formation of bromide. The stronger reducing agents, arsenite and antimonite, reduce the bromate all the way to bromide. Weaker reducing agents reduce the bromate only to free bromine, unless mercuric sulfate is added to the solution. The reduction then proceeds to the bromide owing to the formation of undissociated mercuric bromide. Thus, the oxidation of ferrous sulfate may proceed in two ways:

$$2KBrO_3 + 10FeSO_4 + 6H_2SO_4$$
$$= 2Br^0 + 5Fe_2(SO_4)_3 + K_2SO_4 + 6H_2O$$

$$2KBrO_3 + 12FeSO_4 + 6H_2SO_4 + HgSO_4$$
$$= HgBr_2 + 6Fe_2(SO_4)_3 + K_2SO_4 + 6H_2O$$

The presence of the mercuric sulfate effectively prevents the formation of free bromine.

The substances which can be determined by direct titration with bromate are

Addition of Mercuric; Sulfate Not Necessary		Addition of Mercuric; Sulfate Necessary	
H_3AsO_3	to H_3AsO_4	Fe^{++}	to Fe^{+3}
SbO^+	to H_3SbO_4	Cr^{+3}	to $CrO_4^=$
$Fe(CN)_6^{-4}$	to $Fe(CN)_6^{-3}$	$C_2O_4^=$	to $CO_2 + H_2O$
Hg_2^{++}	to Hg^{++}	NO_2^-	to NO_3^-
		Mn^{++}	to MnO_2

Solutions of potassium bromate are usually made up to approximately the concentration desired and standardized against primary-standard arsenious oxide or against pure metallic iron. Potassium bromate is marketed in highly pure form, has no water of crystallization, is non-hygroscopic, and may undoubtedly be used as a primary-standard material although the point has apparently not been checked exhaustively.

Basic mercuric bromate, $Hg(OH)BrO_3$, is available commercially in sufficiently pure form and has been recommended as a primary-standard bromate. It is prepared from the normal bromate, $Hg(BrO_3)_2$, by hydrolysis. It is soluble in water to the extent of only 0.81 g. per l. at 25°, so that a little hydrochloric acid is required to take it into solution.

The interaction of the bromate ion, BrO_3^-, and the bromide ion in acid solution may be used as a means of providing known amounts of bromine

$$KBrO_3 + 5KBr + 6HCl = 6Br^0 + 6KCl + 3H_2O$$

The measured quantities of bromine thus formed may be utilized in quantitative reactions such as the determination of 8-hydroxyquinoline

This reaction is employed in the volumetric determination of magnesium after its precipitation as the 8-hydroxyquinoline salt. The precipitate, which consists of 2 molecules of 8-hydroxyquinoline per magnesium atom and is insoluble in neutral solution, is filtered off and dissolved in hydrochloric acid. The hydrochloric acid solution is treated with an excess of potassium bromide and then titrated in the hot solution with standard 0.1 N potassium bromate. The equivalence-point is generally determined potentiometrically.

THE DETERMINATION OF ARSENIC AND ANTIMONY

Trivalent arsenic and trivalent antimony may be titrated with potassium bromate in hydrochloric acid solutions, bromate being reduced to bromide:

$$3H_3AsO_3 + KBrO_3 + HCl = 3H_3AsO_4 + HBr + KCl$$

$$6KSbOCl_2 + 2KBrO_3 + 12H_2O$$
$$= 6H_3SbO_4 + 2KBr + 6KCl + 6HCl$$

Arsenic and antimony in the pentavalent state must first be reduced to the trivalent state. This is most conveniently done by passing sulfur dioxide through the hydrochloric acid solution; the excess sulfur dioxide is removed by bubbling a stream of air, or better carbon dioxide, through the solution.

Antimony occurs naturally as the black, sulfide mineral, stibnite, Sb_2S_3. The mineral is easily concentrated by procedures commonly used in mining, and the concentrates fortunately contain very little iron and arsenic. The ore is soluble in dilute hydrochloric acid, $Sb_2S_3 + 6HCl = 2SbCl_3 + 3H_2S$, any residue which remains usually being free of antimony. Antimonous chloride may be volatilized from hydrochloric acid solutions at about 100°, so that the temperature should not exceed this value and the vessel should be closely covered with a cover glass. The addition of a few grams of sodium chloride is said to reduce materially the volatility of the antimonous chloride.

When arsenic and antimony are present together, a preliminary separation must be made before they can be determined by any volumetric oxidation method such as the bromate titration under discussion. One method of effecting their separation involves distilling off arsenic trichloride from a hydrochloric acid solution containing a reducing agent; this is discussed in more detail in Chapter 14 dealing with methods of effecting separations.

Preparation of 0.1 *N Potassium Bromate.* The equivalent weight of potassium bromate is one-sixth of the molecular weight in the reactions with arsenite, antimonite, and ferrous used in the following procedures (reduction to bromide). The equivalent weight is therefore 167/6, or 27.832. Dissolve 2.78 g. of potassium bromate in 1 l. of water and mix thoroughly. Standardize this solution against arsenious oxide as described in the following section.

Procedure for the Titration of Trivalent Arsenic. Carry out the standardization of the potassium bromate solution and the analysis in identical fashion by the following procedure: Samples containing arsenious oxide should not be dried in the oven unless at less than 110° because of the possibility of volatilizing a portion of the arsenious oxide present and thus changing the composition of the sample. For the standardization weigh exactly into 250-ml. beakers several samples of primary-standard arsenious oxide, keeping the weight between 0.17 and 0.23 g.; for the analysis weigh out samples of 0.3 to 0.35 g. To each sample add 0.5 g. of sodium hydroxide and 10 ml. of water. Swirl the contents of the beaker gently until the arsenious oxide has completely dissolved. Add 75 ml. of water and then 15 ml. of concentrated hydrochloric acid. Place a magnetic stirring rotor in the solution and place the beaker on the magnetic stirring apparatus. Adjust the stirring rotor so that the rapid swirling motion produces a cone at the center of the solution. Add 2 drops of 0.2 per cent solution of naphthol blue black indicator (0.2 g. of the dye dissolved in 100 ml. of water). Add 30 to 35 ml. of the standard potassium bromate solution rapidly and then proceed more slowly as the end-point is approached. The color change of the indicator is not reversible. If the indicator fades toward the end of the titration add 2 drops more of the indicator solution. The color changes from green to faint pink at the end-point. At the end-point 10 to 20 seconds are required between drops.

Calculate the normality of the bromate solution by dividing the weight of primary-standard arsenious oxide taken by the milliequivalent weight of the arsenious oxide, 0.049455, and by the number of milliliters of potassium bromate solution used. Calculate the per cent of arsenious oxide in the unknown material analyzed, using the same milliequivalent weight.

Methyl red can be used as indicator in place of naphthol blue black, but 20 to 30 seconds are required between drops at the end of the titration. The indicator error for the amount of naphthol blue black used is negligible, for 1.0 ml. of the indicator solution requires only 0.03 ml. of 0.1 N potassium bromate for oxidation.

The titration may of course be carried out in a flask shaken by hand, but the magnetic stirring is much preferred in view of the time required as the end-point is approached. A titration thief is particularly useful in titrations such as this one in which a non-reversible indicator is used which gives no warning of the approach to the end-point. With part of the solution trapped off in the thief, the end-point may be approached more rapidly; when the premature end-point has been found, the titration thief may be removed, additional indicator added, and the exact end-point found by slow dropwise addition of the oxidizing agent.

Procedure for the Determination of Antimony in Stibnite. Dry the material for analysis for 1 hour in the oven at 100°. Weigh accurately three samples of approximately 1 g. each, transferring each sample to a 400-ml. beaker. To each, add about 5 g. of sodium chloride. Place a cover glass on the beaker. Add 25 ml. of concentrated hydrochloric acid from a graduated cylinder, allowing the acid to flow into the beaker by way of the lip without removing the cover glass. Place a wire gauze on a ring on a ringstand and adjust the flame of a Bunsen burner beneath it so that a small spot at the center of the wire gauze is heated to a dull red. Place the beaker on the hot gauze and swirl it gently, holding it either with beaker tongs or by the fingers protected by short lengths of rubber tubing, Fig. 21. Do not allow the solution to boil, although considerable gaseous hydrogen chloride will be evolved. As soon as the black stibnite has dissolved remove the beaker from the hot gauze and rinse the cover glass and walls with water, using not more than 5 ml. of water.

Place twin cover-glass supports on the beaker, replace the cover glass, and return the beaker to the hot wire gauze. Continue the heating at almost the boiling point until no more hydrogen sulfide is evolved, as tested by odor or, better, by a strip of filter paper moistened with a little dilute lead acetate solution.

As soon as the evolution of hydrogen is complete, remove the beaker from the heat, rinse the cover glass, the cover-glass supports, and the walls of the beaker, and dilute to 100 ml. with water. If at this point the solution yields a precipitate of antimonous sulfide this shows that all the sulfide was not removed as hydrogen sulfide, and the sample is best discarded. If no precipitate of antimonous sulfide appears, drop a magnetic stirring rotor in the beaker and place the beaker on the magnetic stirrer. Adjust the stirring rotor so that the rapid swirling motion produces a cone at the center of the solution. Add 2 drops of a 0.2 per cent solution of naphthol blue black indicator (0.2 g. of the dye dissolved in 100 ml. of water). Place a titration thief in the solution. Add 30 ml. of 0.1 N potassium bromate solution rapidly and then proceed more slowly as the equivalence-point is approached. The indicator changes from green to faint pink at the end-point, but the color change is not reversible. At the end-point, 10 to 20 seconds are required between drops.

With part of the solution trapped off in the thief, the end-point may be approached somewhat more rapidly. When the premature end-point has been found, remove the titration thief, add 1 or 2 drops of indicator if needed, and titrate slowly to the exact end-point.

Standardize the potassium bromate solution against primary-standard arsenious oxide as described under the determination of arsenic in the preceding section. Calculate the per cent of antimony in the sample; the equivalent weight of antimony is one-half the atomic weight, $121.76/2 = 60.88$. If the results are reported as per cent of stibnite, use the equivalent weight, $Sb_2S_3/4$, which has the value 84.93.

THE DETERMINATION OF IRON BY BROMATE OXIDATION. USE OF BASIC MERCURIC BROMATE AS STANDARD SOLUTION

In the determination of iron by titration of the ferrous ion with permanganate, ceric salts, or dichromate, organic matter may not be present in the solution; the presence of such substances as tartaric acid, citric acid, oxalic acid, and alcohol is thus ruled out. For the determination of iron in pharmaceutical products, foods, and similar materials, the organic matter must first be destroyed. The bromate method described below provides a method in which the prior removal of organic matter is not necessary. If not more than 4 g. of tartaric acid or citric acid, or 2 g. of oxalic acid, or more than a few milliliters of methanol or ethanol are present in the original sample, no appreciable change results in the determination of iron.

The oxidation of ferrous iron by bromate is too slow in a sulfuric acid solution to be used for a direct titration. Even in hydrochloric acid the oxidation is too slow to be useful unless a suitable catalyst is added. Cupric chloride catalyzes the reaction in quite remarkable fashion. The iron is first reduced with stannous chloride, and the excess stannous chloride is removed by the addition of mercuric chloride

$$2FeCl_3 + SnCl_2 \;(+\; HCl) = 2FeCl_2 + SnCl_4$$

$$SnCl_2 + 2HgCl_2 \;(+\; HCl) = SnCl_4 + Hg_2Cl_2$$

Cupric chloride oxidizes the ferrous iron, largely because of the great stability of the colorless chlorocuprous ion formed

$$FeCl_2 + CuCl_2 + 2HCl = FeCl_3 + H_2CuCl_3$$

The presence of some phosphoric acid which forms a stable complex with ferric iron helps drive this reaction to the right. The chlorocuprous ion, $CuCl_3^{=}$, is rapidly oxidized by air, so that contact with atmospheric oxygen must be avoided. This is accomplished by the addition of arsenate which is reduced by the chlorocuprous ion to arsenite, which is not oxidized by air. The trivalent arsenic is then oxidized to the pentavalent form by the standard bromate solution,

$$2H_2CuCl_3 + H_3AsO_4 = 2CuCl_2 + H_3AsO_3 + H_2O + 2HCl$$

$$3H_3AsO_3 + KBrO_3 + HCl = 3H_3AsO_4 + HBr + KCl$$

The oxidation can be made either with a solution of potassium bromate, or with one of basic mercuric bromate, $HgOHBrO_3$ which is a primary standard that can be weighed out directly for the preparation of a standard solution.

The irreversible oxidation indicator, naphthol blue black, is used just as in the bromate titration of arsenious acid as described in a preceding section.

Preparation of 0.1 *N Basic Mercuric Bromate.* The equivalent weight of basic mercuric bromate is its molecular weight, 345.534, divided by 6, or 57.589. One liter of 0.1000 N bromate solution contains, therefore, 5.7589 g. of $HgOHBrO_3$. Weigh exactly the amount of primary-standard-grade basic mercuric bromate, or exactly some quantity near this weight, and transfer it to a 600-ml. beaker. Add 400–500 ml. of water to the weighed salt and with vigorous magnetic stirring add dilute hydrochloric acid (1:1) in 0.5-ml. portions until all of the salt has dissolved. Do not add more hydrochloric acid than is just necessary to dissolve the salt. Transfer the solution to a 1-l. volumetric flask, dilute to the mark with water, and mix thoroughly. If an amount of basic mercuric bromate other than that called for was weighed, calculate the normal concentration using the milli-equivalent weight, 0.057,589.

Procedure for the Determination of Iron by Titration with Bromate. Dry the iron ore for 2 hours in the oven at 110°. Weigh accurately three samples for analysis. Make each sample about 1 g. in amount and weigh it directly into a 400-ml. beaker. Cover the beaker and add 30 ml. of dilute hydrochloric acid (1:1). Heat gently to dissolve the ore. When all of the sample has dissolved except perhaps for a small amount of silica, remove the beaker from the heat and rinse down the bottom of the cover glass and the walls of the beaker, using the least volume of water necessary. The yellow color of the solution is due to the ferric chloride, the color being most intense when the solution is hot and the hydrochloric acid concentrated. With the volume of the solution small and the solution kept hot on a wire gauze over a burner, add with vigorous stirring a 1 per cent solution of stannous chloride [1 g. of stannous chloride dissolved in 100 ml. of dilute hydrochloric acid (10:90)]. Reduce only one sample at a time and add the stannous chloride solution dropwise from a pipet or buret until 1 drop discharges the last of the yellow color of ferric chloride. The reduction is rather rapid and can be carried out almost like a titration, the yellow color changing sharply to green. When this has happened add 1 further drop of stannous chloride solution and immediately cool the solution by adding 40–50 ml. of cold water. Add at once 10 ml. of a 10 per cent solution of mercuric chloride. A light, white precipitate of mercurous chloride should form within a minute or two, indicating that an excess of stannous chloride has been added; if no precipitate appears it is probable that the reduction of iron was incomplete. If more than a slight amount of mercurous chloride precipitates, too much stannous chloride was added and the sample must be discarded, for an excessive amount of mercurous chloride causes the reduction of some bromate over that required for the iron. After the reduction with stannous chloride and the addition of mercuric chloride proceed immediately with the titration.

Add 10 ml. of a solution prepared by dissolving 4 g. of cupric sulfate, $CuSO_4 \cdot 5H_2O$, and 100 g. of ammonium arsenate, $(NH_4)_3AsO_4$, in 500 ml. of 85 per cent phosphoric acid and diluting to 1000 ml. with water. Dilute the solution to 100–125 ml. by adding water. Add 2–4 drops of a 0.2 per cent solution of naphthol blue black (0.2 g. of the dyestuff dissolved in 100 ml. of water). Place a titration thief in the solution. Add 30 ml. of 0.1 N basic mercuric bromate solution rapidly and then proceed more slowly as the equivalence-point is approached. The indicator changes from green to faint pink at the end-point, but the color change is not reversible. At the end-point, 10–20 seconds are required between drops. With part of the solution trapped off in the thief, the end-point may be approached somewhat more rapidly. When the premature end-point has been found, remove the titration thief, add 1 or 2 drops of indicator if needed, and titrate slowly to the exact end-point.

Using the normality of the basic mercuric bromate obtained by making up the solution by weight and the volume of the solution used, calculate the per cent of iron in the sample; the milliequivalent weight of iron is 0.055,85. If a solution of potassium bromate is used as the standard solution in this titration, it should be standardized against pure iron as the primary standard.

TITRATIONS WITH IODATE

Iodic acid is a powerful oxidizing agent which can be used in acid solution for the volumetric determination of various materials. The reduction of iodic acid in hydrochloric acid solution proceeds in three ways, depending on the concentration of the acid and the strength of the reducing agent being titrated. In hydrochloric acid, sulfuric acid, or perchloric acid solutions 0.1 to 1 M in strength, iodine is the usual reaction product. Very strong reducing agents carry the reduction all the way to iodide. In strong hydrochloric acid, 4–6 M, iodate is reduced to iodine chloride, ICl, in which the oxidation number of the iodine is $+1$. Typical reactions are:

$$KIO_3 + 6HCl + 5KI = 6I^0 + 6KCl + 3H_2O$$
Low acidity, 0.1 to 1 M HCl

$$KIO_3 + 6TiCl_3 + 6HCl = KI + 6TiCl_4 + 3H_2O$$
Low acidity, 0.1 to 1 M HCl

$$KIO_3 + 6HCl + 2KI = 3ICl + 3KCl + 3H_2O$$
High acidity, 4–6 M HCl

Of these three types of reaction, the reduction to iodine chloride is the most useful in that it may be applied to the determination of a number of materials: arsenic (H_3AsO_3 to H_3AsO_4), antimony (Sb^{+3} to Sb^{+5}), tin (Sn^{+2} to Sn^{+4}), thallium (Tl^+ to Tl^{+3}), thiosulfate ($S_2O_3^=$ to $SO_4^=$), thiocyanate (CNS^- to $CN^- + SO_4^=$), sulfite ($SO_3^=$ to $SO_4^=$), iodide (I^- to ICl), hydrogen peroxide (H_2O_2 to $H_2O + O_2$), and hydrazine ($N_2H_6SO_4$ to $N_2 + H_2O$). The end-point can be determined by shaking the solution with a few milliliters of carbon tetrachloride. Before the end-point the carbon tetrachloride is colored purple by iodine produced by the dissociation of the iodine chloride produced. At the end-point the iodine is converted completely to iodine chloride, and the color changes quite sharply from purple to colorless. The reaction must be carried out in a glass-stoppered flask, and after each drop of iodate added near the equivalence-point the flask is stoppered and shaken vigorously so that the iodine is extracted by the carbon tetrachloride. This makes the procedure tedious.

The determination of iron is particularly noteworthy, for in contrast to the permanganate and cerate methods for the determination of iron, the determination may be carried out in the presence of organic matter such as alcohol, cellulose, citric acid, and tartaric acid. The determination is best performed by adding a solution of iodine chloride to the reduced iron solution, and the iodine liberated is titrated back to iodine chloride by iodate. The iodine chloride solution is prepared, before its addition to the solution of ferrous chloride, by mixing equivalent quantities of potassium iodide and potassium iodate. The reactions are

$$2KI + KIO_3 + 6HCl = 3ICl + 3KCl + 3H_2O$$

$$(ICl + Cl^- = ICl_2^-)$$

$$2FeCl_2 + 2ICl (+ HCl) = 2FeCl_3 + 2I^0$$

$$KIO_3 + 4I^0 + 6HCl = 5ICl + KCl + 3H_2O$$

The end-point is determined with one of the indicators mentioned above.

PROBLEMS

1. Illustrate by equations the reactions involved in the use of potassium acid iodate as a primary standard in (*a*) neutralization; (*b*) the oxidation of iodide in 4–6 *M* hydrochloric acid forming iodine chloride; and (*c*) the oxidation of potassium iodide at lower acid concentration in which free iodine is formed. Calculate the equivalent weight in each case.

2. Tell how to standardize a solution of iodine in two ways, using as primary standard only potassium iodate. A solution of sodium thiosulfate may be used in one method. Calculate the equivalent weights of potassium iodate in each method.

3. A sample of primary-standard arsenious oxide weighing 0.2576 g. was dissolved in a few milliliters of strong sodium hydroxide solution, diluted with water to 150 ml. and acidified with hydrochloric acid. The sample of arsenite was then oxidized with a standard potassium bromate solution, using methyl red as indicator, 48.75 ml. being required. Calculate the normality of the standard bromate solution and the titer of the solution for metallic arsenic.

4. A sample of stibnite weighing 1.000 g. was dissolved in concentrated hydrochloric acid and the hydrogen sulfide formed expelled by heat. The resulting solution of antimony trichloride was diluted and titrated with 0.1259 *N* potassium bromate with naphthol blue black as indicator, 24.1 ml. being required. Calculate the per cent of antimonous sulfide, Sb_2S_3, in the sample.

5. Explain why mercuric sulfate is added in certain procedures employing potassium bromate as a standard oxidizing agent.

6. Explain the function of the copper sulfate, ammonium arsenate, and phosphoric acid added in the potassium bromate procedure for the determination of iron.

7. A sample of ferrous ethylenediammonium sulfate, $FeC_2H_4(NH_3)_2(SO_4)_2 \cdot 4H_2O$, weighing 0.7576 g., was dissolved in hydrochloric acid and treated with cupric

sulfate, ammonium arsenate, and phosphoric acid, and then titrated with a solution of basic mercuric bromate, $HgOHBrO_3$, 19.28 ml. being required to reach the end-point with naphthol blue black as indicator. Calculate the normality of the bromate solution.

8. Write the equation for the reaction of potassium iodate with potassium iodide upon which the preparation of iodine monochloride is based. Calculate the amounts of each salt required to prepare 500 ml. of a solution 0.5000 M in iodine monochloride.

TITRATIONS WITH FERROUS SULFATE

Ferrous sulfate is a rather mild reducing agent and is used only for the titration of strong oxidizing agents such as ceric salts, permanganate, and dichromate. It is useful for back-titrating standard solutions of these oxidizing agents and also for the determination of cerium, manganese, and chromium, for these elements can be readily converted to their higher valence forms.

Ferrous sulfate solutions are slowly oxidized in contact with air and should be standardized the same day used. Ferrous sulfate solutions can be made up from crystalline ferrous sulfate ($FeSO_4 \cdot 7H_2O$), ferrous ammonium sulfate (Mohr's salt, $Fe(NH_4)_2(SO_4)_2 \cdot 6H_2O$), or ferrous ethylenediammonium sulfate (Oesper's salt, $FeC_2H_4(NH_3)_2$-$(SO_4)_2 \cdot 4H_2O$), the latter two being better for the purpose because they are likely to have less of the iron oxidized to the ferric state. Ferrous ethylenediammonium sulfate, indeed, is a primary-standard material, and a solution of it may be made up by weight. Any one of these salts is dissolved in water containing 10 ml. of concentrated sulfuric acid per l. The presence of ammonium sulfate or ethylenediammonium sulfate has no adverse effect on the use of the solution, for these double salts are completely dissociated in water solution.

One particularly important use of standard ferrous sulfate is in the determination of chromium. Chromium may be oxidized by several reagents to chromic acid, H_2CrO_4, the excess oxidizing agent removed, and the chromic acid titrated with ferrous sulfate $2H_2CrO_4 + 6FeSO_4 + 6H_2SO_4 = Cr_2(SO_4)_3 + 3Fe_2(SO_4)_3 + 8H_2O$, using diphenylaminesulfonic acid as indicator. Of the various oxidizing agents which may be employed for the preliminary oxidation, perchloric acid is the most commonly used. Steel samples may be dissolved directly in it, and certain chromium-containing organic materials (chrome-tanned leather and chromatized cat gut, for example) may also be destroyed by boiling with a mixture of perchloric acid and nitric acid. As the concentration of perchloric acid increases and the boiling point rises, the oxidizing power of the perchloric acid becomes greater. It finally oxidizes the chromium to chromic acid. It is only necessary then to dilute the solution and titrate the chromic acid with ferrous sulfate, for, when dilute, perchloric acid has no oxidizing power at all. Manganese present in the sample is not oxidized, probably because the higher valence forms of manganese are oxygen-containing acids which decompose at the temperature of boiling perchloric acid, 204°.

Potassium persulfate, $K_2S_2O_8$, is also a strong oxidizing agent but will convert chromic salts to chromic acid only when a silver salt is present as a catalyst. The excess persulfate is destroyed by boiling, and the silver is precipitated by the addition of enough chloride. The chromic acid may then be titrated with ferrous sulfate. Manganese is oxidized by persulfate to permanganate; in the process of destroying the excess persulfate by boiling, the permanganate is decomposed, partly by heat and partly by reaction with the chloride added. For this reason permanganate cannot be determined by oxidation with persulfate, for no way is known of removing the excess persulfate without boiling.

Two powerful oxidizing agents are available for converting manganese compounds to permanganate: sodium bismuthate ($NaBiO_3$) and potassium periodate (KIO_4). Sodium bismuthate is insoluble, and, after it is oxidized by shaking it with the solution at room temperature, the excess is simply filtered off and the permanganate titrated with ferrous sulfate. The periodate oxidation is made in a hot solution and in one preferably containing phosphoric acid; the excess periodate and the iodate formed in the reaction are precipitated as mercuric salts which are filtered off, leaving the solution ready for titration with ferrous sulfate. Chromium interferes in the determination of manganese by either method.

The Determination of Available Oxygen.   Certain metal oxides, manganese dioxide for example, are used industrially for the oxidation of various materials. The oxygen in such metal oxides which can be used for oxidation is known as *available oxygen*. More precisely, available oxygen is that oxygen in excess of the oxygen in the oxide of the metal in its lowest valence form. Thus, manganese dioxide, MnO_2, has 1 available oxygen, for on reduction manganous salts are formed which are derivatives of manganous oxide, MnO. The higher oxides of lead, PbO_2 and Pb_3O_4, each have 1 replaceable oxygen per molecule.

Available oxygen is determined by dissolving the higher oxide in an acid in the presence of an excess of a standard reducing agent and, after the oxide has dissolved, back-titrating the excess standard reducing agent. A combination of sulfuric acid and ferrous sulfate is a good reducing solvent for the purpose; the excess ferrous sulfate may be titrated with cerate, permanganate, or dichromate. The whole process should be carried out in the absence of air to minimize the oxidation of the ferrous sulfate by oxygen; this can be done by passing carbon dioxide or nitrogen through the flask.

The results are reported simply as per cent available oxygen, the equivalent weight of the oxygen being $O/2$, or 8.000.

Preparation and Standardization of 0.1 *N Ferrous Sulfate.* Weight 39.2 g. of ferrous ammonium sulfate, $Fe(NH_4)_2(SO_4)_2 \cdot 6H_2O$, or 27.8 g. of ferrous sulfate, $FeSO_4 \cdot 7H_2O$, and dissolve it in 1 l. of water containing 10 ml. of concentrated sulfuric acid. Standardize this solution the same day that it is to be used. For the standardization weigh out exactly 0.18 to 0.2 g. of pure potassium dichromate, transferring the salt into a 400-ml. beaker. Dissolve the salt in a little water, add 5 ml. of dilute sulfuric acid (1:1), 5 ml. of concentrated phosphoric acid, and dilute to 200 ml. Add 0.3 ml. of 0.01 M diphenylamine-sulfonic acid and titrate with the ferrous sulfate solution.

Alternatively, the standardization may be made by measuring out with a pipet a convenient volume of a standard solution of potassium dichromate or potassium permanganate the normality of which is known.

PROBLEMS

1. A volume of 40.0 ml. of a solution of ferrous sulfate is required for titrating 32.0 ml. of 0.0900 N potassium permanganate. Calculate the normality of the ferrous sulfate solution.

2. Tell how to determine the amount of ferrous sulfate and chromic sulfate in a solution containing the two and also some free sulfuric acid.

3. Chromous sulfate is an excellent absorbent for oxygen. Exactly 2 l. of gas containing oxygen, measured at 20° and 730 mm. Hg pressure, was bubbled through a solution containing 50.0 ml. of a standard chromous sulfate solution. Afterward the excess of chromous sulfate was titrated with 0.1000 N permanganate, 15.5 ml. being required to oxidize the chromous sulfate to chromic sulfate. Another 50.0 ml. of the chromous sulfate solution required 40.0 ml. of the permanganate solution for titration in the absence of oxygen. Calculate (*a*) the weight of oxygen in grams in the gas sample, (*b*) the volume of this oxygen under standard conditions of temperature and pressure, and (*c*) the volume per cent of oxygen in the sample.

4. Devise a scheme for determining chromic acid and trivalent chromium in the same solution.

5. A volume of 40.0 ml. of 0.125 N iodine required 45.0 ml. of sodium thiosulfate solution for titration. A volume of 40.0 ml. of sulfatoceric acid was treated with potassium iodide, and the liberated iodine was titrated with the same thiosulfate solution; 36.0 ml. was required. Calculate the normality of the sulfatoceric acid solution.

6. A sample of chromite ore weighing 0.6000 g. was fused with sodium peroxide, the melt was dissolved in water and acid, and the chromate was reduced by the addition of 50.0 ml. of 0.3500 N ferrous sulfate. The excess ferrous sulfate was back-titrated with 0.05 N potassium dichromate, 10.5 ml. being required. Calculate the per cent of chromium in the sample.

CHAPTER 12

Volumetric Reactions Involving

the Formation of Insoluble

or Non-Dissociated Compounds

The third class of reactions which find use in volumetric analysis involves the formation of precipitates or of slightly dissociated compounds. In practice such reactions are almost limited to titrations with silver nitrate. Many metals undergo such reactions, but satisfactory indicators for marking the end-points are not known. The silver halides are insoluble, and at least four good methods are available for detecting the equivalence-point when their precipitation is carried out volumetrically. A good many other anions can be determined indirectly because the silver salts of practically all the weak acids are insoluble in neutral solution and their silver content can be determined after their precipitation and filtration (Volhard method). Silver also forms non-dissociated, soluble compounds, those with cyanide and with ammonia being especially useful in volumetric analysis. Largely, then, the present chapter is devoted to titrations with silver nitrate, and the chapter might well be entitled *argentimetry*, meaning measurements involving silver.

EQUIVALENT WEIGHT IN REACTIONS INVOLVING THE FORMATION OF INSOLUBLE OR NON-DISSOCIATED COMPOUNDS

Equivalent weight in this type of volumetric reaction is defined as that amount of material which contains or reacts with 1 gram atom of a univalent metal or $\frac{1}{2}$ gram atom of a bivalent metal.

Thus, the equivalent weight of silver nitrate used in the reaction

$$NaCl + AgNO_3 = AgCl + NaNO_3$$

320

is equal to the molecular weight; that of chromate for the reactions

$$2AgNO_3 + Na_2CrO_4 = Ag_2CrO_4 + 2NaNO_3$$

$$PbCl_2 + Na_2CrO_4 = PbCrO_4 + 2NaCl$$

is one-half the molecular weight. In the reaction

$$NiSO_4 + 4KCN = K_2Ni(CN)_4 + K_2SO_4$$

the equivalent weight of potassium cyanide is twice the molecular weight, for this is the amount which reacts with one-half an atom of the bivalent metal nickel.

As in the other types of volumetric reactions, a material may have several different equivalent weights, depending on the reaction in which it is involved. Thus, although the equivalent weight of potassium cyanide is twice the molecular weight in the reaction above, in the reaction

$$AgNO_3 + NaCN = AgCN + NaNO_3$$

it is equal to the molecular weight; and in the reaction

$$2Cu(NH_3)_4(NO_3)_2 + 7NaCN + H_2O = 2Na_2Cu(CN)_3 + NH_4CNO$$

$$+ 6NH_3 + 3NaNO_3 + NH_4NO_3$$

it is equal to $\frac{7}{4}NaCN$.

FORMATION AND INSTABILITY CONSTANTS

In Chapter 8, dealing with neutralization reactions, the mass-action principle was applied to the ionization of water and of weak acids and bases. The constants in the mathematical expressions defining the equilibrium in these reactions were represented by K_W, K_A, and K_B and were called ionization or dissociation constants. The principle is actually broader in its application than was implied in Chapter 8 because substances other than water and the weak acids and bases are only slightly ionized in solution. In particular, there exists a great class of substances commonly spoken of as *complexes*, which are formed by the union of otherwise apparently saturated molecules. Thus, silver nitrate combines with sodium cyanide to form a new compound

$$AgNO_3 + 2NaCN = NaAg(CN)_2 + NaNO_3$$

and with ammonia to form another

$$AgNO_3 + 2NH_3 = Ag(NH_3)_2NO_3$$

These new products are salts and are completely ionized in the following manner:

$$NaAg(CN)_2 = Na^+ + Ag(CN)_2^-$$

$$Ag(NH_3)_2NO_3 = Ag(NH_3)_2^+ + NO_3^-$$

but the silver-containing ions are themselves ionized only to a minute degree to form silver ions

$$Ag(CN)_2^- = Ag^+ + 2CN^-$$

$$Ag(NH_3)_2^+ = Ag^+ + 2NH_3$$

The extent of ionization of such complex or non-dissociated ions varies greatly from one to another.

The constant defining the equilibrium in these reactions is known as the *instability constant* if the reaction is written as a dissociation

$$Ag(NH_3)_2^+ = Ag^+ + 2NH_3 \qquad K_I = \frac{[Ag^+][NH_3]^2}{[Ag(NH_3)_2^+]} = 6.8 \times 10^{-8}$$

If the reaction is written in reverse, as a formation reaction, the constant is called a *formation constant*

$$Ag^+ + 2NH_3 = Ag(NH_3)_2^+ \qquad K_F = \frac{[Ag(NH_3)_2^+]}{[Ag^+][NH_3]^2} = \frac{1}{6.8 \times 10^{-8}}$$

The formation constant is the reciprocal of the instability constant.

The instability constant may be used to determine the extent to which reactions will occur that involve the formation of non-dissociated compounds. It may also be used to determine whether a precipitate will dissolve in a reagent, owing to the formation of a non-dissociated compound. This is a question of deciding whether the precipitate or the non-dissociated, soluble compound furnishes the greater concentration of metal ions to the solution. The one furnishing the fewer ions to the solution will form at the expense of the other.

As an example, we consider what occurs when 1 g. of silver chloride is treated with 1 l. of 1 M ammonia. If the silver dissolves, the concentration of the silver and of the chloride in the solution will be $1/143 = 0.0070$ M, the molecular weight of silver chloride being 143. This is the concentration of the chloride ion and of the total silver, but not, of course, the concentration of the silver ion as the silver is tied up with ammonia. As long as no precipitate of silver chloride is present the silver ion concentration must be smaller than that indicated by the solubility product of silver chloride for the chloride concentration of the solution; that is

$$[Ag^+][Cl^-] = 1.0 \times 10^{-10}$$

$$[Cl^-] = 0.0070$$

$$[Ag^+] = \frac{1.0 \times 10^{-10}}{7 \times 10^{-3}} = 1.43 \times 10^{-8}$$

If the silver-ion concentration exceeds this, solid silver chloride will precipitate. The concentration of the ammonia is smaller than the original 1 M by the ammonia used to unite with the dissolved silver, that is, $1 - 2 \times 0.007$, or 0.986 M.

The dissolved silver is present largely as the silver ammonia ion; some silver ion is also present, the sum of the two being equal to the molar concentration of the silver which dissolved, $[Ag(NH_3)_2^+] + [Ag^+] = 0.0070$. Inserting these values into the expression for the instability constant of the silver ammonia ion,

$$K_I = \frac{[Ag^+][NH_3]^2}{[Ag(NH_3)_2^+]} = \frac{[Ag^+](0.986)^2}{0.0070 - [Ag^+]} = 6.8 \times 10^{-8}$$

It is apparent that $[Ag^+]$ is going to be so much smaller than 0.0070 that it may be dropped from the expression in the denominator. Solution of the equation then gives

$$[Ag^+] = \frac{6.8 \times 10^{-8} \times 7.0 \times 10^{-3}}{(9.86 \times 10^{-1})^2} = 4.9 \times 10^{-10}$$

This value for the silver ion is a good deal smaller than the value 1.43×10^{-8} calculated above as that concentration of silver needed to cause a precipitation of silver chloride. Hence, silver chloride dissolves in ammonia.

METHODS OF DETECTING THE EQUIVALENCE-POINT IN REACTIONS INVOLVING THE FORMATION OF INSOLUBLE OR NON-DISSOCIATED COMPOUNDS

Owing to the fact that silver chloride coagulates rapidly it is possible to locate the equivalent-point in the titration of chloride with silver nitrate simply by determining when the addition of silver nitrate no longer causes a precipitation of silver chloride. When chloride is present, a cloud or turbidity of silver chloride forms where the drop of silver nitrate strikes the solution. At the so-called *clear point*, marking the point where equivalent amounts of chloride and silver are present, this turbidity is no longer produced. Actually the equivalence-point can be determined quite accurately this way but the titration must be carried out slowly.

A second method of locating the equivalence-point in the chloride titration is based on the formation of a colored precipitate of silver chromate which is more soluble than silver chloride and precipitates only after all the chloride has been precipitated. This procedure is known as the Mohr method and is discussed in detail subsequently.

A third method of detecting the equivalence-point of precipitation reactions involves the formation of a soluble colored compound. The best example of this is the Volhard method in which a soluble silver salt is titrated with potassium thiocyanate. Ferric iron is added as indicator; an excess of thiocyanate reacts with the ferric ion to give an intense red, soluble compound, which serves well to mark the end-point. The Volhard method is of great general utility and is also discussed in detail in a subsequent section.

Still another method employed in locating the equivalence-point of precipitation reactions involves the adsorption of dyestuffs on the surface of the precipitate. These so-called adsorption indicators are also treated in some detail later.

Two volumetric methods involving the formation of soluble, non-dissociated compounds are covered later in the chapter. In one, the determination of cyanide, the equivalence-point is detected by the first appearance of an insoluble material, silver iodide. In the second procedure, a method for calcium using an organic compound called Versene, the equivalence-point is found by the destruction of a soluble, colored, non-dissociated compound of magnesium with a dyestuff by the formation of a less dissociated (more stable) compound of magnesium with the Versene.

Thus we have some six methods of locating the equivalence-point in volumetric reactions involving the formation of insoluble or non-ionized compounds. There are in addition a few other methods which are used in specific titrations; these will be found in more advanced texts.

PRIMARY STANDARDS AND STANDARD SOLUTIONS FOR REACTIONS INVOLVING THE FORMATION OF INSOLUBLE OR NON-DISSOCIATED COMPOUNDS

Silver Nitrate. $AgNO_3$. Mol. wt. 169.89. Equiv. wt. 169.89. Silver nitrate is available in a sufficiently pure grade for use directly as a primary standard. The crystals contain a few hundredths of a per cent of occluded water and in highly precise work are melted to render them perfectly anhydrous.

Although silver nitrate is an excellent primary standard, solutions of it are often made up approximately and standardized by titrating a pure specimen of the material being determined. This procedure eliminates or minimizes the indicator correction, which is appreciable in certain titrations.

Procedure for the Preparation of 0.1 *N Silver Nitrate.* Weigh on a watch glass or glazed paper on the side-shelf balance 17.0 g. of reagent-grade silver nitrate and transfer to a clean, dry weighing bottle. Dry the material in an oven at 110° for 2 hours. Cool the bottle and silver nitrate to room temperature in a desiccator. Weigh the bottle and silver nitrate accurately on the analytical balance. Holding the weighing bottle over a 400-ml. beaker, remove the stopper and carefully pour the crystals of silver nitrate into the beaker. Replace the stopper and weigh the bottle and any crystals which remain in it. Add 150 ml. of water to the beaker and stir the mixture until the salt has dissolved. Transfer the solution to a clean, 1-l. volumetric flask, rinsing the beaker well into the flask. Dilute the solution to the mark and mix thoroughly. Transfer the solution to a clean, dry, glass-stoppered bottle. Finally calculate the normal concentration of the solution by dividing the weight of silver nitrate taken by 169.89.

Potassium Chloride. KCl. Mol. wt. 74.54. Equiv. wt. 74.54. Potassium chloride has a high temperature coefficient of solubility and is easy to recrystallize. The reagent grade is suitable as a primary standard. In highly precise work, the salt is heated to 500° in a stream of hydrogen chloride gas to eliminate the traces of water occluded in the crystal.

Procedure for the Preparation of 0.1 *N Potassium Chloride.* Place in a clean, dry weighing bottle 7.4 g. of reagent-grade potassium chloride and dry the salt at least 2 hours at 110°. Cool the bottle and salt in the desiccator. Weigh the bottle and salt accurately. Holding the weighing bottle over a 400-ml. beaker, remove the stopper, and empty the salt into the beaker. Without attempting to transfer the crystals which adhere to the bottle, replace the stopper, and weigh the bottle accurately. Dissolve the salt in 100 ml. of water and transfer the solution to a clean 1-l. volumetric flask. Wash the beaker well. Dilute to the mark and mix well by shaking vigorously and inverting twenty or thirty times. Transfer the solution to a clean, dry, glass-stoppered bottle. Calculate the normality of this solution by dividing the weight of salt taken by the equivalent weight, 74.54.

Potassium Thiocyanate. KCNS. Mol. wt. 97.18. Equiv. wt. 97.18. Potassium thiocyanate is a satisfactory primary standard if suitably purified and dried. In the Volhard titration, in which it is commonly used as a standard solution, it is practically always standardized against a silver nitrate solution. The standard solution of potassium thiocyanate is simply a water solution of the salt; the solution is stable indefinitely.

THE DETERMINATION OF CHLORIDE BY THE MOHR METHOD

In the titration of chloride with silver nitrate

$$NaCl + AgNO_3 = AgCl + NaNO_3$$

the end-point is found by the appearance of a precipitate of red silver chromate. Silver chromate is more soluble than silver chloride. After all the chloride is precipitated the next drop of silver nitrate causes the precipitation of red silver chromate, marking the end-point:

$$Na_2CrO_4 + 2AgNO_3 = Ag_2CrO_4 + 2NaNO_3$$

By means of the solubility product it is possible to calculate the amount of chromate which should be added to the solution to make the colored silver chromate precipitate exactly at the equivalence-point. At the equivalence-point in the titration 1 atom of silver is present for each atom of chlorine and the solution is saturated with silver chloride:

$$S_{AgCl} = [Ag^+][Cl^-] = 1.0 \times 10^{-10}$$

$$[Ag^+] = [Cl^-]$$

$$[Ag^+]^2 = 1.0 \times 10^{-10}$$

$$[Ag^+] = 1.0 \times 10^{-5}$$

When the silver-ion concentration reaches this value the next drop of silver nitrate should cause the precipitation of silver chromate; this will occur if the chromate concentration is just right:

$$S_{Ag_2CrO_4} = [Ag^+]^2[CrO_4^=] = 5.7 \times 10^{-13}$$

$$[CrO_4^=] = \frac{5.7 \times 10^{-13}}{(1.0 \times 10^{-5})^2} = 5.7 \times 10^{-3}$$

that is, the chromate concentration should be 0.005 M. Experiment has indicated that 0.005 to 0.01 M is the correct value to use. The situation, however, is complicated by two other factors: hydrogen-ion concentration and indicator blank.

The acidity of the solution makes a great deal of difference. Although enough sodium chromate may be added to make the solution 0.01 M in chromate, the actual chromate concentration may be something else owing to the fact that the second replaceable hydrogen atom of chromic acid is a weak acid, $K_2 = 3.2 \times 10^{-7}$ (the first hydrogen is a strong acid). The reaction, $HCrO_4^- = H^+ + CrO_4^=$, is shifted to the left by increasing the hydrogen-ion concentration. At any given pH the ratio of the acid chromate to chromate may be calculated using the expression defining the dissociation of the acid

$$\frac{[CrO_4^=]}{[HCrO_4^-]} = \frac{K_2}{[H^+]}$$

Thus, at various hydrogen-ion concentrations

pH	4	5	6	7	8	9
$\dfrac{[CrO_4^=]}{[HCrO_4^-]}$	0.0032	0.032	0.32	3.2	32	320

It is apparent, then, that if the sodium chromate added is to stay essentially as chromate ion, the pH must be 7 or higher. Thus, if sufficient sodium chromate is added to make the solution 0.01 M in chromate but some is converted to acid chromate, $[CrO_4^=] + [HCrO_4^-] = 0.01$. At pH 7, then,

$$\frac{[CrO_4^=]}{0.01 - [CrO_4^=]} = 3.2$$

$$[CrO_4^=] = 0.0076$$

and at pH 8, $[CrO_4^=] = 0.0097$, even closer to the desired value of 0.01. Fortunately, this is an easy value to attain. The addition of solid calcium carbonate serves to neutralize any acid present and to provide a bicarbonate-carbonic acid buffer of the right pH value.

The solution dare not be made too alkaline as there is then the danger of precipitating some of the silver as the carbonate or hydroxide.

From a practical standpoint the formation of the silver chromate precipitate does not function as a truly ideal indicator. Actually a measurable amount of silver nitrate must be added to form enough silver chromate to be distinctly visible over the heavy white precipitate of silver chloride; the amount of this indicator blank varies with the individual and the lighting. It is best to determine the indicator correction on a solution having the same pH and containing the same concentration of chromate; calcium carbonate can be added to simulate the silver chloride precipitate present in an actual analysis. Usually the correction will amount to 0.05 to 0.15 ml. of silver nitrate.

Limitations and Applications of the Mohr Method. The fact that the titration of chloride using silver chromate precipitation as the end-point must be carried out in neutral solution limits the application largely to hydrochloric acid and the chlorides of the alkali metals. Many metals precipitate as hydroxides or basic salts when neutralized, and many form insoluble chromates. Obviously these metals must be absent. Anions which form insoluble silver salts, such as phosphate, oxalate, and sulfite, must be absent.

The method may be applied to the determination of bromide and cyanide, but not to the determination of iodide or thiocyanate.

Other colored salts of silver can be used as the indicator; the brown arsenate, Ag_3AsO_4, for example, has about the right characteristics.

Procedure for the Determination of Chloride by the Mohr Method. In the Mohr method for the determination of chloride, it is best that the silver nitrate be standardized by titrating pure potassium chloride. This can be done by weighing out a small sample (0.3 g.), dissolving, and titrating with the silver nitrate. Or, a standard solution of potassium chloride can be prepared and portions of the solution titrated with the silver nitrate; this procedure is especially recommended as it provides practice with the end-point before running the determinations.

The preparation of standard 0.1 N solutions of potassium chloride and silver nitrate are given on page 325.

In standardizing the silver nitrate with the 0.1 N potassium chloride solution, place the potassium chloride in one buret and the silver nitrate in another. Measure out into a 250-ml. conical flask 40.0 ml. of potassium chloride. Dilute the solution to 100 ml. and continue the titration as described below, picking up the procedure at the point of addition of the sodium chromate.

If a small weighed sample of pure potassium chloride is to be titrated to standardize the silver nitrate solution, proceed as follows: Dry reagent-grade potassium chloride for at least 2 hours at 110°. Weigh accurately a sample of about 0.3 g. into a 250-ml. conical flask. Dissolve the salt in 100 ml. of water. Continue as described below, picking up the procedure at the point of addition of sodium chromate.

Dry the material to be analyzed for chloride for at least 2 hours at 110°. Weigh accurately samples of 0.3 to 0.4 g. into 250-ml. conical flasks. Dissolve each sample in 100 ml. of water. Add a small piece of litmus paper to the solution. If the sample is alkaline owing to the presence of some alkaline salt such as sodium carbonate, add dilute nitric acid (1:20) dropwise with stirring until the solution is acid. Add 1 g. of calcium carbonate to neutralize the free acid. Add 2.5 ml.

of a 0.4 M solution of sodium chromate (64.8 g. of sodium chromate per l.). Titrate with 0.1 N silver nitrate to the first permanent color change from the clear yellow of the solution. The change in color at the end-point can be detected more readily by preparing a comparison solution. To a similar flask add the same volume of water and indicator and sufficient calcium carbonate to give a suspended insoluble material resembling the precipitate of silver chloride. Titrate until the solution changes distinctly from the color of the blank.

Determine the indicator correction by suspending in the same volume of water a few tenths of a gram of calcium carbonate. Add 2.5 ml. of 0.4 M sodium chromate solution and add dropwise 0.1 N silver nitrate until the same pink color is obtained that was used as the end-point in the determination. Subtract this reading from the volume of silver nitrate used in each titration.

Calculate the normality of the silver nitrate solution. Then calculate and report the per cent of chloride in the sample; the milliequivalent weight of chloride is 0.035,457.

PROBLEMS

1. Calculate the concentration of the silver ion at the equivalence-point in the titration of each of the following salts with silver nitrate: sodium chloride, sodium bromide, sodium iodate, sodium cyanide, sodium thiocyanate, sodium iodide. See Appendix, Table A2, for values of the solubility products.

2. Following up Problem 1, calculate the concentration of chromate which should be present to give a precipitate of silver chromate at the equivalence-point of each substance. In the case of some of the salts the values come out absurdly high. Explain why from a practical standpoint a concentration about like that adopted for the chloride titration would be satisfactory.

3. Assume that sufficient sodium chromate has been added to make a solution 0.01 M in total chromium. Calculate the actual chromate concentration at pH 4, 5, 6, 7, 8, and 9.

4. Calculate the silver-ion concentration which will produce a precipitate of silver hydroxide at a pH of 10.

5. The determination of the chloride in ammonium chloride cannot be made by the Mohr method if the pH is above 7. Explain this.

6. The silver in a sample weighing 0.8500 g. was precipitated by the addition of 40.0 ml. of 0.1250 N sodium chloride. The excess chloride required for back titration 14.5 ml. of 0.0900 N silver nitrate. Calculate the per cent of silver in the sample.

7. Determine from the solubility products involved whether arsenate could be used as indicator in the titration of bromide with silver nitrate in the manner of the Mohr method.

8. A sample containing only potassium chloride and potassium bromide weighing 0.6000 g. required for titration of the chloride and the bromide 63.2 ml. of 0.1000 N silver nitrate. Calculate the per cent of each salt in the sample.

9. Devise a scheme for the determination of the sulfuric acid and hydrochloric acid in a solution, using only volumetric methods.

THE VOLHARD METHOD

The Volhard method is essentially a method for silver, the standard solution being a solution of potassium thiocyanate:

$$AgNO_3 + KCNS = AgCNS + KNO_3$$

Indirectly it is a method for any anion with which silver forms an insoluble salt. There are a great many of these, and the Volhard method is second only to indirect iodometric methods with respect to the number of materials which may be determined by it.

The end-point in the titration of silver with potassium thiocyanate is detected by the formation of the red, soluble compound that thiocyanate forms with ferric iron. The nature of this red, soluble compound is still in doubt; it is probably the ion $FeCNS^{++}$. At any rate, it is not formed until all the silver has been precipitated as the thiocyanate; the next drop of standard thiocyanate solution then reacts to color the solution, $Fe^{+++} + CNS^- = FeCNS^{++}$.

Some silver salts are insoluble in acid solution of not too high acidity, and the determination of these anions is carried out by adding a standard solution of silver nitrate in excess, filtering off the precipitate, and titrating the excess of silver nitrate with potassium thiocyanate. The reactions in the case of the determination of bromide are

$$NaBr + AgNO_3 = AgBr + NaNO_3$$
Excess of
standard
solution

$$AgNO_3 + KCNS = AgCNS + KNO_3$$
Excess

If the silver salt formed is less soluble than silver thiocyanate the precipitate need not be filtered off; this is the case with bromide and iodide. A more soluble salt must be filtered off, otherwise a reaction between the precipitate and the potassium thiocyanate occurs; for example, in the case of chloride, the reaction

$$AgCl + KCNS = AgCNS + KCl$$

takes place even though silver chloride is insoluble, owing to the fact that the silver thiocyanate is less soluble.

An interesting modification of the method is possible in the case of chloride to obviate the need of filtering. Nitrobenzene is immiscible with water but wets silver chloride better than it wets water; if nitrobenzene is added it coagulates the silver chloride and becomes firmly attached to it. The silver chloride does not then react with the potassium thiocyanate. The excess silver nitrate stays in the water layer and is titrated with the potassium thiocyanate.

In the method just outlined for silver salts insoluble in acid solutions two standard solutions are required, silver nitrate and potassium thiocyanate. The anions which must be determined this way are chloride, thiocyanate, bromide, and iodide. If the silver salt is soluble in nitric acid, and this is true of all of the silver salts of weak acids, only one standard solution, potassium thiocyanate, is required. The silver salt is simply precipitated by the addition of an excess of silver nitrate, the precipitate filtered off and then dissolved in nitric acid, and the silver from the precipitate titrated with standard potassium thiocyanate. The reactions for the determination of oxalate by this method are:

$$Na_2C_2O_4 + 2AgNO_3 = Ag_2C_2O_4 + 2NaNO_3$$

$$Ag_2C_2O_4 + 2HNO_3 = H_2C_2O_4 + 2AgNO_3$$

$$2AgNO_3 + 2KCNS = 2AgCNS + 2KNO_3$$

Among the anions that can be determined indirectly in this manner are arsenate, carbonate, chromate, ferricyanide, ferrocyanide, molybdate, oxalate, phosphate, sulfide, and sulfite.

Strong oxidizing agents react with potassium thiocyanate and may not be present when the silver ion is titrated with thiocyanate.

Procedure for the Determination of Chloride by the Volhard Method. Dry the material for 2 hours at 110°. Weigh accurately a sample of 0.3–0.4 g. into a 250-ml. conical flask. Dissolve each sample in water and acidify with 8 to 10 drops of concentrated nitric acid. Add 1 ml. of nitrobenzene. Add 0.1 N silver nitrate from a buret until an excess of 5 ml. or so is present. Stopper the flask with a rubber stopper and shake vigorously until the silver chloride has settled out in large spongy flakes; usually 30 to 40 seconds agitation is enough. Fine droplets of nitrobenzene may remain suspended, but most of the nitrobenzene adheres to the silver chloride precipitate.

Add 1 ml. of ferric alum indicator (a saturated solution of ferric alum containing a few drops of nitric acid) and titrate with approximately 0.1 N potassium thiocyanate solution. Add the thiocyanate solution slowly with gentle swirling until a pink color which persists for 30 seconds is obtained.

Standardize the potassium thiocyanate solution in the following manner: Measure out 40.0 ml. of the silver nitrate solution, add 1 ml. of the ferric alum indicator solution, and titrate with the potassium thiocyanate solution. It is not necessary actually to calculate the normality of the potassium thiocyanate solution but merely to know the equivalent volumes of the two solutions. The volume of silver nitrate added in excess in the determination can then be calculated by a simple proportion.

Standardize the silver nitrate solution with potassium chloride, using either aliquots of a standard solution of potassium chloride or a small, accurately weighed sample. Use the same procedure as in the analysis.

Calculate the volume of silver nitrate solution equivalent to the volume of potassium thiocyanate used to titrate the excess silver nitrate; subtract this volume from the volume of silver nitrate added. From the volume obtained in this manner, which is the volume actually used in the titration, calculate the normality of the silver nitrate, if a sample of pure potassium chloride was titrated; or calculate the per cent of chloride if an unknown was being analyzed.

THE VOLUMETRIC DETERMINATION OF BROMIDE BY THE MODIFIED VOLHARD PROCEDURE

The Volhard process for the determination of chloride, bromide, iodide, and thiocyanate is complicated by the presence of a lightly colored precipitate of silver salts at the equivalence-point. The red color of the ferric thiocyanate compound used to mark the end-point is not easily observed over this mass of precipitate. The procedure may be improved for the determination of bromide, thiocyanate, and mercuric ions by using mercuric perchlorate in place of silver nitrate as the standard solution in the titration. The mercuric and bromide ions combine to form mercuric bromide, which is only very slightly ionized. A similar slightly dissociated compound is formed by mercuric and thiocyanate ions, but mercuric bromide is the less dissociated of the two.

The determination is carried out by adding an excess of a standard solution of mercuric perchlorate to a solution of a soluble bromide in nitric acid, perchloric acid, or sulfuric acid solution

$$2KBr + Hg(ClO_4)_2 = HgBr_2 + 2KClO_4$$

The formation of slightly ionized mercuric bromide removes the bromide from solution as completely as the precipitation of silver bromide, but the solution remains clear and colorless. The excess mercuric perchlorate is then titrated with thiocyanate, using the appearance of the ferric thiocyanate color as the end-point; the soluble, only slightly ionized mercuric thiocyanate is formed, and the solution remains clear and colorless up to the end-point.

$$Hg(ClO_4)_2 + 2KCNS = Hg(CNS)_2 + 2KClO_4$$

$$Fe_2(SO_4)_3 + 2KCNS = 2Fe(CNS)SO_4 + K_2SO_4$$

The end-point in the titration is more distinct if the acid concentration is relatively low. The temporary appearance of a red color where the thiocyanate solution strikes the solution gives ample warning of the approach to the end-point.

Unlike mercuric bromide, mercuric chloride is dissociated to a considerable extent, and the titration of chloride in this manner is not satisfactory. Iodide cannot be determined either, for it forms a slightly soluble complex which is red in color.

Procedure for the Determination of Bromide. Preparation of Solutions. Prepare a solution of mercuric perchlorate, approximately 0.1 N, as follows: Place 10.86 g. of mercuric oxide in a 400-ml. beaker and add 88 ml. of concentrated perchloric acid (72 per cent). Stir the solution until all the oxide has dissolved. Transfer this solution to a bottle, dilute to 1 l., and mix well.

Prepare a 0.1000 N solution of potassium bromide. Weigh exactly 11.901 g. of reagent-grade potassium bromide, dissolve the salt in water, and dilute it to exactly 1000 ml. in a volumetric flask. The solution need not be exactly 0.1000 N, of course, and any weight around 12 g. may be used. The exact weight taken must be known and from it the actual concentration of the solution may be calculated.

Prepare a solution of ammonium thiocyanate, approximately 0.1 N, by dissolving 7.6 g. of the salt in 1 l. of water in a bottle. Mix thoroughly.

Prepare the indicator solution by saturating dilute nitric acid (1:1) with anhydrous ferric sulfate at the boiling point. Filter or decant the solution from the excess ferric sulfate. One to two milliliters of this solution is required per 100 ml. of the solution being titrated.

Using a pipet, transfer 25.00 ml. of the mercuric perchlorate solution to a 400-ml. beaker and dilute with water to 275 ml. Add 3 ml. of ferric sulfate indicator solution. Titrate with the ammonium thiocyanate solution to the first faint pink color. Carry out the titration with uniform stirring and without interruption. No precipitate will appear if the titration is carried out rapidly. This titration gives the ratio of the equivalent volumes of mercuric perchlorate and ammonium thiocyanate.

Using a pipet, transfer 25.00 ml. of the 0.1 N potassium bromide solution to a 400-ml. beaker and dilute to 225 ml. with water. Pipet into this solution 50.00 ml. of the mercuric perchlorate solution. Add 3 ml. of the ferric sulfate solution. Titrate the excess mercuric perchlorate with standard ammonium thiocyanate to the first permanent pink color. Using the mercuric perchlorate-ammonium thiocyanate ratio determined above, calculate the volume of mercuric perchlorate in excess and the volume used to react with the potassium bromide. Then calculate the normal concentration of the mercuric perchlorate.

Weigh exactly a sample of such size that it contains bromide equivalent to about 25 ml. of 0.1 N solution. Thus, if the sample contains about 30 per cent of potassium bromide, use a 1.0-g. sample. Dissolve the sample in water or if necessary in dilute sulfuric acid (1:10). Dilute the solution to 225 ml. and add from a pipet 50.00 ml. of the standard mercuric perchlorate solution. Add 3 ml. of the ferric sulfate indicator solution. Titrate the excess mercuric perchlorate with the standard ammonium thiocyanate solution to the first permanent pink color. Calculate the volume of mercuric perchlorate solution in excess, then that used to titrate the bromide. Finally, calculate the per cent of bromide in the sample. The equivalent weight of bromide is 0.079,916.

PROBLEMS

1. In the Volhard method for the determination of iodide trouble is experienced if the ferric ion is added as indicator before the excess of silver nitrate has been added. Suggest the probable source of the difficulty.

2. A sample weighing 10.000 g. of a solution containing oxalic acid required 40.0 ml. of 0.1000 N sodium hydroxide for complete neutralization. Calculate the volume of 0.1000 N potassium thiocyanate required to precipitate the silver in the silver oxalate derived from the same weight of sample.

3. A solution is in contact with both silver chloride and silver thiocyanate and has stood long enough to come to equilibrium. Calculate the ratio of chloride to thiocyanate in the solution. Calculate the chloride concentration when the thiocyanate concentration is 1×10^{-5}, the concentration of thiocyanate necessary to produce a red color with ferric iron. Calculate, finally, the volume of 0.1 N silver nitrate equivalent to this concentration of chloride assuming a total volume of 150 ml.

4. Tell how to determine the silver in an alloy of zinc and silver, using a volumetric method.

5. A mixture containing only potassium chloride and sodium chloride was dissolved, and the total halide determined by titration with silver nitrate. A sample weighing 0.3250 g. required 50.9 ml. of 0.1000 N solution. Calculate the per cent of each salt in the sample.

6. A sample of pure sodium chloride weighing 0.3000 g. was dissolved and treated with 50.0 ml. of a standard solution of silver nitrate; the silver chloride was filtered off and the excess silver nitrate in the filtrate titrated with potassium thiocyanate of which 7.20 ml. was required. In a separate titration a volume of 40.0 ml. of the silver solution required 35.6 ml. of the thiocyanate solution. Calculate the normality of both solutions.

7. Devise a method for determining the nitric acid and the chromic acid in a solution containing the two, using only volumetric methods. The second ionization constant of chromic acid is 3.2×10^{-7}.

ADSORPTION INDICATORS

Certain organic dyestuff materials have the property of adhering to crystals and of thus imparting a color to them. This phenomenon is a purely surface action, for a change in the composition of the solution surrounding the crystal may cause the color to change.

In the surface layer of a crystal, the ions making up the crystal are only partially surrounded by other ions of the crystal and their valence forces are only partially saturated. These ions attract other ions from the solution and bind them strongly to the surface of the crystal, a phenomenon known as *adsorption*. In general, those ions are adsorbed which form insoluble salts with one of the ions constituting the crystal; that is, a crystal adsorbs its own ions by preference. Thus, silver chloride in contact with a solution of sodium chloride adsorbs chloride ions and becomes negatively charged; on the other hand, when the silver chloride is surrounded by a solution containing silver nitrate, silver ions are adsorbed and the crystal of silver chloride is positively charged.

The dyestuffs which act as adsorption indicators evidently react with this layer of adsorbed ions. Fluorescein and dyestuffs related to it are weak acids and ionize to give a dyestuff anion, which is the substance actually adsorbed. Fluorescein has a greenish yellow fluorescent color. On addition to a suspension of silver chloride in the presence of chloride ions fluorescein has little effect on the silver chloride. If the solution contains silver ions, however, the precipitate becomes highly colored, much as if the silver salt of fluorescein were deposited on its surface, which may indeed be the case. Moreover, the effect is reversible, and the change on passing from an excess of chloride ions to an excess of silver ions is sharp enough to be used to detect the end-point.

The color change occurs on the surface of the precipitate. Anything that can be done to keep the precipitate in a finely divided form aids in improving the sharpness of the end-point. Certain materials called protective colloids prevent the precipitates of silver halides from coagulating and are very useful in this connection; dextrin is such a material. Large amounts of salt and particularly salts of polyvalent ions like aluminum and phosphate act the other way, tending to cause the precipitates to coagulate.

Inasmuch as the adsorption indicators are weak acids their ionization is repressed in acid solution, and so little anion is present that the indicator does not function. When fluorescein is used the pH must be above 7; with dichlorofluorescein, above 4.4; with eosin, which is a much stronger acid, the pH may be as low as 2.

The dyestuffs render the precipitates especially sensitive to light so that the titrations using adsorption indicators must be carried out in diffuse light.

Fluorescein and dichlorofluorescein function well as indicators in the titration of chloride with silver nitrate. In the titration of bromide, iodide, and thiocyanate, eosin (tetrabromfluorescein) is used. The color change is very sharp, to a bright red. Eosin cannot be used in the titration of chloride, for it is so strongly adsorbed on silver chloride that it colors the precipitate even when chloride is in excess.

It is possible to titrate iodide in the presence of chloride, using di-methyl-di-iodofluorescein as indicator.

Another type of dyestuff, the rhodamine dyes, are weak bases rather than weak acids and are adsorbed on the silver halides when the halide ion is in excess; that is, they are adsorbed as cations and function in very strongly acid solutions. In the titration of silver with bromide Rhodamine 6G gives a particularly sharp end-point.

Procedure for the Determination of Chloride by the Adsorption-Indicator Method. It is recommended that a standard 0.1 N solution of potassium chloride be prepared and some experience be gained in detecting the end-point before attempting the analysis of an unknown. The preparation of standard solutions of potassium chloride and silver nitrate are described on page 325.

Place the standard potassium chloride solution in a buret and measure out 40.0 ml. into a 250-ml. conical flask. Add 8 drops of a 0.1 per cent solution of the sodium salt of dichlorofluorescein and 5 ml. of a 1 per cent solution of dextrin. Carry out the titration with 0.1 N silver nitrate in a place where the light is rather poor. Titrate to the point where the color of the silver chloride suddenly turns pink. The color change occurs on the surface of the precipitate and is sharper if the precipitate is not allowed to coagulate. If the end-point is overstepped add more of the potassium chloride solution and titrate again with silver nitrate. Usually just before the equivalence-point is reached the silver chloride coagulates; the stirring must be vigorous after this point.

Dry the material to be analyzed for chloride for at least 2 hours at 110°. Weigh accurately a sample of 0.3 to 0.4 g. into a 250-ml. conical flask. Dissolve each sample in 75 ml. of water. Add 1 drop of phenol-phthalein. If the sample is alkaline owing to the presence of some alkaline salt such as sodium carbonate add dilute nitric acid (1:20) dropwise with good mixing until the phenolphthalein just becomes colorless. Add the indicator and dextrin, and titrate as described above.

The amount of silver nitrate required to change the indicator is very small, and the indicator correction may be ignored. The normality of the silver nitrate solution obtained by making it up by weight may be used, or the silver nitrate solution may be standardized by titrating pure potassium chloride. Report the results of the analysis as per cent of chloride.

THE DETERMINATION OF CYANIDE

Sodium cyanide is used in electroplating baths and in the casehardening of steel; it is an important industrial chemical, and its determination is a matter of some importance. Cyanide forms non-dissociated compounds with a number of metals, and the chemistry of these reactions is particularly interesting. The formulas for some of these undissociated ions are:

$$
\begin{array}{lll}
Ag(CN)_2{}^- & Zn(CN)_4{}^= & Co(CN)_6{}^{-3} \\
Cu(CN)_3{}^= & Cd(CN)_4{}^= & Fe(CN)_6{}^{-4} \\
 & Ni(CN)_4{}^= & Fe(CN)_6{}^{-3}
\end{array}
$$

These materials are formed by adding potassium or sodium cyanide to a metal salt; the simple metal cyanide is first precipitated and is then dissolved on the addition of more potassium cyanide:

$$NiSO_4 + 2KCN = Ni(CN)_2 + K_2SO_4$$

$$Ni(CN)_2 + 2KCN = K_2Ni(CN)_4$$

The compound $K_2Ni(CN)_4$ can be obtained in the form of yellow crystals simply by allowing the solution to evaporate and crystallize.

The statement that these cyanide compounds are non-ionized is a bit exaggerated. Actually all the compounds dissociate somewhat, although they vary greatly in degree. Thus,

$$Zn(CN)_4{}^= = Zn^{++} + 4CN^- \qquad K_I = \frac{[Zn^{++}][CN^-]^4}{[Zn(CN)_4{}^=]} = 1.2 \times 10^{-18}$$

$$Ag(CN)_2{}^- = Ag^+ + 2CN^- \qquad K_I = \frac{[Ag^+][CN^-]^2}{[Ag(CN)_2{}^-]} = 3.8 \times 10^{-19}$$

Written this way as instability constants a small number means a low concentration of the products of the dissociation and therefore a slightly ionized compound. The smaller the number the more stable the compound.

The determination of cyanide is based on the reaction

$$2NaCN + AgNO_3 = NaAg(CN)_2 + NaNO_3$$

At the start the cyanide is in excess, and on the addition of silver nitrate the solution remains clear owing to the formation of the non-dissociated ion $Ag(CN)_2{}^-$. After the ratio of the cyanide to silver has been reduced to 2, the next drop of silver nitrate causes the precipitation of silver cyanide,

$$NaAg(CN)_2 + AgNO_3 = 2AgCN + NaNO_3$$

marking the equivalence-point of the reaction. Unfortunately there is a little difficulty in carrying this out in practice. Where the drop of silver nitrate from the buret strikes the solution there is a local concentration of silver, the ratio of cyanide to silver falls to less than two, and silver cyanide precipitates. Although silver cyanide redissolves in the sodium cyanide solution as the solution is mixed the rate at which it dissolves is very slow; the precipitate of silver cyanide is curdy and appears to be poorly wetted by the liquid. At any rate, the very slow redissolution spoils the method from a practical standpoint.

A modification of the process is based on the formation of another non-dissociated compound of silver, that with ammonia, which ionizes slightly according to the equation

$$Ag(NH_3)_2{}^+ = Ag^+ + 2NH_3 \qquad K_I = \frac{[Ag^+][NH_3]^2}{[Ag(NH_3)_2{}^+]} = 6.8 \times 10^{-8}$$

The silver ammonia ion is not nearly as stable as the silver cyanide ion, the instability constants of the two being 6.8×10^{-8} and 3.8×10^{-19}, respectively. The silver ammonia ion is still sufficiently non-ionized, however, to dissolve silver chloride, meaning that it furnishes fewer silver ions to the solution than silver chloride. In fact, ammonia will dissolve silver chloride, silver cyanide, silver thiocyanate, and some silver bromide, but not silver iodide ($S_{AgI} = 1 \times 10^{-16}$). The silver cyanide ion being more stable, all these salts and silver iodide as well dissolve in solutions of potassium cyanide.

If ammonia is added to the solution of cyanide before the titration with silver nitrate begins, no precipitate of silver cyanide forms at the point where the drop of silver nitrate from the buret strikes the solution, because silver cyanide is soluble in ammonia. In effect, then, we have done away with the end-point. However, by taking advantage of the fact that silver iodide will dissolve in cyanide solutions but not in ammonia, the end-point can still be located. By also adding potassium iodide, a precipitate of silver iodide forms on the next drop of silver nitrate beyond that needed to make the ratio of cyanide to silver 2:1. Moreover, the physical character of the silver iodide precipitate is such that it redissolves instantly in the cyanide solution on mixing, after being precipitated where the drop of silver nitrate strikes the solution. The equivalence-point is marked, then, by the formation of a permanent precipitate of silver iodide which appears as a cream-colored opalescent turbidity. The principal reaction involved in the determination is

$$2NaCN + AgNO_3 = NaAg(CN)_2 + NaNO_3$$

and the next drop of standard silver nitrate solution causes the precipitation of silver iodide

$$KI + AgNO_3 = AgI + KNO_3$$

This end-point is one of the sharpest in the entire field of volumetric analysis.

Inasmuch as 2 molecules of sodium cyanide react with 1 atom of silver in this reaction, the equivalent weight of the sodium cyanide is two times the molecular weight, 2NaCN.

Procedure for the Determination of Cyanide. No convenient, stable, soluble salts of hydrocyanic acid are available for the preparation of solid samples, and the unknowns are therefore given out in the form of solutions. Do not acidify the unknown solution at any stage of the analysis. Solutions of cyanide when acidified give off gaseous hydrogen cyanide which is very poisonous. Solutions of sodium cyanide do not keep well; they decompose slowly to give ammonium formate; the sample must therefore be analyzed within a day or two of the time issued. Drop other work until this determination is completed.

Clean and dry a 250-ml. conical flask closed with a rubber stopper. Label it with name and desk number and leave it with the laboratory instructor for the sample.

Weigh accurately a clean, dry, 125-ml. conical flask closed with a cork. Add 8 to 10 ml. of the unknown cyanide solution, replace the cork, and weigh again. Dilute the solution to about 60 ml. Add one large crystal (0.1 g.) of potassium iodide and 3 ml. of concentrated ammonia. Titrate the solution with 0.1 N silver nitrate, using a black background. Titrate to the appearance of a permanent opalescence of silver iodide.

No primary-standard cyanide is available, so that the normality of the silver nitrate must be obtained by some other method. The best procedure is to make up the silver nitrate solution by weight, for silver nitrate itself is an excellent primary standard.

Calculate the per cent of cyanide in the sample; the milliequivalent weight is 0.052,04.

Pour the solutions containing silver and any standard silver nitrate solution left over into the large crock provided in the hood. The silver will be recovered later.

PROBLEMS

1. Explain why chloride, bromide, and thiocyanate do not interfere in the determination of cyanide.

2. Devise a procedure for the determination of both chloride and cyanide in a mixture of the two.

3. Devise a procedure for the determination of both thiocyanate and cyanide in a mixture of the two.

4. A silver-plating bath consists of silver nitrate dissolved in an excess of sodium cyanide. To a volume of 10.00 ml. of such a bath were added ammonia and potassium iodide. The solution was titrated with 0.2000 N silver nitrate; 20.2 ml. was required to reach the silver iodide end-point. Another sample of the same volume was titrated to the silver chromate end-point, 62.0 ml. of 0.2000 N silver nitrate being required. Calculate the weight of silver and of sodium cyanide in grams per liter.

THE DETERMINATION OF CALCIUM PLUS MAGNESIUM BY TITRATION WITH VERSENE

THE DETERMINATION OF THE HARDNESS OF WATER

The organic acid ethylenediaminetetraacetic acid is marketed under the name *Versene* (abbreviated H_4Y)

$$\underset{\text{HOOC—CH}_2}{\overset{\text{HOOC—CH}_2}{\Large\diagdown}}\hspace{-0.3em}N\text{—CH}_2\text{—CH}_2\text{—}N\hspace{-0.3em}\overset{\text{CH}_2\text{—COOH}}{\underset{\text{CH}_2\text{—COOH}}{\Large\diagup}}$$

This acid forms a series of salts on neutralization with sodium hydroxide, one of which, disodium dihydrogen versenate, $Na_2H_2Y \cdot 2H_2O$, is used in the preparation of the standard solution for the titration of calcium and magnesium. The determination of calcium is based on the formation of a stable, slightly ionized calcium compound,

$$Na_2H_2Y + Ca^{++} = Na_2CaY + 2H^+$$

Magnesium forms a similar compound which is somewhat more dissociated than the calcium compound. The constants for the formation of these non-dissociated calcium and magnesium compounds are 3.0×10^{10} and 5.0×10^8, respectively.

The end-point of this reaction is found by the use of a dyestuff which also forms a soluble, non-dissociated compound with magnesium but which is more highly dissociated than the magnesium versenate compound. Thus, Versene will extract magnesium from the magnesium-dyestuff compound, and, because the dyestuff and its magnesium derivative differ in color, a color change results. Of various hydroxylated azo dyestuffs which have this property of forming non-dissociated magnesium compounds, the best appears to be Eriochromeschwartz T, known also as F241:

F241 is a tribasic acid (abbreviated H_3In) which functions as an acid-base indicator with two color changes:

$$\underset{\text{Wine red}}{NaH_2In} \underset{\text{at }pH\ 6.3}{\overset{\longrightarrow}{\longleftarrow}} \underset{\text{Blue}}{Na_2HIn} \underset{\text{at }pH\ 11.5}{\overset{\longrightarrow}{\longleftarrow}} \underset{\text{Orange}}{Na_3In}$$

Of these three forms only Na_3In forms non-dissociated, colored complexes with magnesium

$$Mg^{++} + \underset{\text{Orange}}{Na_3In} = \underset{\text{Wine red}}{NaMgIn} + 2Na^+$$

The equilibrium constant for this reaction, $K = 10^7$, is so great that in the pH range 8 to 10 the blue form, Na_2HIn, is converted directly to the wine red magnesium compound

$$Mg^{++} + \underset{\text{Blue}}{Na_2HIn} = \underset{\text{Wine red}}{NaMgIn} + Na^+ + H^+$$

On the addition of sodium versenate to such a solution, the magnesium is extracted from the compound NaMgIn, and the color reverses sharply from wine red to blue.

Although calcium forms a relatively weak, soluble, colored compound with Eriochromeschwartz T, the compound is not sufficiently stable to serve as an indicator in the titration of calcium with sodium versenate. Since magnesium is required to function with the indicator, it is added to the sodium versenate solution before it is standardized. Thus, as the titration progresses, magnesium is introduced without requiring a blank correction.

A pH value of about 10 is best for the titration. Above this value, magnesium hydroxide may be precipitated, and at lower values the magnesium is not bound strongly enough to the dye to give the desired wine red compound, NaMgIn. At high pH values, also, the indicator shifts to its most alkaline (orange) form, so that at the end-point a blue color is not obtained. Hydroxides and large amounts of carbonates which raise the pH above 10.5 interfere for this reason, but the bicarbonate ion and the carbonate ion, in themselves, as well as the ions of other weak acids, have no effect on the end-point. A pH of 10 can be readily obtained and maintained by the addition of a sufficient amount of an ammonia-ammonium chloride buffer. At a pH of 10, the color change is sharp and may be approached rapidly.

The hardness of water is due to the presence of calcium and magnesium bicarbonates (carbonate or temporary hardness) and calcium and magnesium sulfates (non-carbonate or permanent hardness). The amounts of calcium and magnesium in water are usually expressed in parts per million (p.p.m., equal to milligrams per liter) of an equivalent amount of calcium carbonate. The total hardness may be anything from 0 to 2500 p.p.m. The Versene titration provides an excellent method of determining the total hardness (calcium plus magnesium, and both carbonate and non-carbonate hardness) with an accuracy of 2 p.p.m. (0.12 grains per U. S. gallon).

One of the remarkable features of this titration is that it is not affected by considerable concentrations of salts. The titration is sharp and accurate in solutions containing up to 15 g. of sodium chloride per 100 ml.

A pure calcium carbonate is used as primary standard, a standard solution being prepared by dissolving a weighed amount in hydrochloric acid and diluting to a definite volume.

Small amounts of certain metals interfere in the determination of calcium and magnesium. Only 0.3 p.p.m. of copper and even smaller amounts of cobalt and nickel render the end-point indistinct. Manganese dioxide and manganate also interfere with the action of the indicator although the manganous ion does not interfere with the indicator, being simply titrated just like calcium and magnesium. Iron does not interfere if the buffer is added to the solution before the indicator is added. Aluminum above 20 p.p.m. causes the end-point to be indistinct. The interference of all these metals except aluminum can be overcome by the addition of hydroxylammonium chloride, which reduces the metals to their lower valence states, and of sodium cyanide, which ties up the metals as very slightly dissociated cyanide compounds. The interference by aluminum is avoided by adding tartrate.

Procedure for the Determination of Calcium and for the Determination of the Total Hardness of Water. For the determination of calcium or for the determination of the total hardness of water, the following routine procedure should be employed. Occasionally interfering ions may be present (copper above 0.3 p.p.m. or large amounts of iron or manganese) which cause the end-point to be indistinct; if so, the alternate procedure employing sodium cyanide should be used.

Buffer Solution. Mix 6.75 g. of ammonium chloride with 57.0 ml. of concentrated ammonium hydroxide and dilute to 100 ml. The pH of this mixture is just over 10.

Standard Calcium Chloride Solution. Dissolve 1.000 g. of pure calcium carbonate in a little dilute hydrochloric acid. Dilute exactly to 1 l. and transfer to a clean, dry, glass-stoppered bottle for storage; 1.00 ml. of this solution is equivalent to 1.00 mg. of calcium carbonate.

Calcium carbonate meeting the A.C.S. specifications is not satisfactory, as the tolerance for magnesium plus alkali metals is too high, 0.5 per cent. A more highly purified grade is required.

Indicator. Weigh on the analytical balance 0.5 g. of analytical reagent-grade Eriochromeschwartz T (F241) and dissolve it in 100 ml. of alcohol.

Standard Sodium Versenate Solution. Weigh 4.00 g. of disodium dihydrogen versenate dihydrate and dissolve it in 750 ml. of water. Weigh 0.100 g. of magnesium chloride, $MgCl_2 \cdot 6H_2O$, and add this to the above solution. Mix the solution well.

Pipet 25.0 ml. of the standard calcium chloride solution prepared above, add 1.0 ml. of the buffer solution and 4 drops of the indicator solution. Titrate with the versenate solution according to the procedure described below for the determination of hardness in water. The sodium versenate solution prepared as indicated above should be equivalent to more than 1.0 mg. of calcium carbonate per ml. Using the volume required for the titration and the total volume of the standard solution, calculate the volume to which the solution must be diluted to make it equivalent to 1.00 mg. of calcium carbonate per ml. Make the required dilution, mix well, and restandardize the solution as a check.

Routine Procedure. Pipet 50.0 ml. of the water sample into a 250-ml. flask. Add about 1 ml. of the buffer solution and mix by swirling. Add 4 drops of the indicator solution. Titrate with the standard sodium versenate solution. At the end-point, the solution should be clear and should change from wine red to pure blue with no reddish tinge remaining. In daylight the color beyond the end-point is sky blue, but under a tungsten-filament lamp it is almost colorless.

Multiply the number of milliliters of standard sodium versenate solution by 20 to obtain the total hardness as parts per million of calcium carbonate. The magnesium added to the standard sodium versenate solution is accounted for in the standardization.

The accuracy of the determination is greatest when the volume of standard solution approaches the maximum volume which can be delivered by the buret. The volume of the sample may be adjusted to take advantage of this. Thus, for waters having a total hardness less than 500 p.p.m., use a 100.0-ml. sample; for waters above 1000 p.p.m., use a 25.0-ml. sample. The factor used in calculating the results must be changed accordingly: 100.0-ml. sample, multiply by 10; 50.0-ml. sample, multiply by 20; 25.0-ml. sample, multiply by 40. A small sample of a very hard water should be diluted to approximately 100 ml. with distilled water before the buffer is added; otherwise, magnesium hydroxide may be precipitated on addition of the buffer and erratic results obtained.

Alternate Procedure. Pipet 50.0 ml. of the water into a 250-ml. flask. Add about 5 ml. of the buffer solution and mix the solution by swirling. Add about 0.02 g. of hydroxylammonium chloride and about 0.25 g. of sodium cyanide; mix well, add 4 drops of indicator solution, and titrate with the standard sodium versenate solution. At the end-point the color will change from wine red to pure blue. On the second titration, modify the size of the sample as discussed in the second paragraph under "Routine Procedure." Calculate the results as described there also.

The extra volume of buffer solution (5 ml. rather than 1 ml.) specified in this alternate procedure is necessary to offset the additional alkalinity resulting from the hydrolysis of the sodium cyanide added.

OTHER REACTIONS INVOLVING THE FORMATION OF INSOLUBLE OR NON-DISSOCIATED COMPOUNDS

Zinc. In addition to the procedures studied in detail in the foregoing pages, there are a few other reactions falling in this general type of volumetric analysis which are of some importance.

The only direct volumetric method for zinc involves the precipitation of the ferrocyanide, $K_2Zn_3[Fe(CN)_6]_2$,

$$3ZnCl_2 + 2K_4Fe(CN)_6 = K_2Zn_3[Fe(CN)_6]_2 + 6KCl$$

The end-point can be determined using uranyl nitrate as an *external indicator;* portions of uranyl nitrate are placed in the depressions of a spot plate and from time to time during the titration a drop of the solution is removed on a stirring rod and added to the uranyl nitrate. At the equivalence-point the excess of ferrocyanide gives a chocolate-colored precipitate of uranyl ferrocyanide. This procedure is slow and inconvenient and, particularly in the first sample titrated, introduces error in removing portions of the solution being titrated.

The end-point can also be found by the use of diphenylamine as internal indicator. The use of an oxidation-reduction indicator is based on the oxidation of the indicator by the addition of a small amount of potassium ferricyanide which converts the indicator to its blue, oxidized form if no ferrocyanide is present. During the titration the ferrocyanide is precipitated by the zinc. At the end-point the excess ferrocyanide causes a sharp reduction in the ferricyanide-ferrocyanide potential and the indicator is reduced to its colorless form. The end-point is quite satisfactory if no oxidizing agents are present. Usually the determination is carried out by adding an excess of standard ferrocyanide and back-titrating with a standard zinc solution.

Nickel. Use is made of the highly undissociated nickel-cyanide ion. An excess of a standard cyanide solution is added to an ammoniacal solution of the nickel salt

$$Ni(NH_3)_4Cl_2 + 4NaCN = Na_2Ni(CN)_4 + 2NaCl + 4NH_3$$

The excess of cyanide is back-titrated with silver nitrate, using the appearance of a silver iodide precipitate as end-point. This was discussed under the determination of cyanide. This method can be applied to nickel in the presence of iron by adding citric acid, which keeps the iron from precipitating as the hydroxide.

CHAPTER 13

Colorimetry

The measurement or matching of the intensity of the light transmitted by a solution may frequently furnish a convenient method for the quantitative determination of materials which are themselves colored or can be made to yield colored compounds. Such methods are usually rapid and over the range to which they are applicable are as accurate as other methods which might be applied. In general, colorimetric methods can be applied only to constituents present in quantities of less than 1 or 2 per cent. Larger amounts of materials can be diluted and an aliquot part taken, but it must be remembered that any error in the colorimetric measurement is then multiplied by the dilution factor. The ranges of concentration over which colorimetric methods are usually adaptable to quantitative work fall between 0.5 and 10 mg. per l., although some methods are not as sensitive as this, and others are sensitive even to such low concentrations as 0.01 mg. per l., or at a dilution of 1 part in 100,000,000. The number of known colorimetric methods is quite large, and methods are available for the determination of a great variety of inorganic and organic materials.

The Laws of Absorption. Two laws determine the absorption of light on its passage through a transparent material. One, Lambert's (or Bouguer's) law, relates the absorption of the light to the thickness of the material; the other, Beer's law, relates the light absorption to the concentration of the colored material. Both laws hold strictly only for monochromatic light. Since colorimeters, photometers, and spectrophotometers measure the extent of light absorption, these laws are of fundamental importance in the field of colorimetry.

Lambert's (or Bouguer's) Law. The rate at which the intensity of monochromatic light decreases at any point on passage through a homogeneous, transparent material is proportional to the intensity of the light at that point. Thus, considering the transparent material shown in Fig. 73, this relation may be expressed mathematically

$$-\frac{dI}{dl} = kI$$

where I is the intensity of the light at a distance l in the material. This is the usual first-order differential equation encountered fre-

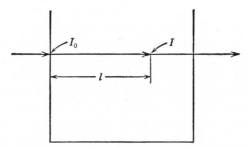

Fig. 73. The transmission of monochromatic light through a transparent material.

quently in natural phenomena ("compound interest" or "snowball" law) and yields easily to solution by separation of the variables and integration

$$-\frac{dI}{I} = kl$$

$$-\ln I = kl + C$$

At the point where the light enters the material $l = 0$, and by definition $I = I_0'$; the constant of integration may be readily evaluated

$$-\ln I_0' = k\cdot 0 + C$$

so that $$-\ln I = kl - \ln I_0'$$

or $$\ln \frac{I}{I_0'} = -kl$$

or, expressed exponentially,

$$\frac{I}{I_0} = e^{-kl}$$

e being the base of natural logarithms and the ratio I/I_0 the fraction of the light transmitted the distance l in the material.

Another way of stating this relation is that each layer of equal thickness absorbs an equal fraction of the light which traverses it; that is, the intensity of the emitted light decreases exponentially as the thickness of the absorbing material increases arithmetically; or, the logarithm of the absorption varies directly with the thickness.

There are no known exceptions to this law for homogeneous materials.

Beer's Law. The constant k of Lambert's law just developed has a characteristic value for each transparent material. If the number or the nature of the molecules in the light path changes, the value of k changes. In the case of gases this change can be brought about by a change in pressure. In pure liquids such changes can be brought about only with difficulty because of the great incompressibility of liquids. Solutions, however, provide a convenient way of varying the number of molecules in the light path. Assuming for the moment that the number of solvent molecules in the light path is constant, the change in k is often linear with the change in the number of molecules of solute, that is, with the concentration of the solute

$$k = Kc + b$$

where c is the concentration and K and b are new constants. This function of k may be introduced into Lambert's law, giving

$$\ln \frac{I}{I_0'} = -(Kc + b)l$$

The constant b may be evaluated by rewriting the expression to give

$$\ln I = -(Kc + b)l + \ln I_0'$$

and defining I_0'' as the intensity of the light entering the cell when the concentration of the light-absorbing material is 0. Thus, for a constant length of cell l when $c = 0$, $I = I_0''$

$$\ln I_0'' = -K(0 + b)l + \ln I_0'$$

and

$$-Kbl = \ln \frac{I_0''}{I_0'}$$

from which

$$\ln I = -Kcl + \ln \frac{I_0''}{I_0'} + \ln I_0'$$

$$= -Kcl + \ln I_0''$$

This is the combined Lambert-Beer law as commonly used, the constant being designated simply as I_0:

$$\ln \frac{I}{I_0} = -Kcl$$

In use the dimensions of c and l are specified, logarithms of base 10 are used rather than natural logarithms, and the constant and the ratio I/I_0 are given suitable names. This law applies to a homogenous, transparent medium containing only one kind of molecule. In the case of a solution in which molecules of solute and solvent are uniformly dispersed among each other the absorption by each takes place independently, and the effects of the solvent (designated by subscripts s) and of the solute (subscripts m) are additive:

$$\ln\left(\frac{I}{I_0}\right)_{\text{Soln.}} = \ln\left(\frac{I}{I_0}\right)_s + \ln\left(\frac{I}{I_0}\right)_m$$

$$\ln\left(\frac{I}{I_0}\right)_{\text{Soln.}} = -K_s l_s - K_m l_m c_m$$

Frequently the light absorption of the solvent is so small that the term $-K_s l_s$ can be ignored or canceled in the process of making the measurement; this is so for water over the portion of the spectrum between 200 and 2000 mμ. The law then reduces to

$$\ln\frac{I}{I_0} = -K_m l_m c_m$$

Strictly also, the law applies only to monochromatic light. The value of K varies with the wave length of the light used. When white light, or light having a broad band of wave lengths is used, the constant has an average value of some sort of the individual values over the region involved, depending on the wave-length response of the eye or photoelectric cell. In analytical work this response may be assumed to remain constant throughout a series of measurements, and so the Lambert-Beer law can be applied in work in which white light is employed.

Many colored systems do not conform to Beer's law. The reasons for this, its consequences, and its use in chemistry are dealt with in detail later.

Definition of Terms. In the general practice of colorimetry the colored solution under examination will be contained in a glass cell with plane parallel sides of uniform thickness, and initial balancing of the instrument with pure solvent in the cell makes it possible to eliminate the light-absorption effects of the glass walls and of the solvent. In other words, the term b in the above development of Beer's law is made equal to zero. This is done in two-celled instruments by placing pure solvent in two identical cells, balancing the optical and electrical components of the system, and then proceeding with the measurement of a colored solution placed in one cell; in one-celled instruments the cell with pure solvent is first "zeroed" or balanced and the solvent then replaced by the solution which is measured, the light source being assumed to remain constant throughout. The intensity of the light measured, then, is a function of the concentration of the colored component and the length l of the cell.

For this situation, which is the one commonly encountered in analytical work, we make the following definitions as related to the Lambert-Beer law:

$$\log_{10} \frac{I}{I_0} = -\epsilon l c$$

or the identical mathematical statement,

$$\frac{I}{I_0} = e^{-\epsilon l c}$$

in which I_0 is the intensity of the light entering the solution; I is the intensity of the light transmitted; l is the length of the cell in centimeters; c is the concentration in moles per liter; and, by definition, ϵ is the molar extinction coefficient; T is the transmittancy, usually expressed in per cent; A is the absorbancy (also frequently referred to as optical density).

$$T = 100 \frac{I}{I_0} = (100)10^{-\epsilon c l}$$

$$A = \log_{10} \frac{I_0}{I} = \epsilon l c$$

$$A = \log_{10} \frac{1}{\dfrac{T}{100}}$$

The use of I/I_0, that is, transmittancy, expressed as per cent, is most common with chemists at present, but some of the instruments read in absorbancy (optical density) as well as per cent transmittancy.

Measurement of the Intensity of Transmitted Light. In analytical work the measurement of the intensity of the light transmitted by a solution is made by one of two methods. The first method involves comparison with a solution of known strength of the same colored material. In such a process the per cent transmittancy of two solutions, unknown and standard, are made equal

$$\left(\frac{I}{I_0}\right)_u = \left(\frac{I}{I_0}\right)_s$$

in which the subscripts u and s refer to unknown and standard, respectively. Because

$$\log\left(\frac{I}{I_0}\right)_u = -\epsilon c_u l_u \quad \text{and} \quad \log\left(\frac{I}{I_0}\right)_s = -\epsilon c_s l_s$$

it follows that

$$-\epsilon c_u l_u = -\epsilon c_s l_s \quad \text{and} \quad c_u l_u = c_s l_s$$

The comparison may be made either by varying the concentration and keeping the depth constant (Nessler-Tube Method) or by keeping the concentration constant and varying the depth of the solution (Duboscq method).

The second method involves a direct measure of the per cent of light transmitted. Although there are visual methods of doing this, in all the instruments in use in this country the measurement is made by a photoelectric cell. The instruments are spoken of as photoelectric colorimeters or spectrophotometers.

The Standard-Series or Nessler-Tube Method. The constant depth of solution used in the standard-series type of colorimetric measurement is most conveniently obtained by the use of a flat-bottomed tube bearing a mark indicating a certain volume and depth, generally, 100 ml. and 30 cm., or 50 ml. and 22.5 cm. Such tubes are referred to as *Nessler tubes.* They should preferably be of clear glass and have perfectly flat bottoms. The comparison is made in a *Nessler rack,* Fig. 74, in which the solutions are viewed vertically, a uniform light being reflected from an opalescent white screen up through the bottoms of the tubes. In a series of these tubes, then, the concentration of the material is varied over a suitable range, and the unknown is placed successively between pairs of tubes until the depth of color falls between two of the standards or matches one. The concentrations of the colored material in the tubes that match are then equal.

In general, the standard-series method is better than the variable-depth method for faint colors, especially yellows, as the depth of solution in the Nessler tubes is much greater than in the cells of the Duboscq-type colorimeters. The standard-series method is also the more convenient method for routine work when a series of stable, permanent standards can be prepared.

When it is possible to add a standard solution of the material being determined directly to the reagents which develop the color and prepare the standard color rapidly in this manner, it is convenient to add the standard solution from a buret until the color of the standard matches that of the unknown. A minor variation in the depth may usually be disregarded. This process is frequently referred to as a colorimetric titration.

Fig. 74.   Nessler tubes and racks.   Left: 100-ml. tubes; right: 50-ml. tubes.

The Duboscq Colorimeter.   The Duboscq colorimeter operates on the variable-depth principle (Fig. 75). The instrument may be arranged for use with either artificial light or daylight. The bottoms of the cups are of clear glass and the walls of clear or black glass. The plungers, about which the cups can be raised and lowered, have clear glass bottoms and black walls. The scales carried on the tube holders read directly the depth of the solution between the bottoms of the cups and the bottoms of the plungers. Below the cups is an adjustable mirror or a milk white plate, which reflects the light up through the cups. By means of an arrangement of mirrors and lenses the rays passing through both cups are brought together in a circular field split by a thin line, each half representing one of the tubes. Equality is obtained by moving the cups up and down (varying the depths of the liquids) until the field appears uniform.

The results are calculated by the relation developed previously, $c_u l_u = c_s l_s$, where c and l are concentrations and depths, respectively,

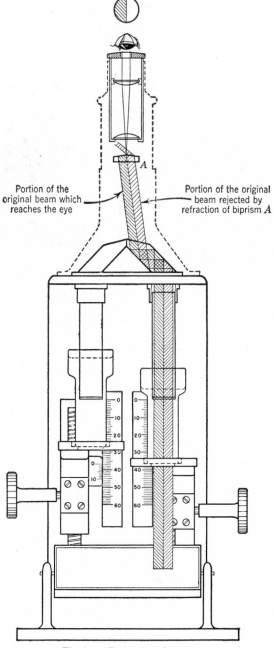

Portion of the original beam which reaches the eye

Portion of the original beam rejected by refraction of biprism *A*

Fig. 75. Duboscq colorimeter.

and u and s refer to unknown and standard. It is evident that concentration and depth are inversely proportional, so that the smaller reading on the colorimeter indicates the more concentrated solution. If the unknown and standard are diluted to different volumes, a calculation must be made to reduce them to the same volume. The concentrations are usually expressed as milligrams per 100 ml. or in some other convenient units. The data are then properly substituted into the formula, and the amount of material in the unknown is calculated. The method is illustrated as follows:

Example. The iron in a sample of limestone weighing 1.0000 g. was converted to ferrous 1,10-phenanthroline sulfate, and the solution was diluted to exactly 250 ml. A standard iron solution was prepared by dissolving 0.0100 g. of metallic iron, converting it to ferrous 1,10-phenanthroline sulfate and diluting to exactly 1 l. On comparison in the Duboscq instrument the depth readings on unknown and standard, respectively, were 24.5 and 30.0. It is apparent that the concentration of iron in the standard is 0.002,50 g. per 250 ml.; therefore

$$c_u(24.5) = (0.002,50)(30.0)$$

$$c_u = 0.003,06 \text{ g. Fe per 250 ml.}$$

Since the sample was diluted to 250 ml., this is the amount of iron in the sample. The per cent of iron in the sample, then, was $(0.00306)(100)/1.000$ = 0.306 per cent.

Use of the Duboscq Colorimeter. Fill both cups of the colorimeter with water, taking care not to fill them above the shoulder and making certain that the outsides and bottoms of the cups are clean and dry. Place the cups in the instrument, being sure that they are seated properly in the cup holders. Adjust the cups so that the plungers are below the surface of the water and the scales have the same reading. Adjust the mirror and light source to give a uniform field of maximum brightness. This is of great importance, for if perfect equality in the halves of the field is not obtained all readings will be in error. If daylight is used, the instrument should be placed preferably in front of a north window and not in direct sunlight.

In making a measurement it is well to adopt one side, say the left, for the standard solution and to place the standard always on the same side. Rinse the cups and plunger with the solutions under examination before filling the cups. As it is desirable to have as long a column of liquid as possible for comparison in order to increase the accuracy, one plunger is set at 50, or at just as great a depth as possible, and balance is produced by moving the other until equality is produced in the two halves of the field. The plungers should always remain below the surface of the liquid. The readings should·be repeated four or five times and the average taken. Since the eye soon becomes fatigued and unable to detect small differences, it is advisable after making the adjustment to close the eyes a minute or to look at something else and then see if the adjustment still appears satisfactory. It is a good plan to approach equality from both above and below.

The colors must be of the same shade for comparison. If one is orange and the other lemon yellow, they can never be matched with any degree of accuracy. If one solution is clear and the other faintly turbid, accurate comparison is impossible. If the unknown and standard do not give approximately similar readings, make up a new standard. They should not be farther apart than a 50:30 ratio, and if the color does not conform to Beer's law they should be very close to a 50:50 ratio.

Compute the results as discussed above.

The Photoelectric Colorimeter. These instruments should more properly be called photometers, as they make an actual measurement of the amount of light transmitted by a solution. The measurement made is not an absolute measurement of the intensity of the transmitted light but rather a relative measure in comparison with a standard, usually the pure solvent in an identical glass cell. Photoelectric colorimeters are usually calibrated to read directly the per cent of light transmitted. They are usually used with white light, but are provided with color filters so that isolated portions of the spectrum may be used for the measurements and the sensitivity of the methods improved. It is, of course, necessary to run calibration curves on the materials being analyzed, and this should be done under conditions closely approximating those which prevail when the unknown is run.

A number of photoelectric photometers have appeared on the market.[1] The instruments are designed with either one or two cells, and they utilize the photovoltaic type of photocell. In the two-celled instruments the light beam is divided, one beam passing through the colored solution and the other passing through a similar cell containing only solvent. Although somewhat less convenient to use than the one-celled instrument, the two-celled instrument can be readily designed electrically to counteract variations in the intensity of the light source. Two-celled instruments, then, can be completely line operated, thus eliminating the necessity of frequently charging or replacing batteries. One-celled instruments must be battery operated to eliminate completely the effects of line-voltage fluctuation. Deterioration

---

[1] See the advertising in the chemical journals, particularly those devoted to analytical chemistry.

of the photocells on aging has relatively little effect on the calibration curve of a two-celled instrument, as a matched pair of cells will deteriorate at about the same rate; on the other hand, deterioration requires that calibration curves with one-celled instruments be checked at frequent intervals.

Two types of photocells are known: photovoltaic, which consists of a copper sheet covered with a film of metallic selenium, and photo-

Fig. 76.   Two-celled photoelectric colorimeter.

emissive, which consists of metallic cesium in a high vacuum.   The photovoltaic (barrier-layer) cell requires no voltage or amplification since it generates sufficient voltage to affect a meter directly; it does require, however, a fairly sensitive galvanometer.   The photovoltaic cell is slow in its response to changes in intensity; this, however, is not serious enough to be a disadvantage in analytical work.   Photoemissive cells have an instantaneous response, but require the application of an external voltage and an electronic amplification system.

Operating directions are furnished with the commercial instruments, and invariably these can be readily followed.   Usually a 0 or 100 per cent adjustment must be made with the solvent only in the cell or cells before a measurement is made on a colored solution.   In any case the precautions mentioned in the preceding section dealing with the conditions which affect colorimetric processes must be fully considered just as when the Duboscq or other colorimeter is used.

The photoelectric photometer shown in Fig. 76 is a two-celled instrument constructed at Iowa State College. It is typical of the two-celled photoelectric colorimeters now in use. It uses spectrally matched photovoltaic cells and the electric circuit shown in Fig. 77, which automatically compensates for fluctuations in the intensity of the light source. The light source is a 110-volt, 100-watt Mazda bulb with a straight helical filament. The bulb may be cooled by a stream of compressed air, although this is not absolutely necessary. Holders are provided for glass filters at F. Usually two glass filters are used in

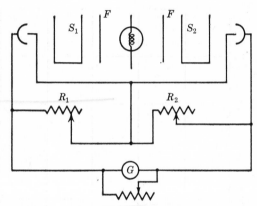

Fig. 77. Electric circuit of two-celled photoelectric colorimeter. S_1 and S_2, cells for solution and solvent, respectively. F, glass filter. R_1, variable resistance for zeroing. R_2, slide wire reading per cent transmittancy.

each light beam, one to select a portion of the visible spectrum to improve the sensitivity of the analytical method, and a second, an Aklo filter, to remove from the incident light the infrared radiation to which the photoelectric cells respond slowly. Holders are provided for glass filters, and spaces are left, large enough to accomodate cells up to 5 cm., although the instrument is customarily used with 1-cm. cells. The galvanometer, G, used is the Leeds and Northrup lamp-and-scale type, sensitivity 0.02 μamp. per mm. Resistance R_1 is an initial adjustment to make the scale read 100 when solvent alone is placed in both cells. The slide wire, R_2, reads directly the per cent transmittancy.

The calibration curve used with a photoelectric colorimeter must be prepared on the particular instrument used and for a certain set of conditions: voltage applied to filament of light bulb, thickness of cell, and glass filters used. A plot of the per cent of transmittancy against concentration is made, using data obtained on known solutions. Usually four or five points are sufficient. A curve which is concave upward is obtained, such as that shown in Fig. 78. A logarithmic plot of the data gives a straight line. This is best done by plotting the absorbancy, which is defined as $\log I_0/I$. Such a plot is shown in Fig. 79. In the operation of most instruments the transmittancy, $100(I/I_0)$, is generally measured. If the instrument does not read also in absorbancy (optical density), absorbancy may be calculated from the transmittancy by the relation

$$ A = \log \frac{I_0}{I} = \log \frac{1}{T/100} = -\log \frac{T}{100} $$

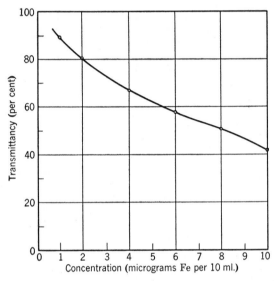

Fig. 78. Calibration curve for the determination of iron with bathophenanthroline. Transmittancy plotted against concentration. See Fig. 79 for another plot of same data. Data was secured using a spectrophotometer at wave length 533 mμ; 1-cm. cells.

Either plot may be used as a working calibration curve. The concentration may be expressed in any convenient units, milligrams per 100 ml., for example.

Use of the Photoelectric Colorimeter. Connect the instrument to the correct power supply. Tungsten-filament, white-light sources operate on either 110 volts or on 6 volts. When a 110-volt a.c. main is used as the power supply it is usually necessary to use a constant-voltage transformer to maintain constant the voltage applied to the filament; connect the voltage regulator to the 110-volt a.c. main and connect the instrument to the regulator. With instruments employing 110-volt lamps no warm-up period is necessary, and it is best to operate the bulb only when needed, to avoid unnecessary heating effects. Instruments having 6-volt lamps are commonly powered by storage batteries. A warm-up period of several minutes is usually necessary for the battery to reach a steady voltage, and it is usually best to leave the lamp on until a series of readings on standards and unknown have been completed. After a battery has been freshly charged its potential

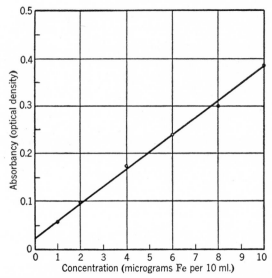

Fig. 79. Calibration curve for the determination of iron with bathophenanthroline. Absorbancy (optical density) plotted against concentration. See also Fig. 78. Straight line does not go through origin in this case because the instrument was balanced with water in reference cell, whereas the colored iron compound was dissolved in a mixture of ethyl and amyl alcohols.

falls off rather rapidly for a time, and it may be necessary to extend the warm-up period to 20 or 30 minutes.

Select the proper filters in accordance with the principles discussed on page 361; for example, for permanganate solutions use Corning Sextant Green (No. 401); for ferrous 1,10-phenanthroline sulfate use Corning Dark Shade Blue Green (No. 430); and for ferrous bathophenanthroline use Corning Heat Resistant Yellow Green (No. 450). Place the filter in the light path, or, if a two-celled colorimeter is used, place a filter in each light path. Insert also Corning Aklo filter, which removes the infrared from the light and causes the photocells to respond more rapidly.

If the colorimeter is a one-celled instrument, fill the cell with distilled water and place the cell in the holder, making certain that it is
perpendicular to the light beam. Turn on the lamp and bring the
needle on the meter to the 100 per cent transmittancy mark by adjusting the zeroing resistors or the diaphragm in the light path as provided
on the instrument. Replace the water in the cell by the solution and
return the cell to the holder. Read the per cent transmittancy (or
optical density).

If the colorimeter is a two-celled instrument fill both cells with water,
place the cells in the holders, making certain that they are perpendicular
to the light beams. Turn on the lamp, adjust the transmittancy scale
to read 100, and bring the galvanometer to the center of the scale,
using the zeroing resistors. Turn off the lamp, replace the water in
the cell on the side marked "solution" with the colored solution. Turn
on the lamp and bring the galvanometer back to 0 by turning the
transmittancy scale. Read the per cent transmittancy.

Usually it will be necessary to run three or four standards to obtain
enough data for a calibration curve. The data may be plotted as per
cent transmittancy *vs.* concentration (curved line) or as absorbancy
vs. concentration (straight line), as discussed above. The transmittancy of the unknown can then be measured and the concentration
of the unknown found by reference to the calibration curve. The
concentration can be expressed in any convenient units.

Conformity to Beer's Law. Whether or not a solution of a colored
material conforms to Beer's law can be easily determined by measuring
the transmittancy of several solutions of differing concentration of the
colored material. As will be seen from the Lambert-Beer law

$$\log (I/I_0) = -\epsilon l c$$

a plot of $\log (I/I_0)$ against the concentration c should yield a straight
line of negative slope passing through 0 (or $+2.00$ if transmittancy is
expressed as per cent). An equivalent method, more in accord with
current practice, is to plot absorbancy (optical density) against
concentration

$$A = \log (I_0/I) = \epsilon l c$$

the slope then being positive and the curve passing through the origin.

The molar extinction coefficient ϵ can be calculated from the slope
of this curve if the units of length are in centimeters and of concentration in moles per liter. The molar extinction coefficient ϵ depends
upon the wave length of the incident light, and on the nature of the
solvent employed, so that these should be specified when values of the
molar extinction coefficient are reported.

Only a minority of solutions of colored materials conform to Beer's law. Strictly, all homogeneous, colored systems conform to the law, and the statement just made really means that the conditions under which the color is measured have not been adequately established to insure that only one colored material is present. Any action in the solution, such as ionization, association, dissociation, and hydration, may affect the nature of the absorbing substance and change the light-absorption characteristics of the solution. The change in color resulting from dilution of a solution of the dichromate ion with water is a familiar example. The equilibrium involving this color transformation may be represented by the equation $Cr_2O_7^= + H_2O = 2HCrO_4^- = 2H^+ + 2CrO_4^=$, the three ions involved having different absorption spectra. The permanganate ion, on the other hand, undergoes no change on dilution or treatment with acids and conforms strictly to Beer's law.

Variation of Transmittancy with Wave Length; Absorption Bands and Filters. Colored materials are, of course, colored because they absorb light in certain definite regions or bands of the visible spectrum. These bands often extend into or exist only in the ultraviolet and infrared portions of the spectrum, and absorption spectroscopy can also be carried out in these regions with suitable apparatus. The transmission curves for various typical colors are shown in Fig. 80, in which transmittancy is plotted against the wave length in millimicrons [$m\mu$; $1\ m\mu = 10$ Å (Ångstroms)]. In these curves the fraction of light transmitted is the portion below the curve, the fraction absorbed is that above the curve (per cent transmittancy plus per cent absorbancy equals 100). Thus it will be seen that a green color transmits the central or green portion of the visible spectrum but absorbs most of the blue or red portion.

The prime importance of this variation of transmittancy with wave length is that the greatest variation in transmittancy with changes in concentration is at the wave length where the transmittancy is at the minimum, that is, the wave length of maximum absorption. This is readily seen from the absorption-spectrum curves of potassium permanganate at various concentrations, Fig. 81. The transmittancy has minimum values at 522 $m\mu$ and at 545 $m\mu$; the greatest change in transmittancy with concentration occurs at these wave lengths. Thus, at 522 $m\mu$, the difference in transmittancy of solutions containing 1.0 and 20.0 p.p.m. of manganese as potassium permanganate is 95.5 − 17.5 of 78 per cent; at 425 $m\mu$, on the other hand, the difference is only 8 per cent, and at 700 $m\mu$ the difference is less than 3 per cent. Accordingly, the most sensitive quantitative measurements of permanganate will be made with white light of wave length about 520 mμ.

Using a simple photoelectric colorimeter which has a tungsten-filament lamp as light source, the photocell would respond to light of all wave lengths. By inserting a green glass in the light path, most of

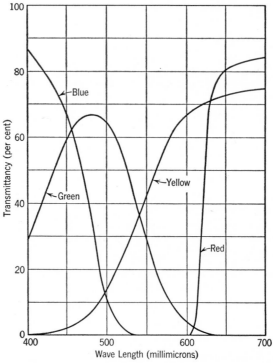

Fig. 80. Transmittancy of colored glasses over the visible spectrum. Spectra shown are for the Corning filters: Dark Theater Blue (503), Signal Green (440), Signal Yellow (330), H.R. Pyrometer Shade Red (2408).

the red and blue light is absorbed and only light of wave lengths between 320 mμ and 580 mμ falls on the photocell (Fig. 80, curve for green glass; wave lengths at 10 per cent transmittancy on either side selected arbitrarily as the limits). The total amount of light falling on the photocell is thus reduced; and changes in the amount of green light falling on the photocell, owing to changes in the concentration of permanganate, produce a greater relative change in the electric output of the photocell. A considerable increase in sensitivity toward permanganate is thus achieved.

The optimum condition is that the filter have its maximum transmittancy in the region of the absorption band of the material being studied and as little transmittancy as possible in the surrounding spectrum. For permanganate, the Corning Signal Green filter is quite satisfactory; the transmittancy curve of this filter is shown in Fig. 80,

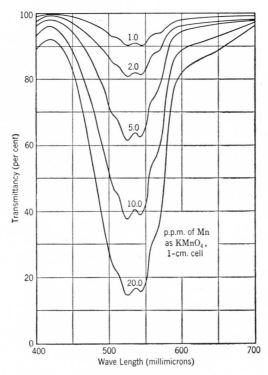

Fig. 81. Transmittancy of potassium permanganate at various wave lengths and concentrations.

the maximum transmittancy occurring at 480 mμ. Another Corning filter, Sextant Green, transmittancy maximum at 520 mμ, is somewhat better in that the maximum lies closer to the minima of permanganate.

If the spectral transmittancy curve for the colored system being measured is not available, the best of a series of filters is the one giving the greatest difference in reading between two concentrations of the colored solution. In general, the complementary color is the filter indicated, as shown in Table 24.

TABLE 24. SUITABLE COLORS FOR FILTERS

Color of Solution	Color of Filter
Purple	Green
Orange to red	Blue to blue green
Yellow	Blue
Green	Purple
Blue	Red

The most precise work, of course, will be done with light that is as nearly monochromatic as possible. Although glass filters if properly chosen increase the sensitivity considerably, they transmit a broad band of the visible spectrum. The Signal Green filter shown in Fig. 80 from 10 per cent transmittancy on the left of the absorption band to 10 per cent transmittancy on the right covers a wave-length band of about 260 mμ. Instruments known as spectrophotometers are available at moderate prices; they break up the white light from the tungsten-filament lamp into the spectrum and select any particular wave length for the photometric measurement. The best measurements can, of course, be made on such an instrument. Actually, however, the greatest errors in colorimetric analyses arise from the apparent departures of the colored material from Beer's law; this matter is discussed in the next section.

The Conditions for Making Colorimetric Comparisons. In the standard-series (Nessler-tube) method, when a match is obtained the concentrations of the colored material in the standard and the unknown are identical. It is apparent that the colored system need not conform to Beer's law. On the other hand, with the variable-depth (Duboscq) instrument conformity to Beer's law is necessary, and the more widely different the depths of the solutions the more essential this conformity becomes. With photoelectric colorimeters a preliminary calibration curve must be obtained, and it is immaterial whether the color conforms to Beer's law.

The shade and intensity of a colored material often vary with the anion present; thus, the intensity of the yellow color of pertitanic acid is deeper in hydrochloric acid than in sulfuric acid solution. Ferric iron in a hydrochloric acid solution is a bright yellow, in a sulfuric acid solution is only a pale yellow-brown, and in a phosphoric acid solution is completely colorless. Advantage is taken sometimes of such behavior to remove one color when another color is to be measured.

Obviously then, the unknown and standard should be alike as far as possible with respect to the nature and the concentration of the salts and acids present in the solution. If the colored material is the salt of a weak acid, the formation of the material, and thus the transmittancy of the solution, will depend on the pH of the solution. In such cases then the solutions of unknown and standard should be of exactly the same pH; the same foreign electrolytes should be present in each, and in about the same amounts; the amount of excess reagent added should be about the same; and, of course, the temperatures of unknown and standard should be identical. Finally, if the color develops slowly or fades on standing, the unknown and standard should be carried through the reaction simultaneously.

Permanent color standards of other similarly colored materials are often made where the color is not stable indefinitely or when a suitable primary-standard material is not available. For example, in the *o*-tolidine method for residual chlorine, permanent standards are prepared by mixing definite amounts of potassium bichromate and copper sulfate solutions of certain strengths.

THE DETERMINATION OF MANGANESE IN STEEL

Manganese is determined colorimetrically as permanganic acid, $HMnO_4$. The best of the various reagents capable of oxidizing manganous salts to permanganate is potassium periodate, KIO_4. The periodate is reduced to iodate

$$2MnSO_4 + 5KIO_4 + 3H_2O = 2HMnO_4 + 5KIO_3 + 2H_2SO_4$$

With an excess of periodate present the permanganate solution is stable indefinitely. The acidity of the solution is immaterial, the system conforms to Beer's law, and in general the method is an excellent one. The upper limit to the amount of manganese which can be determined this way is about 30 mg. per l.

The method is used regularly for the determination of manganese in steel. The steel is dissolved in nitric acid or a mixture of nitric acid and sulfuric acid. Any carbon which is not oxidized is destroyed by heating with potassium persulfate. This oxidizes some manganese to the dioxide, which must be reduced back to the bivalent form before proceeding; this can be done easily by heating with a bit of bisulfite. The solution is then ready for the oxidation with periodate according to the equation above. The large amount of ferric salts present gives the solution a yellow color, but fortunately phosphoric acid does not interfere with the determination of manganese, and the color of the ferric iron can be completely removed by conversion to the slightly dissociated, colorless ferric-phosphate compound.

Procedure for the Colorimetric Determination of Manganese in Steel. Weigh accurately 0.5 to 1.0 g. of the steel into a 400-ml. beaker.

Cover, and add to the sample 70 ml. of dilute nitric acid (1:3). Boil for 1 minute. Remove from the heat and add 0.5 to 1.0 g. of ammonium persulfate. Boil for 10 to 15 minutes to oxidize the carbon and destroy the persulfate. If a permanganate color or dark precipitate of manganese dioxide develops, add a few crystals of sodium bisulfite to clear the solution. Boil for a few minutes to drive off the sulfur dioxide and oxides of nitrogen. Add 40 ml. of water, 10 ml. of concentrated phosphoric acid, and 0.5 g. of potassium periodate. Boil for a few minutes. Cool and dilute to 250 ml. in a volumetric flask. To a similar flask add 200 ml. of water, 10 ml. of concentrated phosphoric acid, and then a measured volume of standard potassium permanganate solution until the color is approximately the same as that of the sample. Dilute to exactly 250 ml., mix well, and compare the two solutions in a Duboscq colorimeter as described on page 352. If the comparison is to be made with a photoelectric colorimeter prepare three or four standards rather than one, using the procedure just given; vary the amount of standard permanganate added to obtain solutions having transmittancy values scattered over the range 10 to 90 per cent. Directions for operating the photoelectric colorimeter are given on page 358.

Report the per cent of manganese in the sample.

THE COLORIMETRIC DETERMINATION OF IRON USING 1,10-PHENANTHROLINE

The organic base 1,10-phenanthroline reacts with ferrous iron to form a red complex ion having the formula $Fe(1,10\text{-phenanthroline})_3^{++}$:

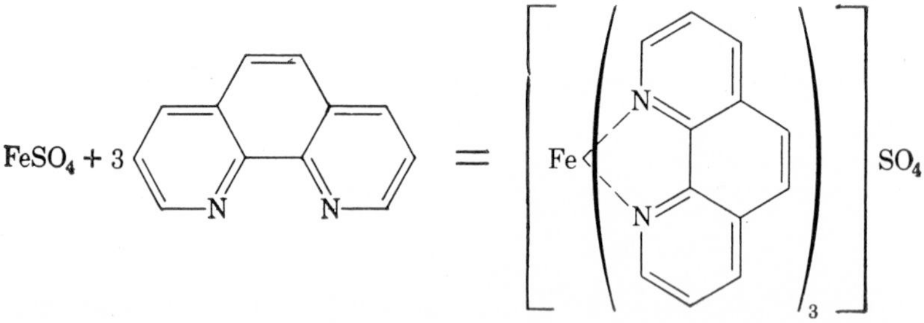

This reaction is a very sensitive test for iron and may be used for its colorimetric determination. The molar extinction coefficient of the $Fe(1,10\text{-phen})_3^{++}$ ion is 11,100. The formation of the ferrous 1,10-phenanthroline ion and the intensity of its color are independent of pH between 2 and 9. To adjust the pH it is usually sufficient to buffer the solution by the addition of sodium acetate. Ferric iron must be reduced to the ferrous state; this is most conveniently done by adding hydroxylammonium chloride, NH_3OHCl.

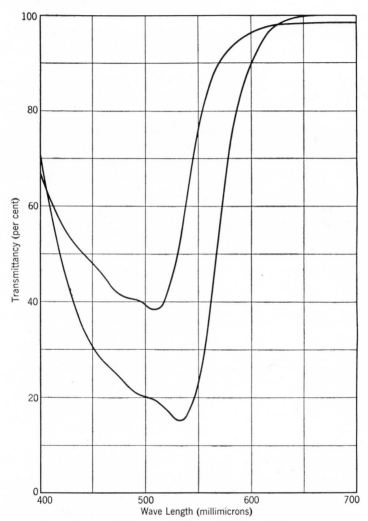

Fig. 82. Transmittancy of ferrous 1,10-Phenanthroline and ferrous bathophenanthroline ions. Upper curve: 2 p.p.m. of iron as ferrous 1,10-phenanthroline sulfate in water. Lower curve: 2 p.p.m. of iron as ferrous bathophenanthroline sulfate in amyl alcohol-ethyl alcohol mixture; 1-cm. cells.

The absorption curve of the 1,10-phenanthroline ion is shown in Fig. 82. The color conforms to Beer's law over the range 0.1 to 6 p.p.m. of iron.

The solution containing the iron to be determined must be colorless and free of any turbidity. If organic material is present, as in wine or blood, it can be destroyed by evaporation with nitric acid and perchloric acid (see pages 43 and 403).

Procedure for the Determination of Iron with 1,10-*Phenanthroline. Reagents.* Prepare a solution of 1,10-phenanthroline by dissolving 0.10 g. of 1,10-phenanthroline monohydrate in 100 ml. of water, heating to 80° to effect the dissolution more rapidly. Ten to fifteen milliliters of this solution is required for each milligram of iron.

Dissolve 10 g. of hydroxylammonium chloride in 100 ml. of water. Dissolve also 10 g. of sodium acetate in 100 ml. of water.

Prepare a standard iron solution by weighing carefully 0.0702 g. of ferrous ammonium sulfate [$Fe(NH_4)_2(SO_4)_2 \cdot 6H_2O$, Mohr's salt] or 0.0684 g. of ferrous ethylenediammonium sulfate [$FeC_2H_4(NH_3)_2$-$(SO_4)_2 \cdot 4H_2O$, Oesper's salt]. Transfer the salt to a 1-l. volumetric flask, and add water to dissolve the salt. Add 2.5 ml. of concentrated sulfuric acid, dilute exactly to the mark, and mix well. This solution contains 0.0100 mg. of iron per ml.

Sample. Choose a size for the sample such that it will contain 0.01 to 0.6 mg. of iron per. 100 ml. in the final solution. If the sample is a ground or surface water, the specific gravity may be assumed to be 1 and the sample may be taken by simply pipetting accurately a volume of suitable size. If the sample contains organic material use the procedure given below to effect its destruction before carrying out the colorimetric determination of the iron.

Determination of Iron in Ground or Surface Water. Obtain a sufficient sample of the water. Rinse the sample bottle several times with the water, fill the bottle completely full, and stopper the bottle in such a manner that no air bubble is left above the water. If the analysis is not to be begun within 1 hour add 2 ml. of concentrated hydrochloric acid per l. of sample.

Carry several solutions through the process together; for example, two samples of the unknown water, three or four standards, and a blank. Into a series of 100-ml. volumetric flasks pipet (*a*) 50.0 ml. of the water being tested, (*b*, *c*, *d*, and *e*) 1.00, 5.00, 10.0, and 50.0 ml. of the standard iron solution, and (*f*) 50 ml. of distilled water. To each solution add 1.0 ml. of 10 per cent hydroxylammonium chloride solution and 5 to 10 ml. of 1,10-phenanthroline solution. Buffer the solution by the addition of 8 ml. of 10 per cent sodium acetate solution, producing the red color of ferrous 1,10-phenanthroline. Dilute the solution to exactly 100 ml. Measure the transmittancy of each solution, using a photoelectric colorimeter with a blue green filter, preferably Corning Filter No. 430, Dark Shade Blue Green. Directions for operating the photoelectric colorimeter are given on page 358. Using the data obtained on the standards, prepare a calibration curve plotting transmittancy against milligrams of iron per 100 ml. Using the transmittancy of the unknown and the calibration curve, find the number of milligrams of iron per 100 ml. in the final solution of the unknown.

Fig. 83. Fume eradicator. Glass hood is connected to a water aspirator. The flask in this picture has a reflux head in the neck to condense perchloric acid vapors.

Subtract the iron found in the blank and then multiply this value by 20 to obtain the number of milligrams of iron per 1000 ml. of the original sample; each milligram per liter corresponds to 1 p.p.m.

Determination of Iron in Organic Matter. Weigh the sample accurately and transfer it to a 500-ml. conical flask, preferably one of Vycor. A suitable decomposition mixture consists of equal volumes of 72 per cent perchloric acid ($HClO_4 \cdot 2H_2O$) and concentrated nitric acid; 20 ml. of such a mixture will decompose 1 g. of organic material, 1 g. of tobacco, for example. Place a refluxing head in the neck of the flask and cover the flask with a fume eradicator (Fig. 83) connected to a water aspirator. Heat the mixture on a hot plate or over a burner. Increase the heat gradually until the organic matter has been destroyed and fumes of perchloric acid are evolved. Cool the mixture, remove the fume eradicator, rinse the reflux head, and dilute the solution to about 20 ml. Add 5 ml. of concentrated sulfuric acid. Return the flask to the hot plate and replace the fume eradicator. Heat the solution until fumes of sulfuric acid appear and all perchloric acid has been expelled. Cool the mixture and dilute with 50 ml. of water. Boil the solution for a few minutes to dissolve any anhydrous ferric sulfate and any calcium sulfate; some silica may remain. Filter the solution, catching the filtrate in a 100-ml. volumetric flask. To the solution add 1.0 ml. of 10 per cent hydroxylammonium chloride solution. Using congo red paper as indicator neutralize the sulfuric acid first with concentrated ammonium hydroxide and finally with dilute ammonium hydroxide (1:50) until the paper turns from blue to pink, pH about 4. Add 5 to 10 ml. of 1,10-phenanthroline solution. Dilute the solution to exactly 100 ml. and mix well.

Prepare a series of standards for the colorimetric comparison as follows: Into a series of 100-ml. volumetric flasks pipet 1.00, 5.00, 10.0, and 50.0 ml. of the standard iron solution (0.0100 mg. Fe per ml.), and into another flask (for a blank) place 50 ml. of distilled water. To each flask add 1.0 ml. of 10 per cent hydroxylammonium chloride solution. Neutralize the solution with dilute ammonia (1:50), using congo red paper, until the paper turns from blue to pink. Add 5 to 10 ml. of 1,10-phenanthroline solution.

Measure the transmittancy of each solution, using a photoelectric colorimeter with a blue green filter, preferably Corning Filter No. 430, Dark Shade Blue Green. Directions for operating the photoelectric colorimeter are given on page 358. Using the data obtained on the standards, prepare a calibration curve, plotting transmittancy against milligrams of iron per 100 ml. Using the transmittancy of the unknown and the calibration curve, find the number of milligrams of iron per 100 ml. in the final solution of the unknown. Subtract the iron found in the blank. Using the net weight of iron and the weight of the sample, calculate the per cent of iron in the sample.

THE COLORIMETRIC DETERMINATION OF IRON WITH BATHOPHENANTHROLINE

The substituted 1,10-phenanthroline, 4,7-diphenyl-1,10-phenanthroline forms a red compound with ferrous iron, just as does 1,10-phenanthroline. The color is more intense, however, and the colored iron compound can be extracted with a solvent immiscible with water.

Considerably lower concentrations of iron can thus be determined with this reagent than with 1,10-phenanthroline. The reagent, which has been given the common name bathophenanthroline, has the structural formula

The molar extinction coefficient of the ion $Fe(bathophen)_3^{++}$ is 22,400, twice as great as that of $Fe(1,10\text{-phen})_3^{++}$. The extraction of the color with an immiscible solvent gives the method a further advantage, for a large sample, 100 ml., for example, may be taken and the colored iron compound extracted into a volume of only 10 ml. for the colorimetric comparison. Whereas 1,10-phenanthroline can be used for the colorimetric determination of iron as low as 0.1 p.p.m., bathophenanthroline can be used for as low as 0.005 p.p.m. of iron. Inasmuch as bathophenanthroline is more difficult to prepare and more expensive, its principal use is in the determination of very low concentrations of iron, such as those found in the treated water from water-softening plants. The method can, however, be applied to larger amounts of iron.

The absorption curve of the bathophenanthroline ferrous ion is shown in Fig. 82. The absorption peak lies at 533 mμ, that is, at a longer wave length than that of the 1,10-phenanthroline ferrous ion. The color conforms to Beer's law over the range 0.001 to 3 p.p.m. When the color measurement is made with a spectrophotometer, the measurement is made at 533 mμ. When the measurement is made with a photoelectric colorimeter, a green filter should be used; Corning Sextant Green (No. 401) is recommended. For very small amounts of iron the comparison with standards is best made in Nessler tubes so that the light passes through a great depth of solution.

For extracting the color, isoamyl alcohol or *n*-hexyl alcohol has been found most satisfactory. The separation of the two immiscible liquids is carried out in a separatory funnel, Fig. 84, page 400. If the volume of water is large, more than 50 ml., two extractions with the immiscible liquid are necessary.

All the iron in the sample must be in the ferrous form. The reduction of any ferric iron is most conveniently brought about by adding hydroxylammonium chloride.

The bathophenanthroline ferrous ion is stable over the pH range 2 to 9 but forms most rapidly in slightly acid solution, pH 4. If the reaction is carried out in a slightly acid solution, one buffered with acetate, copper does not interfere.

In working with very low concentrations of iron, it is necessary that the reagents be free of iron. The solubility of the bathophenanthroline ferrous ion in isoamyl alcohol makes it possible to free the solutions of the reagents by simply adding bathophenanthroline and extracting. The excess bathophenanthroline is extracted quantitatively along with the colored iron compound.

Procedure for the Determination of Iron with Bathophenanthroline.
Reagents. Prepare a 0.001 M solution of bathophenanthroline (4,7-diphenyl-1,10-phenanthroline) by dissolving 33.4 mg. of the solid reagent in a mixture of 50 ml. of ethyl alcohol and 50 ml. of isoamyl alcohol.

Prepare iron-free solutions of hydroxylammonium chloride and sodium acetate in the following manner: Dissolve 10 g. of hydroxylammonium chloride in 100 ml. of distilled water in a 125-ml. separatory funnel. Add 2 ml. of 0.001 M bathophenanthroline and mix well. Add 5 ml. of isoamyl alcohol and shake vigorously. Allow the liquids to separate, and draw off the lower, aqueous layer into a glass-stoppered reagent bottle. Dissolve 10 g. of sodium acetate in 100 ml. of water in a 125-ml. separatory funnel. Add 2 ml. of 10 per cent hydroxylammonium chloride solution. Add 2 ml. of 0.001 M bathophenanthroline and mix well. Add 5 ml. of isoamyl alcohol and shake vigorously. Allow the liquids to separate and draw off the lower, aqueous layer into a glass-stoppered reagent bottle.

Prepare two standard iron solutions, containing respectively 10 μg. and 1 μg. per ml. (μg., microgram, equal to 0.001 mg.). Weigh carefully 0.0702 g. of ferrous ammonium sulfate (Mohr's salt) or 0.0684 g. of ferrous ethylenediammonium sulfate (Oesper's salt) and transfer to a 1-l. volumetric flask. Add water to dissolve the salt, add 2.5 ml. of concentrated sulfuric acid, dilute exactly to the mark, and mix well. Pipet 100 ml. of this solution into a second 1-l. volumetric flask, add 2.5 ml. of sulfuric acid, dilute to the mark with water, and mix well. The first of these solutions contains 10 μg. of iron per ml.; the second contains 1 μg. of iron per ml.

Determination of Iron in Natural or Treated Water. Obtain a sufficient sample of the water. Rinse the sample bottle several times with the water, fill the bottle completely full, and stopper in such a manner that no air bubble is left above the water. If the analysis is not to be begun within 1 hour add 2 ml. of concentrated hydrochloric acid per l. of sample.

Carry several solutions through the process together; for example, two samples of the unknown to be analyzed, three or four standards, and a blank. Once a calibration curve has been established, further standards need not be run.

From a rough estimate or a preliminary determination, decide the size of the sample to be taken for analysis from the accompanying table.

SELECTION OF SIZE OF SAMPLE FOR THE DETERMINATION OF IRON WITH BATHOPHENANTHROLINE

Iron Content (p.p.m.)	Size of Sample to be Taken (milliliters)	Weight of Iron in Sample to be Taken (micrograms)	Procedure to be Used
0.01–0.1 (aerated water)	100	1–10	Special procedure (Nessler tubes)
0.1–1.0	10	1–10	Procedure [a] (photoelectric colorimeter)
1.0–10.0 (raw water)		1–10	Procedure [a] (photoelectric colorimeter)

[a] If a greater volume than 10 ml. is required to fill the colorimeter cell the range will be correspondingly shifted to greater quantities of iron.

For the standards, use various amounts of the second standard iron solution (1 μg./ml.), for example: 1.00, 5.00, and 10.0 ml., corresponding to 1.00, 5.00, and 10.0 μg. of iron.

Pipet the sample (water being tested or standard iron solution) into a 60-ml. separatory funnel. If the sample taken was less than 10 ml. add sufficient distilled water to bring the volume to 10 ml. Use 10 ml. of distilled water for the blank. To each sample add 2 ml. of 10 per cent hydroxylammonium chloride solution. Add 4 ml. of 10 per cent sodium acetate solution. If the original sample of the water had been acidified with hydrochloric acid when taken add an additional 4 ml. of sodium acetate solution. Add 4 ml. of 0.001 M bathophenanthroline and mix. Add 6.0 ml. of isoamyl alcohol, stopper the funnel, and shake the mixture well. Allow the liquids to separate. After not less than 5 minutes after adding the bathophenanthroline and after the liquids have cleanly separated into two layers, draw off and discard the lower, aqueous layer. Shake away any of the aqueous layer remaining in the

stem of the separatory funnel. Drain the isoamyl alcohol layer into a
10-ml. volumetric flask. If more than 10 ml. are required to fill the
cell of the colorimeter to be used later, use a 25-ml. volumetric flask
rather than a 10-ml. flask at this point. Wash out the separatory
funnel with 2 to 3 ml. of ethyl alcohol added from a pipet in such a
manner that the upper stopper of the funnel and the walls of the funnel
are uniformly washed at least twice by a film of alcohol as it drains
from the top to the bottom. Transfer this wash alcohol to the volumetric flask. Dilute the solution in the flask to the mark with ethyl
alcohol and mix by shaking. At this point the solution in the volumetric flask should be clear with no turbidity, the ethyl alcohol added
being sufficient to render miscible the isoamyl alcohol and the few droplets of water which are carried along in separating the layers.

Determine the transmittancy of the solution. If a spectrophotometer
is available make the measurement at 533 mμ. If the measurement
is made with a photoelectric colorimeter, use (in addition to the Aklo
infrared filter) a blue green filter; the Corning filters Sextant Green
(No. 401) or Heat Resistant Yellow Green (No. 450) are especially
recommended, but certain other Corning filters, for example Dark
Theater Blue (No. 503), Colorimeter Blue Green (No. 978), Dark
Shade Blue Green (No. 430), and Signal Green (No. 440), are satisfactory and render the method only slightly less sensitive.

Plot the data secured from the standards as absorbancy (optical
density) A against concentration of iron expressed as micrograms of
iron per 10 ml. of final volume of colored solution. If the instrument
used reads in per cent transmittancy T, calculate the absorbancy,
using the relation $A = -\log (T/100)$, and then plot the absorbancy
against the concentration. The iron-bathophenanthroline color
conforms to Beer's law, so that this plot is a straight line. Using this
graph find the iron concentration in the final, colored solution of the
unknown. This weight of iron was present in the original sample.
From this and the volume of the sample taken calculate the concentration of iron in the unknown in p.p.m.

Example. Volume taken, 1.00 ml.; concentration of iron in final solution,
2.5 μg./10 ml.; weight of iron in sample, 2.5 μg.; concentration of iron in
sample, 2.5 μg./ml., which is equal to 2500 μg./l., or 2.5 mg./l., or 2.5 p.p.m.

Special Procedure for Iron in the Range 0.01 *to* 0.1 *p.p.m.* Carry
several solutions through the process together; for example, two samples
of the unknown, a blank, and three or four standards. The colorimetric
comparison is later to be made in Nessler tubes, and for routine work
a series of standards can be made and preserved for a long period.

Pipet 100 ml. of the water to be tested into a 125-ml. separatory funnel. For the standards pipet the desired volumes, for example, 1.00, 2.00, 3.00, $\cdots$, 10.0 ml., of the standard iron solution (1 μg./ml.) into 100 ml. of distilled water in a 125-ml. separatory funnel. Add 2 ml. of iron-free, 10 per cent hydroxylammonium chloride solution. Add 4 ml. of iron-free, 10 per cent sodium acetate solution; if the sample taken contained any free acid, add additional sodium acetate solution. Add 4 ml. of 0.001 M bathophenanthroline and mix well. Add 10 ml. of isoamyl alcohol. Shake the mixture well and then allow it to stand for 5 minutes. Draw off the aqueous layer into a second 125-ml. separatory funnel. Add to this 10 ml. of isoamyl alcohol, shake well, and allow to stand until the layers have separated. Draw off and discard the aqueous layer. Transfer both colored isoamyl alcohol extracts to a 50-ml. volumetric flask, rinsing both separatory funnels with generous portions of ethyl alcohol. Dilute to the mark with ethyl alcohol and mix thoroughly. Transfer to a 50-ml. Nessler tube. Carry out the comparison by looking down through the full length of the tubes toward a sloping, white, reflecting background, such as found on Nessler racks, Fig. 74.

Inasmuch as unknown and standards were diluted to the same volume, the unknown contains the same weight of iron as that in the standard which it matches. From this weight and the volume of sample taken, calculate the concentration of iron in the sample in p.p.m.

PROBLEMS

1. The manganese in a sample of steel weighing 1.000 g. was determined colorimetrically. After the manganese was oxidized to permanganate the solution was diluted to 500 ml. A colorimetric standard was prepared by diluting 1.42 ml. of a standard potassium permanganate solution to 250 ml. The concentration of the standard permanganate solution was found to be 0.125 N by titrating primary-standard sodium oxalate in acid solution. When compared in the Duboscq colorimeter the readings on the unknown and on the colorimetric standard were 30.0 and 20.0, respectively. Calculate the per cent of manganese in the steel.

2. The titanium in a 1.000-g. sample was converted to yellow pertitanic acid, diluted to 100 ml., and compared in a Duboscq colorimeter with a standard prepared by dissolving 0.0100 g. of pure titanium oxide, TiO_2, converting to pertitanic acid, and diluting to 250 ml. The colorimeter reading of the standard was 30.0, of the unknown, 25.0. Calculate the per cent of titanium in the sample.

3. Using data taken from Fig. 81 confirm that potassium permanganate conforms to Beer's law. Make a plot of log (I_0/I) against concentration at 522 mμ and at 600 mμ. From the slope of the curves calculate the molar extinction coefficient of manganese as permanganate. Parts per million is equal to milligrams per liter.

4. The following data were obtained for the absorbancy (optical density) of three solutions of ferrous 1,10-phenanthroline sulfate.

		Absorbancy		
	Spectro-	Photoelectric		
Iron	photometer	Colorimeter		White
(p.p.m.)	510 mμ	No. 503 [a]	No. 430 [b]	Light
5	1.05	0.650	0.733	0.169
2	0.426	0.270	0.290	0.070
0.5	0.116	0.075	0.076	0.013

[a] Filter No. 503, Dark Theater Blue.
[b] Filter No. 430, Dark Shade Blue Green.

Plot absorbancy against concentration and determine the molar extinction coefficient in each case. On the basis of the molar extinction coefficient determine how much more sensitive the spectrophotometer is than the photoelectric colorimeter. Decide also which of the glass filters is the best to use.

CHAPTER 14

Methods of Effecting Separations

With the probable exception of sampling heterogeneous materials, separations are likely to be the seat of the most numerous and most serious errors in many methods of analysis—*M. G. Mellon.*

The primary objective of any quantitative analysis is to obtain a true measure of the extent to which some component is present in the sample. The actual physical measurements made on the sample and on the component must, of course, be accurately made, and equally important, the measurement on the component must be of the component alone and of nothing else; that is, the measurement must be limited to the substance being determined. Only on rare occasions is the analyst called on to determine a material in the absence of a second material, and in general any foreign material may be expected to exert an adverse effect of some sort on any method of analysis. Usually the substances to be analyzed are mixtures, and, even when they are pure materials, the interest centers on the traces of foreign bodies which are inevitably present. In any analysis, then, specificity is a prerequisite to accuracy.

Many gravimetric, volumetric, and colorimetric methods are quite specific. Many are hardly specific at all. Research has greatly simplified and speeded the methods of analyzing materials of commercial importance, but for a multitude of other materials no direct methods are known. The rapid advance of our chemical civilization continually brings forth new products in which the chemical elements and their compounds are combined in new and complex compositions which are difficult and often baffling to analyze. Direct methods are preferred in the interest of accuracy and economy of time and chemicals. When they are not available the components of the mixture must somehow be separated before the final measurement can be made. Fortunately, the number of devices which effect separations is large, and it is seldom that nothing at all can be done with a given mixture. Unfortunately, the separation processes are often tedious, and frequently they are incomplete and not wholly satisfactory. Next to the sampling operation, the separation step is the most likely source of error in analytical work.

Materials vary greatly in complexity, but the difficulty of analyzing them stems not from their complexity, but from the inadequacies of the known methods which can be applied to effect the necessary separations. In a large measure this is determined by the similarity of the components which must be separated. Some alloy steels are quite complex, having in addition to iron four or five alloying elements: tungsten, molybdenum, chromium, nickel, and vanadium, for example, as well as the inescapable minor constituents silicon, manganese, sulfur, phosphorus, and carbon. Yet the analysis of such an alloy is not too difficult because of the marked differences in the chemistry of the various elements concerned. On the other hand, the analysis of a protein for the individual amino acids comprising it is a most difficult matter, for there are no sharp differences in the properties of the amino acids. In the determination of the alkali metals, sodium and potassium can be separated satisfactorily although not easily; the separation of potassium from rubidium and cesium can hardly be done at all for no really satisfactory method is known.

Separations are primarily brought about by the formation of a new phase, that is, by the formation of a new solid, liquid, or gas. The separation of a solid, the phenomenon of precipitation, is the most important of these phase changes. The separation of a gas from a solid or liquid is used but is of lesser importance. Extraction of a liquid with a liquid is also used but has only a limited number of applications.

In the following material, attention is first directed to the abundance and distribution of the elements with notes on the frequency with which the various elements appear in the analytical laboratory. This is followed by a discussion of the chemical changes which can be employed to enhance the differences between the elements, notably by changes in valence state and by the formation of non-dissociated ions. The subject of precipitation is then taken up in detail, and certain specific reagents and methods are discussed. The chapter ends with sections on distillation and volatilization, on extraction methods, and on the destruction of organic matter.

THE COMPLEXITY OF MATERIALS AND THE ABUNDANCE OF THE VARIOUS ELEMENTS

The aggregates of material encountered by man vary from the elementary particles constituting the atom to the vast collections of stellar matter constituting the galaxies. The province of the analytical chemist is only a limited segment of this broad array of nature, and in view of the multiplicity of materials confronting the chemist in his own narrow domain, he is indeed happy to leave the analysis of the interior of the atom to the physicist and of the outer universe to the astronomer. In Table 25 a summary is presented of the composition

TABLE 25. THE ORDER OF COMPLEXITY OF THE MATERIALS OF NATURE

Substance	Components	Method of Study or Separation of Components
Nuclei of atoms	Protons, neutrons.	Disruption and alteration by high-speed particles (protons, neutrons, deutrons, α-rays).
Atoms (isotopes)	Nuclei, electrons.	Temporary removal or displacement of electrons by light of high energy (x-ray, ultraviolet, visible light).
Elements	Isotopes (atoms of different mass but same nuclear charge and chemical properties).	Physical processes involving mass (deflection of ionized particles in magnetic field, distillation).
Compounds (molecules)	Elements in relatively small, whole-number combinations. Molecular weight usually less than 10,000.	Decomposition by chemical and physical processes. Ultimate analysis for elementary components. Proximate analysis for specific groups or simpler molecular components.
Compositions	Mixtures of elements or compounds in any proportions.	Separation by differences in chemical behavior and physical properties.
Macromolecules (proteins, cellulose, fibers, plastics)	Smaller units polymerized into fibers and films. Molecular weight greater than 10,000.	Separation by high-speed centrifuging; partial breakdown by chemical attack.
Earth	Minerals and organic compounds and compositions making up the core, lithosphere, hydrosphere, and atmosphere.	Mechanical separation.
Solar system	Sun, planets, satellites, asteroids, comets.	Mechanical interpretation of gravitational effects.
Universe	Solar systems, nebulae, galaxies.	Properties of light received.

of the various aggregations of matter and the methods of attack in analyzing them.

The chemist is indeed fortunate that he has only some ninety elements to deal with, and although these can be arranged in an almost infinite number of ways, the number of general types of matter is rather limited.

A first inspection might indicate that most analytical work would deal with the most abundant of the elements on earth, the first ten, for example, oxygen, silicon, aluminum, iron, calcium, sodium, potassium, magnesium, hydrogen, and titanium, which together make up about 98 per cent of the crust of the earth (Table 26). This is not the case,

TABLE 26.　RELATIVE ABUNDANCES OF THE ELEMENTS IN THE LITHOSPHERE, HYDROSPHERE AND ATMOSPHERE [a]

	Lithosphere	Hydrosphere	Atmosphere	Average [b]
Oxygen	46.46	85.79	23.024	49.20
Silicon	27.61			25.67
Aluminum	8.07			7.50
Iron	5.06			4.71
Calcium	3.64	0.05		3.39
Sodium	2.75	1.14		2.63
Potassium	2.58	0.04		2.40
Magnesium	2.07	0.14		1.93
Hydrogen	0.14	10.67		0.87
Titanium	0.62			0.58
Carbon	0.09	0.002		0.08
Chlorine	0.05	2.07		0.19
Bromine		0.008		
Fluorine	0.03			0.03
Phosphorus	0.12			0.11
Sulfur	0.06	0.09		0.06
Manganese	0.09			0.09
Barium	0.04			0.04
Strontium	0.02			0.02
Nitrogen			75.539	0.03
All other elements	0.50		1.437	0.47

[a] F. W. Clark, *U. S. Geological Survey, Bulletin* 770, pages 36 and 45, 1924.
[b] Assuming the lithosphere to be 93 per cent and the hydrosphere 7 per cent of the ten-mile crust.

however. The number of inorganic materials found naturally is surprisingly small, and, although products of the ten most abundant elements make up a big segment of all industrial products, a good part of our civilization is based on another twenty elements whose combined abundance is less than half of one per cent of the known portions of the earth. In Table 27 we have indicated the frequency with which the

TABLE 27. THE FREQUENCY WITH WHICH ELEMENTS ARE
ENCOUNTERED IN ANALYTICAL WORK

Very Frequent	Frequent	Occasional	Rare	Very Rare
Iron	Nickel	Titanium	Rare earths	Helium and
Calcium	Chromium	Beryllium	Selenium	the other
Aluminum	Vanadium	Lithium	Tellurium	rare
Magnesium	Tungsten	Strontium	Rubidium	gases
Copper	Molybdenum	Barium	Cesium	
Tin	Sodium	Oxygen	Zirconium	
Lead	Potassium	Boron	Gallium	
Sulfur	Bromine	Cobalt	Indium	
Chlorine	Iodine	Zinc	Thallium	
Carbon	Phosphorus	Cadmium	Rhenium	
Nitrogen	Mercury	Arsenic	Iridium	
Hydrogen	Fluorine	Antimony	Osmium	
Silicon	Manganese	Bismuth	Ruthenium	
		Silver	Rhodium	
		Uranium		
		Columbium		
		Cerium		
		Thorium		
		Platinum		
		Palladium		
		Gold		

analyst is called on to determine a number of the elements; obviously such estimates are only guesses, for the materials analyzed vary greatly from laboratory to laboratory and depend on a variety of circumstances.

The inorganic materials which are encountered in nature and in industrial products can be placed in several broad groups: minerals and ores, ferrous and non-ferrous metallurgical materials, cement, ceramics, and synthetic chemical compounds.

The materials of industrial importance are not entirely the most common elements. Iron is the fourth most abundant element, and of course its ores are one of the great raw materials of our civilization, and innumerable specimens of it are analyzed daily. Titanium, which is ninth most abundant in the earth's crust, finds a relatively minor, although increasing, industrial use. Copper and its alloys have great industrial importance, yet copper is listed as one of the minor elements in the makeup of the earth's crust. In fact, some of the elements which occur in really insignificant amounts have found important uses in quite astonishing fashions.

Minerals and Ores. A naturally occurring inorganic material is called a *mineral;* the number of these is about 1800. Minerals which are exploited for the recovery of some component are termed *ores;* the foreign or extraneous material in an ore is called the *gangue.* The majority of the minerals are silicates, as might be expected from the abundance of silica and oxygen. The carbonates, such as limestone and dolomite, constitute the next largest group. Sulfides and oxides are common and also chlorides, fluorides, phosphates, and sulfates. A few elements occur in nature as the metals; these are the elements at the positive end of the reduction-potential series: copper, silver, mercury, gold, and the platinum metals.

The metals of the first four groups of the periodic system occur only as salts of oxygen-containing acids (silicates, carbonates, phosphates, and sulfates) or as chlorides or fluorides, but never as sulfides. A number of elements occur primarily as sulfides. These are the metals of the hydrogen sulfide groups of the qualitative-analysis scheme and are the elements of the eighth periodic group (iron, cobalt, nickel and the platinum metals) and the adjacent groups.

Silica (quartz) and silicates constitute the major portion of the sedimentary and igneous rocks of the earth's crust. The common rock-forming minerals are silicates of aluminum, iron, sodium, calcium, magnesium, potassium, and titanium, that is, silicates of the most abundant elements. The great variety of silicate materials results from the property of silica of combining with variable amounts of water to give a variety of silicic acids. All the various silicic acids are very weak acids, but each has at least two or more hydrogen atoms which can be replaced by metals. The crystal structure of the silicates is such that replacement of one atom by another of about equal size may occur (magnesium, ferrous iron, and manganese for calcium; ferric iron for aluminum, for example). This replacement may take place in any proportions, so that between two isomorphous silicates there often exists a whole series of silicates in which an increasing amount of one metal is replaced by a metal like it in valence and size.

Ferrous Materials. The common ores of iron are oxides: hematite, Fe_2O_3; magnetite, Fe_3O_4; and limonite, $Fe_2O_3 \cdot xH_2O$. Cast iron, the product of the reduction of iron ores in the blast furnace, contains considerable carbon and invariably also silicon, sulfur, phosphorus, and manganese. In the process of converting cast iron to steel, the content of carbon, sulfur, and phosphorus is greatly reduced and for special purposes other metallic materials are introduced. The common alloying elements are: nickel, chromium, vanadium, tungsten, molybdenum, manganese, and cobalt. Because scrap metal is also used in the manufacture of steel, other metals are found in small amounts in steel: copper, tin, aluminum, zinc.

A special class of ferrous materials made in the electric furnace are the ferroalloys used to introduce alloying constituents in steel. Ferro-silicon, ferromanganese, and ferrotungsten are typical examples. The amount of the second element in such materials is usually high, 30 to 60 per cent.

Copper-Base Materials. Copper wire for electrical uses is pure copper and very low in impurities. A wide variety of copper alloys is used commercially, such as brass, bronze, aluminum brass, and phos-phor bronze. The metals most commonly associated with copper in such alloys are tin, lead, and zinc. Aluminum, silicon, manganese, and phosphorus are placed in a number of common copper alloys. Beryl-lium copper, which finds many special uses, often has in addition a third metal such as cobalt, chromium, or nickel. Several copper-nickel alloys are also common: cupronickel or German silver; monel.

Aluminum. The principal metals found in aluminum alloys are: copper, zinc, manganese, magnesium, nickel, and silicon.

Die-Casting Alloys. These are primarily zinc-base alloys, con-taining copper, cadmium, tin, lead, and antimony.

White-Metal Alloys. These have tin or lead as the base metal and contain in addition antimony, bismuth, copper, zinc, and aluminum.

Other non-ferrous alloys are magnesium metal and its alloys, and alloys of silver, gold, and platinum.

ADJUSTMENT OF VALENCE STATE AS AN AID IN SEPARATION

The chemical behavior of the elements is greatly altered by changes in valence state and by the formation of non-dissociated ions or mole-cules. Advantage is taken of such changes in a number of analytical methods, many of which have been described in the earlier chapters of this book, especially in volumetric analysis. Such changes are also of great assistance in the processes of effecting separations by precipita-tion, distillation, and extraction.

With the exception of the rare gases, all the elements have at least two valence states if the metallic or elemental form of the element is considered as having a valence of zero. The elemental form of the elements is usually insoluble, so that the applications which can be made of changes in valence state are mostly with elements having two valence states in addition to the valence of zero. The valences of the common elements are given in Table 28, which is arranged according

TABLE 28. VALENCE STATES OF THE COMMON ELEMENTS

Most stable valence state is given first. Other states are listed in the order of their interest in analytical chemistry. All the elements can exist in the elemental state; where a valence of zero is indicated the analytical chemistry is often concerned with the element in the elemental form.

Hydrogen	+1		Iron	+3, +2
			Cobalt	+2, +3
Lithium	+1		Nickel	+2
Sodium	+1		Palladium	+2
Potassium	+1		Platinum	+4, +2
Beryllium	+2		Copper	+2, +1, 0
Magnesium	+2		Silver	+1, 0
Calcium	+2			
Strontium	+2		Zinc	+2, 0
Barium	+2		Cadmium	+2, 0
			Mercury	+2, +1, 0
Boron	+3			
Aluminum	+3		Thallium	+1, +3
Rare earths	+3			
			Tin	+2, +4, 0
Carbon	+4, +2		Lead	+2, +4
Silicon	+4			
Titanium	+4, +3		Arsenic	+5, +3, −3
			Antimony	+5, +3, −3
Nitrogen	−3, +5, +3, 0, +2,		Bismuth	+3, +5
	−1, −2			
Phosphorus	+5, +3, +1, −3		Selenium	+4, +6, −2
			Tellurium	+4, +6, −2
Oxygen	−2, 0, −1			
Sulfur	+6, −2, 0, +4, +2		Fluorine	−1
Chromium	+6, +3, +2		Chlorine	−1, +1, +3, +5,
Molybdenum	+6, +3, +5			+7, 0
Tungsten	+6		Bromine	−1, +5, 0
Uranium	+6, +4		Iodine	−1, +1, +5, +7, 0
Manganese	+2, +7, +4, +3,		Helium	0
	+6		Argon	0

to the periodic groupings. The elements of the first, second, and third groups have only one valence in addition to zero. Most of the remaining elements have two or more additional valences and thus a more complicated chemistry, which provides greater opportunity for effecting separations.

A change in valence is the basis of the oxidation-reduction type of volumetric analysis (Chapter 11). Volumetric methods of this class deal primarily with elements having two valences in addition to zero, although a few methods are known in which the titrated materials are taken from the elemental to some other valence state; iodine as a standard solution is the prime example of this, but methods have been devised involving metallic arsenic, metallic mercury, and bromine, chlorine, and oxygen. The preliminary adjustment of the valence state of the substance being determined is an important part of an oxidation-reduction titration, and a considerable section of Chapter 11 is devoted to a discussion of the various agents by which such adjustments could be made and the methods of removing the excess of the reagents used, Table 20. These reagents can also be used for adjusting the valence state of elements being determined by gravimetric and colorimetric methods; and in addition many other reagents can be used because it is generally not necessary in precipitation and colorimetric methods to remove the excess of the reagent. Thus, nitric acid may be used to oxidize ferrous iron to ferric before precipitating ferric hydroxide, and the excess of nitric acid left does no harm. In oxidation-reduction titrations the presence of nitric acid is usually objectionable, and because there is no convenient method of removing it, it is not often used for such preliminary oxidations.

The difference in the properties of iron in the ferrous and ferric states is frequently used in analysis. Thus, aluminum and ferric iron are both precipitated at pH 4 to 4.5 by hydrolysis, forming the hydrated oxides; ferrous iron is not precipitated at this pH, and aluminum can be separated from iron by first reducing the ferric iron. This is most conveniently done with sulfur dioxide or a sulfite; the aluminum hydroxide is then precipitated with phenylhydrazine, a very weak base.

In the determination of silver by precipitation of the chloride, the interference of mercury is eliminated by oxidizing the mercury to the bivalent form.

There are certain properties which may in a sense be associated with particular valence states. The strengths of the metal hydroxides, for example, vary with the valence of the metal; the univalent metals (the alkalies) form the very strong bases, the bivalent metals weaker bases, the trivalent metals still weaker bases, and the quadrivalent metals the weakest bases of all. The pH at which the various hydroxides (hydrated oxides) are precipitated is a measure of this, Table 30.

FORMATION OF NON-DISSOCIATED IONS

The formation of soluble, non-dissociated compounds is an extremely useful way of changing the nature of a metal in solution, often, in effect, of removing it from solution. The use of the formation constant or its reciprocal, the instability constant, in this connection is discussed in Chapter 12 on volumetric analysis involving the formation of non-dissociated substances. The principal agents for forming such non-dissociated ions are now discussed individually.

Cyanide. Probably the most remarkable agent in forming soluble, non-dissociated compounds of the metals is the cyanide ion. It reacts with the bivalent forms of the elements of the transition groups and the groups immediately on either side of it, that is, with elements 24 through 30 (chromium through zinc, see periodic table in rear cover), 42 through 48, and 74 through 80. The formulas of many of these cyanides and their formation constants are given in Table 29.

TABLE 29. THE SLIGHTLY DISSOCIATED IONS
OF VARIOUS METALS WITH CYANIDE

Chromium [a]	$Cr(CN)_6^{-4}$	Molybdenum [d]	$Mo(CN)_6^{-4}$
	$Cr(CN)_6^{-3}$		$Mo(CN)_6^{-3}$
Manganese [a]	$Mn(CN)_6^{-4}$	Palladium	$Pd(CN)_4^{=}$
	$Mn(CN)_6^{-3}$	Silver	$Ag(CN)_2^{-}$
Iron	$Fe(CN)_6^{-4}$		$K_F = 2.6 \times 10^{18}$
	$Fe(CN)_6^{-3}$	Cadmium	$Cd(CN)_4^{=}$
Cobalt [b]	$Co(CN)_6^{-4}$		$K_F = 7.1 \times 10^{16}$
	$Co(CN)_6^{-3}$	Tungsten [d]	$W(CN)_8^{-4}$
Nickel	$Ni(CN)_4^{=}$		$W(CN)_8^{-3}$
Copper [c]	$Cu(CN)_3^{=}$	Gold	$Au(CN)_4^{-}$
	$K_F = 2 \times 10^{27}$	Mercury	$Hg(CN)_4^{=}$
Zinc	$Zn(CN)_4^{=}$		$K_F = 2.5 \times 10^{41}$
	$K_F = 8.3 \times 10^{17}$		

[a] The trivalent metal hexacyanides are formed by oxidation of the bivalent hexacyanides but not by the direct action of cyanide on a trivalent metal salt.

[b] Bivalent cobalt reacts with cyanide to form $Co(CN)_6^{-4}$ [or perhaps $Co(CN)_5(H_2O)^{-3}$], which is a powerful reducing agent and rapidly reduces water, liberating hydrogen and forming $Co(CN)_6^{-3}$.

[c] A cyanide compound of cupric copper has only a transient existence owing to the reduction of the copper with formation of cyanogen: $2Cu^{++} + 8CN^{-} = 2Cu(CN)_3^{--} + (CN)_2$.

[d] A large number of cyanides of molybdenum and tungsten in various valence states have been reported.

Several very useful volumetric methods are based on the formation of non-dissociated cyanide-metal ions; the determination of cyanide itself, and of silver, copper, nickel, and cobalt.

In electroplating, several of the metals give better deposits from their cyanide derivatives; this is particularly true of silver and cadmium.

Tartaric Acid. Citric Acid. Tartaric and citric acids behave about alike in forming very slightly dissociated compounds with ferric iron, aluminum, trivalent chromium, and copper. The compounds are so stable that none of the metals is precipitated as the hydroxide on making the solutions alkaline.

Use is made of this in the determination of nickel in iron and steel. Nickel dimethylglyoxime is only precipitated from a neutral solution, and tartrate is added to keep the iron, aluminum, and chromium in solution.

Phosphoric Acid. Pyrophosphoric Acid. In acid solution ferric iron reacts with phosphoric acid and with pyrophosphoric acid, forming colorless, non-dissociated ions. These ions are sufficiently stable so that the yellow color of a solution of ferric chloride in hydrochloric acid disappears on the addition of phosphate or pyrophosphate. Iron when tied up in these ions will not oxidize iodide to iodine; use is made of this in certain indirect iodometric processes to eliminate interference by iron.

Fluoride. The fluoride ion forms slightly dissociated ions with a number of the metals, and advantage is taken of this in certain analytical methods.

The compound of ferric iron and fluoride is not so stable that it prevents the precipitation of ferric hydroxide on the addition of ammonia, but it does reduce the concentration of ferric ions present sufficiently that the oxidation of iodide to free iodine does not occur. Use is made of this fact in the iodometric method for copper.

Aluminum also unites with fluoride; the mineral cryolite is K_3AlF_6, and presumably the ion in solution is AlF_6^{-3}.

Stannic salts and fluoride form a very slightly dissociated ion which is not decomposed by hydrogen sulfide; use is made of this fact in the separation of arsenic and antimony from tin by precipitation as the sulfides.

Oxalic Acid. Stannic tin and oxalate form a very stable complex ion from which the tin is not precipitated by hydrogen sulfide.

1,10-*Phenanthroline.* The organic base 1,10-phenanthroline combines with certain metals by secondary valence bonds.[1]   The combination of 1,10-phenanthroline with iron is of particular interest.

$$Fe^{++} + 3 \text{ 1,10-phenanthroline} = [Fe(1,10\text{-phenanthroline})_3]^{++}$$

This red, ferrous compound is highly colored and its formation is a sensitive qualitative test for iron and one of the best colorimetric methods known for iron.   It is oxidized reversibly to a blue ferric compound and thus serves as an oxidation-reduction indicator.   The perchlorate of the ferrous 1,10-phenanthroline ion is sufficiently insoluble that it may be used for the gravimetric determination of perchlorate.   The concentration of ferrous iron in a solution of ferrous 1,10-phenanthroline is so small that aluminum can be precipitated as aluminum hydroxide in its presence without carrying with it a trace of iron.

Bipyridyl,

behaves toward ferrous iron in a manner quite similar to 1,10-phenanthroline.

SEPARATION BY PRECIPITATION.
GENERAL CONSIDERATIONS

Various precipitation processes are discussed in Chapter 6 on gravimetric methods.   The precipitation of barium sulfate and of silver chloride are fairly specific for barium and for silver; in both methods other metals interfere, but their number is quite limited.   The precipitation of calcium as the oxalate, however, is hardly specific for calcium at all, and the same is true of the determination of magnesium by precipitation as magnesium ammonium phosphate.

There is no definite order in which the various separation methods are employed in quantitative analysis as there is in qualitative analysis. In part this is due to the limited complexity of the materials which are commonly analyzed quantitatively and in part to the number of methods which can be called on for limited but specific uses.   Thus, brass and bronze will usually contain copper, zinc, tin, and lead, and the common method of analysis takes into consideration only these metals.   Again, limestone is essentially a carbonate of calcium and

[1] Valence bonds of this type are two-electron, non-ionic bonds in which the two electrons shared by a metal and another atom, usually nitrogen, are contributed by the second atom.   Unlike the ionic bond in salts such as sodium chloride, such bonds are not broken when the material is dissolved in water.   In the older literature such bonds are referred to as *coordination valence* or *secondary valence*.   The coordination compounds which involve this type of valence are very numerous.

magnesium with impurities of silica, iron, and aluminum; the customary method of analysis is designed to determine each of these elements, but it disregards the alkali metals, the titanium, the sulfate, the organic matter, and other elements which are often present in small amounts. Roughly, the order in which the separations are made in a quantitative analysis is that of the qualitative-analysis scheme, but the only really fixed part of this sequence of operations is that the silica, or more generally the acid-insoluble group, is taken out first. From there on the attack varies with the nature of the material. The group separations, that is, the precipitation of the insoluble chlorides, the acid sulfides, the weak bases, and so on, are commonly employed, but usually not all of them in any one analysis nor necessarily always in the order or the manner of the qualitative-analysis scheme.

In general it is best not to load up the solution with foreign electrolytes. They are adsorbed on some precipitates and increase the solubility of others. Sometimes it is even necessary to interrupt an analysis to destroy ammonium salts or to remove acids which may have accumulated.

Inasmuch as each precipitation carries with it some undesired material, and thus causes low results in the remaining determinations, specific methods are preferred to methods involving separations. The rule is to use as many samples for direct determinations and to employ as few separations as possible.

THE ACID-INSOLUBLE GROUP

Strong acids are highly ionized in aqueous solution; weak acids are only slightly ionized, and the very weak acids are not only not ionized at all but break up readily into water and oxide. Carbonic acid is an example of a very weak acid, decomposing readily into water and carbon dioxide. The acids of certain of the metals, notably silicon, tin, and tungsten, also decompose in such fashion, and advantage is taken of these reactions for the isolation and determination of these elements. Inasmuch as this breakdown of very weak acids occurs as soon as an alkali metal salt of one of these acids is acidified with a strong acid, the precipitation of its metal oxides is always the first separation made in an analysis. In the analysis of a silicate rock, for example, silica is invariably the first element removed.

On acidifying a solution of a silicate, silicic acid is formed and decomposes in part, precipitating hydrated silica, $SiO_2 \cdot xH_2O$. The precipitation is made complete only by a dehydration process which removes the water from the soluble silicic acid. Three methods are available for doing this: evaporation to dryness with hydrochloric acid, evaporation followed by boiling with concentrated sulfuric acid, and evaporation followed by boiling with concentrated perchloric acid. The precipitate of silica obtained is gelatinous and adsorbs considerable amounts of foreign materials. The impure precipitate first obtained is treated with hydrofluoric acid, which volatilizes away the silica as silicon tetrafluoride, and the residue of impurities is weighed. The details of the dehydration and purification are found in the discussion of the determination of silica, Chapter 6.

The precipitates of metastannic acid, H_2SnO_3, and tungstic oxide, WO_3, have the same general characteristics as the silica formed by acidifying a solution of a soluble silicate. Precipitation is only complete after a dehydration, the precipitate is colloidal and gelatinous and adsorbs badly, and the ignited oxide first obtained must be subjected to a purification process to obtain a more accurate result.

The gravimetric determination of tin is described in detail in connection with the analysis of brass, Chapter 16. One purification process involves volatilizing the tin as stannic iodide by heating the impure stannic oxide with ammonium iodide.

PRECIPITATION AS CHLORIDE

Three of the metals form chlorides which are sufficiently insoluble for quantitative work: silver, mercury (univalent), and bismuth. Lead chloride is sparingly soluble and is not used for the determination of lead.

The conditions for the determination of silver, particularly the effect of light on the precipitate of silver chloride and the manner in which the results are affected, are discussed in Chapter 6. Interference by mercury in the determination of silver is avoided by oxidizing the mercury to the mercuric form. Bismuth does not interfere if the solution is kept sufficiently acid to prevent the precipitation of bismuthyl chloride and a reprecipitation is made. Silver and lead are better separated by precipitating the lead as phosphate from an ammoniacal solution containing tartrate than by taking advantage of the solubility of lead chloride in hot water.

Mercurous chloride is precipitated in much the same manner as silver chloride, a mild reducing agent such as phosphorous acid being added if the mercury is in the mercuric form. Mercurous chloride is sufficiently volatile at 100° that it cannot be properly dried, and it is best to convert the mercury to another form for weighing: precipitation as mercuric sulfide from an alkaline tartrate solution, for example.

Bismuth is precipitated as bismuthyl chloride, BiOCl, by adding chloride to a solution of a bismuth salt slightly acidified with nitric or perchloric acid. The precipitate is dried at 105° and weighed as bismuthyl chloride.

PRECIPITATION WITH HYDROGEN SULFIDE

Separations involving precipitation with hydrogen sulfide are avoided whenever possible. Precipitates of metal sulfides are often seriously affected by the coprecipitation of other metals: they are always contaminated with free sulfur if formed from an acid solution; they can be weighed directly in only a few cases; and precipitation with hydrogen sulfide is sometimes incomplete, short of several treatments. The separation of certain elements is possible in no other way, however, than by a sulfide precipitation.

The metals which are precipitated from acid solution by hydrogen sulfide are, in the order of their increasing solubility: arsenic, molybdenum, silver, copper, antimony, bismuth, mercury, gold, platinum, tin, cadmium, and lead. These metals constitute the *acid hydrogen sulfide group*. Precipitation of these metals as the sulfide is used to remove them from other metals which are not precipitated from acid solution. The sulfide precipitation of cadmium is about the only way cadmium can be separated from zinc. The precipitation is made from a solution 3 to 4 N in sulfuric acid. The process is rather troublesome, for the precipitation is complete only when the treatment with hydrogen sulfide is repeated once or twice. The cadmium sulfide is converted to cadmium sulfate by treatment with sulfuric acid for weighing.

Zinc is precipitated as zinc sulfide from a solution of pH 2.5 buffered with formic acid and ammonium formate. Zinc is separated in this manner from manganese, iron, nickel, aluminum, chromium, and the alkali and alkaline-earth metals, but not from cobalt.

Cobalt and nickel may be precipitated as sulfides from a solution buffered with acetate; this process separates them from iron, aluminum, chromium, manganese, calcium, and magnesium, but not from zinc.

Mercury is one of the few elements weighed as the sulfide. It may be precipitated from an alkaline solution containing tartrate as mercuric sulfide, filtered off, dried at 110°, and weighed directly. Free sulfur is not formed from an alkaline solution. The mercury must first be separated by some other method from metals forming insoluble sulfides.

THE PRECIPITATION OF HYDRATED OXIDES

The hydroxides of the various metals vary greatly in their strengths as bases. On the one hand are the very strong bases such as sodium hydroxide and potassium hydroxide, the caustic alkalies which are soluble and highly ionized in water. On the other hand are the tri-valent and quadrivalent metal hydroxides, such as aluminum hy-droxide, ferric hydroxide, and titanium hydroxide, which are hardly hydroxides at all but hydrated oxides; they are insoluble and give up water so easily that their composition is more accurately expressed as $Al_2O_3 \cdot xH_2O$, $Fe_2O_3 \cdot xH_2O$, and $TiO_2 \cdot xH_2O$. Between these two extremes, the strong bases and the very weakly basic hydrated oxides, fall the hydroxides of the various common metals. It is convenient to arrange the metals on the pH scale on the basis of the pH at which they are precipitated as hydroxides (Table 30). The material actually

TABLE 30.   THE pH AT WHICH METAL HYDROXIDES OR BASIC
SALTS ARE PRECIPITATED

Metal	pH	Metal	pH
Titanium	2	Cadmium	6.7
Ferric	2.3	Cobalt	6.8
Stannous	3	Mercuric	7.4
Aluminum	4.1	Manganous	8.5
Zinc	5.2	Silver	9
Chromic	5.3	Magnesium	10.5
Cupric	5.4	Barium $\rbrace$ sparingly soluble	
Ferrous	5.5	Calcium	
Lead	6.0	Potassium $\rbrace$ soluble	
Nickel	6.7	Sodium	

precipitated in many cases is not a hydroxide or hydrated oxide but a basic salt; for example, on raising the pH of a solution of cadmium sulfate, the precipitate formed actually has the composition $Cd_4(OH)_6$-$SO_4 \cdot xH_2O$. The pH values given in Table 30 therefore vary some-what, depending on the anion present.

The variation in the pH at which the metals are precipitated as hydroxides or basic salts makes it possible to effect certain separation of one element from another by proper adjustment of the pH of the solution; thus titanium can be separated from aluminum and ferrous iron; aluminum and ferric iron from the bivalent metals cobalt, nickel, and cadmium; the bivalent metals from magnesium. Although pri-marily the problem is simply one of regulating pH the matter is not quite so simple. Coprecipitation is especially serious because of the gelatinous nature of the precipitates, and the anion present has a greater effect on the physical character of the precipitate than might be anticipated.

The simple addition of a base to a solution containing ions of the metals which might be expected to yield a separation leads to sur-prisingly poor results. Ferric iron and copper are precipitated at pH values far enough apart (Table 30, pH 2 to 3 and 5.4, respectively) that a separation appears feasible by simply adding ammonium hydroxide until the pH of the solution reaches 4 to 4.5. Unfortunately, where the drop of ammonium hydroxide strikes the solution there is a region of high pH, and at this spot the pH is high enough to precipitate both ferric and cupric hydroxides. Because of the gelatinous character of the precipitates, the cupric hydroxide surrounded by ferric hydroxide does not redissolve completely when stirred up into the main body of the solution even though the pH of the solution is well below that at which cupric hydroxide is precipitated. An obvious solution to this particular difficulty is reprecipitation; that is, the ferric hydroxide formed can be filtered off and dissolved in hydrochloric acid and the precipitation repeated, less copper being present in the solution during the second precipitation. Inherently, however, the process is so poor that copper remains in the iron even after three such reprecipitations.

A better approach to the problem consists in adjusting the pH of the solution by a reaction which takes place within the solution to liberate a base. The local high concentration of hydroxyl is then avoided. One way of doing this is to use the decomposition of urea in a boiling solution, $CO(NH_2)_2 + 2H_2O = H_2O + CO_2 + 2NH_3$. Carbon dioxide is driven off, and the liberated ammonia raises the pH of the solution. This procedure works out ideally for aluminum, separating it cleanly from copper, cobalt, zinc, and the metals precipitating above pH 5. Because the precipitate formed in this manner is a basic salt rather than simple, hydrated aluminum oxide, the nature of the anion present determines the characteristics of the precipitate. From chloride solutions the precipitate obtained is gelatinous and bulky like the aluminum hydroxide obtained by precipitation with ammonia; from solutions containing sulfate, and especially succinate, the precipitate is crystalline and dense, settles rapidly, and adsorbs foreign materials only slightly. The combination of slow precipitation from a homogeneous solution plus the selection of the proper anion affords an excellent method for the separation and determination of aluminum.

PRECIPITATION AS OXALATE

The oxalates of practically all the metals except the alkalies and ammonium are insoluble in slightly acid or neutral solution. Thorium oxalate is less soluble in hydrochloric acid than any other oxalate and is used to separate thorium from titanium and zirconium. Trivalent cerium and the other rare earths are also quite insoluble in hydrochloric acid solution and are removed from solution as oxalates. The most common of the oxalate precipitation methods is the separation and determination of calcium, discussed in detail in Chapter 6. Such precipitation is used to separate calcium from the alkali metals magnesium and barium. The separation from magnesium is only successful when the calcium oxalate is filtered within a few hours after precipitation. Strontium is completely precipitated with calcium as the oxalate.

Because the metal oxalates can be dissolved in dilute sulfuric acid, the oxalic acid titrated with permanganate, and the determination thus completed volumetrically, precipitation as oxalate has been a favorite method for determining the elements. Zinc and thorium, for which no particularly good, direct volumetric methods are known, are commonly determined this way.

PRECIPITATION AS PHOSPHATE OR DOUBLE PHOSPHATE

Excluding the alkali metals, the phosphates of all the metals are insoluble in slightly acid or neutral solution. With three exceptions, zirconium, aluminum, and bismuth, precipitation as phosphate is little used for separating the metals from each other. Most of the metal phosphates are of rather indefinite composition and not good forms for weighing.

Zirconium is precipitated as the phosphate from very acid solution, 10 per cent in sulfuric acid, as zirconyl hydrogen phosphate, $ZrOHPO_4$. This affords a separation of zirconium from all metals but quadrivalent cerium and titanium. When ignited the precipitate has the approximate composition ZrP_2O_7.

Aluminum is sometimes precipitated as the phosphate from a solution buffered with acetate. If thiosulfate is first added to reduce iron to the ferrous state, such precipitation gives a fair separation of aluminum from iron. The precipitate is ignited and weighed as aluminum phosphate, $AlPO_4$.

Bismuth is precipitated as the phosphate from a hot, acid solution by adding phosphoric acid and then trisodium phosphate until the solution has a pH of 7.0. The precipitate is ignited and weighed as bismuth phosphate. This method separates bismuth from silver, copper, cadmium, mercury, aluminum, zinc, and the alkali and alkaline-earth metals.

Certain bivalent metals are precipitated as double ammonium phosphates from neutral solution and on ignition give pyrophosphates of definite composition which are good forms for weighing. The elements which are handled in this manner are magnesium, manganese, zinc, cadmium, cobalt, and beryllium. Beryllium phosphate is not as definite in composition as could be desired, but for the other metals the method is about the best known. The details of the pyrophosphate method are given under the determination of magnesium, Chapter 6, and zinc, Chapter 16. In none of the six metals mentioned is precipitation as the double ammonium phosphate a separation from any metals but the alkalies. The double ammonium phosphates of magnesium and manganese are insoluble in solutions containing an excess of ammonia. The other metals mentioned must be precipitated from solutions which are practically neutral. In general the double metal ammonium phosphates are filtered, washed, dried, and ignited to their pyrophosphates, $M_2P_2O_7$.

CHEMICAL REDUCTION TO THE METAL

The metals at the positive end of the reduction-potential series are easily reduced to the metal. Gold, platinum, silver, and mercury are reduced by mild reducing agents and are commonly separated from other metals in this fashion. Bismuth, antimony, and copper require strong reducing agents for their reduction to the metal, and the metals between copper and zinc are best reduced to the metal from aqueous solution by the action of the electric current.

Gold is reduced to the metal by hydroquinone, a mild reducing agent which does not reduce copper or bismuth. Silver if present with the gold must be precipitated previously as the chloride.

Hypophosphorous acid, H_3PO_2, a powerful reducing agent, reduces all the metals mentioned including copper, antimony, and bismuth.

Gold, silver, and platinum when precipitated as the metal can be ignited and weighed as the metal. Mercury can be weighed as the metal but must be dried at room temperature with acetone or alcohol to avoid loss by volatilization. Copper, antimony, and bismuth are best redissolved and converted to other forms for weighing.

The deposition of metals by electrolysis is taken up in detail in Chapter 15.

DIMETHYLGLYOXIME

$$\begin{array}{c} H_3C\!-\!C\!-\!C\!-\!CH_3 \\ \| \quad \| \\ N \quad N \\ \diagup \qquad \diagdown \\ OH \qquad\quad OH \end{array}$$

Nickel is quantitatively precipitated by dimethylglyoxime from very weakly acid or ammoniacal solution as a scarlet compound of striking color and definite composition. Palladium also is precipitated by dimethylglyoxime as a yellow compound, from solutions as strongly acid as pH 1. Dimethylglyoxime acts as a monobasic acid in the formation of these metallic derivatives, 2 molecules uniting with 1 atom of the metal. The second oxime group also becomes attached to the metal by secondary valence forces, forming a ring structure:

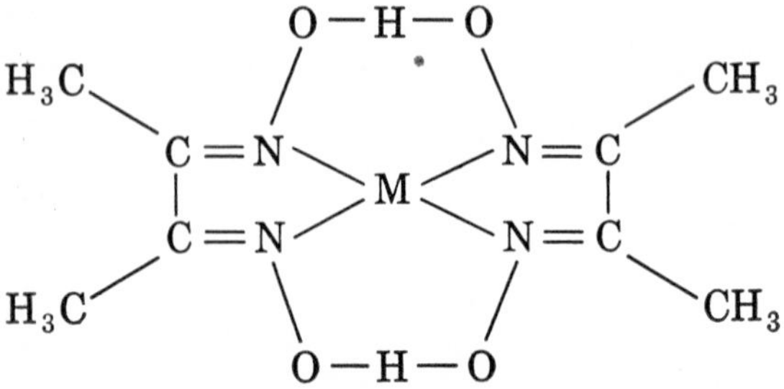

Nickel is almost invariably determined by precipitation with dimethylglyoxime. Inasmuch as the precipitation must be carried out in a neutral solution, the weak bases such as ferric iron and aluminum, which are precipitated as hydroxides, interfere. Such interference by ferric iron and aluminum can be avoided by the addition of tartaric acid which forms stable, complex ions with these metals, keeping them from precipitating as the hydroxides. Nickel can be separated from large amounts of iron in this way, and this is the usual method for the determination of nickel in steel. Cobalt forms a soluble compound with dimethylglyoxime, and sufficient reagent must be added to combine with both the cobalt and the nickel. Curiously, cobalt and ferric iron when present together give a red precipitate with dimethylglyoxime; if the iron is reduced to the ferrous state, this material does not form. Large amounts of copper also interfere in the determination of nickel with dimethylglyoxime. With the exceptions just mentioned the precipitation of nickel from an ammoniacal tartrate solution is specific and serves to separate nickel from practically all the metals, including chromium, manganese, zinc, cadmium, and the alkali and alkaline-earth metals.

The nickel dimethylglyoxime precipitate is rather bulky, and in general the amount of nickel being precipitated should not exceed 40 or 50 mg. The nickel and palladium derivatives of dimethylglyoxime are anhydrous, dried at 110°, and weighed directly.

CUPFERRON

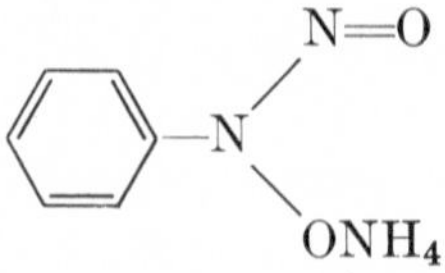

The ammonium salt of nitrosophenylhydroxylamine, known as cupferron, yields insoluble compounds with a number of metals. Ferric iron, tin, and titanium are precipitated quantitatively from solutions containing 5 to 10 parts by volume of sulfuric or hydrochloric acid. Copper, mercury, bismuth, and certain other metals are precipitated from more weakly acid solutions.

One of the principal uses of cupferron is the removal of ferric iron prior to the determination of aluminum. The cupferron precipitates are of rather indefinite composition and must be ignited to the metal oxide for weighing.

A 6 per cent solution of cupferron is used as reagent; it should be made up fresh when needed as the solution does not keep for more than a few days. Precipitation is always made in the cold as cupferron is decomposed when heated. Precipitation may be made from hydrochloric, perchloric, or sulfuric acid solutions but not from solutions containing nitric acid, as cupferron is rapidly attacked by oxidizing agents. The precipitates should be filtered fairly promptly, using filter-paper pulp to aid the digestion. The excess cupferron in the filtrate may easily be destroyed by oxidation with nitric acid.

8-HYDROXYQUINOLINE (OXINE)

The common name *oxine* has been applied to 8-hydroxyquinoline, which is a useful reagent for the precipitation of various metals. 8-Hydroxyquinoline is selective in its action rather than specific. Certain metals, of which the common ones are ferric iron, aluminum, titanium, copper, zinc, cadmium, cobalt, and nickel, are precipitated by 8-hydroxyquinoline from a solution buffered with acetic acid and ammonium acetate, whereas under these conditions magnesium, lead, the alkali metals, and the alkaline-earth metals are not precipitated. Precipitation of aluminum in this manner is one of the best ways to separate aluminum from beryllium and phosphate. Magnesium is precipitated from an ammoniacal or alkaline solution of pH 9 to 12; large amounts of ammonium salts and of the alkali metal salts do not interfere, making the method particularly good for the determination of magnesium in limestone.

The metal derivatives of 8-hydroxyquinoline are usually crystalline and are frequently hydrated. They may be dried to the anhydrous state for weighing, a temperature of 135 to 150° usually being employed. Some of the metal derivatives may be weighed as hydrates. Magnesium 8-hydroxyquinoline, for example, may be dried at 105 to 110° and weighed as $Mg(C_9H_6NO)_2 \cdot 2H_2O$ or at 130 to 140° and weighed as anhydrous $Mg(C_9H_6NO)_2$.

The precipitates may also be ignited and the metal weighed as oxide. The precipitate is usually covered with a layer of oxalic acid before such an ignition; this assists in burning away the organic material and prevents loss of metal by sublimation of the metal hydroxyquinolate.

There is also a convenient volumetric method for completing the determination. The metal hydroxyquinolate is dissolved in hydrochloric acid, treated with bromine derived from a standard bromate-bromide solution, the excess bromine converted to an equivalent amount of iodine, and the iodine titrated with thiosulfate. The reactions, illustrating with aluminum, are:

$$AlCl_3 + 3C_9H_7NO + 3NH_4OH = Al(C_9H_6NO)_3 + 3NH_4Cl + 3H_2O$$

$$Al(C_9H_6NO)_3 + 3HCl = 3C_9H_7NO + AlCl_3$$

$$KBrO_3 + 5KBr + 6HCl = 2Br^0 + 6KCl + 3H_2O$$

$$C_9H_7NO + 4Br^0 = C_9H_5NOBr_2 + 2HBr$$

$$Br^0(excess) + KI = I^0 + KBr$$

$$2I^0 + 2Na_2S_2O_3 = 2NaI + Na_2S_4O_6$$

Twelve atoms of bromine are involved per atom of aluminum in these reactions, so that the equivalent weight of aluminum in this determination is one-twelfth the atomic weight.

Directions for the determination of magnesium by this volumetric 8-hydroxyquinoline procedure are given in the section dealing with bromate oxidations, Chapter 11.

DISTILLATION AND VOLATILIZATION

Separations can often be effected in a convenient and clean-cut manner by evolving some component of the sample as a gas. The process may be carried out on a solid or liquid and may or may not be accompanied by a chemical reaction. Frequently volatilization is used simply to remove a substance which is interfering with another determination.

The Kjeldahl method for the determination of nitrogen, in which ammonia is distilled from a sodium hydroxide solution, collected, and titrated, is a good example of the distillation method. The determination of carbon dioxide in a limestone, in which the carbon dioxide is evolved by treatment with acid and the carbon dioxide absorbed in ascarite and weighed, is another good example.

Adsorbed water or water of crystallization is often determined by heating the material to a sufficiently high temperature and taking the loss in weight as the weight of the water expelled. This is the method employed for the determination of the water of crystallization of hydrated barium chloride, Chapter 6. Water may also be determined by heating the sample in a tube through which a stream of dry air or nitrogen is passing; the gas is then passed through a weighed U-tube containing an absorbent for the water. The actual weight of water is obtained in this manner, and the result may be more nearly correct than the value obtained by the loss in weight method, which may be inexact owing to oxidation of the sample or the simultaneous evolution of carbon dioxide or some other component. In still another method the water is distilled away from the sample by means of a high-boiling, immiscible solvent such as toluene (boiling point 111°) or xylene (boiling point 135 to 140°), both liquids are condensed, and the volume of the water is measured. This method is applied most often to grain and petroleum products.

Boron is separated prior to its determination by the distillation of methyl borate. It is only necessary to add methyl alcohol and sulfuric acid or phosphoric acid to the solution. On heating, methyl borate is formed, which distills over and is collected in a solution of sodium hydroxide. The sodium hydroxide hydrolyzes the ester to boric acid, which can then be determined.

One of the sharpest and most convenient separations of arsenic, antimony, and tin from each other involves a sequence of distillations of the chlorides of these metals. Of the chlorides of these metals, arsenic trichloride is the most volatile. To separate arsenic from antimony and tin by distillation the arsenic is reduced by hydrazine to the trivalent state and the concentrated hydrochloric acid solution distilled in an all-glass distillation flask and condenser. The arsenic chloride is collected in water, and, after the distillation, is determined by titration with bromate. Antimony is distilled by raising the temperature to 160°. In the presence of tin, phosphoric acid is added, which prevents the tin from distilling with the antimony. After the removal of the antimony, the tin is distilled by adding hydrobromic acid and distilling at 140°.

EXTRACTION WITH IMMISCIBLE SOLVENTS

Numerous inorganic materials are soluble in ether, amyl alcohol, and other organic solvents which do not mix with water. Advantage may

be taken of this to separate such substances from others which are not soluble; ferric chloride, for example, may be separated from the chlorides of aluminum, copper, and other elements, and this separation is widely used for the determination of these elements in iron and steel.

Actually, of course, a given material has some solubility in both the immiscible solvent and the water. The substance is distributed between the two solvents, and if the mixture is well shaken up a definite ratio is always reached for the concentrations of the substance in the two liquids. This ratio is known as the *distribution coefficient* and is defined by the expression

$$K = C_s/C_w$$

in which C_s and C_w represent the concentrations in the immiscible solvent and water, respectively.

The distribution coefficient of ferric chloride between ether and water (the water containing hydrochloric acid and the ether saturated with hydrochloric acid) is 99. An equal volume of ether shaken up with a water solution containing ferric chloride will extract 99 per cent of the ferric chloride. If the layers are separated and a second portion of ether added, 99 per cent of the remaining ferric chloride will be extracted.

Fig. 84.   Separatory funnel.

Since the concentration of the substance in the immiscible solvent occurs in the numerator of the expression defining the distribution coefficient, extractions are more complete for higher numerical values of the distribution coefficient. Extraction is more effective from a concentrated aqueous solution than from a dilute solution.

Extractions are usually carried out in a separatory funnel, Fig. 84, which tapers toward the stopcock so that the meniscus becomes smaller as the lower layer is drained away, and a sharp separation of the two layers can be made.

The effectiveness of the separation increases directly with the volume of the immiscible solvent and with the power of the number of extractions made. The expression defining the distribution coefficient may be written in terms of the amounts of the substance extracted and the volumes of the liquids:

$$K = \frac{C_s}{C_w} = \frac{\dfrac{W_0 - W}{V_s}}{\dfrac{W}{V_w}}$$

W_0 being the weight of the substance originally present, W the weight remaining in the water layer, and V_s and V_w the volumes of solvent and water, respectively. $W_0 - W$ is the weight of substance passing into the immiscible solvent. For the first extraction, then, the weight of substance remaining unextracted is W_1, which may be obtained by solving the above equation

$$K = \frac{\dfrac{W_0 - W_1}{V_s}}{\dfrac{W_1}{V_w}} = \frac{V_w}{V_s} \frac{W_0 - W_1}{W_1}$$

$$K \frac{V_s}{V_w} = \frac{W_0}{W_1} - 1$$

$$W_1 = W_0 \left[\frac{V_w}{KV_s + V_w} \right]$$

In the second extraction

$$W_2 = W_1 \left[\frac{V_w}{KV_s + V_w} \right]$$

and so

$$W_2 = W_0 \left[\frac{V_w}{KV_s + V_w} \right] \left[\frac{V_w}{KV_s + V_w} \right]$$

$$= W_0 \left[\frac{V_w}{KV_s + V_w} \right]^2$$

By similar reasoning, the weight of substance remaining in the water layer after n extractions is

$$W_n = W_0 \left[\frac{V_w}{KV_s + V_w} \right]^n$$

This assumes that the same volume of immiscible solvent was used for each extraction.

In addition to ferric chloride, the chlorides of trivalent gold, gallium, thallium, and hexavalent molybdenum are extracted by ether. Several other chlorides, notably stannic, stannous, antimonic, and arsenious, are quite soluble in ether. The extent of such extraction for a number of metal chlorides is shown in Table 31. The maximum extraction of

TABLE 31. EXTRACTION OF METAL CHLORIDES
WITH DIETHYL ETHER

Metal	Per Cent Extracted	Metal	Per Cent Extracted
Al	0	$Fe(Fe^{III})$	99
$Sb(Sb^{III})$	2	$Fe(Fe^{II})$	0
$Sb(Sb^{V})$	100	Pb	0
	6.5–8.5 M HCl	Mn	0
$As(As^{III})$	68	$Hg(Hg^{II})$	0–2
$As(As^{V})$	2–4	$Mo(Mo^{VI})$	80–90
Be	0		100 with Fe^{III}
Bi	0	Ni	0
Ca	0	$P(H_3PO_4)$	12–27
Cd	0	Ag	0
Cr	0	Th	0
Co	0	$Tl(Tl^{III})$	90–95
Cu	0.05	$Sn(Sn^{IV})$	17
Ga	97	$Sn(Sn^{II})$	15–30
Ge	40–60	Ti	0
$Au(Au^{III})$	95	Zn	0.2

ferric chloride by ether occurs when the aqueous solution is 6.2 N in hydrochloric acid; the distribution coefficient at this acidity is about 140. The substance which is actually extracted is probably not ferric chloride but tetrachloroferric acid, $HFeCl_4$. The extraction of ferric chloride is used widely for removing the iron from a large sample of iron or steel for the determination of minor elements such as aluminum, titanium, and copper. Not all the iron is removed, for some ferric chloride is reduced by light in the presence of ether and escapes extraction. Ferrous chloride is not extracted by ether at all.

Isopropyl ether and dichlorodiethyl ether have higher boiling points than common or diethyl ether and are more convenient to work with than diethyl ether. The behavior of the various metal chlorides is about the same in these ethers as in diethyl ether. The hydrochloric acid concentration of the aqueous solution is not as critical as with common ether, and photochemical reduction is less.

REMOVAL OF AMMONIUM SALTS AND OXALATES BY WET OXIDATION

In the complete analysis of some materials, notably limestone and silicate rock, the elements must be determined successively on a single sample. During such a sequence of operations the amount of ammonium salts present in the solution becomes undesirably large because the various reagents and wash solutions are usually added as ammonium salts. In the determination of magnesium, which is usually the last determination made, the presence of large amounts of ammonium salts and of oxalate, added during the calcium determination, is very undesirable. Ammonium salts may be removed by evaporating the solution to dryness and baking the residue at a sufficiently high temperature to volatilize the salts. A better procedure, and the one generally employed, depends on the wet oxidation of the ammonium ion to nitrogen and nitrogen oxides. Nitric acid and hydrochloric acid are added, and the mixture is digested near the boiling point. Usually the operation is combined with an evaporation. If the solution is evaporated to dryness the residue consists of a mixture of the nitrates, chlorides, and other non-volatile acids which may have been present. If ammonium sulfate is treated with nitric acid and hydrochloric acid in this manner, the final residue consists of sulfuric acid. Similarly ammonium perchlorate is converted into perchloric acid. The oxidation of ammonium salts in this fashion is vigorous, and the beaker should be kept well covered and the cover glass raised off it only after the main reaction is over. Occasionally, and only when the conditions happen to be just right, the mixture of ammonium salts and nitric and hydrochloric acids evaporate to moist dryness and ignite, the ammonium salt (probably the nitrate) burning with a brilliant flame; this reaction is startling, but if a cover glass is on the beaker no loss of material results.

Oxalates are rather slowly destroyed by a mixture of nitric acid and hydrochloric acid, and the operation usually must be repeated several times to complete the oxidation. Oxalates are rapidly destroyed by oxidation with perchloric acid. The solution is acidified with perchloric acid and concentrated to the point where constant-boiling perchloric acid (72 per cent $HClO_4$) is present. After this stage the oxalic acid is destroyed in a few minutes. Nitric acid and hydrochloric acid may be present in the solution but are of course removed during the concentration. The residue consists of the perchlorates of the metals present and excess perchloric acid. Sulfuric acid in more than small amounts should not be present.

WET OXIDATION OF ORGANIC MATTER

The destruction of organic material is often necessary before the determination of inorganic components of a material can be carried out. A wet oxidation to remove the organic material is generally preferable to dry combustion, for there is less chance of losing certain elements by volatilization. A mixture of nitric acid and perchloric acid is particularly efficacious for the destruction of organic material. Carbon is oxidized to carbon dioxide, hydrogen and oxygen form water, nitrogen passes to free nitrogen or nitrogen oxides, sulfur goes to sulfuric acid, and the various metals such as iron, aluminum, copper, lead, calcium, magnesium, potassium, and sodium are left in their highest valence states as perchlorates; arsenic, phosphorus, and silica also are retained in the solution.

The mixture used is made up of about equal volumes of concentrated nitric acid (70 per cent HNO_3) and 72 per cent perchloric acid. The sample taken may be small or may amount to 5 or 10 g. or more. At 100° this acid mixture will dissolve cellulose, sugar, protein, collagen, and many other types of organic material. The acid mixture is added to the sample at room temperature and heated gradually. At room temperature, the nitric acid begins the oxidation with the evolution of brown fumes of nitrogen oxides. As the temperature rises, the intensity of the nitric acid oxidation increases, reaching its full effectiveness at 100 to 140°. During this period the more easily oxidized organic matter is smoothly burned away. As the temperature rises further, the nitric acid is boiled away and around 150° the perchloric acid begins its work. As the temperature mounts, the effectiveness of the perchloric acid increases. By the time the temperature reaches 195 to 200° no organic material is left except for a very few unusually resistant types (Teflon, for example). Chromic acid or ammonium vanadate, if it does not interfere with the later operations, may be added to catalyze the oxidation; 20 to 30 mg. of either smooths the oxidation and often cuts in half the time required. In addition, the chromium serves as an indicator to determine when the destruction of the organic material is complete; the chromium remains green until all traces of organic material have been oxidized, and then turns red.

The precautions which should be observed when using perchloric acid are discussed on page 46. A suitable apparatus for preventing acid fumes from poisoning the atmosphere is shown in Fig. 83, page 369.

PROBLEMS

1–16. Devise schemes for the analysis of each alloy. Give the principal steps, indicating the form in which each element is separated, the essential conditions for the separation, and the form in which the element is finally weighed. Make use of the data in Table 9, Chapter 6.

1. Cu (95 per cent), Si	10. Hg, Bi
2. Cu, Sn	11. Zn, Al, Sn
3. Ag, Si	12. Zn, Ni, Mg
4. Sn, Pb	13. Mg (90 per cent), Al,
5. Ag, Mn, Al	Mn (0.1 per cent)
6. Ag, Sn, Zn	14. Cu, Ni
7. Ag, Cd, Zn	15. Cu, Co, Ni
8. Bi, Sn	16. Al (99 per cent), Cu, Fe
9. Hg, Mg, Cd	

17. Outline a scheme for the determination of small amounts of copper and aluminum in electrolytic iron in which no carbon, silicon, or phosphorus is present.

18. Eyeglass frames are commonly made by wrapping a solid covering of gold ribbon around a core of iron-nickel wire. Give the steps in a scheme of analysis of such a material.

19. Outline a scheme for the analysis of the mineral calamine, a zinc silicate ($ZnSiO_3$) containing small amounts of iron and calcium, which is soluble in hydrochloric acid.

20. The distribution coefficient of ferric chloride between 6.2 N hydrochloric acid and ether is 140. Calculate the amount of iron remaining after the first and second extractions under the following conditions, assuming that no photochemical reduction of the ferric chloride occurs: 1.000 g. of iron present as ferric chloride in 50.0 ml. of 6.2 N hydrochloric acid, 50.0 ml. of ether used in each extraction.

21. Outline the steps in the determination of the silica, iron, and calcium in a sample of seed.

CHAPTER 15

Electrodeposition

The electrochemical theory presented in Chapter 10 deals mainly with single-electrode potentials, cells at equilibrium, indicator and reference electrodes, and reaction constants. In general, the study referred only to equilibrium conditions (the potentials after the substances had been given time to interact), and in general no current was passed through the cell other than the intentionally negligible amounts needed for the operation of the potentiometer. Now we approach the problem from a new viewpoint and study the effects produced by deliberately putting a considerable quantity of electricity through the cell. It will be assumed that Chapter 10 dealing with electrochemical theory has already been mastered. References will be made to the tables of standard reduction potentials given on pages 20 and 236.

One of the effects of electrolysis, the electrodeposition of a metal on the cathode, turns out to be quite useful, for if done properly the metal may be completely removed from the solution in a form suitable for weighing. As in most analytical methods, however, there are difficulties and limitations. Not all the metallic elements can be determined by electrodeposition; indeed, not even all the metals positive to hydrogen in the reduction potential series. A few can be determined with great accuracy, but a number which ought to deposit nicely fail to do so in a most exasperating manner.

The electrical circuit and apparatus required are shown in Fig. 85. The direct current from the battery can be adjusted by the variable resistance R. The voltage applied to the cell and the current passing are measured by the meters V and A, respectively. The electrodes are cylinders of platinum gauze. The glass stirring rod is driven by a motor not shown in the figure. The metal is deposited at the negative electrode. For example, in the determination of copper a solution containing cupric sulfate, ammonium nitrate, and a little nitric acid is used as electrolyte. The reaction taking place at the cathode is $Cu^{++} + 2e^{-} = Cu^{0}$. The electrons enter the cell from the external circuit and react with the cupric ions to form metallic copper. At the anode oxygen is evolved and the electrons leave the solution by way of the positive electrode. The overall cell reaction, obtained by adding

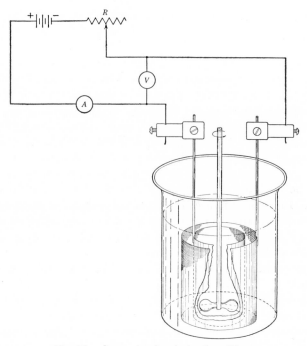

Fig. 85. Apparatus for electrodeposition.

together the reactions at the cathode and anode in such a manner that the electrons cancel,

$$Cu^{++} + 2e^- = Cu^0$$

$$H_2O - 2e^- = \tfrac{1}{2}O_2 + 2H^+$$

$$\overline{Cu^{++} + H_2O = Cu^0 + \tfrac{1}{2}O_2 + 2H^+}$$

amounts to the replacement of copper ions by hydrogen ions. If the conditions are adjusted properly all the copper can be plated out and the electrode removed from the solution, dried, and weighed.

A few metals are oxidized to higher oxides and deposited on the anode. Lead is the only element commonly determined in this way.

The flow of electricity through the wire and the electrodes consists in the movement of electrons through the metal, the electrons leaving the electrolytic cell at the anode and returning via the cathode. In the solution itself the current is conducted by the ions present in the solution, the positively charged ions of hydrogen and copper moving toward the negatively charged electrode (*cations* because they are attracted to the cathode) and the negatively charged ions, sulfate, nitrate, and hydroxyl, moving toward the positive electrode (*anions* because they are attracted to the anode). Ions are much bigger than electrons, and the resistance to their movement is much greater; the electrical resistance to the electrolytic type of conduction which occurs in solution is much greater than that toward the metallic conduction which occurs in a wire.

Apparatus. Electrodes and Stirring. Platinum electrodes are almost invariably used in electroanalytical work because of their resistance to chemical attack. The most satisfactory form for the cathode is a cylinder of platinum gauze made of sufficiently heavy wire to be mechanically strong. The form of the anode is less important. In some apparatus it is a second cylinder of platinum gauze which can be rotated to stir the solution; in others it is a stationary platinum foil or spiral of wire, and the stirring is accomplished with a mechanically driven glass stirring rod.

Vigorous mechanical stirring is essential. With effective stirring higher currents can be used and the time required for the electrolysis correspondingly reduced. A rotating platinum anode provides satisfactory stirring if ruggedly built and driven with sufficient speed; such an electrode is easily bent, however, and a rotating glass rod is usually more effective and less trouble. The stirring should throw the solution sideways through the gauze electrodes rather than move it up and down parallel to the surface of the electrodes. If the stirring is poor the solution next to the cathode becomes depleted in metal ions and the polarization becomes greater. If hydrogen is liberated simultaneously with the deposition of metal in such cases, the metal deposit is often spongy, adheres poorly to the electrode, and is easily detached.

Direct current is, of course, required for an electrodeposition. Direct current can be obtained from a storage battery, a motor-generator set, or a dry-plate rectifier.

A variable resistance in the external circuit is convenient for adjusting the potential applied to the cell.

Definition of Terms. The meanings of such terms as *single-electrode potential, electrolytic cell, electrode reaction, and reduction potential* are given in Chapter 10. A few more terms must be defined in order to describe accurately the phenomena which occur when a current is passed through a cell. The *cathode* is that electrode at which reduction occurs; the *anode* is that electrode at which oxidation occurs. These definitions hold, irrespective of whether the cell itself is generating the current or being driven in reverse by the application of a greater potential. Which of the two electrodes is the cathode and which the anode is determined by the manner in which the cell is operating, but in either operation the chemical reduction which takes place does so at the *cathode* and the concomitant oxidation goes on at the *anode*.

As in all natural phenomena as soon as a force is exerted an opposing force arises. In the case of a reaction at an electrode this phenomenon takes the form of a depletion or an accumulation of material in the neighborhood of the electrode, which tends to make the process more difficult. If copper is being deposited at the cathode, the copper ions in the layer immediately surrounding the electrode are removed and in accord with the electrode-potential equation the electrode potential is shifted in the negative direction so that a greater potential is required to maintain the current. This effect is termed *polarization,* and the potential which is developed is termed the *polarization potential.* If a gas is being evolved at the electrode, the polarization potential is several times greater than that arising when the electrode reaction involves only a metal and its ions. Such polarization is then spoken of as *overvoltage.* Inasmuch as the constituents of water appear at the electrodes as gases, overvoltage is a matter of great importance. More precisely, *polarization* (and *overvoltage*) is the departure of a single electrode potential from the value given by the electrode-potential equation, which results from the flow of current.

The Laws of Electrolysis. The laws governing the quantities of materials and electricity involved in the passage of current through a cell can be summarized in a single equation

$$G = \frac{1}{F} It \frac{M}{n}$$

in which G is the weight in grams, I is the current in amperes, t is the time in seconds, M is the molecular weight, n is the number of electrons involved in the electrode reaction, and F is the faraday. Thus, the weight of material reacting at the electrode is proportional to the current and also to the time. The term M/n is the electrochemical equivalent weight. For a given quantity of electricity, the weight of material reacting is directly proportional to the electrochemical equivalent weight. The term $1/F$ is the proportionality constant; its numerical value is 96,500 coulombs per electrochemical equivalent. Thus, in the deposition of copper from a solution of cupric sulfate, $Cu^{++} + 2e^- = Cu^0$, two electrons are required, $n = 2$, and the electrochemical equivalent weight is one-half the atomic weight of copper, or $63.54/2 = 31.77$. The deposition of 1 g. electrochemical equivalent weight requires the passage of 96,500 coulombs. One ampere is equal to the passage of 1 coulomb for 1 second, so that 96,500 amp.-sec. are required to deposit 1 g. electrochemical equivalent weight. The deposition of 31.77 g. of copper then requires a current of 1 amp. flowing for 96,500 seconds (approximately 26.8 hours).

In chemical analysis by electrodeposition the current efficiency is of secondary interest, although in commercial electroplating it is a matter of considerable importance. In analytical work an attempt is made to deposit every bit of the metal. Toward the end of the process especially, conditions are such that other reactions occur at the cathode, such as the formation of hydrogen or the reduction of nitrate to ammonia. The laws of electrolysis still hold, there being apparently no exceptions to them, but the current is simply used in part for the side reactions. In electroanalysis a good deal more current must be passed than that necessary to deposit solely the metal.

Cathode Reaction. When several reducible ions are present in the solution, the ion having the most positive reduction potential will be reduced first. Thus, if a solution containing potassium permanganate, silver nitrate, and copper nitrate were electrolyzed, the permanganate would be reduced to manganous sulfate first ($E^0 = +1.52$ volts), then the silver would be reduced ($E^0 = +0.799$ volts), then the copper ($E^0 = +0.345$ volts), and finally hydrogen would be discharged. The actual potentials, of course, depend on the concentration of the metal ions in the solution according to the second term of the electrode-potential equation

$$E = E^0_{M^{n+},M^0} + (0.059/n) \log [M^{n+}]$$

The metals which are positive to hydrogen can be deposited from acid solutions because the metal is more easily reduced than the hydrogen ion. At first sight it appears that the metals negative to hydrogen should not be deposited electrolytically at all; actually, however, the metals between hydrogen and zinc can be deposited from alkaline solution for two reasons: (1) In alkaline solution the hydrogen-ion concentration is very low and the potential at which hydrogen is discharged is shifted to more negative values. Thus, in a solution of pH 7,

$$E = E^0{}_{H^+,\frac{1}{2}H_2} + 0.059 \log [H^+]$$

$$= 0 + 0.059(-7) = -0.433 \text{ volt}$$

whereas, at a pH of 10,

$$E = 0 + 0.059(-10) = -0.59 \text{ volt}$$

(2) The second effect has to do with the overvoltage phenomenon. Overvoltage shifts the potential at which hydrogen is discharged to more negative values. The corresponding effect with metal ions (polarization) is much smaller, and the result is that metals even as negative as zinc ($E^0 = -0.762$ volt) are deposited from alkaline solutions. The phenomenon of overvoltage is discussed below in more detail.

In all but the simplest analytical problems it is necessary to separate one metal from another. In the determination of copper by electrodeposition the question arises immediately as to whether the method can be applied to the determination of copper in copper ore and in brass, two common commercial materials. Unfortunately it cannot be, for sulfide ores contain antimony and arsenic, and brass usually contains tin and lead; all four of these metals are deposited more or less simultaneously with the copper. For the determination of copper in ore a good volumetric method is available, the iodometric method, in which arsenic and antimony do not interfere. In the analysis of brass the tin may first be removed by precipitation as metastannic acid, the lead removed by precipitation as lead sulfate, and the copper then deposited electrolytically.

Using the simple technique described above, the separations which can be effected by electrodeposition are limited to the separation of metals positive to hydrogen from those negative to hydrogen. In acid solution the metals positive to hydrogen are deposited, then hydrogen is evolved, but the more negative metals do not deposit. In alkaline solutions the metals negative to hydrogen can be deposited but no separations can be effected. In general, then, the electrodeposition method finds its principal utility in separating metals positive to hydrogen from those negative to hydrogen and in providing a convenient weighing form for metals after suitable separations have been made by other methods.

There is a more elaborate scheme for carrying out the electrodeposition of metals, called the *controlled cathode-potential method*, by which metals lying close together in the reduction-potential series can be separated. This technique is outlined in a later section.

In addition to the reduction occurring at the cathode which results in the deposition of a metal, certain other reduction reactions may also occur which do not result in the deposition of metal but which do reduce the current efficiency and influence the character of the metal deposit. The liberation of hydrogen, the reduction of ferric iron to ferrous, and the reduction of nitrate to ammonia are the principal side reactions encountered in common practice.

In general, the evolution of hydrogen simultaneously with the deposition of a metal causes the metal to deposit in a spongy form unsuitable for quantitative work. This effect has been ascribed to the formation of metal hydrides and their subsequent decomposition. The evolution of hydrogen can be prevented by working in ammoniacal or alkaline solutions when permissible. In the case of copper, where the deposition must be made from an acid solution, the addition of ammonium nitrate stops the evolution of hydrogen and leads to a better copper deposit. The nitrate ion is reduced in preference to the hydrogen ion, $NO_3^- + 8e^- + 10H^+ = NH_4^+ + 3H_2O$. As will be seen from the equation a great deal of hydrogen ion is used up in the reduction of nitrate; so much in fact, that a solution initially acid may become ammoniacal on continued electrolysis and change the nature of the electrodeposition. The reduction of nitrate greatly reduces the current efficiency, of course, but in analytical work this is not of great concern as time and cost are of secondary consideration.

Anode Reaction. If several oxidizable materials are present in a solution being electrolyzed, the reaction at the anode consists in the oxidation of the one with the most negative single-electrode potential. Three general types of reactions may occur: the dissolution of the metal of the anode, the oxidation of some material in the solution to a higher state of oxidation (stannous ions to stannic, for example), or the evolution of a gas such as oxygen, chlorine, or nitrogen. In electroanalytical work platinum electrodes are used so that the anode is not attacked. The second type of anode reaction is usually not a source of trouble, for the common practice is to adjust the composition of the electrolyte so that a gas is evolved at the anode, usually oxygen.

The hydroxyl ion probably carries the charge to the anode:

$$2OH^- - 4e^- = O_2 + 2H^+$$

The reduction potential for this reaction in a solution 1 M in hydroxyl ions is $+0.401$ volt; in a neutral solution, $[OH^-] = 10^{-7}$, this is raised to $+0.815$ volt, whereas in a solution 1 M in hydrogen ions the value is $+1.229$ volts. This means that oxygen should be liberated at an anode potential of $+1.229$ volts, but actually, owing to overvoltage, the potential is 0.4 to 0.5 volt higher. If hydrochloric acid solutions are being electrolyzed chlorine is evolved in preference to oxygen even though the reduction potential is higher ($E^0 = +1.36$ volts), for there is little chlorine overvoltage. The oxygen-containing anions, sulfate, nitrate, and perchlorate, are not discharged at the anode, presumably because they require too high a potential; the anode reaction in such electrolytes is the liberation of oxygen.

The favored electrolytes for the deposition of metals are solutions of sulfuric acid, nitric acid, and perchloric acid. In general, hydrochloric acid solutions are avoided: the free chlorine liberated at the anode attacks the platinum, and the platinum introduced into the solution is deposited on the cathode. In addition, the free chlorine is swirled about in the solution and attacks the metal on the cathode. On occasion, hydrochloric acid solutions are employed as electrolytes, but the evolution of chlorine at the anode is then avoided by the addition of hydroxylammonium chloride. This substance is more readily oxidized to nitrogen than chloride ion is oxidized to free chlorine, and, at the anode, then, nitrogen is liberated which has no deleterious effects on the electrolysis operation.

Composition of the Electrolyte. The cathode potential at which a metal is deposited and the character of the metallic deposit depend greatly on the nature of the ions of the metal in the electrolyte. For the most part the simple ions of the metal are present in nitrate, sulfate, or perchlorate solutions. Undissociated metal compounds are seldom formed with nitrate and never with perchlorate. The standard reduction potentials reported in Tables 2 and 17 were determined by measurements on perchlorate or nitrate solutions and therefore can be used in calculating the cathode potentials at which the metals are electrodeposited from such solutions.

The situation is quite different in solutions containing chloride, fluoride, oxalate, tartrate and other anions, quite the reverse often being the case. These anions form non-dissociated compounds or ions with many metals. Actually, of course, the non-dissociated compound does undergo some dissociation, the extent varying greatly from one compound to another. The effect, however, is to decrease greatly the concentration of the simple metal ion. Such a decrease in the metal-ion concentration shifts the potential at which the metal is deposited in the negative direction. A greater potential must then be applied to the cell to cause the deposition to proceed. Fewer metal ions are present in the solution, and they are therefore laid down on the metal of the electrode more slowly. The metal deposit formed by the electrolysis of solutions in which the metal is tied up in a non-dissociated compound is much more dense and crystalline.

Silver is one of the most striking cases of the changes which result from the formation of a non-dissociated compound. When a solution of silver nitrate is electrolyzed, silver is deposited on the cathode as a mass of individual crystals. These crystals grow quite large and even become large enough to drop off the electrode. Such a deposit is unsuitable for quantitative work. When deposited from a solution of silver nitrate containing a slight excess of sodium cyanide, a solution in which the silver is present as the non-dissociated ion $Ag(CN)_2^-$, silver forms a smooth, uniform, white plate which is closely adherent to the metal of the electrode. The shift in the potential on the formation of such non-dissociated compounds is quite astonishing. Given the instability constant (or its reciprocal, the formation constant) of the non-dissociated ion it is possible to calculate the potential at which the metal will be deposited. For silver.

$$Ag(CN)_2^- = Ag^+ + 2CN^- \qquad K_I = \frac{[Ag^+][CN^-]^2}{[Ag(CN)_2^-]} = 3.8 \times 10^{-19}$$

Solving for the silver-ion concentration gives

$$[Ag^+] = \frac{K_I[Ag(CN)_2^-]}{[CN^-]^2}$$

Combining this with the electrode-potential equation,

$$E = E^0_{Ag^+,Ag^0} + 0.059 \log [Ag^+]$$

$$= E^0_{Ag^+,Ag^0} + 0.059 \log \frac{K_I[Ag(CN)_2^-]}{[CN^-]^2}$$

The constants may be combined to give a new reduction potential characteristic of the slightly dissociated ion $Ag(CN)_2^-$:

$$E = E^0_{Ag^+,Ag^0} + 0.059 \log K_I + 0.059 \log \frac{[Ag(CN)_2^-]}{[CN^-]^2}$$

$$= E^0_{Ag(CN)_2^-,Ag^0} + 0.059 \log \frac{[Ag(CN)_2^-]}{[CN^-]^2}$$

Since $\quad E^0_{Ag^+,Ag^0} = +0.799$ volt $\quad$ and $\quad K_I = 3.8 \times 10^{-19}$

therefore, for the reaction,

$$Ag(CN)_2^- + e^- = Ag^0 + 2CN^- \qquad E^0_{Ag(CN)_2^-,Ag^0} = -0.286 \text{ volt}$$

that is, although silver will plate from a 1 M solution of silver nitrate at a cathode potential $+0.8$ volt, from a solution 1 M in silver and 1 M in cyanide it will only plate when the cathode potential has been made -0.29 volt.

As a consequence of the shift in the cathode potential which results from the formation of non-dissociated ions it is sometimes possible to effect separations of metals which cannot be separated in solutions of their simple ions. Silver cannot be separated from copper in sulfate, nitrate, or perchlorate solutions; although the silver is deposited first because of its more positive reduction potential, the cathode potential is shifted progressively negative as the silver is removed from the solution (logarithm term of the electrode-potential equation) and ultimately reaches a value at which the copper is also deposited. Thereafter the two metals are deposited simultaneously. The addition of cyanide to the solution shifts the reduction potential more negative, but the shift is far greater for copper than for silver. On the addition of cyanide to a cupric salt, the copper is first reduced to cuprous cyanide with formation of cyanogen and the cuprous cyanide is then dissolved in excess cyanide

$$2CuSO_4 + 4KCN = 2CuCN + 2K_2SO_4 + (CN)_2$$

$$CuCN + 2KCN = K_2Cu(CN)_3$$

The dissociation constant for this ion is

$$Cu(CN)_3^= = Cu^+ + 3CN^- \qquad K_I = \frac{[Cu^+][CN^-]^3}{[Cu(CN)_3^=]} = 5 \times 10^{-28}$$

The reduction potentials are

$$Cu^+ + e^- = Cu^0 \qquad\qquad E^0 = +0.522 \text{ volt}$$

$$Cu(CN)_3^= + e^- = Cu^0 + 3CN^- \qquad E^0 = -1.09 \text{ volts}$$

This shifts the cathode potential so far negative that silver can be easily deposited and separated from copper.

Both copper and zinc form non-dissociated ions with cyanide. That with copper is so stable that the reduction potentials of the tricyanocuprous ion and the tetracyano zinc ion are about the same; that of the zinc is

$$Zn(CN)_4^= + 2e^- = Zn^0 + 4CN^- \qquad E^0 = -1.26 \text{ volts}$$

If the concentrations happen to be about right, the copper and zinc plate out simultaneously. This is the basis of brass plating.

Polarization and Overvoltage. Polarization and overvoltage have been spoken of previously as the departure of a single electrode potential from the reversible single-electrode potential, resulting from the flow of current. Previously we have attributed polarization to the depletion or the accumulation of metal ions in the layer of solution immediately surrounding the electrode. This at least gives the direction of the effect, although actually the phenomenon is not so simple. Thus, in the deposition of copper, a decrease in the concentration of the copper ions in solution shifts the reversible potential in the negative direction (logarithm term of the electrode-potential equation). The polarization resulting when a current is being passed to cause the copper to plate shifts the cathode potential in the same direction. The polarization potential may be as much as 0.3 volt. Typical values for the polarization during the deposition of copper are shown in Table 32. As would be expected, the polarization potential in-

TABLE 32. POLARIZATION DURING THE ELECTRODEPOSITION
OF COPPER [a]

| Current (amperes) | Potential of Cathode toward Saturated Calomel Electrode | | Polarization Potential (volts) |
	Current On (volts)	Current Off (volts)	
4.4	−0.339	−0.152	0.187
1.6	−0.388	−0.250	0.138
1.0	−0.388	−0.263	0.125
0.50	−0.388	−0.288	0.100
0.17	−0.388	−0.320	0.068

[a] Measured during the course of a deposition of copper from hydrochloric acid solution. The cathode potential was being held constant at 0.388 volt negative to the saturated calomel electrode during the deposition. The change in the equilibrium cathode-calomel potential (current off) reflects the decrease in the copper concentration as the deposition proceeded. Note that the polarization shifts the single-electrode potential in the negative direction.

creases with the current. It depends also on the effectiveness of the stirring. It depends in addition on the nature of the metal. It is higher for ions of a metal other than the metal of the electrode. This may be a matter of some importance where metals having reduction potentials quite close together are being separated; unfortunately, this is a subject which has not received much study.

Polarization in the case of hydrogen and oxygen (overvoltage) is much greater than in the deposition of metal on metal, being as high as 1.5 volts under some conditions. Again, the overvoltage is a function of the current, the stirring, and the nature of the metal. The relation between hydrogen overvoltage and current is expressed fairly well by the relation $P_{H_2} = a + b \log CD$, in which CD is the current density, usually expressed in amperes per square centimeter or am-

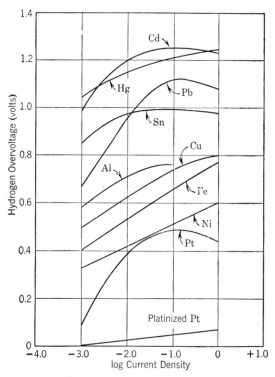

Fig. 86. Hydrogen overvoltage on various metals as a function of current density; 1 M hydrochloric acid solutions. Current density in amperes per square centimeter. [Data of Hickling and Salt, *Trans. Faraday Soc.*, **36**, 1226 (1940).]

peres per square decimeter, and a and b are constants; b has about the same value for a wide variety of metals. Hydrogen overvoltage is highest on mercury, cadmium, and lead and practically zero on platinized platinum, as will be seen from Fig. 86.

Inasmuch as overvoltage varies with the nature of the metal of the electrode, it is apparent that the phenomenon is not the simple formation of a film of gaseous hydrogen. A number of theories have been proposed to account for overvoltage. One, for example, assumes that the hydrogen atoms first released accumulate as a film and are slow to combine to give hydrogen molecules. Another theory assumes that the slow reaction is the transfer of an electron from the electrode to the hydrogen ion. These theories are discussed in detail in the treatises on electrochemistry.

The importance of hydrogen overvoltage in electrodeposition is that it makes possible the deposition of metals having reduction potentials negative to hydrogen in the reduction-potential scale; such metals would not otherwise deposit because the liberation of hydrogen would constitute the reaction at the cathode.

The Various Potentials in an Electrolytic Cell. The potential applied to the cell to cause the electrolysis to take place is measured by the voltmeter connected between the cathode and anode, V in Fig. 85. Within the cell this potential consists of the sum of the single-electrode potentials at the cathode and anode, the cathode-polarization potential, the anode-polarization potential, and the IR drop through the solution:

$$V = E^r_{a(\text{Ox.})} + E^r_{c(\text{Red.})} - P_a - P_c - IR$$

In this equation $E^r_{a(\text{Ox.})}$ and $E^r_{c(\text{Red.})}$ stand for the reversible single-electrode potentials at the anode (expressed as an oxidation potential) and at the cathode (expressed as a reduction potential), respectively; P_c and P_a are the polarization potentials; I is the current passing through the cell; and R the internal resistance of the cell. The term IR is equal to a potential because, by Ohm's law, current multiplied by resistance is equal to potential.

The potential E^r_c consists of the standard reduction potential and the logarithmic term involving the concentration of the metal ion:

$$E^r_c = E^0_{M^{n+},M^0} + (0.059/n) \log [M^{n+}]$$

The anode potential consists of the standard oxidation potential and a logarithmic term involving concentration. Addition of the reversible, single-electrode potentials at the cathode (written as a reduction potential) and at the anode (written as an oxidation potential) gives the equilibrium potential of the cell,[1] that is, the potential when no current is flowing through the cell. The potential of the cell is negative, indicating that the reaction does not take place spontaneously

---

[1] This method of combining two single-electrode potentials to obtain the potential of a cell is explained on page 231. The addition of a reduction potential and an oxidation potential is equivalent to taking the difference between the two single-electrode potentials when they are expressed on the same basis, that is, both as reduction potentials or both as oxidation potentials.

as written but is being forced by the application of an external potential just slightly greater in magnitude.

When current flows through the cell, three additional potential
drops occur within the cell: the IR drop already mentioned and the

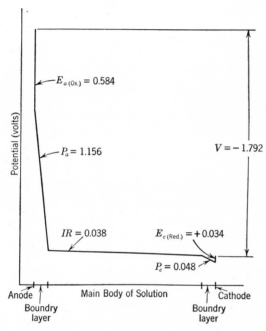

Fig. 87.   Distribution of potentials through cell at one stage in the electrodeposition of copper from a dilute nitric acid solution.

$$V = E_{a\,(Ox.)} + E_{c(Red.)} - P_a - P_c - IR$$

$$= -0.584 + 0.034 - 1.156 - 0.048 - 0.038$$

$$= -1.792 \text{ volts}$$

two polarization potentials.   The cathode polarization potential P_c
shifts the cathode potential in the negative direction.   Conversely,
the anode polarization, P_a, shifts the anode potential in the positive
direction.   All three oppose the potential applied to the cell and hence
are given negative values in computing the potential of the cell.

These potentials can perhaps be best understood from a graph.
Figure 87 shows the actual potentials involved at one stage in the
electrodeposition of copper as carried out in the determination of
copper by deposition at the cathode.   The reaction at the platinum

anode is the evolution of oxygen. Figure 88 shows similar data for the deposition of cadmium.

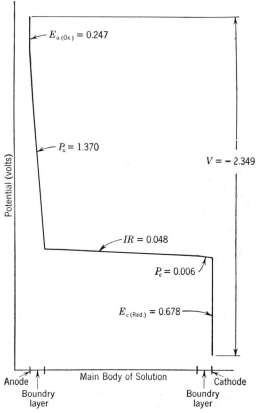

Fig. 88. Distribution of potentials through cell at one stage in the electrodeposition of cadmium from a solution buffered with ammonium acetate.

$$V = E_{a(\text{Ox.})} + E_{c(\text{Red.})} - P_a - P_c - IR$$
$$= -0.247 - 0.678 - 1.370 - 0.006 - 0.048$$
$$= -2.349 \text{ volts}$$

It is evident that V, the potential applied to the cathode and anode, is not a guide to any changes occurring in the solution, owing to the reaction taking place at the cathode. The terms P_a, P_c, and IR depend on the current which varies with R, the resistance of the solution, and therefore in turn with the composition of the solution. Both E_c and E_a involve the concentration of materials in the solution and thus change during the electrolysis. In the simple method of carrying out an electrodeposition, sufficient potential V is applied to cause the electrolysis to proceed, and beyond adjusting the composition of the electrolyte little can be done to control the process. An electro-deposition carried out in this simple manner is called a *constant-current process*. It is possible by introducing a third electrode, a reference electrode, to control the process in such a manner as to effect certain separations; these *controlled cathode-potential processes* are described in the next section.

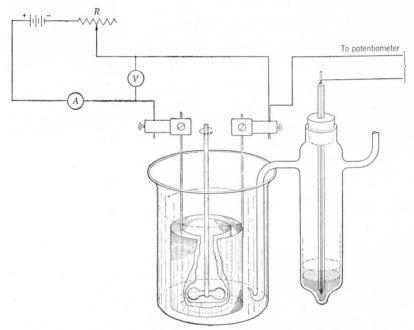

Fig. 89. Apparatus for electrodeposition with controlled cathode potential.

Electrodeposition with Cathode-Potential Control. By intro-ducing into the electrolysis cell a reference electrode, that is, a third electrode in the form of a saturated calomel electrode (page 238) and measuring the potential between it and the cathode, it is possible to follow the change in the cathode potential during the electrolysis. In effect this isolates from all the various potentials within the cell the one of particular interest in the electrodeposition of a metal, that is, the cathode potential. The cathode potential consists of the reversible, single-electrode potential and the polarization potential:

$$E_c = E^0_{M^{n+}, M^0} + (0.059/n) \log [M^{n+}] - P_c$$

By measuring the cathode potential the changes in the concentration of the metal ions in solution can be followed during the deposition, and by limiting the cathode potential to certain values it is possible to separate a metal from one negative to it in the reduction-potential series.

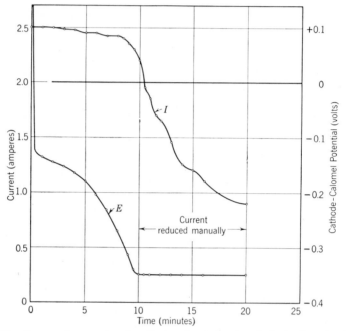

Fig. 90.   Course of current and cathode-saturated calomel electrode potential in the separation of copper from tin in a sulfate solution.

The apparatus for carrying out a controlled cathode potential electrolysis is the same as that used before (Fig. 85), with the addition of the reference electrode and a potentiometer to measure the cathode-calomel potential (Fig. 89).

Since the concentration of the metal ion decreases as the metal is being plated out, the cathode potential becomes more negative. Each tenfold change causes the cathode potential to become more negative by $0.059/n$ volt. If two metals are present in the solution the more positive metal is plated first, but, as its concentration decreases, the cathode potential becomes more negative and ultimately reaches a value at which the second metal is deposited. By decreasing the potential applied to the cell) by increasing the resistance R in the circuit), the cathode potential can be held at some potential just short of the deposition of the second metal. If the difference in E^0 values of the two metals is 0.3 volt or greater it is possible to deposit the first metal completely and separate it from the more negative metal.

The separation of copper from tin is possible by such a process. Thus, in Fig. 90 are plotted the cathode-reference cell potential E and the electrolyzing current I against time for the deposition of copper from a solution containing about 0.4 g. of copper, 0.2 g. of tin, and 15 per cent of sulfuric acid. The cathode potential became more negative rapidly at the beginning of the electrolysis as the platinum electrode was covered with copper and as the copper was deposited. By the time the cathode potential had fallen to −0.35 volt toward the saturated calomel electrode the current had dropped slightly owing to the increased resistance of the solution. The cathode was not allowed to become more than 0.35 volt negative to the calomel electrode by reducing the applied potential (that is, to the cathode and the anode) by increasing the resistance R. In this manner the copper was separated from the tin. In the analysis from which the data of Fig. 90 was taken the amount of copper taken was 0.3805 g., the copper found, 0.3802 g.

APPLICATIONS OF ELECTRODEPOSITION TO THE DETERMINATION OF VARIOUS ELEMENTS

Silver. Silver may be deposited from an ammoniacal or alkaline cyanide solution.

$$Ag^+ + e^- = Ag^0 \qquad E^0 = +0.799 \text{ volt}$$

$$Ag(NH_3)_2{}^+ + e^- = Ag^0 + 2NH_3 \qquad E^0 = +0.374 \text{ volt}$$

$$Ag(CN)_2{}^- + e^- = Ag^0 + 2CN^- \qquad E^0 = -0.288 \text{ volt}$$

It tends to form large, loose crystals when deposited from nitric acid solution, so that such a solution is not satisfactory for the quantitative determination of more than small amounts of silver. The deposits from ammonia or cyanide solutions are bright, smooth, and adherent. The separation of silver from copper may be effected by depositing the silver from either an ammoniacal solution or from an alkaline cyanide solution.

Copper. Copper is most commonly plated at the cathode from a dilute nitric acid or sulfuric acid solution containing ammonium nitrate

$$Cu^{++} + 2e^- = Cu^0 \qquad E^0 = +0.3448 \text{ volt}$$

Good deposits are not obtained from solutions containing sulfate alone as the anion; the addition of a gram or so of ammonium nitrate corrects the situation, the nitrate probably functioning as a cathode depolarizer to prevent the evolution of hydrogen. The electrolyte should contain about 1 to 2 ml. of concentrated nitric acid per 200 ml. The deposition of copper from such a solution serves to separate copper from zinc, cadmium, cobalt, nickel, small amounts of iron, and of course from manganese, aluminum, and the alkali and alkaline-earth metals. The separation of copper from these metals succeeds because the deposition of hydrogen follows the deposition of the copper and continues as long as the solution remains acid. On continued electrolysis of a nitrate solution the solution may become alkaline owing to the reduction of nitrate to ammonia; and then other metals, even those as negative as zinc, may deposit and the copper redissolve owing to oxidation by oxygen and the stability of the cupric-ammonia ion. The deposition of copper cannot be made in the presence of tin, arsenic, antimony, bismuth, or silver. Phosphate when present in the electrolyte appears in the deposit as some reduced form of phosphorus, which renders the deposit unsuitable for weighing. Small amounts of chloride are deposited with the metal, probably as insoluble cuprous chloride, making the results high.

The method described above is commonly used for the determination of copper in brass and bronze after the removal of tin as metastannic acid and lead as lead sulfate. Small amounts of lead can be determined simultaneously with copper by deposition as lead dioxide on the anode; the electrolyte in this case is a 3 per cent nitric acid solution, about the highest acidity of nitric acid the copper deposit can tolerate.

The separation of copper from tin and lead can be made by the controlled cathode-potential method. The copper from a strong hydrochloric acid solution containing hydroxylammonium chloride is deposited by limiting the cathode potential to 0.40 volt negative to the saturated calomel electrode. The method is excellent but has not found commercial application because of the complexity of the apparatus.

Lead. When determined electrolytically, lead is always deposited as the dioxide, PbO_2, on the anode. Deposition on the cathode from an alkaline solution invariably leads to low results. The dioxide is deposited from a solution containing 15 per cent nitric acid, although this concentration may be cut down to the point where copper can be deposited simultaneously on the cathode. The dioxide always contains an excess of oxygen, and the empirical factor 0.8640 is used in converting the dioxide to lead rather than the theoretical factor 0.8660. A number of metals interfere. Silver, manganese, and bismuth form higher oxides at the anode. Tin, arsenic, antimony, and the anions chloride and phosphate delay or contaminate the deposit and must be absent. Lead may be separated from tin if hydrofluoric acid is added to the nitric acid solution.

Nickel and Cobalt. The electrodeposition of nickel by the constant-current method is of value only for getting the metal into a satisfactory form for weighing rather than for accomplishing its separation from zinc. It is usually deposited from an ammoniacal sulfate solution. Cobalt accompanies nickel when a solution of the two metals is electrolyzed. When cobalt is deposited from a solution containing no nickel or only a small amount, sodium sulfite must be added to the ammoniacal solution.

Cadmium. Satisfactory electrodeposits of cadmium can be obtained from acetic acid; also from alkaline cyanide solutions, where the results tend to be high by about 1 per cent. The principal separation of cadmium is from zinc. This separation can be effected only by the controlled cathode-potential method, using an alkaline cyanide bath and limiting the cathode potential to 1.3 volts negative to the saturated calomel electrode.

Zinc. Zinc may be deposited electrolytically from an ammoniacal chloride or sulfate solution or from a strong sodium hydroxide solution, but the results are frequently disappointing. Small amounts of nitrate interfere.

PROBLEMS

1. Write the equation for the half-cell reaction, and calculate the electrochemical equivalent weight of the substance reduced, in each of the following cathode reactions: (a) Ni^{++} to Ni^0; (b) Fe^{+++} to Fe^{++}; (c) MnO_4^- to Mn^{++}; (d) NO_3^- to NH_4^+; (e) Cu^{++} to $CuCl_3^=$. Note that hydrogen ions are involved in the reduction of materials containing oxygen.

2. A current was allowed to flow through a cell long enough to deposit 1.5000 g. of silver. Calculate the number of coulombs which passed.

3. Calculate the time in minutes required to deposit 0.7000 g. of copper by the electrolysis of an acid solution of cupric sulfate with a current of 5.00 amp. assuming the current efficiency to be 50.0 per cent.

4. Calculate the number of (a) ampere-minutes and (b) ampere-hours required to effect a change of 1 gram electrochemical equivalent weight.

5. Calculate how many grams of ferric sulfate can be reduced to ferrous sulfate at the cathode by a current of 8.0 amp. in 20 minutes.

6. Calculate the kilowatt-hours of work expended in Problem 3 if the potential applied to cathode and anode was 5.0 volts.

7. The cadmium in 100.0 ml. of a solution of cadmium sulfate was deposited by electrodeposition, and a weight of 0.6530 g. was obtained. The solution was

titrated with a standard solution of sodium hydroxide of which 45.0 ml. was required. Write equations for the reaction at each electrode and for the overall reaction of the cell. Calculate the normality of the sodium hydroxide solution.

8. Two cells were operated in series for a certain length of time. In one cell 0.7500 g. of copper was deposited from a cupric sulfate solution. The second cell was arranged for the deposition of cadmium on the cathode. Calculate the weight of cadmium deposited, assuming no secondary reactions occurred in either cell.

9. Calculate the volume of hydrogen gas under standard conditions formed at a platinum cathode in a solution of potassium sulfate on the passage of 5.0 amp. for 40 minutes.

10. A porous membrane was used to separate the electrolyte surrounding the cathode from the solution around the anode. The catholyte consisted of a solution of ferric sulfate in dilute sulfuric acid, the anolyte of a potassium sulfate solution. A current of 1.50 amp. was passed through the cell for 12.5 minutes. Calculate the number of milliliters of 0.1250 N potassium permanganate required to titrate the ferrous sulfate formed, assuming that no ferrous iron diffused through the membrane.

11. Occasionally in the electrodeposition of copper a student will allow the electrolysis of the dilute nitric acid solution containing the copper and ammonium nitrate to run overnight. On returning he finds a bare platinum electrode and a dark blue solution. Explain what has happened.

12. The instability constant of the non-dissociated zinc-cyanide ion is

$$Zn(CN)_4^= = Zn^{++} + 4CN^- \qquad K_I = 1.2 \times 10^{-18}$$

and the reduction potential of the normal zinc ion is -0.762. Calculate the E^0 for the reaction

$$Zn(CN)_4^= + 2e^- = Zn^0 + 4CN^-$$

13. Calculate the single-electrode potential of a copper electrode dipping into a solution 0.1 M in cupric ion. Repeat the calculation for concentrations 1×10^{-3} M, 1×10^{-5} M, and 1×10^{-7} M. From the viewpoint of a quantitative determination of copper decide which of these concentrations would represent complete deposition.

14. Starting with a solution 1.00 M in both silver and cupric ions, calculate the concentration of silver in the solution at the point where copper just begins to deposit on the silver. Assume that the polarization potential of copper on silver is negligible.

CHAPTER 16

The Analysis of Brass

Strictly speaking, brass is an alloy of copper and zinc which contains relatively little lead and little or no tin. Bronze is a copper alloy containing a considerable amount of tin. In this chapter the term brass is used to mean both brass and bronze. Some tin and appreciable amounts of lead are present in brass, so that the method of analysis of the two materials is the same. On occasion a brass prepared from virgin copper and zinc and free of tin is encountered; the analysis can be considerably shortened in such cases. Included under the general title of brass are a variety of other names applied to copper-base alloys: muntz metal, yellow brass, red brass, commercial bronze, free-turning brass, naval brass, admiralty metal, and others.

Quite a few metals are used commonly as alloying elements with copper. Beside the usual components already mentioned, tin, lead, and zinc, are silicon, manganese, aluminum, beryllium, nickel, phosphorus, arsenic, and antimony. The variation in percentage of each of these in commercial alloys is

Copper	50–95	Nickel	0–5
Lead	0–27	Iron	0–4
Tin	0–20	Manganese	0–6
Zinc	0–50	Phosphorus	0–1
Silicon	0–5	Arsenic	0–1
Aluminum	0–12	Antimony	0–1
Beryllium	0–2		

The presence of these elements necessitates modifications in the basic procedure given below for copper, lead, zinc, and tin.

Unfortunately, methods are not available for the direct determination of each of the elements in copper alloys. Rather, it is necessary to separate the elements one at a time, arranging the procedure to take advantage of the separations that are possible. More specifically, tin is removed first as insoluble metastannic acid, lead next as lead sulfate, copper third by electrodeposition, and finally zinc as the double phosphate. Traces of iron are invariably present in copper-base alloys and must be removed as the hydroxide before the zinc is precipitated. Aluminum if present is precipitated with the iron. Nickel appears in the filtrate from the zinc.

Samples of brass for analysis are taken from the metal under examination by drilling or cutting on a milling machine or lathe. The cut should be made dry, that is, without oiling the cutting tool, to obviate later washing with gasoline or benzene. Brass samples high in lead are likely to be inhomogeneous owing to the segregation of lead as a separate phase during cooling. In general, segregation is a serious problem in non-ferrous alloys, and care should be taken to drill through the whole piece of metal and otherwise attempt to eliminate the effects of the variation in composition with depth.

TIN

Tin is precipitated as metastannic acid, H_2SnO_3, when tin salts are heated with nitric acid. In many respects the precipitation of tin in this way resembles the determination of silica. Both materials are hydrated oxides which are partially soluble when first formed. Both are amorphous in character, adsorb badly, and after ignition to the oxide must be corrected for impurities.

When a brass sample is dissolved in nitric acid the metastannic acid is precipitated directly:

$$CuSn + 4HNO_3 = Cu(NO_3)_2 + H_2SnO_3 + 2NO + H_2O$$

Metastannic acid need not actually be dehydrated like silica, but it should be digested with nitric acid for some time. The precipitate carries with it some iron, copper, and lead, and when ignited and weighed always gives somewhat high results.

The impure stannic oxide may be corrected for the impurities by heating it with ammonium iodide; the tin is volatilized as stannic iodide. The iron and copper remain behind as the iodides which are then converted to nitrates, ignited to the oxides, and weighed. The tin is found by the loss in weight. The residue of oxides can be dissolved and returned to the filtrate.

Stannic oxide is very easily reduced to metallic tin, and care must be exercised in burning away the filter paper.

Small amounts of antimony are carried down quantitatively with the tin and are present in the ignited residue as antimony tetroxide, Sb_2O_4. Antimony is volatilized with the tin in the ammonium iodide procedure.

Any phosphate in the sample is carried down with the metastannic acid. Phosphorus in a brass is oxidized to phosphate, and the stannic oxide obtained is thus the sum of the tin, antimony, and phosphorus.

Tin may be determined volumetrically by direct titration with iodine,

$$SnCl_2 + 2I + 2HCl = SnCl_4 + 2HI$$

The precipitate of metastannic acid is dissolved in hydrochloric acid and the tin reduced with metallic lead. If the solution is cooled to below 5° after the reduction, the titration with iodine can be carried out without removing the lead. Stannous chloride must not be allowed to come in contact with air during the titration since it is quickly oxidized; the air in the flask can be expelled by passing carbon dioxide through the flask. Arsenic and antimony if present do not interfere because the titration with iodine is carried out in an acid solution.

Procedure for the Gravimetric Determination of Tin. Weigh accurately a sample of 1.0 to 1.5 g. of the brass into a 400-ml. beaker. Cover the beaker and add 25 ml. of dilute nitric acid (1:1). Heat the mixture in a hood on the steam plate or with a burner. Allow the solution to evaporate until solids have separated, but do not allow it to go to dryness. Add 50 ml. of water and allow the mixture to digest on the hot plate for 1 hour. Add filter-paper pulp prepared by tearing a sheet of ashless filter paper to pieces and stirring it with a few milliliters of concentrated nitric acid in a test tube. Filter off the metastannic acid, using a close-texture filter paper. Wash the filter and precipitate several times with hot, dilute nitric acid (1:50). Save the filtrate for the determination of lead, copper, and zinc.

Place the precipitate in a porcelain crucible previously ignited and weighed. Char and burn the paper away at as low a temperature as possible, and ignite the residue at the full heat of a Meker burner for 30 minutes, keeping the crucible inclined and the flame toward the back of the crucible. Cool and weigh. The stannic oxide is usually brown owing to the presence of ferric oxide.

Report the results as per cent of impure tin. The amount of impurity depends on the amount of tin; with 5 per cent tin the impurity will be 0.2 to 0.3 per cent.

The impure tin can be corrected by the ammonium iodide volatilization method as follows: Add to the impure stannic oxide about fifteen times its weight of ammonium iodide and mix the two intimately with a small spatula. Use a small brush to remove the particles from the spatula when the spatula is withdrawn. Place the crucible in an electric muffle at a temperature of 425 to 475° for 15 minutes. Cool the crucible, add 2 to 3 ml. of concentrated nitric acid. Evaporate to dryness and decompose the residual nitrates over a low flame. Ignite the residue at a low red heat. Cool and weigh. The loss in weight represents the amount of pure stannic oxide present. Dissolve the oxide residue out of the crucible by digestion with a few milliliters of hot, concentrated hydrochloric acid. Dilute the resulting solution and filter to remove any silica that may have accumulated. Add the filtrate to the filtrate being evaporated with sulfuric acid for the determination of lead.

Procedure for the Volumetric Determination of Tin. Dissolve the sample of brass in nitric acid, digest the mixture, and filter as described above. Wash the precipitate thoroughly with a 1 per cent solution of ammonium chloride to remove all of the nitrate.

Equip a 500-ml. conical flask with a three-hole stopper carrying an inlet tube for bubbling carbon dioxide through the solution, an air condenser (about 30 cm. of 10-mm. glass tubing), and an opening for the buret tip, this opening being plugged with a piece of glass rod during the first part of the procedure.

Place the filter paper containing the metastannic acid in the flask and add 200 ml. of water and 75 ml. of concentrated hydrochloric acid. Add 5 g. of granulated lead, pass a slow stream of carbon dioxide through the solution, and boil gently until all the stannic salts have been reduced, generally about 30 minutes. Cool the solution to below 5° and then, with a slightly faster stream of carbon dioxide flowing, add 5 ml. of freshly prepared starch solution. Insert the tip of the buret and titrate with standard iodine or iodate-iodide solution until the first permanent blue color appears. For small amounts of tin use a 0.01 N solution; for larger amounts (greater than 0.1 per cent) use a 0.1 N solution. Standardize the solutions against a sample of pure tin in the same manner.

LEAD

After tin is removed as metastannic acid, lead is precipitated as the sulfate. The solubility of lead is greatly increased by the presence of acids other than sulfuric; fortunately the nitric acid introduced in the determination of tin can be removed simply by evaporating with sulfuric acid.

The solubility of lead sulfate in water at room temperature is about 5 mg. per 100 ml. This solubility is reduced sufficiently by the presence of sulfuric acid to make the precipitation acceptable as a quantitative method. The very minimum of wash water necessary to remove all of the mother liquor and its salts should be used. Lead salts are very easily reduced to metallic lead, and lead sulfate must be filtered on porous-bottom filtering crucibles rather than on filter paper. Above 700° lead sulfate begins to give off sulfur trioxide, so that the ignition must be conducted at a temperature well below this.

Small amounts of lead can be determined electrolytically by deposition as lead dioxide on the anode from a nitric acid solution. The amount of lead which can be handled in this way is distinctly limited; for quantities of lead more than 20 to 30 mg. (2 to 3 per cent on a 1-g. sample) the lead dioxide tends to fall off the electrode. The best electrolyte is one containing about 15 per cent nitric acid. In a brass analysis the lead if determined electrolytically is determined simultaneously with the copper; in this case the nitric acid concentration must be reduced to about 3 per cent. The lead dioxide deposited electrolytically is always slightly heavy owing to the presence of excess oxygen or perhaps to water; an empirical factor is used to convert the lead dioxide to lead.

The directions for depositing lead electrolytically are given under the electrolytic determination of copper.

Procedure for the Determination of Lead as the Sulfate. To the filtrate from the metastannic acid precipitate (to which has been added the dissolved residue from the ammonium iodide process for correcting the impure stannic oxide, if used) add 10 ml. of dilute sulfuric acid (1:1). Evaporate to dense, white fumes of sulfuric acid to expel the nitric acid. Cool and wash down the walls of the beaker with water and again evaporate to dense white fumes. Cool and dilute to 75 to 100 ml. Allow the solution to stand 2 hours with occasional stirring. Filter through a porous-bottom filtering crucible previously ignited and weighed. Wash the precipitate with dilute sulfuric acid (1:20). Reserve the filtrate for the determination of copper. Place the filtering crucible in a porcelain crucible and heat gently at first and finally at a barely visible red heat for 30 minutes. Carry out the ignition in an electric muffle at 500 to 600°, if one is available. Calculate the per cent of lead in the sample.

COPPER

The electrolytic determination of copper is discussed in Chapter 15. The deposition of copper from a dilute nitric acid solution separates the copper from nickel, zinc, and the small amounts of iron normally found in a brass.

Procedure for the Electrolytic Determination of Copper and Lead. To the filtrate from the determination of lead as the sulfate add 1 ml. of nitric acid and 1 g. of ammonium nitrate; deposit the copper electrolytically as described below. If lead was not removed by precipitation but is to be determined electrolytically, neutralize the solution with filtered ammonia (1:1) until a precipitate of cupric hydroxide just persists. Dissolve the precipitate by the dropwise addition of nitric acid. Add 3 ml. of nitric acid for each 100 ml. of solution and electrolyze as described below.

Clean the platinum gauze electrodes by dipping them into dilute nitric acid (1:3), wash well with water, and dry in the oven at 110°. Weigh the cathode and the anode if lead is to be determined electrolytically. Mount the cathode and anode on the binding posts provided on the electrolysis board, bringing the anode up concentrically about the glass stirring shaft. Bring the cathode up around the anode concentrically. Arrange the electrodes symmetrically and at the same height. Bring the beaker containing the solution up from below so that the bottom of the beaker is about 1 cm. below the bottom of the electrodes. Dilute the solution until all but the top 6 or 8 mm. of the cathode is immersed. Cover the beaker with split cover glasses. Start the motor driving the stirrer. Turn on the current and adjust the resistance to give a current of 5 amp. Allow the electrolysis to run 40 to 50 minutes. Toward the end wash down the cover glasses and walls of the beaker with a little water from the wash bottle. When copper no longer deposits on the bare platinum electrode brought into contact with the solution as the level is raised by the wash water, the electrolysis is finished. Without turning off the current lower the beaker, at the same time washing the electrodes with a stream of water. Turn off the stirring motor and current. Remove the cathode, wash it thoroughly with water, and dry it in the oven at 110° for 20 to 30 minutes. Remove the anode, wash it once or twice with water, and dry it at 110° for 20 minutes. The anode must be handled very carefully as the lead dioxide deposit is fragile and easily knocked off the electrode. Save the solution for the determination of iron, zinc, and nickel. Finally, weigh the cathode, and from the weight of copper deposited calculate the per cent of copper in the sample. Weigh the anode and compute the per cent of lead in the sample, using the factor 0.864 for converting lead dioxide to lead.

IRON

Following the separation of copper it is necessary to remove the iron by precipitation as ferric hydroxide before carrying out the determination of zinc, because the zinc is later precipitated from a neutral solution. Some zinc will be carried down by the ferric hydroxide so that the latter must be reprecipitated. Usually the amount of iron in a brass is so small that one reprecipitation is enough to separate the iron completely from the zinc.

As indicated in the section dealing with the gravimetric determination of iron, aluminum, titanium, and manganese (if an oxidizing agent is present) accompany the iron in the ammonia precipitation. Some copper-base alloys are quite high in aluminum and manganese, so that such special alloys require a modification of the procedure at this point.

Procedure for the Determination of Iron Plus Aluminum. To the solution remaining from the copper determination add 2 to 3 ml. of bromine water and evaporate the solution to about 125 ml. Add a few drops of methyl red to the solution. Heat the solution and add filtered ammonia (1:1) dropwise until the methyl red is distinctly yellow; then add 5 ml. more. Keep the solution hot for 15 minutes. Filter through a medium paper. Wash the filter and precipitate with dilute ammonia (1:100). Place a clean beaker under the funnel and dissolve the hydroxide precipitate on the filter by pouring over it 25 ml. of hot, dilute hydrochloric acid (1:10). Reprecipitate the hydroxides as before. Filter through the same paper. Add the filtrate to the main solution and set the main solution aside for the determination of zinc. Place the filter and hydroxide precipitate in a porcelain crucible previously ignited and weighed. Burn away the paper and ignite the residue at the full heat of a Meker burner. Calculate the per cent of iron in the sample, assuming that all the material is ferric oxide.

ZINC

One of the best methods for the determination of zinc is the precipitation as zinc ammonium phosphate, $ZnNH_4PO_4$, followed by ignition to the pyrophosphate, $Zn_2P_2O_7$. A number of bivalent metals can be determined in this way (for example magnesium, discussed in Chapter 6), and in general the precipitation as the double phosphate is not a separation of the bivalent metal being precipitated from anything but the alkali metals and ammonium. Precipitation of zinc as the double phosphate is a convenient method for determining zinc in brass, and fortunately the small amounts of nickel which may be present in the solution do not interfere.

Zinc forms a non-dissociated ion with ammonia, $Zn(NH_3)_4^{++}$, which is sufficiently stable that most salts of zinc including the double phosphate are soluble in ammonia. Zinc ammonium phosphate is also soluble in acids owing to the fact that it is the salt of a weak acid.

The precipitation of zinc ammonium phosphate must therefore be made in a strictly neutral solution. The monohydrogen phosphate-dihydrogen phosphate system provides a convenient buffer, holding the pH of the solution near 7.

On the addition of phosphate, a flocculent precipitate, probably a normal zinc phosphate, is first precipitated. On digestion this material passes over into crystals of the double phosphate.

Procedure for the Determination of Zinc as the Pyrophosphate. To the filtrate from the iron determination add 25 ml. of nitric acid and 25 ml. of hydrochloric acid and evaporate the solution to dryness or to fumes of sulfuric acid to destroy the major part of the ammonium salts which have accumulated in the solution. If convenient leave the beaker on the hot plate overnight with the cover glass raised from the beaker by means of glass hooks.

Dilute the solution to 75 ml. If the solution is not clear owing to the presence of some silica, filter and wash the filter well with dilute hydrochloric acid (1:50). Add methyl red to the solution and neutralize the solution exactly with filtered ammonia (1:1). Prepare a solution of 6 g. of diammonium hydrogen phosphate, $(NH_4)_2HPO_4$, in 30 ml. of water; add a drop of phenolphthalein and then add just enough ammonia to color the solution pink. Heat the zinc solution to boiling and add the phosphate solution with stirring. Digest the solution for 30 minutes, then set the solution aside for 2 hours to cool. The precipitate should be crystalline and settle rapidly at this point. The solution should be at room temperature when filtered. Filter through a porous-bottom filtering crucible previously ignited and weighed. Wash the zinc ammonium phosphate with cold water, attempting to complete the transferring and washing with not more than 100 ml. Use small portions of wash water. Save the filtrate for the determination of nickel. Place the filtering crucible inside a porcelain crucible and heat gradually to a red heat. Finally, ignite the precipitate for 30 minutes at the full heat of a Meker burner. Cool and weigh. Report the per cent of zinc in the sample; the factor for converting zinc pyrophosphate to zinc is 0.4291.

NICKEL

Nickel is practically always determined by precipitation as nickel dimethylglyoxime. The precipitate is dried at 120° and weighed as such. Nickel dimethylglyoxime is insoluble in neutral and alkaline solutions; in the analysis of brass the filtrate from the zinc determination is buffered at a pH of about 7, and nothing more need be done to the solution than add dimethylglyoxime. Dimethylglyoxime is not very soluble in water (40 mg. per 100 ml.), and the reagent is made up as a 1 per cent alcohol solution. Care should be exercised to avoid adding too big an excess of reagent, as water throws the reagent out of the alcohol solution so that it contaminates the nickel salt.

Procedure for the Determination of Nickel. Warm the filtrate from the zinc determination to about 70°. Add 5 ml. of a 1 per cent solution of dimethylglyoxime in alcohol. Heat and stir for a few minutes and then allow the solution to cool. Filter the scarlet precipitate of nickel dimethylglyoxime on a porous-bottom filtering crucible previously dried and weighed. Wash with water. Dry the precipitate at 110° for 1.5 hours; cool and weigh. Multiply the weight of nickel dimethylglyoxime by 0.2032 to obtain the weight of nickel.

PROBLEMS

1. Devise a scheme for the determination of each of the elements in an alloy consisting of copper, silver, aluminum, and zinc.

2. Devise a procedure for the analysis of an alloy of lead, nickel, and tin.

3. Tin can be volatilized from a sulfuric, hydrochloric or perchloric acid solution by the addition of hydrobromic acid. Tell what use could be made of this in the analysis of a brass containing several per cent of silicon.

4. In the analysis of a brass the order in which the four major constituents, tin, lead, copper, and zinc, are determined cannot be altered. Explain why this is so.

5. Arsenical copper contains 0.3 to 0.5 per cent arsenic, the balance being copper. Devise a method of determining the arsenic in such material.

6. Devise a scheme for the analysis of an alloy of copper (98 per cent), chromium (1 + per cent), and silicon (difference).

CHAPTER 17

The Analysis of Limestone

Calcium carbonate occurs widely in nature in a variety of forms, the common, crystalline form being designated by the mineral name *calcite*. The massive, more or less impure deposits of calcite are called limestone. The calcium carbonate of limestone was laid down originally as the shells of various marine organisms such as coral and oysters. In the course of geological ages such shells become fused together, first forming masses called coquina from which the individual shells can still be pried loose; as the process of fusion progresses the mass becomes more densely compacted into limestone, the hardness varying greatly from one deposit to another. Under certain conditions of pressure such as occur in the uplift of mountains the calcium carbonate of limestone may undergo recrystallization and form *marble*. Some calcium carbonate deposits result also from the precipitation of calcium carbonate from solution by the reversal of the reaction: $CaCO_3 + H_2CO_3 = Ca(HCO_3)_2$. The stalagmites, stalactites and travertine found in caves originate in this way. Frequently calcium carbonate occurs in beautifully crystalline forms known as *dogtooth spar, satin spar,* and *Iceland spar*. Iceland spar crystals are highly pure chemically and are transparent; they are used as a primary standard in analytical work as well as for optical parts in work with polarized light.

Limestone constitutes a good part of the sedimentary rocks, calcium being the fifth most abundant element in the crust of the earth. Commercially limestone is used as building stone, as crushed rock for ballast, as a blast-furnace flux, and as an ingredient in the manufacture of Portland cement and glass. It is the cheapest of all materials capable of neutralizing acids. It is used in agriculture primarily to neutralize the acids in soil. When ignited, limestone forms calcium oxide, and the calcium oxide when treated with water gives calcium hydroxide, a strong base. Limestone, and calcium oxide and hydroxide derived from it, are widely used in the chemical industry as cheap alkalies, in the Solvay process, for example.

The analysis of limestone is therefore a matter of considerable importance. Unfortunately there is no way of determining directly the calcium or the magnesium present. Rather, the silica, iron, and aluminum which are always present as impurities must be removed first, then the calcium determined, and finally any magnesium in the sample determined. The silica impurity may be present either as silica (SiO_2, quartz) or as a silicate (salt of silicic acid, $KAlSiO_4$, for example) and may vary in amount from zero to such high percentages that the material might be classed as an argillaceous (clay-bearing) limestone or even a calcareous (lime-bearing) shale or sandstone. The principal impurity in a limestone, however, is magnesium. This comes about because of the similarities in the chemical and physical properties of calcium and magnesium. Magnesium carbonate also occurs naturally in vast deposits, as the mineral known as *magnesite*. Magnesite and calcite are isomorphous, that is, have the same crystal form, and the calcium in calcite can be replaced by magnesium and the magnesium in magnesite by calcium. Because of this, materials are found in nature varying in composition from pure calcite at one end of a series to pure magnesite at the other end. One material, in which the ratio of calcium to magnesium is one to one, is especially common; it is known as *dolomite*, $CaMg(CO_3)_2$.

The aluminum impurity in limestone is generally present as a silicate. Iron and manganese, on the other hand, are generally present as carbonates, for ferrous carbonate and manganous carbonate are also isomorphous with calcite.

Limestone may also contain as impurities calcium sulfate (gypsum), iron sulfide (pyrite, FeS_2), and small amounts of sodium and potassium. Occasionally also it contains organic matter, sometimes in appreciable amounts.

A complete analysis for all the constituents of a limestone is seldom required. Usually, only the following determinations are made: (1) loss on ignition, (2) silica, (3) $R_2O_3(Fe_2O_3, Al_2O_3, TiO_2, Mn_3O_4$, and P_2O_5 combined), (4) calcium oxide, (5) magnesium oxide, and (6) carbon dioxide.

LOSS ON IGNITION

When heated above $850°$ calcium carbonate is decomposed into calcium oxide and carbon dioxide. The loss of weight on ignition, then, is a measure of the carbon dioxide in the sample. Secondary reactions may also occur. Any organic material present is burned away and lost. Sulfides present are converted in part to sulfate and in part to oxide.

Ferrous iron and manganese are oxidized to higher-valent forms. And, of course, any water in the sample is lost.

Procedure for the Determination of Loss on Ignition. Dry the finely ground limestone to be analyzed at least 2 hours at 110°. Weigh accurately a sample of about 1 g. into a platinum crucible. Heat the crucible gradually to a red heat; if the heating is too rapid the evolution of carbon dioxide may take place so suddenly that part of the solids will be carried away. Heat at the full heat of a Meker burner for 30 minutes or in an electric muffle at 1000° if available. Keep the platinum crucible in the oxidizing flame, that is, above the tips of the blue cones of the flame above the grid of the burner. Cool, and transfer to the desiccator when the crucible is almost cool enough to pick up with the fingers. Cool for 30 minutes in the desiccator and weigh. Do not allow the crucible to remain in the desiccator longer than 1 hour before weighing as it will absorb moisture from the calcium chloride in the desiccator. Weigh quickly. Ignite a second time for 20 minutes and again cool and weigh. The problem of igniting calcium oxide to constant weight is discussed in more detail in the section dealing with the determination of calcium.

Calculate the per cent loss in weight.

THE DETERMINATION OF SILICA

Although calcium carbonate and magnesium carbonate dissolve readily in hydrochloric acid, any siliceous impurity will usually not dissolve. Insoluble silicates are generally decomposed for analysis by fusion with sodium carbonate. In the present case, however, it is not necessary to add a base, for on ignition of limestone calcium oxide is formed which accomplishes the same purpose. Occasionally a highly impure limestone is encountered where the oxide formed is not sufficient and some additional sodium carbonate must be added. Usually a 30-minute ignition of the limestone is sufficient to render soluble the silicate present. The sample may then be dissolved in hydrochloric acid and the dehydration for silica begun.

The determination of silica is discussed in detail, page 114. Either the hydrochloric acid or the perchloric acid dehydration can be employed in the analysis of a limestone, but the sulfuric acid method is inapplicable owing to the sparing solubility of calcium sulfate. After correcting the silica for impurities the residue of iron, aluminum, calcium, and magnesium is dissolved and added to the main solution.

The silica content of a high-grade limestone or dolomite may be as low as a few hundredths of 1 per cent. In others it may be anything up to 99 per cent, as in a sandstone contaminated with limestone.

Procedure for the Determination of Silica. Dry the finely ground limestone for analysis at least 2 hours at 110°. Weigh accurately a sample of 1 to 1.5 g. into a platinum crucible. This can be done by weighing the platinum crucible, adding the sample to it, and weighing again; or the weighing bottle and sample may be weighed, the sample transferred carefully to the platinum crucible, and the bottle again weighed. Heat the crucible gradually to a red heat to decompose the carbonate; if the heating is too rapid the evolution of carbon dioxide may be so vigorous that some of the sample may be expelled mechanically. Then heat at the full heat of the Meker burner for 30 minutes. Keep the platinum crucible in the oxidizing flame, that is, above the tips of the blue cones of flame above the grid of the burner. Cool, and place the crucible in a 400-ml. beaker.

Cover the beaker and add 15 ml. of water and 15 ml. of concentrated hydrochloric acid a little at a time. Wash down the cover glass and dilute the solution to 50 ml. With a hooked stirring rod remove the platinum crucible, washing it well inside and out with a stream of water from the wash bottle as it is withdrawn. Evaporate the solution to dryness on a hot plate, continuing the evaporation until the solid residue, beaker, and cover glass are completely dry. Add 5 ml. of concentrated hydrochloric acid to dissolve the basic salts and then 20 ml. of water. Cover and warm until the salts have all dissolved, leaving a precipitate of fine silica. Dilute to about 100 ml. and filter, using a hard paper (Whatman No. 42, for example). Wash with dilute hydrochloric acid (1:99) until no trace of yellow ferric iron remains on the paper, and then wash two or three times with water.

Evaporate the filtrate to dryness again and as before take up with hydrochloric acid and water. Filter through a new filter paper and again wash with dilute hydrochloric acid and finally with water. Reserve the filtrate for the subsequent determinations of R_2O_3, calcium, and magnesium.

Transfer both filters to a crucible previously ignited and weighed; if only impure silica is desired a porcelain crucible is satisfactory, but if the silica is to be corrected for impurities a platinum crucible is necessary. See page 40 for the use and care of platinumware. Dry and burn away the papers, keeping the temperature low until the paper is burned away. Be careful not to allow the paper to break into flame, as silica is light and easily swept away in the gas stream. Finally ignite the precipitate at the full heat of the burner for 20 minutes. Cool the crucible and silica in a desiccator and weigh. Calculate the per cent of impure silica, SiO_2, if this is to be reported.

Moisten the silica in the platinum crucible with a drop or two of sulfuric acid. Add about 5 ml. of hydrofluoric acid,[1] pouring the acid directly from the polyethylene bottle into the crucible unless a plastic graduated cylinder is available. Evaporate cautiously to dryness, using a good hood. Fume away the sulfuric acid and heat at the full heat of a Meker burner for 5 minutes. Cool and weigh the residue. The loss in weight represents the pure silica in the sample. Report the results as per cent silica, SiO_2 (corrected).

If R_2O_3 (iron and aluminum) are to be determined on the same sample, fuse the residue with a little sodium carbonate, dissolve the melt in dilute hydrochloric acid, and add the solution to the filtrate from the silica; alternatively, the weight of the residue from the hydrofluoric acid-sulfuric acid treatment may simply be added to the weight of the ammonia precipitate (R_2O_3).

Continue the analysis as described in the next section dealing with the determination of R_2O_3.

THE DETERMINATION OF R_2O_3

Precipitation with ammonia is discussed on page 120. In a limestone analysis the elements precipitated by ammonia are filtered, ignited and weighed as a group. The result is then reported as per cent R_2O_3, which includes Fe_2O_3, Al_2O_3, TiO_2, Mn_3O_4, and P_2O_5.

Procedure for the Determination of R_2O_3. To the filtrate from the determination of silica add the solution obtained by dissolving the oxide residue remaining after correcting the silica with hydrofluoric acid and sulfuric acid. Add 1 ml. of bromine water to the solution and carefully boil for 4 or 5 minutes to make certain that all the iron is in the ferric state. Add a few drops of methyl red; if the indicator is destroyed, boil the solution a few minutes longer to expel the remaining bromine and add a few drops more of indicator. Add filtered, dilute ammonia (1:1) until the indicator changes color, and then an excess of 1 ml. Boil the solution gently for 8 or 10 minutes and then filter through a loose-texture filter paper. Wash the funnel and precipitate a few times with a 1 per cent solution of ammonium nitrate.

Place the beaker in which the precipitation was made under the funnel and dissolve the hydroxide precipitate by pouring onto the

---

[1] Precautions must be taken in the use of hydrofluoric acid. Unlike other strong acids, hydrofluoric acid causes no pain when it comes in contact with the skin, the acid apparently acting as a local anesthetic. Pain begins after a few hours of contact and is accompanied by serious swelling and inflammation which spreads. Severe burns may require amputation. Great care should therefore be taken to avoid breathing hydrofluoric acid vapors or spattering the acid on the skin and any acid touching the skin should be washed off immediately with water. A wise precaution is to wash the hands after every use of hydrofluoric acid.

funnel 20 ml. of hot, dilute hydrochloric acid (1:10). Wash the filter a few times with water. Add a few drops of methyl red to the solution and reprecipitate the R_2O_3 with filtered, dilute ammonia as before. Digest the solution for 10 minutes and filter, using the same filter paper. Wash six or eight times with 1 per cent ammonium nitrate solution. Combine the filtrates and reserve the solution for the determination of calcium.

Place the filter and precipitate of hydroxides in a porcelain crucible previously ignited and weighed. Burn away the paper. Ignite the precipitate 20 minutes at the full heat of a Meker burner with the crucible in an inclined position so that the oxides have free access to air. Cool and weigh. Calculate and report the per cent of R_2O_3 in the sample.

THE DETERMINATION OF CALCIUM

The separation and determination of calcium are discussed in detail on page 124.

Procedure for the Determination of Calcium. To the filtrate from the determination of iron, add 10 ml. of concentrated hydrochloric acid. Evaporate the solution to a volume of about 175 ml. Add a solution of 1.1 g. of ammonium oxalate, $(NH_4)_2C_2O_4 \cdot H_2O$, or 1.0 g. of oxalic acid, $H_2C_2O_4 \cdot H_2O$, dissolved in about 25 ml. of water. A part of the calcium may precipitate when the oxalate is added. Add 2 drops of methyl red and heat the solution to boiling. Add filtered, dilute ammonia (1:3) dropwise with stirring until the indicator becomes yellow, and then add a few drops in excess. Digest the precipitate for 1.5 hours, keeping the solution hot but not necessarily boiling. Cool to room temperature. Filter the calcium oxalate, using a medium, ashless paper (for example, Whatman No. 40). Wash the precipitate four or five times with a solution containing 1.0 g. of ammonium oxalate per l. Use small portions of the wash water and allow the liquid to drain away before adding more.

Carefully remove the filter paper from the funnel and place it in the same beaker in which the first precipitation of calcium was made. Add 3 to 4 ml. of concentrated hydrochloric acid and 7 to 8 ml. of water. With a stirring rod break up the paper. Heat gently and stir until the calcium oxalate has dissolved and only suspended shreds of paper are visible in the solution. Dilute the solution to 175 ml. with distilled water. Precipitate the calcium a second time just as described in the preceding paragraph; that is, add 1.1 g. of ammonium oxalate or 1.0 g. of oxalic acid. Add 2 drops of methyl red and heat the solution to boiling. Add filtered, dilute ammonia (1:3) dropwise with stirring until the indicator becomes yellow, and add a few drops in excess. Digest the precipitate 1.5 hours. Cool to room temperature. Filter, using a medium paper. Wash the precipitate with a solution containing 1.0 g. of ammonium oxalate per l. until the filtrate running through is free of chloride. In testing for chloride, collect a few milliliters of the filtrate in a clean test tube, add 2 drops of nitric acid and then a little silver nitrate; test the wash water to be sure it is chloride free.

Combine the filtrates from the two filtrations and use the resulting solution for the determination of magnesium.

Transfer the paper and calcium oxalate to a weighed crucible, preferably one of platinum, although porcelain will be satisfactory. Dry and burn away the paper and ignite at the full heat of a Meker burner with the crucible in a chimney of some sort. Chimneys of fire brick can be purchased from the supply houses, but cylinders of asbestos paper are easy to make and will last for a few determinations. Make the cylinder about 3 to 4 cm. larger in diameter than the crucible and cut slots up from the bottom so it will rest on the wire triangle and extend below the crucible 2 cm.

If an electric muffle is available ignite the precipitate at 1000° to 1100°; at this higher temperature calcium oxide is "dead burned" and is not as hygroscopic as when ignited at the lower temperature of a burner.

After removing the crucible from the burner or electric muffle, allow it to cool until it can almost be touched with the hand and then place it in a desiccator. As soon as it has reached room temperature, weigh. Do not delay more than 30 minutes, as calcium oxide will absorb water from the fresh air in the desiccator and later will extract it from the calcium chloride in the desiccator. Carry out the weighings as rapidly as possible. Ignite the crucible as before for 20 minutes, cool, and again weigh. This time have the weights already on the balance so that only the final adjustment of the rider is necessary and the weighing can be made quickly. A third ignition may be necessary if the weight is found to be increasing rapidly when the weighing is complete.

Report the per cent of calcium oxide.

THE DETERMINATION OF MAGNESIUM

The precipitation of magnesium as the double ammonium phosphate is discussed on page 128. As pointed out there the precipitate does not have the correct composition when precipitated from a solution containing considerable ammonium salts, although all the magnesium is precipitated. Two alternatives are open. Either the ammonium salts can be destroyed by evaporation with nitric and hydrochloric acids, or the first precipitate can be dissolved and reprecipitated. The complete destruction of the ammonium salts, particularly with oxalate present, is slow, and reprecipitation of the magnesium ammonium phosphate is desirable anyway, so that the reprecipitation procedure is recommended.

Procedure for the Determination of Magnesium. To the solution remaining from the determination of calcium add 10 ml. of concentrated hydrochloric acid and evaporate the solution to a volume of 150 ml. Cool the solution to room temperature. Add 10 ml. of a solution containing 25 g. of diammonium hydrogen phosphate, $(NH_4)_2HPO_4$, per 100 ml. Add a few drops of methyl red indicator. Add filtered ammonium hydroxide with stirring until the indicator has turned distinctly yellow. Stir for a few minutes and then add an additional 5 ml. of concentrated ammonium hydroxide. Allow the solution to stand at least 4 hours or overnight.

Filter the magnesium ammonium phosphate on ashless paper of medium texture. First decant the supernatant liquid through the filter and then transfer the precipitate to the filter. Loosen the precipitate from the beaker with a rubber-tipped stirring rod. Wash the precipitate with dilute ammonium hydroxide (5:100) five or six times, using just enough wash water to wet the precipitate well and allowing the water to drain away completely between washings. Dissolve the precipitate by pouring over it on the filter paper 50 ml. of warm, dilute hydrochloric acid (1:9). Wash the paper thoroughly with hot, dilute hydrochloric acid (1:99). Dilute the solution to 125 to 150 ml., add 0.25 g. of diammonium hydrogen phosphate, and cool the solution to room temperature. Add a few drops of methyl red indicator. Add filtered ammonium hydroxide with stirring until the indicator has turned distinctly yellow. Stir for a few minutes and then add an additional 5 ml. of concentrated ammonium hydroxide. Allow the solution to stand at least 4 hours or overnight.

Filter the magnesium ammonium phosphate on a porous-bottom filtering crucible previously washed, ignited, and weighed. Decant the supernatant liquid through the filter and then transfer the precipitate from the beaker with a rubber-tipped stirring rod. Wash the precipitate with dilute ammonium hydroxide (5:100) until the filtrate is free of chloride (acidify the sample of filtrate taken for the test with nitric acid before adding the silver nitrate). To minimize the loss due to solubility use as little of the wash water as is just necessary to effect the washing. Dry the precipitate in the drying oven or over a low flame. Place the filtering crucible in a larger porcelain crucible to protect the porous bottom and the precipitate from the flame. Heat the precipitate rather slowly at first, and then finally ignite it at the full heat of a Meker burner for 1 hour. Cool and weigh. Ignite the precipitate again for 30 minutes and again cool and weigh. The loss in weight should not be greater than 0.3 mg. If an electric muffle is available carry out the ignition in it at 1000°; constant weight will be attained rapidly at this temperature. The magnesium pyrophosphate is usually quite dark in color after the ignition.

From the weight of magnesium pyrophosphate calculate the per cent of magnesium oxide in the sample; the conversion factor is 0.3623.

THE DETERMINATION OF CARBON DIOXIDE

Samples of naturally occuring carbonate minerals such as limestone ($CaCO_3$), magnesite ($MgCO_3$), dolomite [$CaMg(CO_3)_2$], rhodochrosite

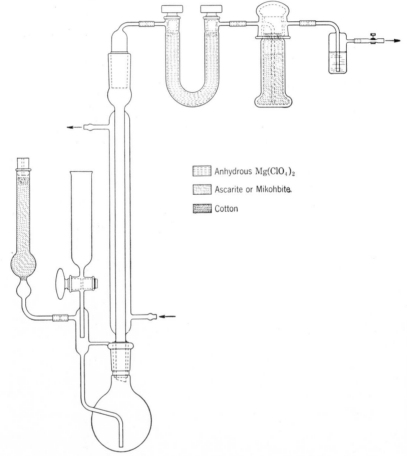

Anhydrous $Mg(ClO_4)_2$

Ascarite or Mikohbite.

Cotton

Fig. 91. Apparatus for the determination of carbon dioxide in carbonates.

($MnCO_3$), and siderite ($FeCO_3$) dissolve readily in strong acids with the evolution of carbon dioxide. The carbon dioxide present in such materials may be determined by carrying out the reaction in a closed vessel and sweeping the carbon dioxide liberated into a suitable absorbent so that it can be weighed. A suitable apparatus is that shown in Fig. 91.

Carbon dioxide is removed from the air stream in the absorption tube at the left. The sample is treated with perchloric acid added through the dropping funnel after the system has been swept free of carbon dioxide. The major part of the water in the air stream is removed by the water-cooled condenser and the remainder by a drying agent in the U-tube. The air then passes through the weighed absorption tube and through a bubbler containing sulfuric acid so that its rate can be estimated. The increase in the weight of the absorption vessel represents the carbon dioxide in the sample.

Limestone occasionally has some pyrite as impurity which yields hydrogen sulfide on treatment with perchloric acid. Hydrogen sulfide is absorbed by alkaline absorbents along with carbon dioxide, and to eliminate this interference potassium dichromate is added to the reaction mixture; sulfide is then oxidized to sulfate as soon as formed.

Absorbents for Carbon Dioxide. The absorbents for carbon dioxide take advantage of the acidic properties of the gas; that is, they are strong alkalies. Sodium hydroxide and potassium hydroxide are most commonly used, but occasionally barium hydroxide is employed. It is more convenient to use these absorbents as solids rather than as liquids if the weight of carbon dioxide absorbed is to be measured. The solid hydroxides present little surface for absorption in the form in which they are usually marketed, that is, as sticks or pellets. It is necessary to disperse the materials on some inert base to increase their porosity. Asbestos or exploded mica is used. *Ascarite* is a composition of sodium hydroxide and asbestos; *mikohbite* is a composition of sodium hydroxide and mica.

The capacity of these preparations is rather high, and their effectiveness in removing carbon dioxide from a gas stream is excellent, for they are highly porous and all the alkali is used. Both change in color as carbon dioxide is absorbed, giving warning of the exhaustion of the absorbent. Water is produced on the absorption of carbon dioxide, $CO_2 + 2NaOH = Na_2CO_3 + H_2O$. Inasmuch as this water is part of the absorbent when it is weighed, this water must be retained. Neither ascarite nor mikohbite are strong absorbents for water, so that it is necessary to charge the final portion of the absorption tube with a good drying agent such as anhydrous magnesium perchlorate.

Neither ascarite nor mikohbite is a specific absorbent for carbon dioxide. Rather, they absorb all acidic gases, for example, hydrogen chloride, hydrogen sulfide, sulfur dioxide, and hydrogen cyanide.

Weighing Large Absorption Bulbs. Absorption bulbs of several different designs are available from the apparatus supply houses. The Turner bulb shown in Fig. 91 is a very convenient form.

Owing to changes in the amount of moisture condensed or adsorbed on the large surface of an absorption vessel and the possible changes this film may undergo with changes in humidity, absorption bulbs are always weighed with a counterpoise. The best counterpoise is a second absorption bulb similar in size and shape. The two are given identical treatment. The counterpoise is part of the weights and must be treated carefully. Bulbs should be picked up by tongs or with a strip of paper. They should not be wiped with a rag after once being filled and placed in use.

Static charges accumulating on absorption bulbs will cause erratic fluctuations in the oscillations of the balance. This can be quite troublesome, particularly in periods of low humidity. Some things can be done to dissipate static charges but in general the best procedure is simply to wait until the charge naturally leaks away.

Absorption bulbs should be kept closed except when used. Heating and cooling effects and changes in barometric pressure can cause the air pressure inside the bulb to be different from that outside. This can cause an appreciable change in weight and can be avoided by opening the bulb momentarily before weighing.

Procedure for the Determination of Carbon Dioxide. Mount the apparatus as shown, using single buret clamps to hold the major pieces. Use a good grade of rubber tubing for the joints between the tube from the condenser and U-tube, and between U-tube and absorption bulb; the inside diameter of the tubing should be slightly smaller than the glass tubing so that a snug fit will be secured. Place glass to glass in making the connections. Place ascarite or mikohbite in the drying tube at the air inlet, using plugs of cotton batting to keep the absorbent in place. Fill the U-tube with anhydrous magnesium perchlorate, placing short lengths of cotton plugs above the absorbent in both arms. If the U-tube is not provided with glass stopcocks, close the ends of the U-tube with corks cut almost flush with the ends of the U-tube and seal them over smoothly with sealing wax. In two absorption bulbs, identical in size and shape, place ascarite or mikohbite, filling each two-thirds to three-fourths full. Fill the remaining space with the same drying agent used in the U-tube, leaving room for a plug of cotton. Place concentrated sulfuric acid in the bubbler.

Connect the bubbler to a water aspirator and place a screw clamp on the suction line so that the rate of flow of air may be adjusted.

Weigh accurately into the reaction flask a sample of such size that it will yield 0.3 to 0.6 g. of carbon dioxide; this will usually mean a sample of 1 to 10 g. As a check on the operation of the apparatus and procedure it is recommended that a material of known composition be run first, preferably a good grade of calcium carbonate. Add two or three small pieces of porous plate to the flask. Grease the ground-glass joints of the condenser lightly and assemble the apparatus, turning the joints to distribute the grease evenly. Slip the rubber-tubing connections over the glass tubing without grease or moisture, bringing the ends of the glass tubing together. Run 20 to 30 ml. of water through the dropping funnel into the reaction flask. Pass a stream of air through the system for 15 minutes, adjusting the flow to about 2 bubbles per second. Disconnect the absorption bulb and weigh it, using the second bulb as counterpoise. Replace the bulb, and continue the air stream for 15 minutes. Disconnect the bulb and weigh it again. The change in weight would not exceed 0.2 or 0.3 mg.

When a satisfactory blank has been obtained, replace the absorption bulb, adjust the air stream, and pass cooling water through the condenser. Add through the dropping funnel 20 ml. of dilute perchloric acid (1:3), adding the acid in small portions over a period of 2 to 3 minutes. Heat the solution with a burner and boil gently for 5 minutes. Continue the air stream for 20 to 30 minutes. Disconnect the absorption bulb. Allow it to come to the temperature of the balance and the counterpoise. Open the stopcocks of both absorption bulb and counterpoise momentarily, and weigh the absorption bulb, taking care that bulb, counterpoise, and weights are on the same sides of the balance as before. Calculate the per cent of carbon dioxide in the sample. The results on a known material should check the theoretical value within 0.2 per cent.

PROBLEMS

1. List the elements which may be found in limestone in addition to calcium, carbon, and oxygen, indicating in what form each is present.

2. Write equations for the decomposition of an insoluble silicate, feldspar, $NaAlSi_3O_8$, for example, during the ignition of a limestone sample.

3. During the preliminary ignition of a limestone to render silicates soluble, explain

(a) Why the ignition must be done in a platinum crucible rather than in one of porcelain.

(b) Why the heat should be applied gradually.

(c) Why all the loss in weight during the ignition may not be due to the volatilization of carbon dioxide from the carbonate.

4. In connection with the determination of silica in limestone, explain

(a) When a second dehydration of silica is necessary.

(b) Why a filtration must precede the second dehydration.

(c) Why a new filter paper should be used following the second dehydration.

(d) Why dilute hydrochloric acid is used to wash silica rather than water.

(e) Why the silica finally obtained is often pink.

5. Write equations for all the reactions which occur in correcting silica for impurities of ferric, aluminum and calcium oxides. Explain why the addition of a few drops of sulfuric acid to the silica followed by ignition before the first weighing is desirable.

6. Tell what happens when hydrofluoric acid is left in contact with the skin more than momentarily.

7. Write equations for the reactions involved in the sodium carbonate fusion and hydrochloric acid treatment given the residue left after correcting silica so that it may be returned to the main solution.

8. In connection with the determination of R_2O_3 in limestone, explain

(a) Why it is necessary to oxidize iron to the ferric state prior to precipitation.

(b) Why the ammonia used must first be filtered.

(c) Why a large excess of ammonia must be carefully avoided.

(d) Why a reprecipitation of the hydrated oxides is necessary.

(e) The reasons for the choice of wash water employed.

(f) Why precautions are taken to avoid reduction during the ignition of the R_2O_3 precipitate.

9. In connection with the determination of calcium oxide in limestone, explain:

(a) Why the hydrogen-ion concentration is a factor in the precipitation of calcium oxalate.

(b) What is meant by post-precipitation and how it enters into a limestone analysis.

(c) The relative merits of igniting calcium oxalate to calcium carbonate and to calcium oxide for weighing.

(d) How the determination can be concluded volumetrically.

10. Write equations for the destruction of ammonium chloride by nitric acid plus hydrochloric acid. The mechanism undoubtedly involves the hydrochloric acid, but the overall oxidation takes place at the expense of the nitric acid. The ammonia is oxidized to nitrogen.

11. Write equations showing the oxidation of oxalic acid to carbon dioxide by nitric acid (plus hydrochloric acid).

12. In connection with the determination of magnesium in limestone, explain

(a) Why ammonium salts must be destroyed before magnesium is precipitated.

(b) What alternative to destroying ammonium salts may be followed.

(c) The effect of large amounts of sodium and potassium salts on the determination.

(d) Why precipitation of magnesium ammonium phosphate in an unscratched beaker is recommended.

(e) The choice of wash solution used.

(f) Why iron, aluminum, and calcium interfere.

13. In connection with the determination of carbon dioxide in a limestone, explain

(a) Why the absorption bulb containing ascarite is also charged with dehydrite.

(b) Why a counterpoise is used in weighing the absorption bulb.

(c) Why opening the absorption bulb momentarily before weighing is recommended.

(d) How provision must be made to eliminate adverse effects of pyrite present in the sample.

14. Explain why the results of analyses of oxygen-containing materials such as carbonates, sulfates, and silicates are reported as oxides, for example, as per cent of Na_2O, CaO, Al_2O_3, CO_2, SiO_2, SO_3.

15. Calculate the volume of hydrofluoric acid, specific gravity 1.15, 48 per cent HF, required to volatilize 0.1000 g. of silica as silicon tetrafluoride.

16. A precipitate of magnesium ammonium phosphate was ignited in a closed tube in a stream of air which was conducted from the tube into 50.00 ml. of 0.1000 N hydrochloric acid. The excess acid required for titration to the methyl red end-point 9.00 ml. of 0.1200 N sodium hydroxide. Calculate the weight of magnesium oxide in the sample.

17. The per cent of carbon dioxide in a limestone sample was found to be 47.80. Calculate the per cent of calcium carbonate and of magnesium carbonate, assuming the sample to consist only of calcium and magnesium carbonates. Determine the empirical formula of the material.

18. Calculate the volume of carbon dioxide at standard conditions which will be liberated on treating an excess of limestone with 54.0 ml. of 0.2000 N hydrochloric acid.

19. Calculate the volume of carbon dioxide at standard conditions which will be liberated on heating 1 g. of magnesium carbonate at 1000°.

20. It is desired to know the total amount of acid which can be neutralized by a carload (50 tons) of limestone. Decide which of the following methods of analysis to use, keeping in mind (1) the information desired, and (2) the economic value of the shipment, and (3) the time required for the analysis.

(a) Loss on ignition.

(b) A determination of the volume of carbon dioxide liberated on treatment with an excess of acid. Time required: 10 minutes; accuracy ±0.4 per cent carbon dioxide.

(c) A gravimetric determination of carbon dioxide.

(d) An analysis of the limestone for silica, R_2O_3, calcium oxide, and magnesium oxide.

(e) Treatment of a weighed sample with excess standard acid, boiling to expel carbon dioxide, and back titration with standard alkali.

21. Limestone for agricultural purposes is sold on the basis of its calcium carbonate content, any magnesium carbonate being reported as calcium carbonate. Calculate the percentage of calcium carbonate which would be reported for dolomite being sold as limestone.

CHAPTER 18

The Determination of pH;

Colorimetric and Potentiometric

Methods

The pH scale as a method of expressing hydrogen-ion concentration is introduced in Chapter 8; this concept together with at least the major elements of the theory of neutralization given in the same chapter should be mastered before one attempts to understand the following material. In the later sections of this chapter, those dealing with the potentiometric measurement of pH, it is assumed that Chapter 10, which deals with electrochemical theory, has also been studied.

In any chemical system involving water, the hydrogen-ion concentration is a factor influencing the equilibrium. Practically all the reactions of analytical chemistry are conducted in aqueous solutions, and the effects of hydrogen-ion concentration are thus a primary concern in chemical analysis. All plant and animal life is carried on with water as the solvent, and here also the hydrogen-ion concentration is a matter of the utmost importance. As long as the earth's surface is dominantly water and its crust is permeated with this same ubiquitous solvent, and until some future unearthly variation of the species *Homo sapiens* settles on Jupiter and Saturn and adapts itself to life in liquid ammonia and methane, hydrogen-ion concentration will determine the equilibrium conditions and chemists will be measuring pH.

Of the two general methods of determining hydrogen-ion concentration, the colorimetric method is the simpler to carry out, but it is subject to greater errors; the potentiometric method requires more elaborate apparatus but is capable of greater accuracy and with modern electronic equipment (pH meters) is more convenient and rapid.

COLORIMETRIC METHODS

In the colorimetric determination of hydrogen-ion concentration use is made of organic dyestuffs which have the property of changing color with changing hydrogen-ion concentration. These so-called *indicators* change color over a range of hydrogen-ion concentration, and within the transition range the color has a characteristic and reproducible shade which depends on the concentration of the hydrogen ion. If a series of solutions having known hydrogen-ion concentrations of progressively varying values is prepared and each solution is treated with the same amount of a suitable indicator, the successive solutions will display a uniform transition in color from one end to the other. A solution of unknown hydrogen-ion concentration may be treated with the same amount of the same indicator and its pH determined by simply matching the color with one of the known solutions. In the following material the theory of indicators is discussed, the method of preparing buffers or solutions of known hydrogen-ion concentration is then taken up, and then a simple and also a more elaborate method of matching the colors is described. The section is concluded with a discussion of the sources of error to which the colorimetric method is subject.

Indicators. The organic materials which act as hydrogen-ion indicators, changing color with changing pH, are themselves weak acids or weak bases. They ionize to varying degrees and form salts on neutralization with bases and acids. They have also the further property that the anions and cations so produced have colors differing from the colors of the undissociated compounds. These color changes are produced by rather complicated rearrangements of the atoms within the molecule.[1] Being weak acids or bases, they are amenable to the

[1] Phenolphthalein, for example, is actually a tribasic acid having the complicated structural formula a in acid solution, the six-sided rings representing rings of 6 carbon atoms. On neutralization with 2 molecules of hydroxide the two forms

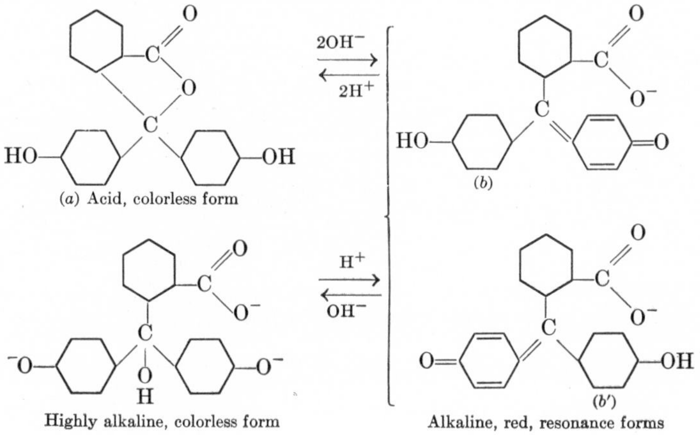

(a) Acid, colorless form

(b)

Highly alkaline, colorless form

Alkaline, red, resonance forms

(b′)

same general treatment that was applied to weak acids and bases in Chapter 8. Thus, an acid indicator may be designated as HIn and its ionization represented by

$$\text{HIn} = \text{H}^+ + \text{In}^-$$

Acid form   Alkaline form

In the titration of a weak acid there is a gradual rise in the pH of the solution as the acid is neutralized. Thus in Fig. 51, page 177, curve *B*, there is an increase in pH from 3.6 to 5.5, or about 1.9 pH units on going from 10 per cent titrated (2.5 ml.) to 90 per cent titrated (22.5 ml.). This means that in the case of an indicator which is a monobasic acid that the color change will take place over a band of about 1.9 pH units if it is assumed that 90 per cent of one color will completely cover up 10 per cent of the other color. The position of this band on the pH scale depends on the dissociation constant of the indicator. An indicator having a dissociation constant about the same value as that of acetic acid $(K_A = 1.75 \times 10^{-5})$ will change over the range of pH 3.6 to 5.5. The indicators which are very weak acids change at higher pH values, and those which are stronger acids will change at lower values. Conversely, the indicators which are weak bases will change at low pH and the stronger bases at higher pH.

The mass-action principle may be applied to the dissociation of an indicator just as to any weak acid. The dissociation constant for the reaction written above is

$$K_{\text{HIn}} = \frac{[\text{H}^+][\text{In}^-]}{[\text{HIn}]}$$

This equation may be rewritten

$$[\text{H}^+] = K_{\text{HIn}} \frac{[\text{HIn}]}{[\text{In}^-]}$$

By taking the negative logarithm of each side of the equation, a new equation is obtained in terms of pH and pK_{HIn}:

$$pH = pK_{\text{HIn}} + \log \frac{[\text{In}^-]}{[\text{HIn}]}$$

Or
$$pH = pK_{\text{HIn}} + \log \frac{[\text{Alkaline form}]}{[\text{Acid form}]}$$

This equation determines the position and the width of the pH band over which the indicator changes color. From the equation it is evident

b and *b'* are formed, which are equivalent and coexist in resonance with each other and are responsible for the red color. The addition of a third molecule of base, which occurs in a highly alkaline solution, produces a second colorless form.

that when pH equals pK_{HIn} that the concentrations of the acid and alkaline forms of the indicator are equal. This may not occur at the midpoint of the color change band, however, because the intensity of the color of the indicator in one form may be greater than in the second form. The red color of methyl red in acid solution is much more intense than the yellow color in the alkaline form; consequently the useful color band lies farther to the acid side than expected. If an apparent pK_{HIn} is determined by color measurements (rather than potentiometrically as for ordinary acids) then the equation is applicable.

The intensities of the colors of the two forms of the indicator also affect the width of the pH bands over which the indicator changes color. Roughly, for a two-color indicator (methyl orange or methyl red as contrasted to phenolphthalein which is colorless in acid form), 10 per cent of one form is concealed by 90 per cent of the other. This gives a band as shown above of about 1.9 pH units; that is, the conversion from log (10/90) to log (90/10) is about 1.9 pH. If the color of one form is much more intense than that of the other, 20 or 30 per cent of the weaker color may be required before the weaker color can

TABLE 33. COLORS AND TRANSITION RANGES OF THE COMMON INDICATORS

A	Amber	G	Green	Pu	Purple
B	Blue	O	Orange	R	Red
C	Colorless	P	Pink	V	Violet
				Y	Yellow

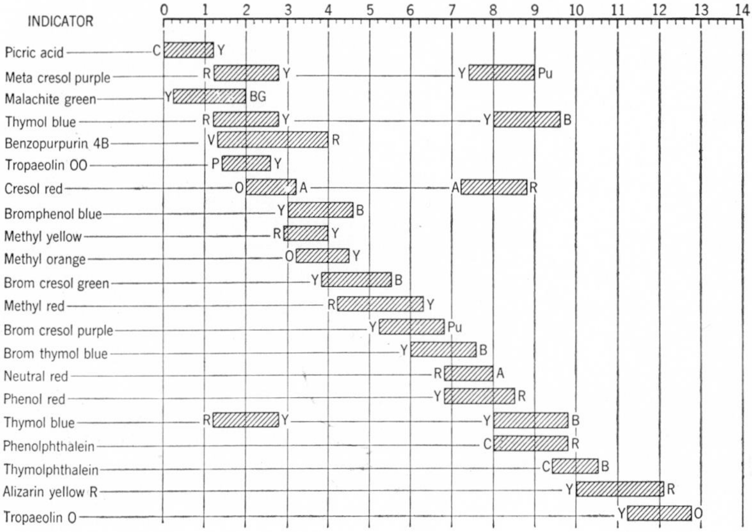

be detected and the pH band will then be narrower. If the indicator is a dibasic acid and the two ionization constants have about the same magnitude, the color change is more abrupt than for an indicator which is a monobasic acid.

Indicators which are dibasic acids with ionization constants of quite different values sometimes have two color transitions; for example, thymol blue which is red at pH 1 and yellow at pH 3 undergoes a second shift from yellow to blue between 8 and 9.5. Many of the numerous indicators which have been studied are bases rather than acids, but the same general considerations apply. In Table 33, in which the colors and transition bands of the more commonly used indicators are given, no attempt is made to differentiate the acidic from the basic indicators, for they function in quite identical fashion.

Buffer Solutions. The solutions of known pH necessary for making colorimetric determinations of pH are best prepared by mixing appropriate volumes of certain standard solutions. Procedures for doing this have been worked out in detail by McIlvaine, by Clark and Lubs, and by others. The composition of these buffer solutions is given in Tables 34 and 35. The McIlvaine buffers are relatively easy to prepare

TABLE 34. COMPOSITION OF McILVAINE'S BUFFERS

Measure out the volume of solution A required for the desired pH and add sufficient volume of solution B to bring the volume to 10.00 ml.

	Ml.		Ml.		Ml.		Ml.		Ml.
pH	A	pH	A	pH	A	pH	A	pH	A
2.2	0.20	3.4	2.85	4.6	4.67	5.8	6.05	7.0	8.24
2.4	0.62	3.6	3.22	4.8	4.93	6.0	6.32	7.2	8.70
2.6	1.09	3.8	3.55	5.0	5.15	6.2	6.61	7.4	9.09
2.8	1.58	4.0	3.85	5.2	5.36	6.4	6.92	7.6	9.37
3.0	2.05	4.2	4.14	5.4	5.57	6.6	7.27	7.8	9.58
3.2	2.47	4.4	4.41	5.6	5.80	6.8	7.72	8.0	9.73

Solution A, 0.200 M Disodium Hydrogen Phosphate. Dissolve 145 g. of disodium hydrogen phosphate ($Na_2HPO_4 \cdot 12H_2O$) in 2 l. of water. Titrate 10.00 ml. of this solution with 0.100 N hydrochloric acid and a drop of methyl orange until the color matches that of an equal volume of indicator in an equal volume of a solution prepared by dissolving 2.28 g. of potassium dihydrogen phosphate and 1.00 g. of sodium chloride in 250 ml. of water. Dilute the solution so that 20.00 ml. of 0.100 N hydrochloric acid will be required to titrate another 10.00-ml. portion.

Solution B, 0.100 M Citric Acid. Dissolve 45 g. of citric acid in 2 l. of water. Titrate 10.00 ml. of the solution with 0.100 N sodium hydroxide to the phenolphthalein end-point. Dilute the citric acid solution so that 30.00 ml. of 0.100 N sodium hydroxide will be required to titrate another 10.00-ml. portion of the solution.

TABLE 35. COMPOSITION AND pH OF CLARK AND LUBS BUFFERS, 20°

Dilute the following volumes to 100 ml.

pH	0.2 N HCl (milliliters)	0.2 N KCl (milliliters)	pH	0.1 N NaOH (milliliters)	0.1 M KHC$_8$H$_4$O$_4$ (milliliters)
1.0	48.50	25.00	4.0	0.40	50.0
1.2	32.25	25.00	4.2	3.70	50.0
1.4	20.75	25.00	4.4	7.50	50.0
1.6	13.15	25.00	4.6	12.15	50.0
1.8	8.30	25.00	4.8	17.70	50.0
2.0	5.30	25.00	5.0	23.85	50.0
2.2	3.35	25.00	5.2	29.95	50.0
			5.4	35.45	50.0
			5.6	39.85	50.0
			5.8	43.00	50.0
			6.0	45.45	50.0

pH	0.1 N HCl (milliliters)	0.1 M KHC$_8$H$_4$O$_4$ (milliliters)	pH	0.1 N NaOH (milliliters)	0.1 M KH$_2$PO$_4$ (milliliters)
2.2	46.70	50.00	6.0	5.70	50.0
2.4	39.60	50.00	6.2	8.60	50.0
2.6	32.95	50.00	6.4	12.60	50.0
2.8	26.42	50.00	6.6	17.80	50.0
3.0	20.32	50.00	6.8	23.65	50.0
3.2	14.70	50.00	7.0	29.63	50.0
3.4	9.90	50.00	7.2	35.00	50.0
3.6	5.97	50.00	7.4	39.50	50.0
3.8	2.63	50.00	7.6	42.80	50.0
			7.8	45.20	50.0
			8.0	46.80	50.0

pH	0.1 N NaOH (milliliters)	0.1 M H$_3$BO$_3$ (milliliters)
7.8	2.61	50.0
8.0	3.97	50.0
8.2	5.90	50.0
8.4	8.50	50.0
8.6	12.00	50.0
8.8	16.30	50.0
9.0	21.30	50.0
9.2	26.70	50.0
9.4	32.00	50.0
9.6	36.85	50.0
9.8	40.80	50.0
10.0	43.90	50.0

and cover the pH range of 2.2 to 8.0, which includes the pH of all biological systems and most of the solutions used in analytical chemistry. The Clark and Lubs buffers cover a greater range of pH, 1.0 to 10.0, but require a greater number of standard solutions.

Matching Unknown and Standard. In making the comparison between the unknown solution and the solution of known pH (buffer solution), equal volumes of the two solutions should be taken and as

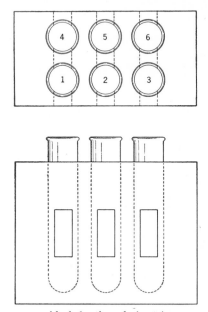

Fig. 92. Comparator block for the colorimetric measurement of pH.

nearly as possible equal amounts of the indicator solution added to each. An indicator must be chosen so that its transition range includes the pH of the solution being examined. Normally this will require a few preliminary tests to determine the approximate pH and to select a suitable indicator. Having the proper indicator, three buffer solutions can then be prepared, differing in value by 0.1 or 0.2 pH, such that the middle solution matches the unknown and the color of those on either side are noticeably different, one being more acidic, the other more basic.

If the solution being examined has no color of its own, the matching can be done quite satisfactorily in simple, clear-glass test tubes held against a white background. If the solution being tested has a color of its own which is not too intense, a colorimetric determination of pH may still be made but a more elaborate technique must be used. By means of the comparator block shown in Fig. 92, conditions can be arranged to cancel the effects of the color of the water. The block is drilled to accommodate six test tubes which are viewed in pairs sidewise through the block when the block is held up to the light. In holes 1 and 3 are placed tubes containing two buffers having slightly different values of pH, each containing 10 drops of indicator solution. In tube 5 is placed the solution being tested plus 10 drops of indicator. In tube 2 is placed distilled water with no indicator, and in tubes 4 and 6 are placed the solution being tested with no indicator. In this manner when the solutions are examined the tubes are viewed in pairs, and in each pair one solution containing the solution being tested and the second distilled water. Each pair also has the same amount of indicator. The color of the solution is thus compensated, and the buffer solutions may be varied until the desired match is secured.

Errors Affecting the Colorimetric Determination of pH. *Acid Error. Isohydric Indicators.* Inasmuch as indicators themselves are acids or bases, their addition to an aqueous solution must change the pH of the solution. If the solution is well buffered, the pH may not be significantly altered by the relatively small amount of indicator necessary. On the other hand, if the solution is not buffered the change may be considerable. Hard waters, such as those taken from wells and streams in many places, are well buffered by the carbonic acid and calcium bicarbonate which they carry in solution. Other natural waters may contain relatively little dissolved salts, and thus a determination of their pH by the direct addition of an acidic or basic substance such as an indicator is not possible. Obviously, a more subtle approach is required in such cases. If the pH of the indicator solution is the same as that of the solution, the pH of the solution will not change. An indicator so adjusted is spoken of as being *isohydric* with the solution.

A simple test will tell if the solution and indicator are isohydric. If the pH changes on the addition of more indicator they are not. The indicator can then be treated with a little very dilute acid or base as required, and the test repeated until the pH does not change on the addition of more indicator. A somewhat more convenient way to carry out the pH adjustment of the indicator is to prepare two solutions of the indicator, one in the acid form and the second in the alkaline form. These can be mixed in various ratios, either by counting drops or by delivering the solutions from measuring pipets. The ratio can be quickly altered by varying the volumes of the two solutions taken. When an indicator solution is finally obtained which has the same pH as the solution being tested the result is not affected by the amount of indicator added.

Effects of Salts, Protein, and Miscible Solvents. High concentrations of salt cause a shift in the ionization constant of the indicator. This results in a shift in the pH band of the indicator and may lead to erroneous results if the buffer does not contain a roughly similar salt concentration. The salt effect varies greatly from one indicator to another. With some indicators the error may be as great as 0.2 pH units for salt concentrations of 0.1 M; with others the effect is absent in salt concentrations as high as 0.5 M. Buffer solutions are made up with a salt concentration about 0.1 M. In the case of most indicators used on solutions of lower salt concentration the pH values obtained are low.

The dissociation constant of indicators is often changed also by the presence of dissolved or suspended protein material. This effect depends on the nature of the protein, the charge it carries, and on the indicator. The colorimetric determination of the pH of biological solutions will therefore always be subject to uncertainties, and the pH of such solutions is best determined potentiometrically.

The dissociation constant of an indicator is also changed by any variation in the nature of the solvent and thus by the addition of solvents miscible with water, such as alcohol. With ethyl alcohol the effect is not significant until the amount of alcohol exceeds 10 per cent.

Procedure for the Colorimetric Determination of pH. Dip a strip of litmus paper into the solution; if the paper turns red, it is evident that the solution is acid and that in further tests the indicators can be confined to those which change at values of pH less than 7. If the paper turns blue the pH is greater than 7 and the indicators changing in the acid range are eliminated from further consideration. The intensity of the red or blue color developed will give some additional information; if only a weak pink develops, the pH is probably between 5 and 7. Determine the pH of the solution approximately, to within 0.5 pH units or so, by testing 1 to 2 ml. of the sample with a drop of each of the various indicators in turn. In separate tests with distilled water containing a little acid or a little alkali observe the full acid and full alkaline forms of the various indicators used. Select an indicator which gives neither the full acid color nor the full alkaline color when placed in the solution being tested, since this shows that the pH of the sample falls in the transition range of the indicator.

Prepare a series of standard pH solutions corresponding to the range covered by the indicator, using either the McIlvaine or the Clark and Lubs buffers, mixing the standard solutions in the proportions given in Tables 34 and 35. Measure exactly 10.0 ml. of each of the standard pH solutions and the unknown solution into a series of uniform test tubes in a rack. The test tubes must be of the same size and must be uniform as to color on visual examination. Add exactly the same volume, 2 to 5 drops, of the indicator to each of the standard pH solutions and to the sample. Compare the color developed in the sample with the colors of the standard pH solutions, estimating the pH to the nearest 0.1 unit. Comparison is best made by observing the test tubes against a white background, using reflected light. Observe the test tubes sidewise rather than through the length of the test tubes.

If the solution to be tested has a slight color of its own it is necessary to carry out the comparison in a comparator block. Place the test tube containing the sample with indicator added in one of the center holes of the block, and place test tubes containing the solution without indicator on either side of it. In the remaining center hole place a test tube containing distilled water. In the holes on each side of the tube of distilled water place two solutions of known pH, differing from each other by 0.2 pH, which appear to match the color of the unknown. With your back to a window, hold the comparator block in one hand and with the other hand hold a sheet of white paper about 1 foot from the block and in such a position as to reflect diffused light through the horizontal holes in the block. Carefully compare the colors. If the color of the unknown does not match the color of one of the standards or does not appear to be intermediate in shade between the two colors, replace the standards with two other consecutive ones until such a match is obtained. The pH of the unknown solution is the same as the pH of the standard solution which it matches, or the average of the pH values of two solutions which lie on either side. Report the pH of the solution and also the indicator used.

PROBLEMS

1. The acid dissociation constant of the indicator methyl red as determined visually is 7.9×10^{-6}. Calculate the pH of a solution of the indicator in which (a) the indicator is 90 per cent in the acid form and 10 per cent in the alkaline form, and (b) the indicator is 10 per cent in the acid form and 90 per cent in the alkaline form. Use the equation for the dissociation constant and convert to pH only after obtaining values for $[H^+]$. Decide if the pH range covered by the transition from situation a to situation b depends on the value of the dissociation constant of the indicator.

2. The indicator methyl red has a molecular weight of 269 and a dissociation constant as an acid of 7.9×10^{-6}. A 0.1 per cent solution is used as indicator. Calculate the pH of 10.0 ml. of distilled water to which 10 drops (0.5 ml.) of this indicator solution has been added.

3. In Table 34, which gives the composition of McIlvaine's buffers, directions are given for the preparation of two standard solutions. Confirm the procedures given and tell in somewhat greater detail just how the final dilutions to the specified normalities are calculated and made.

4. Using the data of Table 34, which gives the composition of McIlvaine's buffers, plot pH against milliliters of solution *A*. Compare the curve with the titration curves of Chapter 8 and explain why disodium hydrogen phosphate and citric acid were chosen for these buffer mixtures, in preference, for example, to sodium hydroxide and acetic acid.

5. Prove that the pH range over which an indicator changes color is only 0.95 pH units if the indicator is a dibasic acid for which the two hydrogen ions are about equally dissociated. *Hint:* K_1 and K_2 are about equal, and the overall ionization can be handled by another constant, $K = K_1K_2$; assume as in Problem 1 that 90 per cent of one color completely covers up 10 per cent of the other color.

THE POTENTIOMETRIC DETERMINATION OF pH

The potentiometric determination of pH is based on the measurement of the electrical potential developed by an electrode whose potential depends on the hydrogen-ion concentration of the solution. The single-electrode potential of any electrode must be measured in conjunction with a second electrode dipping into the same solution; that is, the potential actually measured is the potential of a cell which is the difference of two single-electrode potentials. This was explained in Chapter 10. If one electrode, the *reference electrode*, is made to assume a constant potential toward the solution irrespective of the composition of the solution, then the second electrode, the *indicator electrode*, can be made to respond to changes in the composition of the solution. The reference electrode commonly used is the saturated calomel electrode. Three indicator electrodes for hydrogen ions are of interest: the hydrogen electrode, the quinhydrone electrode, and the glass electrode. The hydrogen electrode is of fundamental importance in having been chosen as the arbitrary zero of the oxidation-reduction series but is of little importance in the actual, routine measurement of pH. The quinhydrone electrode, which was the most widely used of the various hydrogen electrodes during the period 1920 to 1940, has now been displaced almost completely by the glass electrode. The quinhydrone electrode is simple to use, and, although subject to limitations, does not require the elaborate measuring apparatus required for the glass electrode; therefore it is still valuable in occasional work when the more expensive glass-electrode equipment is not available.

The actual electrical measurement of the potential of the cell must be made with the potentiometer so that practically no current is drawn from the cell. The principle and operation of the potentiometer are discussed on pages 240 and 266. The potentiometer must be modified for the measurement of the potential of the glass electrode; the reasons for this and the modification necessary are discussed later in the chapter under the glass electrode.

The Hydrogen Electrode. The technique of dissolving gaseous hydrogen in finely divided platinum and of thus establishing equi-

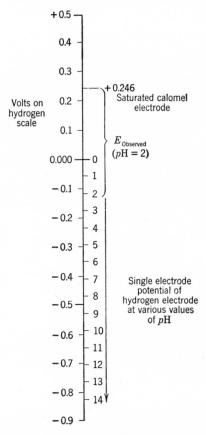

Fig. 93. Potential relations in measuring pH with hydrogen electrode-saturated calomel electrode system.

librium between gaseous hydrogen, hydrogen ions, and electrons, $H^+ + e^- = \frac{1}{2}H_2$, is described in Chapter 10. The hydrogen electrode can be used either as a reference electrode, or as an indicator electrode for hydrogen ions. When used as a reference electrode, the platinized foil and its surrounding tube through which gaseous hydrogen is passed are dipped into a solution of known hydrogen-ion concentration, and electrical contact is made to the second solution through a salt bridge; see Fig. 62, page 237. The potential is then measured. The potentials involved when the electrode pair consists of the hydrogen (indicator) electrode and the saturated-calomel (reference) electrode are shown graphically in Fig. 93. The single-electrode potential of the hydrogen electrode is shifted to more negative values with decreasing hydrogen-ion concentration, the shift amounting to 0.0592 volt for each tenfold change (25°). The saturated calomel electrode maintains a constant potential of +0.246 volt. The potential of the cell, then, gradually increases with decreasing hydrogen-ion concentration. At pH 2, that is, $[H^+] = 0.01$, the potential of the cell is +0.246 − (−0.118) = +0.362 volt. In general, then, if E is the potential of the cell,

$$E = +0.246 - 0.059 \log [H^+]$$

or $$pH = \frac{E - 0.246}{0.059}$$

When some other reference electrode is used its potential on the hydrogen scale is substituted for the 0.246 volt in this equation.

There are certain limitations on the hydrogen electrode. Metals positive to hydrogen in the reduction-potential series are reduced by the hydrogen gas in the presence of the platinum black of the electrode, and such a reaction alters the potential of the electrode. Strong oxidizing agents, such as dichromate, ferric iron, and permanganate, are similarly reduced and must also be absent from the solution. Very strong reducing materials must also be absent, chromous salts, stannous chloride, and sulfites, for example. The hydrogen electrode is easily poisoned by various substances, hydrogen sulfide, cyanide, certain types of protein, and many organic compounds, for example, so that pH measurements in the presence of these materials are unreliable. The hydrogen gas bubbling through the solution sweeps out some of any gases dissolved in the solution; if the hydrogen-ion concentration of the solution depends on some equilibrium involving carbon dioxide, the pH may change appreciably owing to the removal of carbon dioxide in this manner. Because the hydrogen electrode is inconvenient to use and is subject to these limitations, it is not used in the practical measurement of hydrogen-ion concentration. Still another objection, particularly valid in potentiometric titrations, is the time required for the electrode and surrounding solution to reach equilibrium. Frequently the time required is several minutes, and titrations under such conditions are time consuming and tedious.

The Quinhydrone Electrode. The two organic substances, quinone and hydroquinone, form an oxidation-reduction couple:

$$C_6H_4O_2 + 2H^+ + 2e^- = C_6H_4(OH)_2$$

Quinone   Hydroquinone

The electrode potential as applied to this reaction is

$$E = E^0_{\text{Quinone, Hydroquinone}} + \frac{0.059}{2} \log \frac{[\text{Quinone}][\text{H}^+]^2}{[\text{Hydroquinone}]}$$

The equilibrium and consequently the electrode potential involve the hydrogen-ion concentration. Quinone and hydroquinone have the further property of uniting in a ratio of 1:1 to form a new compound, quinhydrone

Quinone   Hydroquinone   Quinhydrone

Quinhydrone is somewhat soluble, and if added to a solution introduces a definite quantity of quinone and of hydroquinone in equivalent amounts. This means that, in the electrode-potential equation above, the concentration terms of quinone and hydroquinone become equal and cancel, leaving

$$E = E^0_{\text{Quinhydrone}} + 0.059 \log [\text{H}^+]$$

The potential developed depends only on the hydrogen-ion concentration, and the quinhydrone electrode is thus an indicator electrode for hydrogen ions. The electrode consists simply of a platinum foil, the usual indicator electrode for an oxidation-reduction system, dipping into the solution to which has been added a bit of solid quinhydrone. For the measurement of *p*H a reference electrode is inserted, and the potential between the platinum wire and the reference electrode is measured. For a saturated calomel reference electrode, the potential of the cell and the pH are related by the equation

$$E_{Cell} = E_{Quinhydrone} - E_{Sat. cal. elec.}$$

$$= E^0_{Quinhydrone} + 0.059 \log [H^+] - E_{Sat. cal. elec.}$$

$$pH = \frac{E^0_{Quinhydrone} - E_{Sat. cal. elec.} - E_{Cell}}{0.059}$$

$E^0_{Quinhydrone} = +0.699$ volt and $E_{Sat. cal. elec.} = +0.246$ volt, so that

$$pH = \frac{0.699 - 0.246 - E_{Cell}}{0.059}$$

The quinhydrone electrode is positive to the saturated calomel electrode. The difference in potential between the two decreases with decreasing hydrogen-ion concentration. At a pH of 7.68 the difference is zero, and at higher pH values the quinhydrone electrode is negative to the saturated calomel electrode. In the above equation a positive value is substituted for E_{Cell} if the wire from the quinhydrone electrode (platinum foil) is connected to the positive terminal of the potentiometer and negative if attached to the negative terminal.

The quinhydrone electrode is very simple to use. Only a few milligrams of quinhydrone are needed to saturate the solution, and the system comes to equilibrium quickly. Its only disadvantage is that it cannot be used in solutions having a pH greater than 8 or in solutions containing strong oxidizing and reducing agents. Hydroquinone acts as a weak acid and in alkaline solution is converted to its sodium salt which disturbs the equilibrium. Hydroquinone is very susceptible to oxidation in alkaline solution, and strong oxidizing agents effect its oxidation even in acid solution. Quinone is reduced by stannous chloride, ferrous salts, chromous salts, and sulfites, so that such strong reducing agents must be absent from the solution being measured. In carrying out a potentiometric titration, it is necessary to titrate the acid with the base because of the error in alkaline solution. If an alkali is to be titrated, it is necessary to add an excess of standard acid and back-titrate with a standard base. The quinhydrone electrode indicates a lower pH than the actual pH of alkaline solutions, reaching a maximum error of about 2.3 at pH 11, the error being greatly minimized if the solution is strongly buffered.

The Glass Electrode. The glass electrode is not an electrode at all in the normal sense but a unique device for measuring hydrogen-ion concentration. When solutions of different hydrogen-ion concentration are placed on opposite sides of a thin glass membrane, a potential difference exists across the membrane. The magnitude of this potential is determined principally by the difference in the hydrogen-ion concentrations of the two solutions. A reference electrode is inserted in each of the two solutions, and the potential between them is measured. The glass electrode thus consists of the cell

Reference Electrode	Solution of Known pH	Glass Membrane	Solution of Unknown pH	Reference Electrode

The potential of this cell is given by the expression $E = 0.059 \log [\text{H}^+]_1 - 0.059 \log [\text{H}^+]_2$. If the hydrogen-ion concentration of one solution is some known, constant value, the potential of the glass electrode varies linearly with the pH of the other solution: $E = E^0 - 0.059 \log [\text{H}^+]$. The potential developed is thus the same as that of the hydrogen electrode, but the mechanism is that of a concentration cell rather than that of a single-electrode potential.

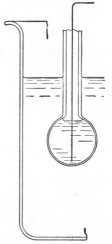

In practice the two reference electrodes used may not be identical. One commonly used for the known solution consists of a buffer solution of a certain pH which is saturated with quinhydrone, electrical contact being made through a platinum wire. The solution is hermetically sealed inside the glass membrane, which is usually in the form of a bulb. The outer reference electrode is commonly a saturated calomel electrode. The potential difference between the two reference electrodes is included in the E^0 term.

Fig. 94. Glass electrode. Inner reference electrode consists of a platinum wire dipping into a buffer solution saturated with quinhydrone. Outer reference electrode, not shown, is usually a saturated calomel electrode.

When the same solution is placed on each side of the glass membrane there usually exists across the membrane a slight residual potential known as the *asymmetry potential*. The cause of this potential is not known with certainty, but it is related to the unsymmetrical character of the surface and to strains in the glass. It varies in a rather unpredictable manner, so that in precise work it becomes necessary to calibrate the glass electrode against a buffer solution of known pH having a value in the general range of the solution to be subsequently measured. The asymmetry potential may change slightly from day to day or may be materially altered temporarily by exposure of the glass surface to very strong acid or alkali.

One of the great merits of the glass electrode is that it can be used in solutions containing oxidizing and reducing agents. It is unaffected by gases, dissolved organic matter, colloids, or suspended matter. It does not disturb the equilibrium of the solution as the hydrogen electrode does, and it is therefore particularly useful in determining the pH of biological solutions or of other solutions where the passage of hydrogen gas disturbs the equilibrium by sweeping away the gases dissolved in the solution. It is practically the only method of measuring the pH of solutions which are unbuffered. No chemicals need be introduced, so that the solution is left unaltered by the measurement. The glass electrode can be used in certain non-aqueous solutions and water-solvent mixtures if dehydrating agents are avoided. The glass electrode cannot be used in strongly alkaline solutions, above pH of 9, although this depends on the composition of the solution and the type of glass used. Special glass electrodes, made of lithium silicate, can be used in solutions of pH as high as 11 or 12.

Fig. 95. Commercial glass electrode. Inner reference electrode is a saturated calomel electrode. Used in conjunction with a second saturated calomel reference electrode.

The electrical resistance of the glass electrode is very high, being of the order of 500,000 ohms in very thin-walled and fragile membranes and as high as 200,000,000 ohms in rugged commercial makes. The measurement of the potential of the glass electrode cannot be made with an ordinary potentiometer because the current which passes through the glass membrane under the very low potential of the cell is insufficient to affect a galvanometer. Vacuum-tube amplifying devices, capable of registering minute currents, can be substituted for the galvanometer, however, and the measurement of the potential of such high resistance cells can be made successfully. Essentially, then, the commercial pH meter is an ordinary potentiometer in which the galvanometer has been replaced by a vacuum-tube device for indicating balance between the potential being measured and the potential taken from the slidewire. Vacuum-tube amplifiers require only minute current for their operation and may be left connected to the cell.

Inasmuch as every 0.0592 volt is equal to 1 unit of pH (at 25°), the slidewire can be calibrated to read directly in pH. Commercial pH meters are designed to take into account differences in the values of the two reference electrodes used and any asymmetry potential if present in the initial balancing. Usually also temperature compensation is provided for, the term RT/nF being equal to 0.0592 volt only at 25°. The commercial pH meters currently available are well designed and quite reliable. Explicit directions, usually placed in the cover of the instrument, are provided, and the operation of the instruments is generally quite simple. The first operation is usually that of adjusting the current in the working circuit so that the slidewire has the correct potential drop over its length, by balancing against a standard cell. The instrument is then calibrated with a buffer solution of known pH; the McIlvaine or Clark and Lubs buffers may be used for this purpose or one selected from those given in Table 36, which are

TABLE 36. CONVENIENT BUFFERS FOR CALIBRATION OF pH
METERS

Use McIlvaine or Clark and Lubs buffers, or those of this table, which are somewhat more easily prepared.

pH	Solution
3.57	Saturated solution of potassium hydrogen tartrate, $KHC_4H_4O_6$.
4.01	0.05 M potassium acid phthalate. Dissolve 1.021 g. of $KHC_8H_4O_4$ in 100 ml. of water.
6.86	0.025 M potassium dihydrogen phosphate, KH_2PO_4, plus 0.025 M disodium hydrogen phosphate, Na_2HPO_4.
9.18	0.05 M sodium tetraborate, $Na_2B_4O_7$.

more quickly prepared. It is best to standardize the meter with a buffer in about the same range of pH as the solution to be measured subsequently.

The mechanism whereby the potential across the glass membrane is established is obscure. It appears that within the glass membrane there exist hydrogen ions which migrate through the membrane, causing a transport of electricity in much the same manner as electricity is carried electrolytically through solutions of electrolytes. It is possible that a portion of the current is carried through the glass by sodium ions which are much more numerous in the glass, and that an exchange occurs at the surface between the hydrogen ions and the sodium ions.

The glass recommended as being most suitable for the glass electrode is Corning 015, a soda-lime glass, having the composition: 22 per cent Na_2O, 6 per cent CaO, and 72 per cent SiO_2. This glass has a low electrical resistance and is more sensitive to hydrogen ions than other glasses. As mentioned before such a glass cannot be used at pH values above 9, above which it begins to function as a sodium electrode. Glass electrodes made of lithium silicate can be used up to pH of 13 or 14 in solutions containing sodium salts; these are available commercially.

POTENTIOMETRIC TITRATION OF ACIDS AND BASES

The electrical circuit and electrodes required for following the course of neutralization reactions potentiometrically are the same as those outlined in the preceding sections on the potentiometric determination of pH. About the only additional features required are provisions for stirring and for the exclusion of carbon dioxide when necessary. A suitable potentiometric titration apparatus is shown in Fig. 67, page 265. The magnetic stirrer which is used is more convenient than a motor-driven glass stirring rod in that it leaves the opening at the top less congested.

The potentiometric titration of acids and bases can be carried out with any of a number of possible combinations of reference and hydrogen-ion indicator electrodes. The most common reference electrode is the saturated calomel electrode. The most convenient of the hydrogen-ion indicator electrodes is the glass electrode. The glass electrode requires that a vacuum-tube indicating device be employed to indicate the balance of the potentiometer. Fortunately the manufacturers of the better commercial pH meters have designed the equipment so that it can be adapted to titration work. The Leeds and Northrup pH meter as adapted for carrying out a neutralization reaction is shown in Fig. 96. The leads from the cell to the meter must be kept as short as possible unless they are special shielded leads provided by the manufacturer. The magnetic stirrer does not disturb the operation of the electronic amplifier if the case of the stirrer is grounded. The pH meter is convenient also in that it reads directly in pH.

If a glass electrode pH meter is not available and the ordinary potentiometric apparatus must be used, the quinhydrone electrode is the second choice. For the reasons pointed out above in the section on the quinhydrone electrode, the titration must always be made with standard alkali, back titration being made after the addition of standard acid when an alkali is being determined.

The potential of the hydrogen electrode is shifted in the negative direction as the hydrogen-ion concentration decreases. This is shown graphically in Fig. 93. The titration curves shown in Chapter 8, Figs. 48 to 57, were obtained with a glass-electrode apparatus, and the

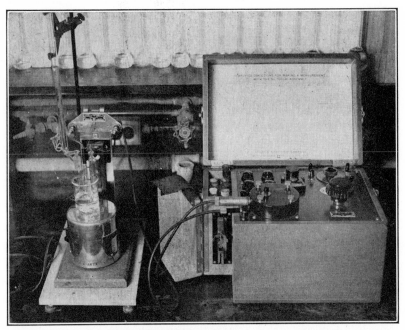

Fig. 96. Apparatus for potentiometric titrations involving neutralization reactions, using a pH meter, glass electrode, and saturated calomel electrode. (*Courtesy of Leeds and Northrup Co.*)

data is plotted to conform with the reduction potential scale as shown in Fig. 93.

The potentiometric method is slower to carry out than a titration with a visual indicator. It is usually necessary to plot the data, at least near the end-point, in order to locate the equivalence-point. On the other hand, the potentiometric method is successful in many titrations where visual indicators fail either because the solution is highly colored or the reactants are too weak to give the sharp change in pH necessary to change the indicator abruptly. Good illustrations of this are the titrations of cyanuric acid, $K_A = 2 \times 10^{-7}$, and of boric acid, $K_A = 5.8 \times 10^{-10}$, shown in Fig. 51, Chapter 8. No visual indicator will mark even roughly the end-point in the titration of acids as weak as these; on the other hand, the equivalence-point can be located with quite satisfactory precision by an inspection of the potentiometric titration curves. The equivalence-point in the titration of acetic acid with ammonia, Fig. 53, can be exactly located on the potentiometric titration curve, but no indicator is known which will give other than a gradual change in color over the end-point region. The most important aspect of potentiometric titrations, however, is probably the insight it has provided into the chemistry of the neutralization process. From a potentiometric titration curve it is possible to determine the dissociation constant of the acid or base titrated, choose the most suitable indicator for later, routine, visual-indicator titrations, measure the extent of hydrolysis of salts, and follow the course of slow reactions involving hydrogen or hydroxyl ions.

The amounts of material which can be titrated and the strengths of the standard solutions used is considerably lower by the potentiometric method than with visual indicators. Solutions as dilute as 0.001 N can be titrated without difficulty. The principal precaution which must be observed when working with such dilute solutions is the exclusion of carbon dioxide. This can be easily done by bubbling through the flask air which has been freed of carbon dioxide by passage over ascarite.

PROBLEMS

1. To 100 ml. of a solution of an acid being titrated was added 0.5 ml. of a 0.1 per cent solution of an indicator having a molecular weight of 250. Assuming that the indicator was a monobasic acid and that 50 per cent of the indicator had to be converted to the alkaline form to produce a color change sufficient to mark the end-point, calculate the error in the titration resulting from the neutralization of the indicator. Express the results as the volume of (a) 0.01 N and (b) 0.1 N sodium hydroxide required.

2. The potential of a cell consisting of a saturated calomel reference electrode and a hydrogen electrode was found to be 0.521 volt at 25°, the calomel electrode being positive. Calculate the pH of the solution.

3. Calculate the potential of a cell consisting of a saturated calomel reference electrode and a quinhydrone electrode dipping into a solution of pH 2. State which electrode is positive.

CHAPTER 19

Errors;

Accuracy and Precision;

Confidence Limits

Man errs, so long as he is striving—*Goethe*.

The measurement of any physical quantity is subject to some uncertainty, which is spoken of as the error in the measurement. In general, the average of a series of measurements will be considerably more reliable than a single measurement. The fact that the members of a series of measurements on the same quantity agree well amongst themselves, however, is no guarantee of the accuracy of the result, for all the measurements may be adversely affected to the same extent by some defect in the method or some maladjustment in the measuring device. Such systematic errors when discovered can usually be eliminated: a bad weight in a set may be replaced, a more accurate mark may be placed on the neck of a volumetric flask, or, in an analysis, steps can be taken to reduce the solubility of a precipitate or to drive a reaction more fully to completion.

Even when systematic errors cannot be eliminated, their effects can sometimes be offset by corrections. The determination of lead by the electrodeposition of lead dioxide at the anode is subject to a serious, systematic error, for the deposit invariably contains more oxygen than is accounted for by the formula PbO_2. The amount of extra oxygen deposited is quite constant, and the method can still be used, provided the empirical conversion factor 0.8640 instead of the theoretical factor 0.8660 is used to convert the weight of lead dioxide to weight of lead.

In addition to systematic errors are the accidental or indeterminate errors which arise because not all of the factors which enter into the measurement have been properly controlled. These errors are both positive and negative and are scattered about both sides of the average; by increasing the number of measurements an average is obtained which is more reliable than any individual reading. The accidental errors set a definite limit on the accuracy of a measurement, however, and the mere multiplication of the number of readings will not insure an appreciably more accurate result. Rather, it is necessary, if an inherently more accurate measurement is desired, to control more carefully the factors which affect the measurement. Frequently such added control or refinement is difficult to achieve. It may be so time-consuming and expensive that the value of the measurement may not justify the additional trouble. Thus, weight can be measured on the scales commonly used in stores with an error of about 1 part in 100, although comparable weights can be measured on an equal-arm balance to 1 part in 1000 or 1 part in 10,000. Obviously, in weighing groceries and meat, the extra time required to make a weighing with an equal-arm balance is hardly justified by the price of the product.

The effects of systematic and accidental errors just discussed are reflected in the use of the terms *precision* and *accuracy*. *Precision* is a measure of the reproducibility of a measurement. *Accuracy* is a measure of the departure of the measurement from the true value. A series of readings of a given quantity may be precise but not accurate. Thus, a crucible was weighed by ten different students who obtained the results in column A. It was weighed again ten times by one individual who obtained the results in column B. Finally, the weight of

A	B
13.1273	13.1283
13.1280	13.1281
13.1277	13.1284
13.1275	13.1280
13.1267	13.1281
13.1287	13.1282
13.1280	13.1283
13.1289	13.1284
13.1259	13.1283
13.1265	13.1282

Average 13.1275   *Average* 13.1282

the crucible was determined by the double-weighing method with a set of weights certified by the National Bureau of Standards, the value found being 13.12705. It is apparent that the deviations from the average are less in column B than in column A; that is, the measurements by the individual were more precise than those by the ten students. However, if 13.12705 is accepted as the true weight, it is apparent that the average of the ten results by the students using different sets of weights is closer to the true weight than that of the individual. In fact, it was found later that the set of weights used to obtain the weighings in column *B* contained one defective weight which was used in all the weighings.

Relative and Absolute Error. When expressed in the same units as those in which a measurement is made, the error in a measurement is called the *absolute error*. When the error is expressed as a fractional part of the value measured, the error is called the *relative error*. Absolute error has dimension, relative error is a pure number and is expressed as per cent or as parts per thousand. Thus, weighings made on the balances commonly employed in analytical laboratories will not usually be more reliable than 0.0001 g. The absolute error in such weighings is therefore 0.0001 g.; it is the same for an object of any weight weighed on the balance. The relative error, however, depends on the weight of the object. For an object weighing 1.0000 g., the relative error in the measurement is 0.0001 g. in 1.0000 g., or 1 part in 10,000; for an object weighing 0.1000 g. the relative error is 0.0001 g. in 0.1000 g., or 1 part in 1000. Relative error may also be expressed in per cent; thus in the two examples just cited the relative errors are $(0.0001/1.0000)100 = 0.01$ per cent and $(0.0001/0.1000)100 = 0.1$ per cent, respectively. The results of chemical analyses are usually expressed as the per cent of some constituent, and absolute error is then expressed as the per cent of the constituent; to avoid confusion it is best to express relative error in parts per thousand rather than in per cent.

Both methods of expressing the error in a measurement or an analysis are useful. Absolute error is particularly useful in interpreting the results of analyses. Thus, if the iron content of a 50-ton shipment of ore is reported to be 49.3 per cent with a maximum error of 0.2 per cent iron, there is little difficulty in computing the total weight of iron in the shipment and of deciding how much coke it will take to reduce it or how much hydrochloric acid will be required to dissolve it.

Relative error, on the other hand, is more useful in comparing one method of analysis with another and in evaluating the error in the result of some analysis which arises from the errors in the individual measurements which are combined to give the result.

A comparison of the different methods by which a certain element may be determined must often be made. Copper, for example, can be determined gravimetrically, volumetrically, and colorimetrically, the inherent errors in each procedure differing considerably:

Method	Relative Error
Gravimetric (electrodeposition)	1 part in 5000
Volumetric (iodometric)	1 part in 1000
Colorimetric (as $Cu(NH_3)_4SO_4$)	1 part in 50

Obviously in the analysis of a brass where the copper content must be determined within 0.05 per cent copper, the colorimetric method cannot be used and the volumetric method is just barely suitable. For, if the copper content happens to be 70 per cent, the error must be less than 0.05 in 70 or 5 parts in 7000, which is 1 part in 1400. On the other hand, for the small amount of copper in cast iron or in plant material, an error of 1 part in 50 may be perfectly permissible and the colorimetric method is the one to use. Actually, of course, this works the other way; the colorimetric method is the only method applicable to the determination of small amounts of copper, and the analyst must be content with whatever minimum relative error he can obtain under the circumstances.

Usually a result can be no more accurate than the least accurate of the measurements or operations which enter into the process leading to the result. If the error in weighing a sample for analysis is 1 part in 1000, there will be an error in the result of 1 part in 1000, no matter how carefully the other phases of the analysis are carried out. Thus, if the sample analyzed happens to be an iron ore and is found to contain 50.00 per cent iron, there is an uncertainty in the result of 1 part in 1000, or 5 parts in 5000, which is equal to 0.05 per cent iron. Indeed, in the gravimetric determination of iron four weighings are involved: the weight of the weighing bottle before and after the sample is removed, and the crucible empty and containing the final ferric oxide. The error in each of the four weighings may cause the final result to be incorrect in the same direction; the error in the result may then be 4 parts in 1000, or 0.2 per cent iron. The gravimetric determination of iron is inherently better than 0.2 per cent iron, and for this reason a sufficiently large sample is taken so that the error caused by the uncertainties in the weighings will be considerably less than this. If a 1.000-g. sample is taken, the absolute error in the two weighings involved is 0.0002 g. and the relative error is only 2 parts in 10,000, or 1 part in 5000. The weight of ferric oxide obtained will be about 0.7 g., and the error in the two weighings measuring it will be 0.0002 g., or 2 parts in 7000, or 1.4 parts in 5000. The sum of the errors in all the weighing operations, then, is about 2.4 parts per 5000, corresponding to 0.024 per cent iron on this particular sample.

Significant Figures. In computing the relative error in a measurement, either as percentage or as parts per thousand, the position of the decimal point is lost. If a measurement is made with an accuracy of 1 part in 1000, four figures have meaning irrespective of the position of the decimal point. Thus, the weights of three objects, each known with an accuracy of 1 part in 1000, might be 123.4 ± 0.1,

12.34 ± 0.01, and 1.234 ± 0.001. In each case figures beyond the 4 have no meaning and should be omitted.

Because a result can usually be no more accurate than the least accurate of the measurements entering into its determination, it is evident that there can be no more significant figures in the result than in the least accurate measurement. In the calculation of the final result involving a multiplication or a division there is a great tendency to include more figures than are significant.[1] A good rule in such arithmetical computations is to include one more than the number of significant figures and drop the rest.

Range.   Average Deviation.   Standard Deviation. If systematic errors are excluded, the best value of a series of measurements is the arithmetic mean, that is, the average of all the measurements. The deviations of the individual readings from the average is a measure of the precision of the measurement. There are several ways of recording the size of the deviations. One way is to state simply the interval between the greatest positive and the greatest negative deviations from the average; this quantity is termed the *range*. Another way is to report the average deviation. The *average deviation* is the average of the deviations from the mean computed without regard to sign. Thus, for the weighings reported in column A above, the average deviation is 0.74 mg.:

	Weight (grams)	Deviation (milligrams)	Square of Deviation (milligrams)
	13.1273	−0.2	0.04
	13.1280	+0.5	0.25
	13.1277	+0.2	0.04
	13.1275	0.0	0.00
	13.1267	−0.8	0.64
	13.1287	+1.2	1.44
	13.1280	+0.5	0.25
	13.1289	+1.4	1.96
	13.1259	−1.6	2.56
	13.1265	−1.0	1.00
Sum	131.2752	7.4	8.18
n	10		

Average 13.1275   *Average deviation* = 7.4/10 = 0.74   *Standard deviation* = $\sqrt{8.18/10}$ = 0.90

[1] Sportsmen and journalists occasionally push significant figures a few decimals too far: "Driving his famed Bluebird over the Bonneville Salt Flats in Utah in 1935, he was the first to crack the five-mile-minute mark (he hit 301.1292 m.p.h.); he switched to speedboats, and four years later, on Lake Coniston, England, established a record 141.74 m.p.h., which has never been equaled."—*Time*, January 10, 1949.

Expressed mathematically the average of a series of measurements and the average deviation are

$$M = \frac{M_1 + M_2 + M_3 + \cdots + M_n}{}$$

and

$$d = \frac{\left|(M_1 - M)\right| + \left|(M_2 - M)\right| + \left|(M_3 - M)\right| + \cdots \left|(M_n - M)\right|}{n}$$

in which M_1, M_2, etc., are individual measurements, M is the arithmetic average or mean, d is the average deviation, and the vertical lines indicate that the absolute values of the deviations are taken without regard to sign. These expressions are often condensed by the use of the symbol Σ (the Greek capital letter sigma):

$$M = \frac{\Sigma M_i}{n}$$

in which ΣM_i means the sum of all the terms from $i = 1$ to $i = n$, that is, the sum: $M_1 + M_2 + \cdots + M_n$, and

$$d = \frac{\Sigma \left| M_i - M \right|}{n}$$

in which $\Sigma \left| M_i - M \right|$ means the sum of all the terms from $i = 1$ to $i = n$ of the differences, $M_1 - M$, $M_2 - M$, $\cdots M_n - M$, without regard to sign.

Another method of expressing the error in a series of measurements is the *standard deviation*, which has greater significance than the average deviation from the standpoint of statistics. The standard deviation, σ (the Greek lower case letter sigma), is defined as the square root of the sum of the squares of the deviations divided by the number of observations. Expressed mathematically

$$\sigma = \sqrt{\frac{\Sigma(M_i - M)^2}{n}}$$

in which the symbols have the same meanings given in the preceding paragraph. The standard deviation of the series of weighings given above is 0.90, the calculation being given in the third column. The standard deviation is always greater than the average deviation, and, as will be learned in the following sections, can be used to make certain estimates as to the reliability of the measurements.

Distribution of Errors. In a series of measurements of the same value the deviations from the arithmetic mean will be distributed symmetrically about the mean if the errors are purely accidental,

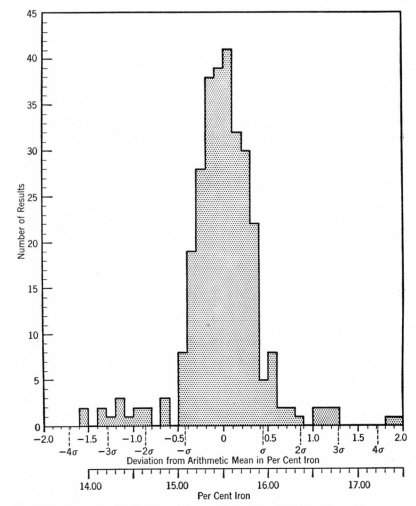

Fig. 97. Frequency distribution of the results and the deviations from the average by 298 students on the determination of iron in iron ore.

that is, are due to a lack of control on several factors which influence the measurement in a minor way. Small errors occur most frequently, large errors occur less frequently, and very large errors do not occur at all.

The frequency with which deviations of various sizes occur is illustrated in Fig. 97. The data used are the results of 298 students at Iowa State College on the gravimetric determination of iron in iron ore. The average of all these results was first calculated (15.50 per cent

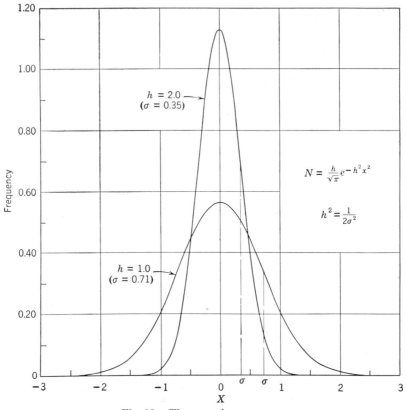

Fig. 98. The normal error curve.

iron), and then the deviation of each result from the average was calculated. The number of results falling into intervals of 0.1 per cent iron on each side of the average was then obtained. This information was then plotted, Fig. 97. The distribution is fairly symmetrical about the average, for there are 144 negative deviations, 151 positive deviations, and three zero deviations. In the process of taking the average, the areas under the curve on each side of the average are made equal. Although most of the results are grouped about the mean there are several results which are quite badly off, deviations of 1.0 per cent iron and more. It would be of interest to learn if such results arose from purely random errors, that is, are due to the workings of chance, or were more likely caused by some gross error, the improper addition of the weights during a weighing, for example, or a loss of material during handling. Fortunately, the theory of probability, in which the standard deviation plays a part, supplies a fair answer to this problem.

If the number of results on the measurement of a certain quantity is large and if the errors, that is, the deviations from the average, are distributed perfectly at random, the frequency plot forms a smooth symmetrical curve, known as the *normal error curve*. This curve conforms to the equation

$$N = \frac{h}{\sqrt{\pi}} e^{-h^2 x^2}$$

x being the deviation, N the frequency with which deviations of the size of x occur, h an arbitrary constant, and e the base of natural logarithms. This equation has been derived theoretically from considerations of the principles governing chance and probability. Plots of the curve are shown in Fig. 98 for two values of the constant h. The constant h is a measure of the precision of the measurements, for the greater the value of h the more greatly the curve is humped in the middle, that is, the closer the deviations lie to the average. The constant h is related to the standard deviation by the relation

$$h^2 = \frac{1}{2\sigma^2}$$

The curve given in Fig. 98 for $h = 2$ ($\sigma = 0.35$ corresponds in general shape to the frequency plot of the results of the students on the gravimetric determination of iron, $\sigma = 0.43$ (Fig. 97).

The frequency N is usually expressed as a fraction of the total number of observations (per cent iron, or deviation from the average in the illustration used above). The total area under the curve is then constant and equal to 1 irrespective of the shape of the curve. The point of inflection always occurs at a value of x equal to the standard deviation. Integration of the error equation shows that 68.27 per cent of the area under the curve lies between values of x equal to the average minus the standard deviation and the average plus the standard deviation, that is, in the interval $M - \sigma$ and $M + \sigma$; also, that 95.45 per cent of the area lies between $M - 2\sigma$ and $M + 2\sigma$; and 99.73 per cent between $M - 3\sigma$ and $M + 3\sigma$. If deviations are plotted rather than the values of the measurements made, M is zero; compare the two horizontal scales of Fig. 97.

Inasmuch as the area under the curve represents probability, it can immediately be concluded that in a thousand results on the measurement of some single quantity, 997 of the results should fall in the range of the average plus and minus three times the standard deviation, and that 954 should fall within the average plus and minus two times the standard deviation. Returning to the student results, Fig. 97, it will be seen that six results exceed 3σ, although theory predicts only 3 in 1000 or 1 in 300 should do so. It is likely, therefore, that five of the six results are due to gross errors; perhaps some of the solution was spilled on the table top.

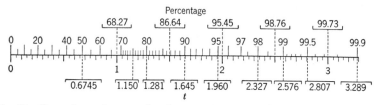

Fig. 99. Percentage of area under the normal error curve falling between $M - t\sigma$ and $M + t\sigma$. M is the average of a set of measurements, σ is the standard deviation of the set, and t is simply the multiple of σ.

The percentages of the area under the error curve for different multiples of the standard deviation are independent of the shape of the curve, that is, they are independent of the actual numerical value of the standard deviation. Two normal-error curves are given in Fig. 98; $\sigma = 0.71$ and $\sigma = 0.35$ respectively; under each curve 68.27 per cent of the area falls in the range $-\sigma$ to $+\sigma$ and 99.73 per cent in the range -3σ to $+3\sigma$.

The area under the normal-error curve can be obtained from a table of the probability integral which will be found in handbooks and books on statistics. A convenient plot of this integral in terms of the standard deviation rather than x is given in Fig. 99. For multiples of σ of 1.0, 2.0, and 3.0, the areas under the curve are 68.27, 95.45, and 99.73 per cent respectively, the percentages mentioned in the preceding three paragraphs. Using this chart the percentage of measurements falling in the range $M \pm t\sigma$ may be obtained, t being simply some multiple of the standard deviation. For example, for $t = 1.645$, nine out of every ten measurements will fall in the range between $M - 1.645\sigma$ and $M + 1.645\sigma$.

Rejection of Part of the Data. It often occurs in analytical work that one value in a series of otherwise quite concordant results deviates markedly from the others.   If the measurement leading to the anomalous result is known to have been subject to an error there is no question that the result should be rejected.   In the absence of any definite reason for discarding a result it is best to include the result, compute the average and the standard deviation, and then reject the result if its deviation from the average is greater than three times the standard deviation.   A result which deviates from the average by more than three times the standard deviation has a probability of only 3 in 1000 of being due to the working of chance only; that is, the chances are 997 in 1000 that some gross error was involved in the measurement.

Actually, the probability figure given here is not strictly correct, for it rests on the assumption that a large number of observations was used in calculating the standard deviation.   This is seldom the case in analytical work where the number of samples analyzed is usually two or three and is seldom more than five.   Methods of treating the results when the number of samples is small were devised in certain classical investigations in the field of statistics by "Student."   The matter is not simple, and the reader is referred to textbooks on statistics for a discussion of Student's work and in particular for the applications of Student's t.   Applied to the problem of rejecting a result which has an excessively large deviation from the average, the small number of results simply reduces the probability that the result is a gross error. Specifically, for three, four, or five results, the probability of a purely random result falling outside the average, plus or minus three times the standard deviation, is about 50 in 1000 rather than the 3 in 1000 predicted from the area under the normal error curve.   Or, putting this another way, a result deviating from the average by more than three times the standard deviation has a probability of only 5 in 100 of having been caused by a purely random error.   The 3σ test is thus still a fair criterion for rejecting a result even though the number of samples is small.

Limits of Uncertainty of an Observed Average.   When the number of samples of a material analyzed is small, the average of the results will vary from the true average which would be obtained if a large number of samples were run.   The observed average M tends to depart more widely from the true average M_t the smaller the number of samples.   Limits can be set for the difference between M and M_t if the measurements made are subject only to random fluctuations; that is, if many measurements were made they would give a distribution about the average conforming to the normal-error curve.   Fortunately, this is the case in analytical work where the various steps in a procedure are usually under careful control.

For a given series of results, the average and the standard deviation are first calculated. The limits are then given by $M_t = M \pm a\sigma$, the value of a being taken from Table 37. If a is taken from the $P_s = 0.90$

TABLE 37.   LIMITS WITHIN WHICH THE TRUE AVERAGE MAY BE EXPECTED TO LIE

$M_t = M \pm a\sigma$. M_t is the true average, M the observed average, σ the standard deviation, n the number of samples, and a simply a multiple of σ taken from the table.

	a	
n	$P_s = 0.90$ (Chances, 9 in 10)	$P_s = 0.99$ (Chances, 99 in 100)
4	1.360	3.372
5	1.066	2.302
6	0.901	1.803
7	0.793	1.513
8	0.716	1.322
9	0.658	1.186
10	0.611	1.083
11	0.573	1.002
12	0.542	0.936
13	0.514	0.882
14	0.491	0.835
15	0.471	0.796
16	0.453	0.761
17	0.437	0.730
18	0.422	0.703
19	0.409	0.678
20	0.397	0.656
21	0.386	0.636
22	0.376	0.618
23	0.366	0.601
24	0.357	0.585
25	0.349	0.571

greater than 25 $a = 1.645/\sqrt{n-3}$ $a = 2.576/\sqrt{n-3}$

column of Table 37, the chances are that the true average will fall within $M \pm a\sigma$ nine out of ten times. If the value of a is taken from the $P_s = 0.99$ column of the table, the chances are 99 out of 100 that the true average will fall within the limits $M \pm a\sigma$.

As an illustration, we make use of the first five results turned in by 64 students determining sulfur trioxide in a pure potassium sulfate:

Analyst	Per cent SO_3	
1	45.22	$n = 5$
2	45.48	$\sigma = 0.13$
3	45.31	$a = 1.07$ from Table 37
4	45.33	$M_t = M \pm a\sigma$
5	45.08	$= 45.28 \pm 0.14$

Average 45.28

The chances are nine in ten that the true average falls between 45.14 and 45.42. The average of all 64 results was 45.28. As a further check, the same calculation was made for the remaining groups of five with the following results:

Analysts	$M \pm (1.07)\sigma$	Analysts	$M \pm (1.07)\sigma$
6–10	45.46 ± 0.21	36–40	45.22 ± 0.34
11–15	45.43 ± 0.52	41–45	45.19 ± 0.45
16–20	45.28 ± 0.31	46–50	45.09 ± 0.45
21–25	45.19 ± 0.06	51–55	45.31 ± 0.08
26–30	45.06 ± 0.54	56–60	45.22 ± 0.22
31–35	45.37 ± 0.28		

In only one of the twelve groups, the 21–25 group, did the true average (45.28 per SO_3) fall outside the observed average for the group plus or minus 1.07 times the standard deviation for the group.

It is possible to obtain values of a for P_s (statistical probability) values other than 0.90 and 0.99 as given in Table 37. A nomograph for obtaining such values for P_s values between 0.50 and 1.00 and for n greater than 4 is found in the very useful booklet *A.S.T.M. Manual on Quality Control of Materials.*[1]

PROBLEMS

1. The aluminum in a sample of silicate rock was determined by precipitation with ammonium hydroxide and ignition to the oxide; the results obtained, reported as aluminum oxide, were 5.83, 5.87, 5.86, 5.85 per cent. Later the titanium in the sample was found to be 0.20 per cent. Explain why the results obtained for aluminum were precise but not accurate.

2. A long series of analyses, by students, of the sulfate in a pure, high-grade sample of potassium sulfate averaged 45.20 per cent SO_3, the theoretical value being 45.95 per cent SO_3. Obviously all the analyses were affected by some systematic error. Suggest two or three possible causes.

3. From an examination of the table of atomic weights in the cover of this book, find an element whose atomic weight is known with an accuracy of 1 part in 100,000. Oxygen must not be considered, of course, for its value is assumed to

[1] American Society for Testing Materials, 1916 Race St., Philadelphia 3, Pa.

be exactly 16.0000. Find another element whose atomic weight is known less accurately than 1 part in 1000.

4. The carbon content of a steel is 1.00 per cent and is to be determined within 0.01 per cent carbon. Decide how accurately a sample of about 1 g. of steel must be weighed.

5. A sample weighing 1.0000 g. yielded on analysis 0.0057 g. of ferric oxide. The factor for converting ferric oxide to iron is 0.6994, so that the calculation yields 3.9866 per cent iron. State how the results should be reported: 3.9866, 3.987, 3.99, or 4.0 per cent iron. Give the reason for the selection made.

6. Assuming that a buret can be read to 0.02 ml., calculate the relative error in parts per thousand for the following volumes delivered from the buret: 1 ml., 10 ml., 40 ml., and 50 ml. Note that two readings are required for each volume measured.

7. In the standardization of an approximately 0.1 N sodium hydroxide solution an amount of primary-standard sulfamic acid was weighed out such that 40 ml. of the alkali solution was used in the titration. Assuming that the error in each reading of the buret is 0.02 ml. and that the two errors do not compensate each other, determine the error in the normality of the sodium hydroxide solution due to the error in reading the buret. Determine the error if 50 ml. was used; 10 ml.; 1 ml.

8. Compute the average deviation and the standard deviation in the series of weighings given in column B, page 472. Compare the average and standard deviations of ten analysts weighing the crucible with those for one analyst weighing the same crucible, page 475.

9. The following results were obtained by students at Iowa State College in the fall of 1950 on the analysis of pure, reagent-grade potassium sulfate. Each value given is the average of three determinations. By *range* is meant the difference between the highest and lowest results of the three. All the analysts used a 50 per cent excess of barium chloride and a 2-hour digestion.

	Per cent SO₃	
Analyst	Range	Average
Magnus	1.46	45.52
Jelinck	0.75	44.17
Buckley	0.18	45.47
Noss	0.51	45.16
Iliff	0.22	45.31
Damon	0.60	45.53
Fritz	0.43	45.26
Pennell	0.91	45.08
Thornburg	0.90	45.01
Fairchild	0.30	44.91
Adams	0.40	45.00
Hokman	0.63	45.19
Robertson	0.70	45.07
Tunison	0.30	44.99

Compute the average per cent sulfur trioxide found by these analysts and compare this grand average with the theoretical value for the sulfur trioxide content of potassium sulfate. Compute the average range and the standard deviation (tables of squares will be found in the handbooks).

10. The following series of results on the determination of sulfur trioxide in pure potassium sulfate were obtained by students at Iowa State College in their

second quarter of quantitative analysis after they had gained experience by carrying out a dozen successful quantitative analyses. All used a 50 per cent excess of barium chloride and a 2-hour digestion. The values given are the range and average of three results by each student.

	Per cent SO_3	
Analyst	Range	Average
Robertson	1.31	44.72
Thornburg	0.33	44.99
Herriott	0.35	45.08
Fellows	0.14	44.83
Day	0.64	45.63
Dahms	0.13	45.31
Young	0.46	45.03
Pennell	1.12	44.88
Holdridge	0.08	45.16
Gaston	0.12	45.11
Roennau	0.20	45.30

Calculate the grand average per cent sulfur trioxide, the average range, and the standard deviation. Compare the results with those of Problem 9 and decide if there was any improvement in the sulfate determination as a result of the experience gained.

11. On page 475 is given a series of weighings of a crucible, together with the average and the standard deviation. Using Fig. 99, determine what multiple of the standard deviation will give the range which should contain nine of the ten observations. Check the data for confirmation. Repeat, finding the range which should contain five of the ten weighings.

12. The following student results on the analysis of pure potassium sulfate are part of the data used to illustrate the computation of confidence limits, page 483.

Analyst	51	52	53	54	55
Per cent SO_3	45.28	45.38	45.35	45.16	45.37

Calculate the average and the standard deviation of this group of results. Using Table 37 to find values of a, obtain the limits within which the true average for this analysis will fall (a) nine times out of ten, and (b) ninety-nine times out of one hundred.

Appendix

TABLE A1. COMPOSITION OF CONCENTRATED COMMON
ACIDS AND AMMONIUM HYDROXIDE AS MARKETED

Acid and Formula	Specific Gravity	Per Cent Acid
Acetic Acid, $HC_2H_3O_2$	1.05	99.5
Hydrochloric Acid, HCl	1.19	37
Hydrofluoric Acid, HF	—	48
Nitric Acid, HNO_3	1.42	72
Perchloric Acid, $HClO_4$	1.68	72.5
Phosphoric Acid, H_3PO_4	1.69	85
Sulfuric Acid, H_2SO_4	1.83	95
Ammonium Hydroxide, NH_4OH	0.90	28 (as NH_3)

Concentrations of diluted acids and ammonium hydroxide, except when standardized, are stated as a ratio of the number of volumes of concentrated reagent to be diluted with a given number of volumes of water; for example, dilute nitric acid (5:95) means 5 volumes of concentrated nitric acid, sp. gr. 1.42, diluted with 95 volumes of water.

TABLE A2. SOLUBILITY-PRODUCT CONSTANTS OF VARIOUS COMPOUNDS

The solubility-product constant has the dimensions (moles/liter)^n, n being the number of ions formed when the compound ionizes in solution. The values given are for room temperature except where specifically stated.

Aluminum
hydroxide	3.7×10^{-15}	iodide	1.1×10^{-12}
Arsenious		sulfide	2.5×10^{-50}
sulfide (As$_2$S$_3$)	1.1×10^{-33}	thiocyanate	4.0×10^{-14}
Barium		Ferric	
arsenate	3.5×10^{-14}	hydroxide	3.8×10^{-38}
carbonate	4.9×10^{-9}	Ferrous	
chromate	2.0×10^{-10}	carbonate	2.1×10^{-11}
fluoride	1.7×10^{-6}	hydroxide	4.8×10^{-16}
hydroxide	5.0×10^{-3}	oxalate	2.1×10^{-7}
iodate	1.3×10^{-9}	sulfide	4.0×10^{-19}
manganate	2.5×10^{-10}	Lanthanum	
oxalate		hydroxide	5.9×10^{-10}
(BaC$_2$O$_4 \cdot$		iodate	5.9×10^{-10}
3.5H$_2$O)	1.7×10^{-7}	oxalate	2×10^{-28}
sulfate (25°)	1.08×10^{-10}	tartrate	2×10^{-19}
(50°)	1.98×10^{-10}	Lead	
Cadmium		bromide	7.9×10^{-5}
carbonate	2.5×10^{-14}	carbonate	1.5×10^{-13}
hydroxide	1.2×10^{-14}	chloride	2.4×10^{-4}
oxalate	2.8×10^{-8}	chromate	1.8×10^{-14}
sulfide	1.4×10^{-28}	fluoride	3.7×10^{-8}
Calcium		iodate	3.0×10^{-13}
carbonate	4.8×10^{-9}	iodide	8.7×10^{-9}
chromate	2.3×10^{-2}	oxalate	3.4×10^{-11}
fluoride	3.9×10^{-11}	phosphate	1.5×10^{-32}
hydroxide	7.9×10^{-6}	sulfate	2.3×10^{-8}
iodate	1.9×10^{-6}	sulfide	1.0×10^{-29}
oxalate	2.3×10^{-9}	Magnesium	
sulfate	6.1×10^{-5}	ammonium	
tartrate	7.7×10^{-7}	phosphate	2.5×10^{-13}
Cerous		carbonate	1.0×10^{-5}
iodate	3.5×10^{-10}	fluoride	7.0×10^{-9}
oxalate	2.6×10^{-29}	hydroxide	1.2×10^{-11}
tartrate	9.7×10^{-20}	oxalate	8.6×10^{-5}
Cobalt		Manganous	
sulfide	3×10^{-26}	hydroxide	4.5×10^{-14}
Cupric		sulfide	1.4×10^{-15}
iodate	1.4×10^{-7}	Mercuric	
oxalate	2.9×10^{-8}	bromide	8.0×10^{-20}
sulfide	8.5×10^{-45}	hydroxide	1.4×10^{-26}
Cuprous		iodide	3.2×10^{-29}
bromide	5.3×10^{-9}	sulfide	4.0×10^{-53}
chloride	1.8×10^{-7}		

TABLE A2 (*continued*)

Mercurous
bromide	1.3×10^{-21}
chloride	1.1×10^{-18}
chromate	1.8×10^{-14}
iodate	3.0×10^{-20}
iodide	4.5×10^{-29}
oxalate	1.0×10^{-13}

Nickel
carbonate	1.4×10^{-7}
hydroxide	1.6×10^{-16}
sulfide	1.4×10^{-24}

Potassium
bitartrate	3×10^{-4}
chloroplatinate	1.1×10^{-5}
perchlorate	1.1×10^{-2}

Silver
arsenate	3.07×10^{-18}
benzoate	9.3×10^{-5}
bromate	5×10^{-5}
bromide	3.3×10^{-13}
carbonate	8.2×10^{-12}
chloride (5°)	0.227×10^{-10}
(10°)	0.388×10^{-10}
(20°)	1.00×10^{-10}
(25°)	1.70×10^{-10}
(50°)	13.3×10^{-10}
(100°)	210×10^{-10}
chromate	5.7×10^{-13}
cyanide	2.7×10^{-12}
cyanate	1.0×10^{-12}
dichromate	2.0×10^{-7}
ferrocyanide	1.5×10^{-41}
hydroxide	2×10^{-8}
iodate	5.3×10^{-8}

iodide	8.5×10^{-17}
nitroprusside $(Ag_2[Fe(CN)_5\text{-}NO])$	7.8×10^{-13}
oxalate	1.1×10^{-11}
phosphate	1.4×10^{-18}
salicylate	1.4×10^{-5}
sulfate	7.0×10^{-5}
sulfide	1.6×10^{-49}
thiocyanate	3.0×10^{-12}

Stannous
sulfide	7.8×10^{-29}

Strontium
carbonate	1.6×10^{-9}
chromate	3.6×10^{-5}
fluoride	3.0×10^{-9}
hydroxide	3.2×10^{-4}
oxalate	5.0×10^{-8}
sulfate	2.8×10^{-7}

Thallous
bromate	3.9×10^{-4}
bromide	3.6×10^{-6}
chloride	2.56×10^{-4}
iodate	4.5×10^{-6}
iodide	5.8×10^{-8}
sulfide	4.5×10^{-23}
thiocyanate	1.4×10^{-4}

Zinc
carbonate	6.0×10^{-11}
hydroxide	1.0×10^{-17}
oxalate	7.5×10^{-9}
sulfide	4.5×10^{-24}

TABLE A3. IONIZATION CONSTANTS OF VARIOUS ACIDS AND BASES (25°)

Inorganic Acids	K_A	pK_A $(= -\log K_A)$
Arsenic, first step	5×10^{-3}	2.7
second step	4×10^{-5}	4.4
third step	6×10^{-10}	9.2
Arsenious	6×10^{-10}	9.2
Boric	5.8×10^{-10}	9.24
Carbonic, first step	4.47×10^{-7}	6.35
second stép	5.62×10^{-11}	10.25
Chromic, second step	3.2×10^{-7}	7.0
Hydrazoic	1.9×10^{-5}	4.7
Hydrocyanic (HCN)	7.25×10^{-10}	9.14
Hydrofluoric	1.7×10^{-5}	4.8
Hydrosulfuric (H_2S), first step	6.3×10^{-8}	7.2
second step	1.3×10^{-12}	11.9
Hypoiodous (HIO)	3×10^{-11}	10.52
Iodic	1.9×10^{-1}	0.73
Nitrous	4×10^{-4}	3.4
Periodic (HIO_4)	2.3×10^{-2}	1.6
Phosphoric, first step	7.54×10^{-3}	2.12
second step	6.23×10^{-8}	7.20
third step	4.79×10^{-13}	12.32
Pyrophosphoric, first step	1.4×10^{-1}	0.85
second step	1.1×10^{-2}	1.96
third step	2.9×10^{-7}	6.5
fourth step	4×10^{-10}	9.4
Sulfamic	1×10^{-2}	2
Sulfuric, second step	1.20×10^{-2}	1.92
Sulfurous, first step	1.7×10^{-2}	1.8
second step	1×10^{-7}	7.0

Organic Acids	K_A	pK_A $(= -\log K_A)$
Acetic	1.75×10^{-5}	4.75
Acrylic	5.62×10^{-5}	4.25
Benzoic	6.32×10^{-5}	4.20
n-Butyric	1.51×10^{-5}	4.82
iso-Butyric	1.51×10^{-5}	4.82
Cinnamic (cis)	1.32×10^{-4}	3.88
Cinnamic (trans)	3.63×10^{-5}	4.44
Citric, first step	8.7×10^{-4}	3.1
second step	1.8×10^{-5}	4.7
third step	3.9×10^{-7}	6.4
Chloroacetic	1.38×10^{-3}	2.85
Cyanuric	2.0×10^{-7}	6.8
Formic	1.77×10^{-4}	3.75
Fumaric, first step	9.57×10^{-4}	3.02
second step	4.13×10^{-5}	4.37
Furoic	2.9×10^{-2}	1.54

TABLE A3 (*continued*)

Organic Acids	K_A	pK_A $(= -\log K_A)$
Glycolic	1.48×10^{-4}	3.83
Lactic	1.38×10^{-4}	3.86
Maleic, first step	1.20×10^{-2}	1.92
second step	5.95×10^{-7}	6.23
Malonic, first step	1.45×10^{-3}	2.84
second step	2.00×10^{-6}	5.70
o-Nitrophenol	1.55×10^{-8}	7.21
Oxalic, first step	5.01×10^{-2}	1.30
second step	5.13×10^{-5}	4.29
Phenol	1.20×10^{-10}	9.92
Phthalic, first step	1.29×10^{-3}	2.89
second step	3.80×10^{-6}	5.42
Propionic	1.34×10^{-5}	4.87
Salicylic, first step	1.06×10^{-3}	2.97
second step	1×10^{-13}	13
Succinic, first step	6.31×10^{-5}	4.20
second step	2.51×10^{-6}	5.60
Tartaric, first step	9.8×10^{-4}	3.01
second step	2.8×10^{-5}	4.55
2,4,6-Trinitrobenzoic	4.16×10^{-3}	2.38

Inorganic Bases	K_B	pK_B $(= -\log K_B)$
Ammonia	1.75×10^{-5}	4.76
Hydrazine, first step	8.5×10^{-7}	6.07
second step	8.9×10^{-16}	15.05
Hydroxylamine	6.6×10^{-9}	8.18

Organic Bases [a]	K_B	pK_B $(= -\log K_B)$
Aniline	2.68×10^{-10}	9.57
Diethylamine	1.46×10^{-3}	2.84
Dimethylamine	8.92×10^{-4}	3.05
Diphenylamine	6.3×10^{-14}	13.2
Ethylamine	3.97×10^{-4}	3.40
Ethylenediamine, first step	1.14×10^{-4}	3.94
second step	1.13×10^{-7}	6.95
Methylamine	3.62×10^{-4}	3.44
Phenylhydrazine	1.6×10^{-9}	8.8
Pyridine	1.07×10^{-9}	8.97
Triethylamine	6.53×10^{-4}	3.18
Trimethylamine	6.15×10^{-5}	4.21

[a] The organic bases are derivatives of ammonia in which one or more hydrogen atoms have been replaced by organic groups, for example, methylamine, CH_3NH_2. Like ammonia, the amines add on water to form hydroxides: methylammonium hydroxide, CH_3NH_3OH. The salts formed on neutralization are analogous to ammonium salts, thus, methylammonium chloride, CH_3NH_3Cl (known in the older literature as methylamine hydrochloride).

TABLE A4. INSTABILITY CONSTANTS, K_I, OF VARIOUS NON-DISSOCIATED IONS

$Ag(NH_3)_2^+ = Ag^+ + 2NH_3$	6.8×10^{-8}
$Ag(S_2O_3)_2^{\equiv} = Ag^+ + 2S_2O_3^{=}$	4.2×10^{-14}
$Ag(CN)_2^- = Ag^+ + 2CN^-$	3.8×10^{-19}
$Ag(SO_3)_2^{\equiv} = Ag^+ + 2SO_3^{=}$	3.0×10^{-9}
$Zn(CN)_4^{=} = Zn^{++} + 4CN^-$	1.2×10^{-18}
$Zn(NH_3)_4^{++} = Zn^{++} + 4NH_3$	2.6×10^{-10}
$Cd(CN)_4^{=} = Cd^{++} + 4CN^-$	1.4×10^{-17}
$Cd(NH_3)_4^{++} = Cd^{++} + 4NH_3$	1×10^{-7}
$Cu(CN)_3^{=} = Cu^+ + 3CN^-$	5×10^{-28}

TABLE A5. RELATIONS AMONG THE UNITS OF MASS IN THE METRIC SYSTEM

μg.—microgram   kg.—kilogram
mg.—milligram   M.T.—metric ton
g.—gram   Gg.—geogram

	μg.	mg.	g.	kg.	M.T.	Gg.
μg.	1	10^{-3}	10^{-6}	10^{-9}	10^{-12}	10^{-26}
mg.	10^3	1	10^{-3}	10^{-6}	10^{-9}	10^{-23}
g.	10^6	10^3	1	10^{-3}	10^{-6}	10^{-20}
kg.	10^9	10^6	10^3	1	10^{-3}	10^{-17}
M.T.	10^{12}	10^9	10^6	10^3	1	10^{-14}
Gg.	10^{26}	10^{23}	10^{20}	10^{17}	10^4	1

TABLE A6. CORRECTION TO WEIGHT IN VACUUM

The correction of weighings made in air to weight in vacuum is discussed on page 62. The formula for making this correction is

$$W_{\text{Vac.}} = W_{\text{Air}} + W_{\text{Air}} \left[\frac{d_{\text{Air}}}{d_{\text{Obj.}}} - \frac{d_{\text{Air}}}{d_{\text{Wt.}}} \right]$$

In the following table are given values of the quantity in the brackets for air of different values of density. The density of air may be computed by the formula given on page 63. For air of average humidity and room temperature, it is sufficient to use the following values:

Barometric pressure	760	740	720	700	680	640	620
Density	1.20	1.10	1.10	1.10	1.00	1.00	0.90

The figures given are for brass weights (density 8.4); for stainless-steel weights (density 7.82) subtract 0.000,01 from each value.

Density of Object	Density of Air 0.001,20	0.001,10	0.001,00	0.000,90
0.2	+0.005,86	+0.005,37	+0.004,88	+0.004,39
0.3	.003,86	.003,54	.003,21	.002,88
0.4	.002,86	.002,62	.002,38	.002,13
0.5	.002,26	.002,07	.001,88	.001,68
0.6	.001,86	.001,70	.001,55	.001,38
0.7	.001,57	.001,43	.001,31	.001,17
0.8	.001,36	.001,24	.001,13	.001,01
0.9	.001,19	.001,09	.000,99	.000,88
1.0	.001,06	.000,97	.000,88	.000,78
1.2	.000,86	.000,79	.000,71	.000,63
1.4	.000,72	.000,66	.000,59	.000,51
1.6	.000,61	.000,56	.000,51	.000,44
1.8	.000,53	.000,48	.000,44	.000,38
2.0	.000,46	.000,42	.000,38	.000,33
2.2	.000,41	.000,37	.000,33	.000,29
2.4	.000,36	.000,33	.000,30	.000,26
2.6	.000,32	.000,29	.000,26	.000,23
2.8	.000,29	.000,26	.000,23	.000,20
3.0	.000,26	.000,24	.000,21	.000,18
3.5	.000,20	.000,18	.000,17	.000,14
4.0	.000,16	.000,14	.000,13	.000,11
5	.000,10	.000,09	.000,08	.000,06
6	.000,06	.000,05	.000,05	.000,03
7	.000,03	.000,03	.000,02	.000,01
8	.000,01	.000,01	.000,01	−0.000,01
9	−0.000,01	−0.000,01	−0.000,01	− .000,02
10	− .000,02	− .000,02	− .000,02	− .000,03
12	− .000,04	− .000,04	− .000,04	− .000,04
14	− .000,05	− .000,05	− .000,05	− .000,06
16	− .000,06	− .000,06	− .000,06	− .000,06
18	− .000,07	− .000,07	− .000,06	− .000,07
20	− .000,08	− .000,07	− .000,07	− .000,07

TABLE A7. SOLUTION OF QUADRATIC EQUATIONS. BINOMIAL THEOREM

An equation containing one variable which is present as a squared term is called a quadratic equation. To solve such an equation, first rearrange the terms in the equations into the general form

$$ax^2 + bx + c = 0$$

A quadratic equation has two solutions (roots) which can be obtained by using the equation:

$$x = \frac{-b \pm \sqrt{b^2 - 4ac}}{2a}$$

If $b^2 > 4ac$, the roots are real numbers.
If $b^2 = 4ac$, the roots are equal.
If $b^2 < 4ac$, the roots are imaginary (involve $\sqrt{-1}$)

Example. The hydrogen-ion concentration of a solution 0.100 M in acetic acid is calculated by the formula

$$[H^+]^2 = K_A(C_{HA} - [H^+])$$
$$= 1.75 \times 10^{-5}(0.100 - [H^+])$$

On rearrangement this equation becomes

$$[H^+]^2 + 1.75 \times 10^{-5}[H^+] - 1.75 \times 10^{-6} = 0$$

In this case
$$a = 1 \qquad b = 1.75 \times 10^{-5} \qquad c = -1.75 \times 10^{-6}$$
so that

$$[H^+] = \frac{-1.75 \times 10^{-5} \pm \sqrt{3.06 \times 10^{-10} - (4)(-1.75 \times 10^{-6})}}{2}$$

$$= \frac{-1.75 \times 10^{-5} \pm \sqrt{70{,}003 \times 10^{-10}}}{2}$$

$$= \frac{-1.75 \times 10^{-5} \pm 264.6 \times 10^{-5}}{2}$$

Only the positive root has any physical significance

$$[H^+] = \frac{262.8 \times 10^{-5}}{2} = 1.31 \times 10^{-3}$$

BINOMIAL THEOREM

$$(a + b)^n = a^n + na^{n-1}b + \frac{n(n - 1)}{2 \cdot 1} a^{n-2}b^2 + \frac{n(n - 1)(n - 2)}{3 \cdot 2 \cdot 1} a^{n-3}b^3 + \cdots$$

n may be positive, negative, or fractional.

Glossary

Accuracy. A measure of the divergence of a given value from the most probable or theoretically correct value. Accuracy is an expression of the reliability of a value. Accuracy and precision are not the same.

Acidimetry. The titration of an alkaline substance with a standard acid solution.

Aliquot part. A portion of the whole, usually some simple fraction. In volumetric analysis, the process of diluting to a known volume and removing a portion for analysis is called *taking an aliquot.*

Alkali metal. One of the elements of periodic group 1A: lithium, sodium, potassium, rubidium, cesium, and francium. The ammonium ion, which resembles the alkali metal ions in many respects, is often included in the group.

Alkalimetry. The titration of an acid substance with a standard solution of an alkali.

Alkaline-earth metal. One of the elements of periodic group 2A: calcium, strontium, barium, and radium. Magnesium and manganese in the bivalent state behave in many respects like the alkaline-earth metals; that manganese is an alkaline earth has been upheld by the United States Supreme Court.

Analysis. The separation, identification, or the determination of the amount of a component of an aggregation of matter. The term *analysis* refers to the method used. Thus, *the determination of copper in brass* and *the analysis of brass for copper* are correct usage, but *the analysis of copper in brass* is incorrect.

Anion. A negatively charged ion.

Anode. An electrode to which a positive charge is applied. The electrode toward which negatively charged ions move. The electrode at which oxidation occurs.

Apparent weight. The weight of an object as obtained in normal fashion on the equal-arm balance. Weight in vacuum is calculated from apparent weight by correcting for the buoyant effect of air on the object and on the weights. Weight in vacuum is greater than weight in air if the density of the weights is greater than the density of the object, and vice versa.

Buffer. A mixture which maintains the pH of the solution constant in spite of the addition of strong acid or base.

495

Bumping. The sudden conversion of superheated liquid to vapor. Bumping may be violent enough to eject liquid from a container or split a beaker. It may be avoided by placing pieces of porous plate or silicon carbide in the solution (but not added while the liquid is superheated!).

Cathode. An electrode to which a negative charge is applied. The electrode toward which positively charged ions move. The electrode at which reduction occurs.

Cation. A positively charged ion.

Chromatographic analysis. Chromatography. The separation of substances by the selective adsorption on the surface of a solid of one component of a solution.

Colorimetry. The process of ascertaining the quantity of a substance by a measurement of the intensity of light transmitted by a solution of the substance.

Concentration. Weight per volume. Commonly expressed in several ways: (a) grams per 100 ml., often written 1:100 meaning 1 g. of substance per 100 ml. of water; (b) molar, the number of gram molecular weights per liter of solution; (c) normal, the number of gram equivalent weights per liter of solution. The equivalent weight varies with the type of reaction involved; (d) formal, the number of gram molecular weights per liter of solution. Formal concentration is the same as molar concentration; the term is used in the specification of some physical property, for example, the reduction potential, to indicate that the measurement has not been corrected for the actual activity of the substance in solution.

Cubic centimeter. One thousandth of a cubic decimeter. Not used in analytical chemistry; replaced by milliliter. See liter.

Desiccator. A container for storing materials in a clean, dry place. An apparatus for removing water from a substance. Note that desiccator is spelled with one *s* but two *c*'s.

Determination. The process or result of measuring the amount of a substance.

Digestion. The process of keeping a solid in contact with the liquid from which it was precipitated. The particle size of crystalline precipitates increases during digestion.

Displacement titration. The titration of a salt of a weak acid with a strong acid, or the titration of a salt of a weak base with a strong base.

Dissolution. The process by which two phases (solid, liquid, or gas) become one phase.

Double phosphate. The bivalent metal ammonium phosphates having the general formula MNH_4PO_4. M may be magnesium, manganese, zinc, cadmium, cobalt, or beryllium.

Electrodeposition. The formation of a solid on an electrode by the action of the electric current.

End-point. The completion of a reaction in volumetric analysis as marked by an indicator.

Equivalence-point. The theoretical completion of a reaction in volumetric analysis; the stage in a titration at which exactly stoichiometric amounts of the reacting materials have been mixed.

Equivalent weight. A combining weight; a multiple or submultiple of the molecular weight depending on the reaction in which the material is involved: (*a*) in neutralization reactions, the molecular weight divided by the number of replaceable hydrogen atoms that the material contains or with which it reacts; (*b*) in oxidation-reduction reactions, the molecular weight divided by the change in oxidation number that the material undergoes; (*c*) in precipitation and non-dissociated compound-formation reactions, the molecular weight divided by the number of atoms of a univalent metal with which the substance reacts.

Faraday. The quantity of electricity required to effect a reaction involving one electrochemical equivalent weight in grams; 96,500 coulombs.

Filter. In colorimetry, a colored glass used to select light of a certain wave length.

Formal concentration. A formal solution is one containing a gram molecular weight of a substance in 1 liter of solution. See concentration.

Formal reduction potential. A standard reduction potential measured at a specified concentration of a specified acid.

Gram (abbreviated g.). Unit of weight in the metric system; see page 155. The United States nickel weighs almost exactly 2 g. A milligram (mg.) is a thousandth of a gram (0.001 g.). A microgram (µg.) is a millionth of a gram (0.000,001 g.).

Gross sample. The preliminary sample taken from a large body of material for further reduction in particle size and amount.

Hygroscopic. Capable of absorbing water.

Ignite. In chemistry, to heat at a high temperature.

Indicator electrode. An electrode making contact with a solution so that the potential developed depends on and can be used to measure the concentration of some particular ion in solution.

Isohydric. Having the same hydrogen-ion concentration or pH.

Liter. The volume occupied by a mass of 1 kilogram of pure water at its maximum density under normal atmospheric pressure; equal to 1000.028 cubic centimeters.

Meniscus. The upper curved surface of a liquid in a tube.

Micro. A millionth of some quantity, as a microgram (µg.), microliter (µl.). Used as a prefix to indicate operation on a small scale, as in microanalysis.

Milligram. One thousandth of a gram; 0.001 g.

Millimicron (abbreviated mµ). A unit of length equal to 10^{-9} meter; equal to 10 Ångstroms.

Molar extinction coefficient. The constant ϵ in the Beer-Lambert law, $\log I/I_0 = -\epsilon lc$, relating the intensity of transmitted light to the path length in centimeters and the molar concentration of the colored material.

Nominal value. The value (weight, volume, etc.) marked on a piece of apparatus; usually a good first approximation to the true value.

Occlusion. The process by which water is trapped mechanically within a crystal.

Overvoltage. Polarization potential at an electrode at which a gas is liberated. See *polarization potential.*

Oxidation. The process of raising the valence state of an element; the loss of electrons.

pH. A measure of the acidity of a solution. The negative logarithm of the hydrogen-ion concentration. Mathematically the expressions

$$p\mathrm{H} = -\log[\mathrm{H}^+] \qquad p\mathrm{H} = \log\frac{1}{[\mathrm{H}^+]} \qquad \text{and} \qquad [\mathrm{H}^+] = 10^{-p\mathrm{H}}$$

are all equivalent. $p\mathrm{H} = 1$, very acid; $p\mathrm{H} = 7$, neutral; $p\mathrm{H} = 14$, very alkaline.

Parts per million (abbreviated p.p.m.). Equal to 1 milligram in a kilogram or 1 gram in a metric ton. Also equal to 0.0001 per cent.

Polarization potential. The departure of a single-electrode potential from the reversible single-electrode potential (as given by the electrode-potential equation) owing to the accumulation or depletion of material next to the electrode and resulting from the passage of current.

Precision. The reproducibility or the spread in a series of measurements of a given value.

Primary standard. A material of definite, known composition, usually 100 per cent pure, which can be used to determine the concentration of a solution to be used in volumetric analysis.

Reduction. The process of lowering the valence state of an element; the gain of electrons.

Reference electrode. An electrode used to make electrical contact to a solution in such a manner that the potential developed is constant and reproducible.

Rider. The platinum wire moved along the beam of a balance as part of the weights.

Single-electrode potential. The electrical potential set up at the surface of a metal in contact with a liquid; a single-electrode potential cannot be measured directly.

Standard oxidation potential. The single-electrode potential of an oxidation-reduction couple when the molar concentrations of the soluble forms are equal to 1; corresponds to a half-cell written as an oxidation reaction; opposite in sign to reduction potential.

Standard reduction potential. The single-electrode potential of an oxidation-reduction couple when the molar concentrations of the soluble forms are equal to 1; corresponds to a half-cell written as a reduction; opposite in sign to oxidation potential.

Standard solution. A solution of known concentration used in volumetric analysis.

Thief. A device for isolating a portion of a liquid for sampling or to prevent overstepping the end-point in a titration.

Titer. The strength of a standard solution expressed in terms of a specific substance determined by titration with the solution. Titer is obtained by multiplying the normal concentration of a solution by the milliequivalent weight of the substance being determined. Milliliters of standard solution multiplied by titer gives grams of substance determined.

Titration. A determination of the amount of a substance in solution by a measurement of the volume of a solution of known strength required to react with it.

Titrimetric analysis. An analysis involving a titration. A somewhat more correct term for the method usually called *volumetric analysis.*

Volumetric analysis. Strictly, an analysis by measurement of volume. Common for analyses involving titrations, in which the volume of a standard solution used in a reaction is measured.

Weight in vacuum. The true weight of an object as calculated from the apparent weight by correcting for the buoyancy effects on object and weights.

Zero point. The center of swings of a balance with no load on the pans.

N	0	1	2	3	4	5	6	7	8	9	Prop. Parts
100	00 000	043	087	130	173	217	260	303	346	389	
01	432	475	518	561	604	647	689	732	775	817	
02	00 860	903	945	988	*030	*072	*115	*157	*199	*242	
03	01 284	326	368	410	452	494	536	578	620	662	

	44	**43**	**42**
1	4.4	4.3	4.2
2	8.8	8.6	8.4
3	13.2	12.9	12.6
4	17.6	17.2	16.8
5	22.0	21.5	21.0
6	26.4	25.8	25.2
7	30.8	30.1	29.4
8	35.2	34.4	33.6
9	39.6	38.7	37.8

N	0	1	2	3	4	5	6	7	8	9
04	01 703	745	787	828	870	912	953	995	*036	*078
05	02 119	160	202	243	284	325	366	407	449	490
06	531	572	612	653	694	735	776	816	857	898
07	02 938	979	*019	*060	*100	*141	*181	*222	*262	*302
08	03 342	383	423	463	503	543	583	623	663	703
09	03 743	782	822	862	902	941	981	*021	*060	*100
110	04 139	179	218	258	297	336	376	415	454	493
11	532	571	610	650	689	727	766	805	844	883
12	04 922	961	999	*038	*077	*115	*154	*192	*231	*269
13	05 308	346	385	423	461	500	538	576	614	652

	41	**40**	**39**
1	4.1	4	3.9
2	8.2	8	7.8
3	12.3	12	11.7
4	16.4	16	15.6
5	20.5	20	19.5
6	24.6	24	23.4
7	28.7	28	27.3
8	32.8	32	31.2
9	36.9	36	35.1

N	0	1	2	3	4	5	6	7	8	9
14	05 690	729	767	805	843	881	918	956	994	*032
15	06 070	108	145	183	221	258	296	333	371	408
16	446	483	521	558	595	633	670	707	744	781
17	06 819	856	893	930	967	*004	*041	*078	*115	*151
18	07 188	225	262	298	335	372	408	445	482	518
19	555	591	628	664	700	737	773	809	846	882
120	07 918	954	990	*027	*063	*099	*135	*171	*207	*243
21	08 279	314	350	386	422	458	493	529	565	600
22	636	672	707	743	778	814	849	884	920	955
23	08 991	*026	*061	*096	*132	*167	*202	*237	*272	*307

	38	**37**	**36**
1	3.8	3.7	3.6
2	7.6	7.4	7.2
3	11.4	11.1	10.8
4	15.2	14.8	14.4
5	19.0	18.5	18.0
6	22.8	22.2	21.6
7	26.6	25.9	25.2
8	30.4	29.6	28.8
9	34.2	33.3	32.4

N	0	1	2	3	4	5	6	7	8	9
24	09 342	377	412	447	482	517	552	587	621	656
25	09 691	726	760	795	830	864	899	934	968	*003
26	10 037	072	106	140	175	209	243	278	312	346
27	380	415	449	483	517	551	585	619	653	687
28	10 721	755	789	823	857	890	924	958	992	*025
29	11 059	093	126	160	193	227	261	294	327	361
130	394	428	461	494	528	561	594	628	661	694
31	11 727	760	793	826	860	893	926	959	992	*024
32	12 057	090	123	156	189	222	254	287	320	352
33	385	418	450	483	516	548	581	613	646	678

	35	**34**	**33**
1	3.5	3.4	3.3
2	7.0	6.8	6.6
3	10.5	10.2	9.9
4	14.0	13.6	13.2
5	17.5	17.0	16.5
6	21.0	20.4	19.8
7	24.5	23.8	23.1
8	28.0	27.2	26.4
9	31.5	30.6	29.7

N	0	1	2	3	4	5	6	7	8	9
34	12 710	743	775	808	840	872	905	937	969	*001
35	13 033	066	098	130	162	194	226	258	290	322
36	354	386	418	450	481	513	545	577	609	640
37	672	704	735	767	799	830	862	893	925	956
38	13 988	*019	*051	*082	*114	*145	*176	*208	*239	*270
39	14 301	333	364	395	426	457	489	520	551	582
140	613	644	675	706	737	768	799	829	860	891
41	14 922	953	983	*014	*045	*076	*106	*137	*168	*198
42	15 229	259	290	320	351	381	412	442	473	503
43	534	564	594	625	655	685	715	746	776	806

	32	**31**	**30**
1	3.2	3.1	3
2	6.4	6.2	6
3	9.6	9.3	9
4	12.8	12.4	12
5	16.0	15.5	15
6	19.2	18.6	18
7	22.4	21.7	21
8	25.6	24.8	24
9	28.8	27.9	27

N	0	1	2	3	4	5	6	7	8	9
44	15 836	866	897	927	957	987	*017	*047	*077	*107
45	16 137	167	197	227	256	286	316	346	376	406
46	435	465	495	524	554	584	613	643	673	702
47	16 732	761	791	820	850	879	909	938	967	997
48	17 026	056	085	114	143	173	202	231	260	289
49	319	348	377	406	435	464	493	522	551	580
150	17 609	638	667	696	725	754	782	811	840	869
N	**0**	**1**	**2**	**3**	**4**	**5**	**6**	**7**	**8**	**9**

Prop. Parts

N	0	1	2	3	4	5	6	7	8	9
150	17 609	638	667	696	725	754	782	811	840	869
51	17 898	926	955	984	*013	*041	*070	*099	*127	*156
52	18 184	213	241	270	298	327	355	384	412	441
53	469	498	526	554	583	611	639	667	696	724
54	18 752	780	808	837	865	893	921	949	977	*005
55	19 033	061	089	117	145	173	201	229	257	285
56	312	340	368	396	424	451	479	507	535	562
57	590	618	645	673	700	728	756	783	811	838
58	19 866	893	921	948	976	*003	*030	*058	*085	*112
59	20 140	167	194	222	249	276	303	330	358	385
160	412	439	466	493	520	548	575	602	629	656
61	683	710	737	763	790	817	844	871	898	925
62	20 952	978	*005	*032	*059	*085	*112	*139	*165	*192
63	21 219	245	272	299	325	352	378	405	431	458
64	484	511	537	564	590	617	643	669	696	722
65	21 748	775	801	827	854	880	906	932	958	985
66	22 011	037	063	089	115	141	167	194	220	246
67	272	298	324	350	376	401	427	453	479	505
68	531	557	583	608	634	660	686	712	737	763
69	22 789	814	840	866	891	917	943	968	994	*019
170	23 045	070	096	121	147	172	198	223	249	274
71	300	325	350	376	401	426	452	477	502	528
72	553	578	603	629	654	679	704	729	754	779
73	23 805	830	855	880	905	930	955	980	*005	*030
74	24 055	080	105	130	155	180	204	229	254	279
75	304	329	353	378	403	428	452	477	502	527
76	551	576	601	625	650	674	699	724	748	773
77	24 797	822	846	871	895	920	944	969	993	*018
78	25 042	066	091	115	139	164	188	212	237	261
79	285	310	334	358	382	406	431	455	479	503
180	527	551	575	600	624	648	672	696	720	744
81	25 768	792	816	840	864	888	912	935	959	983
82	26 007	031	055	079	102	126	150	174	198	221
83	245	269	293	316	340	364	387	411	435	458
84	482	505	529	553	576	600	623	647	670	694
85	717	741	764	788	811	834	858	881	905	928
86	26 951	975	998	*021	*045	*068	*091	*114	*138	*161
87	27 184	207	231	254	277	300	323	346	370	393
88	416	439	462	485	508	531	554	577	600	623
89	646	669	692	715	738	761	784	807	830	852
190	27 875	898	921	944	967	989	*012	*035	*058	*081
91	28 103	126	149	171	194	217	240	262	285	307
92	330	353	375	398	421	443	466	488	511	533
93	556	578	601	623	646	668	691	713	735	758
94	28 780	803	825	847	870	892	914	937	959	981
95	29 003	026	048	070	092	115	137	159	181	203
96	226	248	270	292	314	336	358	380	403	425
97	447	469	491	513	535	557	579	601	623	645
98	667	688	710	732	754	776	798	820	842	863
99	29 885	907	929	951	973	994	*016	*038	*060	*081
200	30 103	125	146	168	190	211	233	255	276	298

Prop. Parts

	29	28
1	2.9	2.8
2	5.8	5.6
3	8.7	8.4
4	11.6	11.2
5	14.5	14.0
6	17.4	16.8
7	20.3	19.6
8	23.2	22.4
9	26.1	25.2

	27	26
1	2.7	2.6
2	5.4	5.2
3	8.1	7.8
4	10.8	10.4
5	13.5	13.0
6	16.2	15.6
7	18.9	18.2
8	21.6	20.8
9	24.3	23.4

	25
1	2.5
2	5.0
3	7.5
4	10.0
5	12.5
6	15.0
7	17.5
8	20.0
9	22.5

	24	23
1	2.4	2.3
2	4.8	4.6
3	7.2	6.9
4	9.6	9.2
5	12.0	11.5
6	14.4	13.8
7	16.8	16.1
8	19.2	18.4
9	21.6	20.7

	22	21
1	2.2	2.1
2	4.4	4.2
3	6.6	6.3
4	8.8	8.4
5	11.0	10.5
6	13.2	12.6
7	15.4	14.7
8	17.6	16.8
9	19.8	18.9

N	0	1	2	3	4	5	6	7	8	9
200	30 103	125	146	168	190	211	233	255	276	298
01	320	341	363	384	406	428	449	471	492	514
02	535	557	578	600	621	643	664	685	707	728
03	750	771	792	814	835	856	878	899	920	942
04	30 963	984	*006	*027	*048	*069	*091	*112	*133	*154
05	31 175	197	218	239	260	281	302	323	345	366
06	387	408	429	450	471	492	513	534	555	576
07	597	618	639	660	681	702	723	744	765	785
08	31 806	827	848	869	890	911	931	952	973	994
09	32 015	035	056	077	098	118	139	160	181	201
210	222	243	263	284	305	325	346	366	387	408
11	428	449	469	490	510	531	552	572	593	613
12	634	654	675	695	715	736	756	777	797	818
13	32 838	858	879	899	919	940	960	980	*001	*021
14	33 041	062	082	102	122	143	163	183	203	224
15	244	264	284	304	325	345	365	385	405	425
16	445	465	486	506	526	546	566	586	606	626
17	646	666	686	706	726	746	766	786	806	826
18	33 846	866	885	905	925	945	965	985	*005	*025
19	34 044	064	084	104	124	143	163	183	203	223
220	242	262	282	301	321	341	361	380	400	420
21	439	459	479	498	518	537	557	577	596	616
22	635	655	674	694	713	733	753	772	792	811
23	34 830	850	869	889	908	928	947	967	986	*005
24	35 025	044	064	083	102	122	141	160	180	199
25	218	238	257	276	295	315	334	353	372	392
26	411	430	449	468	488	507	526	545	564	583
27	603	622	641	660	679	698	717	736	755	774
28	793	813	832	851	870	889	908	927	946	965
29	35 984	*003	*021	*040	*059	*078	*097	*116	*135	*154
230	36 173	192	211	229	248	267	286	305	324	342
31	361	380	399	418	436	455	474	493	511	530
32	549	568	586	605	624	642	661	680	698	717
33	736	754	773	791	810	829	847	866	884	903
34	36 922	940	959	977	996	*014	*033	*051	*070	*088
35	37 107	125	144	162	181	199	218	236	254	273
36	291	310	328	346	365	383	401	420	438	457
37	475	493	511	530	548	566	585	603	621	639
38	658	676	694	712	731	749	767	785	803	822
39	37 840	858	876	894	912	931	949	967	985	*003
240	38 021	039	057	075	093	112	130	148	166	184
41	202	220	238	256	274	292	310	328	346	364
42	382	399	417	435	453	471	489	507	525	543
43	561	578	596	614	632	650	668	686	703	721
44	739	757	775	792	810	828	846	863	881	899
45	38 917	934	952	970	987	*005	*023	*041	*058	*076
46	39 094	111	129	146	164	182	199	217	235	252
47	270	287	305	322	340	358	375	393	410	428
48	445	463	480	498	515	533	550	568	585	602
49	620	637	655	672	690	707	724	742	759	777
250	39 794	811	829	846	863	881	898	915	933	950

Prop. Parts

	22	21
1	2.2	2.1
2	4.4	4.2
3	6.6	6.3
4	8.8	8.4
5	11.0	10.5
6	13.2	12.6
7	15.4	14.7
8	17.6	16.8
9	19.8	18.9

	20
1	2
2	4
3	6
4	8
5	10
6	12
7	14
8	16
9	18

	19
1	1.9
2	3.8
3	5.7
4	7.6
5	9.5
6	11.4
7	13.3
8	15.2
9	17.1

	18
1	1.8
2	3.6
3	5.4
4	7.2
5	9.0
6	10.8
7	12.6
8	14.4
9	16.2

	17
1	1.7
2	3.4
3	5.1
4	6.8
5	8.5
6	10.2
7	11.9
8	13.6
9	15.3

N	0	1	2	3	4	5	6	7	8	9
250	39 794	811	829	846	863	881	898	915	933	950
51	39 967	985	*002	*019	*037	*054	*071	*088	*106	*123
52	40 140	157	175	192	209	226	243	261	278	295
53	312	329	346	364	381	398	415	432	449	466
54	483	500	518	535	552	569	586	603	620	637
55	654	671	688	705	722	739	756	773	790	807
56	824	841	858	875	892	909	926	943	960	976
57	40 993	*010	*027	*044	*061	*078	*095	*111	*128	*145
58	41 162	179	196	212	229	246	263	280	296	313
59	330	347	363	380	397	414	430	447	464	481
260	497	514	531	547	564	581	597	614	631	647
61	664	681	697	714	731	747	764	780	797	814
62	830	847	863	880	896	913	929	946	963	979
63	41 996	*012	*029	*045	*062	*078	*095	*111	*127	*144
64	42 160	177	193	210	226	243	259	275	292	308
65	325	341	357	374	390	406	423	439	455	472
66	488	504	521	537	553	570	586	602	619	635
67	651	667	684	700	716	732	749	765	781	797
68	813	830	846	862	878	894	911	927	943	959
69	42 975	991	*008	*024	*040	*056	*072	*088	*104	*120
270	43 136	152	169	185	201	217	233	249	265	281
71	297	313	329	345	361	377	393	409	425	441
72	457	473	489	505	521	537	553	569	584	600
73	616	632	648	664	680	696	712	727	743	759
74	775	791	807	823	838	854	870	886	902	917
75	43 933	949	965	981	996	*012	*028	*044	*059	*075
76	44 091	107	122	138	154	170	185	201	217	232
77	248	264	279	295	311	326	342	358	373	389
78	404	420	436	451	467	483	498	514	529	545
79	560	576	592	607	623	638	654	669	685	700
280	716	731	747	762	778	793	809	824	840	855
81	44 871	886	902	917	932	948	963	979	994	*010
82	45 025	040	056	071	086	102	117	133	148	163
83	179	194	209	225	240	255	271	286	301	317
84	332	347	362	378	393	408	423	439	454	469
85	484	500	515	530	545	561	576	591	606	621
86	637	652	667	682	697	712	728	743	758	773
87	788	803	818	834	849	864	879	894	909	924
88	45 939	954	969	984	*000	*015	*030	*045	*060	*075
89	46 090	105	120	135	150	165	180	195	210	225
290	240	255	270	285	300	315	330	345	359	374
91	389	404	419	434	449	464	479	494	509	523
92	538	553	568	583	598	613	627	642	657	672
93	687	702	716	731	746	761	776	790	805	820
94	835	850	864	879	894	909	923	938	953	967
95	46 982	997	*012	*026	*041	*056	*070	*085	*100	*114
96	47 129	144	159	173	188	202	217	232	246	261
97	276	290	305	319	334	349	363	378	392	407
98	422	436	451	465	480	494	509	524	538	553
99	567	582	596	611	625	640	654	669	683	698
300	47 712	727	741	756	770	784	799	813	828	842

Prop. Parts

	18	17	16	15	14
1	1.8	1.7	1.6	1.5	1.4
2	3.6	3.4	3.2	3.0	2.8
3	5.4	5.1	4.8	4.5	4.2
4	7.2	6.8	6.4	6.0	5.6
5	9.0	8.5	8.0	7.5	7.0
6	10.8	10.2	9.6	9.0	8.4
7	12.6	11.9	11.2	10.5	9.8
8	14.4	13.6	12.8	12.0	11.2
9	16.2	15.3	14.4	13.5	12.6

N	0	1	2	3	4	5	6	7	8	9	Prop. Parts
300	47 712	727	741	756	770	784	799	813	828	842	
01	47 857	871	885	900	914	929	943	958	972	986	
02	48 001	015	029	044	058	073	087	101	116	130	
03	144	159	173	187	202	216	230	244	259	273	
04	287	302	316	330	344	359	373	387	401	416	
05	430	444	458	473	487	501	515	530	544	558	
06	572	586	601	615	629	643	657	671	686	700	
07	714	728	742	756	770	785	799	813	827	841	
08	855	869	883	897	911	926	940	954	968	982	
09	48 996	*010	*024	*038	*052	*066	*080	*094	*108	*122	
310	49 136	150	164	178	192	206	220	234	248	262	
11	276	290	304	318	332	346	360	374	388	402	
12	415	429	443	457	471	485	499	513	527	541	
13	554	568	582	596	610	624	638	651	665	679	
14	693	707	721	734	748	762	776	790	803	817	
15	831	845	859	872	886	900	914	927	941	955	
16	49 969	982	996	*010	*024	*037	*051	*065	*079	*092	
17	50 106	120	133	147	161	174	188	202	215	229	
18	243	256	270	284	297	311	325	338	352	365	
19	379	393	406	420	433	447	461	474	488	501	
320	515	529	542	556	569	583	596	610	623	637	
21	651	664	678	691	705	718	732	745	759	772	
22	786	799	813	826	840	853	866	880	893	907	
23	50 920	934	947	961	974	987	*001	*014	*028	*041	
24	51 055	068	081	095	108	121	135	148	162	175	
25	188	202	215	228	242	255	268	282	295	308	
26	322	335	348	362	375	388	402	415	428	441	
27	455	468	481	495	508	521	534	548	561	574	
28	587	601	614	627	640	654	667	680	693	706	
29	720	733	746	759	772	786	799	812	825	838	
330	851	865	878	891	904	917	930	943	957	970	
31	51 983	996	*009	*022	*035	*048	*061	*075	*088	*101	
32	52 114	127	140	153	166	179	192	205	218	231	
33	244	257	270	284	297	310	323	336	349	362	
34	375	388	401	414	427	440	453	466	479	492	
35	504	517	530	543	556	569	582	595	608	621	
36	634	647	660	673	686	699	711	724	737	750	
37	763	776	789	802	815	827	840	853	866	879	
38	52 892	905	917	930	943	956	969	982	994	*007	
39	53 020	033	046	058	071	084	097	110	122	135	
340	148	161	173	186	199	212	224	237	250	263	
41	275	288	301	314	326	339	352	364	377	390	
42	403	415	428	441	453	466	479	491	504	517	
43	529	542	555	567	580	593	605	618	631	643	
44	656	668	681	694	706	719	732	744	757	769	
45	782	794	807	820	832	845	857	870	882	895	
46	53 908	920	933	945	958	970	983	995	*008	*020	
47	54 033	045	058	070	083	095	108	120	133	145	
48	158	170	183	195	208	220	233	245	258	270	
49	283	295	307	320	332	345	357	370	382	394	
350	54 407	419	432	444	456	469	481	494	506	518	
N	0	1	2	3	4	5	6	7	8	9	Prop. Parts

Prop. Parts

15
1 | 1.5
2 | 3.0
3 | 4.5
4 | 6.0
5 | 7.5
6 | 9.0
7 | 10.5
8 | 12.0
9 | 13.5

14
1 | 1.4
2 | 2.8
3 | 4.2
4 | 5.6
5 | 7.0
6 | 8.4
7 | 9.8
8 | 11.2
9 | 12.6

13
1 | 1.3
2 | 2.6
3 | 3.9
4 | 5.2
5 | 6.5
6 | 7.8
7 | 9.1
8 | 10.4
9 | 11.7

12
1 | 1.2
2 | 2.4
3 | 3.6
4 | 4.8
5 | 6.0
6 | 7.2
7 | 8.4
8 | 9.6
9 | 10.8

Prop. Parts		N	0	1	2	3	4	5	6	7	8	9
		350	54 407	419	432	444	456	469	481	494	506	518
		51	531	543	555	568	580	593	605	617	630	642
		52	654	667	679	691	704	716	728	741	753	765
		53	777	790	802	814	827	839	851	864	876	888
	13											
1	1.3	54	54 900	913	925	937	949	962	974	986	998	*011
2	2.6	55	55 023	035	047	060	072	084	096	108	121	133
3	3.9	56	145	157	169	182	194	206	218	230	242	255
4	5.2											
5	6.5	57	267	279	291	303	315	328	340	352	364	376
6	7.8	58	388	400	413	425	437	449	461	473	485	497
7	9.1	59	509	522	534	546	558	570	582	594	606	618
8	10.4											
9	11.7	360	630	642	654	666	678	691	703	715	727	739
		61	751	763	775	787	799	811	823	835	847	859
		62	871	883	895	907	919	931	943	955	967	979
		63	55 991	*003	*015	*027	*038	*050	*062	*074	*086	*098
		64	56 110	122	134	146	158	170	182	194	205	217
		65	229	241	253	265	277	289	301	312	324	336
	12	66	348	360	372	384	396	407	419	431	443	455
1	1.2											
2	2.4	67	467	478	490	502	514	526	538	549	561	573
3	3.6	68	585	597	608	620	632	644	656	667	679	691
4	4.8	69	703	714	726	738	750	761	773	785	797	808
5	6.0											
6	7.2	370	820	832	844	855	867	879	891	902	914	926
7	8.4											
8	9.6	71	56 937	949	961	972	984	996	*008	*019	*031	*043
9	10.8	72	57 054	066	078	089	101	113	124	136	148	159
		73	171	183	194	206	217	229	241	252	264	276
		74	287	299	310	322	334	345	357	368	380	392
		75	403	415	426	438	449	461	473	484	496	507
		76	519	530	542	553	565	576	588	600	611	623
		77	634	646	657	669	680	692	703	715	726	738
	11	78	749	761	772	784	795	807	818	830	841	852
		79	864	875	887	898	910	921	933	944	955	967
1	1.1											
2	2.2	380	57 978	990	*001	*013	*024	*035	*047	*058	*070	*081
3	3.3											
4	4.4	81	58 092	104	115	127	138	149	161	172	184	195
5	5.5	82	206	218	229	240	252	263	274	286	297	309
6	6.6	83	320	331	343	354	365	377	388	399	410	422
7	7.7											
8	8.8	84	433	444	456	467	478	490	501	512	524	535
9	9.9	85	546	557	569	580	591	602	614	625	636	647
		86	659	670	681	692	704	715	726	737	749	760
		87	771	782	794	805	816	827	838	850	861	872
		88	883	894	906	917	928	939	950	961	973	984
		89	58 995	*006	*017	*028	*040	*051	*062	*073	*084	*095
	10	390	59 106	118	129	140	151	162	173	184	195	207
1	1.0	91	218	229	240	251	262	273	284	295	306	318
2	2.0	92	329	340	351	362	373	384	395	406	417	428
3	3.0	93	439	450	461	472	483	494	506	517	528	539
4	4.0											
5	5.0	94	550	561	572	583	594	605	616	627	638	649
6	6.0	95	660	671	682	693	704	715	726	737	748	759
7	7.0	96	770	780	791	802	813	824	835	846	857	868
8	8.0											
9	9.0	97	879	890	901	912	923	934	945	956	966	977
		98	59 988	999	*010	*021	*032	*043	*054	*065	*076	*086
		99	60 097	108	119	130	141	152	163	173	184	195
		400	60 206	217	228	239	249	260	271	282	293	304
Prop. Parts		N	0	1	2	3	4	5	6	7	8	9

N	0	1	2	3	4	5	6	7	8	9	Prop. Parts
400	60 206	217	228	239	249	260	271	282	293	304	
01	314	325	336	347	358	369	379	390	401	412	
02	423	433	444	455	466	477	487	498	509	520	
03	531	541	552	563	574	584	595	606	617	627	
04	638	649	660	670	681	692	703	713	724	735	
05	746	756	767	778	788	799	810	821	831	842	
06	853	863	874	885	895	906	917	927	938	949	
07	60 959	970	981	991	*002	*013	*023	*034	*045	*055	
08	61 066	077	087	098	109	119	130	140	151	162	
09	172	183	194	204	215	225	236	247	257	268	
410	278	289	300	310	321	331	342	352	363	374	
11	384	395	405	416	426	437	448	458	469	479	
12	490	500	511	521	532	542	553	563	574	584	
13	595	606	616	627	637	648	658	669	679	690	
14	700	711	721	731	742	752	763	773	784	794	
15	805	815	826	836	847	857	868	878	888	899	
16	61 909	920	930	941	951	962	972	982	993	*003	
17	62 014	024	034	045	055	066	076	086	097	107	
18	118	128	138	149	159	170	180	190	201	211	
19	221	232	242	252	263	273	284	294	304	315	
420	325	335	346	356	366	377	387	397	408	418	
21	428	439	449	459	469	480	490	500	511	521	
22	531	542	552	562	572	583	593	603	613	624	
23	634	644	655	665	675	685	696	706	716	726	
24	737	747	757	767	778	788	798	808	818	829	
25	839	849	859	870	880	890	900	910	921	931	
26	62 941	951	961	972	982	992	*002	*012	*022	*033	
27	63 043	053	063	073	083	094	104	114	124	134	
28	144	155	165	175	185	195	205	215	225	236	
29	246	256	266	276	286	296	306	317	327	337	
430	347	357	367	377	387	397	407	417	428	438	
31	448	458	468	478	488	498	508	518	528	538	
32	548	558	568	579	589	599	609	619	629	639	
33	649	659	669	679	689	699	709	719	729	739	
34	749	759	769	779	789	799	809	819	829	839	
35	849	859	869	879	889	899	909	919	929	939	
36	63 949	959	969	979	988	998	*008	*018	*028	*038	
37	64 048	058	068	078	088	098	108	118	128	137	
38	147	157	167	177	187	197	207	217	227	237	
39	246	256	266	276	286	296	306	316	326	335	
440	345	355	365	375	385	395	404	414	424	434	
41	444	454	464	473	483	493	503	513	523	532	
42	542	552	562	572	582	591	601	611	621	631	
43	640	650	660	670	680	689	699	709	719	729	
44	738	748	758	768	777	787	797	807	816	826	
45	836	846	856	865	875	885	895	904	914	924	
46	64 933	943	953	963	972	982	992	*002	*011	*021	
47	65 031	040	050	060	070	079	089	099	108	118	
48	128	137	147	157	167	176	186	196	205	215	
49	225	234	244	254	263	273	283	292	302	312	
450	65 321	331	341	350	360	369	379	389	398	408	
N	0	1	2	3	4	5	6	7	8	9	Prop. Parts

Prop. Parts:

11

1	1.1
2	2.2
3	3.3
4	4.4
5	5.5
6	6.6
7	7.7
8	8.8
9	9.9

10

1	1.0
2	2.0
3	3.0
4	4.0
5	5.0
6	6.0
7	7.0
8	8.0
9	9.0

9

1	0.9
2	1.8
3	2.7
4	3.6
5	4.5
6	5.4
7	6.3
8	7.2
9	8.1

N	0	1	2	3	4	5	6	7	8	9
450	65 321	331	341	350	360	369	379	389	398	408
51	418	427	437	447	456	466	475	485	495	504
52	514	523	533	543	552	562	571	581	591	600
53	610	619	629	639	648	658	667	677	686	696
54	706	715	725	734	744	753	763	772	782	792
55	801	811	820	830	839	849	858	868	877	887
56	896	906	916	925	935	944	954	963	973	982
57	65 992	*001	*011	*020	*030	*039	*049	*058	*068	*077
58	66 087	096	106	115	124	134	143	153	162	172
59	181	191	200	210	219	229	238	247	257	266
460	276	285	295	304	314	323	332	342	351	361
61	370	380	389	398	408	417	427	436	445	455
62	464	474	483	492	502	511	521	530	539	549
63	558	567	577	586	596	605	614	624	633	642
64	652	661	671	680	689	699	708	717	727	736
65	745	755	764	773	783	792	801	811	820	829
66	839	848	857	867	876	885	894	904	913	922
67	66 932	941	950	960	969	978	987	997	*006	*015
68	67 025	034	043	052	062	071	080	089	099	108
69	117	127	136	145	154	164	173	182	191	201
470	210	219	228	237	247	256	265	274	284	293
71	302	311	321	330	339	348	357	367	376	385
72	394	403	413	422	431	440	449	459	468	477
73	486	495	504	514	523	532	541	550	560	569
74	578	587	596	605	614	624	633	642	651	660
75	669	679	688	697	706	715	724	733	742	752
76	761	770	779	788	797	806	815	825	834	843
77	852	861	870	879	888	897	906	916	925	934
78	67 943	952	961	970	979	988	997	*006	*015	*024
79	68 034	043	052	061	070	079	088	097	106	115
480	124	133	142	151	160	169	178	187	196	205
81	215	224	233	242	251	260	269	278	287	296
82	305	314	323	332	341	350	359	368	377	386
83	395	404	413	422	431	440	449	458	467	476
84	485	494	502	511	520	529	538	547	556	565
85	574	583	592	601	610	619	628	637	646	655
86	664	673	681	690	699	708	717	726	735	744
87	753	762	771	780	789	797	806	815	824	833
88	842	851	860	869	878	886	895	904	913	922
89	68 931	940	949	958	966	975	984	993	*002	*011
490	69 020	028	037	046	055	064	073	082	090	099
91	108	117	126	135	144	152	161	170	179	188
92	197	205	214	223	232	241	249	258	267	276
93	285	294	302	311	320	329	338	346	355	364
94	373	381	390	399	408	417	425	434	443	452
95	461	469	478	487	496	504	513	522	531	539
96	548	557	566	574	583	592	601	609	618	627
97	636	644	653	662	671	679	688	697	705	714
98	723	732	740	749	758	767	775	784	793	801
99	810	819	827	836	845	854	862	871	880	888
500	69 897	906	914	923	932	940	949	958	966	975

Prop. Parts

	10
1	1.0
2	2.0
3	3.0
4	4.0
5	5.0
6	6.0
7	7.0
8	8.0
9	9.0

	9
1	0.9
2	1.8
3	2.7
4	3.6
5	4.5
6	5.4
7	6.3
8	7.2
9	8.1

	8
1	0.8
2	1.6
3	2.4
4	3.2
5	4.0
6	4.8
7	5.6
8	6.4
9	7.2

N	0	1	2	3	4	5	6	7	8	9	Prop. Parts
500	69 897	906	914	923	932	940	949	958	966	975	
01	69 984	992	*001	*010	*018	*027	*036	*044	*053	*062	
02	70 070	079	088	096	105	114	122	131	140	148	
03	157	165	174	183	191	200	209	217	226	234	
04	243	252	260	269	278	286	295	303	312	321	
05	329	338	346	355	364	372	381	389	398	406	
06	415	424	432	441	449	458	467	475	484	492	
07	501	509	518	526	535	544	552	561	569	578	**9**
08	586	595	603	612	621	629	638	646	655	663	1 0.9
09	672	680	689	697	706	714	723	731	740	749	2 1.8
510	757	766	774	783	791	800	808	817	825	834	3 2.7 / 4 3.6 / 5 4.5 / 6 5.4
11	842	851	859	868	876	885	893	902	910	919	7 6.3
12	70 927	935	944	952	961	969	978	986	995	*003	8 7.2
13	71 012	020	029	037	046	054	063	071	079	088	9 8.1
14	096	105	113	122	130	139	147	155	164	172	
15	181	189	198	206	214	223	231	240	248	257	
16	265	273	282	290	299	307	315	324	332	341	
17	349	357	366	374	383	391	399	408	416	425	
18	433	441	450	458	466	475	483	492	500	508	
19	517	525	533	542	550	559	567	575	584	592	
520	600	609	617	625	634	642	650	659	667	675	
21	684	692	700	709	717	725	734	742	750	759	
22	767	775	784	792	800	809	817	825	834	842	**8**
23	850	858	867	875	883	892	900	908	917	925	1 0.8
24	71 933	941	950	958	966	975	983	991	999	*008	2 1.6 / 3 2.4
25	72 016	024	032	041	049	057	066	074	082	090	4 3.2
26	099	107	115	123	132	140	148	156	165	173	5 4.0 / 6 4.8
27	181	189	198	206	214	222	230	239	247	255	7 5.6
28	263	272	280	288	296	304	313	321	329	337	8 6.4
29	346	354	362	370	378	387	395	403	411	419	9 7.2
530	428	436	444	452	460	469	477	485	493	501	
31	509	518	526	534	542	550	558	567	575	583	
32	591	599	607	616	624	632	640	648	656	665	
33	673	681	689	697	705	713	722	730	738	746	
34	754	762	770	779	787	795	803	811	819	827	
35	835	843	852	860	868	876	884	892	900	908	
36	916	925	933	941	949	957	965	973	981	989	
37	72 997	*006	*014	*022	*030	*038	*046	*054	*062	*070	**7**
38	73 078	086	094	102	111	119	127	135	143	151	1 0.7
39	159	167	175	183	191	199	207	215	223	231	2 1.4 / 3 2.1
540	239	247	255	263	272	280	288	296	304	312	4 2.8
41	320	328	336	344	352	360	368	376	384	392	5 3.5 / 6 4.2
42	400	408	416	424	432	440	448	456	464	472	7 4.9
43	480	488	496	504	512	520	528	536	544	552	8 5.6
44	560	568	576	584	592	600	608	616	624	632	9 6.3
45	640	648	656	664	672	679	687	695	703	711	
46	719	727	735	743	751	759	767	775	783	791	
47	799	807	815	823	830	838	846	854	862	870	
48	878	886	894	902	910	918	926	933	941	949	
49	73 957	965	973	981	989	997	*005	*013	*020	*028	
550	74 036	044	052	060	068	076	084	092	099	107	
N	0	1	2	3	4	5	6	7	8	9	Prop. Parts

Prop. Parts	N	0	1	2	3	4	5	6	7	8	9
	550	74 036	044	052	060	068	076	084	092	099	107
	51	115	123	131	139	147	155	162	170	178	186
	52	194	202	210	218	225	233	241	249	257	265
	53	273	280	288	296	304	312	320	327	335	343
	54	351	359	367	374	382	390	398	406	414	421
	55	429	437	445	453	461	468	476	484	492	500
	56	507	515	523	531	539	547	554	562	570	578
	57	586	593	601	609	617	624	632	640	648	656
	58	663	671	679	687	695	702	710	718	726	733
	59	741	749	757	764	772	780	788	796	803	811
	560	819	827	834	842	850	858	865	873	881	889
	61	896	904	912	920	927	935	943	950	958	966
8	62	74 974	981	989	997	*005	*012	*020	*028	*035	*043
1 0.8	63	75 051	059	066	074	082	089	097	105	113	120
2 1.6											
3 2.4	64	128	136	143	151	159	166	174	182	189	197
4 3.2	65	205	213	220	228	236	243	251	259	266	274
5 4.0	66	282	289	297	305	312	320	328	335	343	351
6 4.8											
7 5.6	67	358	366	374	381	389	397	404	412	420	427
8 6.4	68	435	442	450	458	465	473	481	488	496	504
9 7.2	69	511	519	526	534	542	549	557	565	572	580
	570	587	595	603	610	618	626	633	641	648	656
	71	664	671	679	686	694	702	709	717	724	732
	72	740	747	755	762	770	778	785	793	800	808
	73	815	823	831	838	846	853	861	868	876	884
	74	891	899	906	914	921	929	937	944	952	959
	75	75 967	974	982	989	997	*005	*012	*020	*027	*035
	76	76 042	050	057	065	072	080	087	095	103	110
	77	118	125	133	140	148	155	163	170	178	185
	78	193	200	208	215	223	230	238	245	253	260
	79	268	275	283	290	298	305	313	320	328	335
	580	343	350	358	365	373	380	388	395	403	410
	81	418	425	433	440	448	455	462	470	477	485
7	82	492	500	507	515	522	530	537	545	552	559
1 0.7	83	567	574	582	589	597	604	612	619	626	634
2 1.4											
3 2.1	84	641	649	656	664	671	678	686	693	701	708
4 2.8	85	716	723	730	738	745	753	760	768	775	782
5 3.5	86	790	797	805	812	819	827	834	842	849	856
6 4.2											
7 4.9	87	864	871	879	886	893	901	908	916	923	930
8 5.6	88	76 938	945	953	960	967	975	982	989	997	*004
9 6.3	89	77 012	019	026	034	041	048	056	063	070	078
	590	085	093	100	107	115	122	129	137	144	151
	91	159	166	173	181	188	195	203	210	217	225
	92	232	240	247	254	262	269	276	283	291	298
	93	305	313	320	327	335	342	349	357	364	371
	94	379	386	393	401	408	415	422	430	437	444
	95	452	459	466	474	481	488	495	503	510	517
	96	525	532	539	546	554	561	568	576	583	590
	97	597	605	612	619	627	634	641	648	656	663
	98	670	677	685	692	699	706	714	721	728	735
	99	743	750	757	764	772	779	786	793	801	808
	600	77 815	822	830	837	844	851	859	866	873	880
Prop. Parts	N	0	1	2	3	4	5	6	7	8	9

N	0	1	2	3	4	5	6	7	8	9	Prop. Parts
600	77 815	822	830	837	844	851	859	866	873	880	
01	887	895	902	909	916	924	931	938	945	952	
02	77 960	967	974	981	988	996	*003	*010	*017	*025	
03	78 032	039	046	053	061	068	075	082	089	097	
04	104	111	118	125	132	140	147	154	161	168	
05	176	183	190	197	204	211	219	226	233	240	
06	247	254	262	269	276	283	290	297	305	312	
07	319	326	333	340	347	355	362	369	376	383	
08	390	398	405	412	419	426	433	440	447	455	
09	462	469	476	483	490	497	504	512	519	526	
610	533	540	547	554	561	569	576	583	590	597	
11	604	611	618	625	633	640	647	654	661	668	
12	675	682	689	696	704	711	718	725	732	739	
13	746	753	760	767	774	781	789	796	803	810	
14	817	824	831	838	845	852	859	866	873	880	
15	888	895	902	909	916	923	930	937	944	951	
16	78 958	965	972	979	986	993	*000	*007	*014	*021	
17	79 029	036	043	050	057	064	071	078	085	092	
18	099	106	113	120	127	134	141	148	155	162	
19	169	176	183	190	197	204	211	218	225	232	
620	239	246	253	260	267	274	281	288	295	302	
21	309	316	323	330	337	344	351	358	365	372	
22	379	386	393	400	407	414	421	428	435	442	
23	449	456	463	470	477	484	491	498	505	511	
24	518	525	532	539	546	553	560	567	574	581	
25	588	595	602	609	616	623	630	637	644	650	
26	657	664	671	678	685	692	699	706	713	720	
27	727	734	741	748	754	761	768	775	782	789	
28	796	803	810	817	824	831	837	844	851	858	
29	865	872	879	886	893	900	906	913	920	927	
630	79 934	941	948	955	962	969	975	982	989	996	
31	80 003	010	017	024	030	037	044	051	058	065	
32	072	079	085	092	099	106	113	120	127	134	
33	140	147	154	161	168	175	182	188	195	202	
34	209	216	223	229	236	243	250	257	264	271	
35	277	284	291	298	305	312	318	325	332	339	
36	346	353	359	366	373	380	387	393	400	407	
37	414	421	428	434	441	448	455	462	468	475	
38	482	489	496	502	509	516	523	530	536	543	
39	550	557	564	570	577	584	591	598	604	611	
640	618	625	632	638	645	652	659	665	672	679	
41	686	693	699	706	713	720	726	733	740	747	
42	754	760	767	774	781	787	794	801	808	814	
43	821	828	835	841	848	855	862	868	875	882	
44	889	895	902	909	916	922	929	936	943	949	
45	80 956	963	969	976	983	990	996	*003	*010	*017	
46	81 023	030	037	043	050	057	064	070	077	084	
47	090	097	104	111	117	124	131	137	144	151	
48	158	164	171	178	184	191	198	204	211	218	
49	224	231	238	245	251	258	265	271	278	285	
650	81 291	298	305	311	318	325	331	338	345	351	
N	0	1	2	3	4	5	6	7	8	9	Prop. Parts

Prop. Parts

	8
1	0.8
2	1.6
3	2.4
4	3.2
5	4.0
6	4.8
7	5.6
8	6.4
9	7.2

	7
1	0.7
2	1.4
3	2.1
4	2.8
5	3.5
6	4.2
7	4.9
8	5.6
9	6.3

	6
1	0.6
2	1.2
3	1.8
4	2.4
5	3.0
6	3.6
7	4.2
8	4.8
9	5.4

Prop. Parts	N	0	1	2	3	4	5	6	7	8	9
	650	81 291	298	305	311	318	325	331	338	345	351
	51	358	365	371	378	385	391	398	405	411	418
	52	425	431	438	445	451	458	465	471	478	485
	53	491	498	505	511	518	525	531	538	544	551
	54	558	564	571	578	584	591	598	604	611	617
	55	624	631	637	644	651	657	664	671	677	684
	56	690	697	704	710	717	723	730	737	743	750
	57	757	763	770	776	783	790	796	803	809	816
	58	823	829	836	842	849	856	862	869	875	882
	59	889	895	902	908	915	921	928	935	941	948
	660	81 954	961	968	974	981	987	994	*000	*007	*014
	61	82 020	027	033	040	046	053	060	066	073	079
7	62	086	092	099	105	112	119	125	132	138	145
1 0.7	63	151	158	164	171	178	184	191	197	204	210
2 1.4	64	217	223	230	236	243	249	256	263	269	276
3 2.1	65	282	289	295	302	308	315	321	328	334	341
4 2.8	66	347	354	360	367	373	380	387	393	400	406
5 3.5	67	413	419	426	432	439	445	452	458	465	471
6 4.2	68	478	484	491	497	504	510	517	523	530	536
7 4.9	69	543	549	556	562	569	575	582	588	595	601
8 5.6	**670**	607	614	620	627	633	640	646	653	659	666
9 6.3	71	672	679	685	692	698	705	711	718	724	730
	72	737	743	750	756	763	769	776	782	789	795
	73	802	808	814	821	827	834	840	847	853	860
	74	866	872	879	885	892	898	905	911	918	924
	75	930	937	943	950	956	963	969	975	982	988
	76	82 995	*001	*008	*014	*020	*027	*033	*040	*046	*052
	77	83 059	065	072	078	085	091	097	104	110	117
	78	123	129	136	142	149	155	161	168	174	181
	79	187	193	200	206	213	219	225	232	238	245
	680	251	257	264	270	276	283	289	296	302	308
	81	315	321	327	334	340	347	353	359	366	372
6	82	378	385	391	398	404	410	417	423	429	436
1 0.6	83	442	448	455	461	467	474	480	487	493	499
2 1.2	84	506	512	518	525	531	537	544	550	556	563
3 1.8	85	569	575	582	588	594	601	607	613	620	626
4 2.4	86	632	639	645	651	658	664	670	677	683	689
5 3.0	87	696	702	708	715	721	727	734	740	746	753
6 3.6	88	759	765	771	778	784	790	797	803	809	816
7 4.2	89	822	828	835	841	847	853	860	866	872	879
8 4.8	**690**	885	891	897	904	910	916	923	929	935	942
9 5.4	91	83 948	954	960	967	973	979	985	992	998	*004
	92	84 011	017	023	029	036	042	048	055	061	067
	93	073	080	086	092	098	105	111	117	123	130
	94	136	142	148	155	161	167	173	180	186	192
	95	198	205	211	217	223	230	236	242	248	255
	96	261	267	273	280	286	292	298	305	311	317
	97	323	330	336	342	348	354	361	367	373	379
	98	386	392	398	404	410	417	423	429	435	442
	99	448	454	460	466	473	479	485	491	497	504
	700	84 510	516	522	528	535	541	547	553	559	566
Prop. Parts	N	0	1	2	3	4	5	6	7	8	9

N	0	1	2	3	4	5	6	7	8	9	Prop. Parts
700	84 510	516	522	528	535	541	547	553	559	566	
01	572	578	584	590	597	603	609	615	621	628	
02	634	640	646	652	658	665	671	677	683	689	
03	696	702	708	714	720	726	733	739	745	751	
04	757	763	770	776	782	788	794	800	807	813	
05	819	825	831	837	844	850	856	862	868	874	
06	880	887	893	899	905	911	917	924	930	936	
07	84 942	948	954	960	967	973	979	985	991	997	
08	85 003	009	016	022	028	034	040	046	052	058	
09	065	071	077	083	089	095	101	107	114	120	
710	126	132	138	144	150	156	163	169	175	181	
11	187	193	199	205	211	217	224	230	236	242	
12	248	254	260	266	272	278	285	291	297	303	
13	309	315	321	327	333	339	345	352	358	364	
14	370	376	382	388	394	400	406	412	418	425	
15	431	437	443	449	455	461	467	473	479	485	
16	491	497	503	509	516	522	528	534	540	546	
17	552	558	564	570	576	582	588	594	600	606	
18	612	618	625	631	637	643	649	655	661	667	
19	673	679	685	691	697	703	709	715	721	727	
720	733	739	745	751	757	763	769	775	781	788	
21	794	800	806	812	818	824	830	836	842	848	
22	854	860	866	872	878	884	890	896	902	908	
23	914	920	926	932	938	944	950	956	962	968	
24	85 974	980	986	992	998	*004	*010	*016	*022	*028	
25	86 034	040	046	052	058	064	070	076	082	088	
26	094	100	106	112	118	124	130	136	141	147	
27	153	159	165	171	177	183	189	195	201	207	
28	213	219	225	231	237	243	249	255	261	267	
29	273	279	285	291	297	303	308	314	320	326	
730	332	338	344	350	356	362	368	374	380	386	
31	392	398	404	410	415	421	427	433	439	445	
32	451	457	463	469	475	481	487	493	499	504	
33	510	516	522	528	534	540	546	552	558	564	
34	570	576	581	587	593	599	605	611	617	623	
35	629	635	641	646	652	658	664	670	676	682	
36	688	694	700	705	711	717	723	729	735	741	
37	747	753	759	764	770	776	782	788	794	800	
38	806	812	817	823	829	835	841	847	853	859	
39	864	870	876	882	888	894	900	906	911	917	
740	923	929	935	941	947	953	958	964	970	976	
41	86 982	988	994	999	*005	*011	*017	*023	*029	*035	
42	87 040	046	052	058	064	070	075	081	087	093	
43	099	105	111	116	122	128	134	140	146	151	
44	157	163	169	175	181	186	192	198	204	210	
45	216	221	227	233	239	245	251	256	262	268	
46	274	280	286	291	297	303	309	315	320	326	
47	332	338	344	349	355	361	367	373	379	384	
48	390	396	402	408	413	419	425	431	437	442	
49	448	454	460	466	471	477	483	489	495	500	
750	87 506	512	518	523	529	535	541	547	552	558	
N	0	1	2	3	4	5	6	7	8	9	Prop. Parts

Prop. Parts

7
1 | 0.7
2 | 1.4
3 | 2.1
4 | 2.8
5 | 3.5
6 | 4.2
7 | 4.9
8 | 5.6
9 | 6.3

6
1 | 0.6
2 | 1.2
3 | 1.8
4 | 2.4
5 | 3.0
6 | 3.6
7 | 4.2
8 | 4.8
9 | 5.4

5
1 | 0.5
2 | 1.0
3 | 1.5
4 | 2.0
5 | 2.5
6 | 3.0
7 | 3.5
8 | 4.0
9 | 4.5

Prop. Parts	N	0	1	2	3	4	5	6	7	8	9
	750	87 506	512	518	523	529	535	541	547	552	558
	51	564	570	576	581	587	593	599	604	610	616
	52	622	628	633	639	645	651	656	662	668	674
	53	679	685	691	697	703	708	714	720	726	731
	54	737	743	749	754	760	766	772	777	783	789
	55	795	800	806	812	818	823	829	835	841	846
	56	852	858	864	869	875	881	887	892	898	904
	57	910	915	921	927	933	938	944	950	955	961
	58	87 967	973	978	984	990	996	*001	*007	*013	*018
	59	88 024	030	036	041	047	053	058	064	070	076
	760	081	087	093	098	104	110	116	121	127	133
	61	138	144	150	156	161	167	173	178	184	190
6	62	195	201	207	213	218	224	230	235	241	247
1 0.6	63	252	258	264	270	275	281	287	292	298	304
2 1.2											
3 1.8	64	309	315	321	326	332	338	343	349	355	360
4 2.4	65	366	372	377	383	389	395	400	406	412	417
5 3.0	66	423	429	434	440	446	451	457	463	468	474
6 3.6											
7 4.2	67	480	485	491	497	502	508	513	519	525	530
8 4.8	68	536	542	547	553	559	564	570	576	581	587
9 5.4	69	593	598	604	610	615	621	627	632	638	643
	770	649	655	660	666	672	677	683	689	694	700
	71	705	711	717	722	728	734	739	745	750	756
	72	762	767	773	779	784	790	795	801	807	812
	73	818	824	829	835	840	846	852	857	863	868
	74	874	880	885	891	897	902	908	913	919	925
	75	930	936	941	947	953	958	964	969	975	981
	76	88 986	992	997	*003	*009	*014	*020	*025	*031	*037
	77	89 042	048	053	059	064	070	076	081	087	092
	78	098	104	109	115	120	126	131	137	143	148
	79	154	159	165	170	176	182	187	193	198	204
	780	209	215	221	226	232	237	243	248	254	260
5	81	265	271	276	282	287	293	298	304	310	315
1 0.5	82	321	326	332	337	343	348	354	360	365	371
2 1.0	83	376	382	387	393	398	404	409	415	421	426
3 1.5											
4 2.0	84	432	437	443	448	454	459	465	470	476	481
5 2.5	85	487	492	498	504	509	515	520	526	531	537
6 3.0	86	542	548	553	559	564	570	575	581	586	592
7 3.5											
8 4.0	87	597	603	609	614	620	625	631	636	642	647
9 4.5	88	653	658	664	669	675	680	686	691	697	702
	89	708	713	719	724	730	735	741	746	752	757
	790	763	768	774	779	785	790	796	801	807	812
	91	818	823	829	834	840	845	851	856	862	867
	92	873	878	883	889	894	900	905	911	916	922
	93	927	933	938	944	949	955	960	966	971	977
	94	89 982	988	993	998	*004	*009	*015	*020	*026	*031
	95	90 037	042	048	053	059	064	069	075	080	086
	96	091	097	102	108	113	119	124	129	135	140
	97	146	151	157	162	168	173	179	184	189	195
	98	200	206	211	217	222	227	233	238	244	249
	99	255	260	266	271	276	282	287	293	298	304
	800	90 309	314	320	325	331	336	342	347	352	358
Prop. Parts	N	0	1	2	3	4	5	6	7	8	9

N	0	1	2	3	4	5	6	7	8	9	Prop. Parts
800	90 309	314	320	325	331	336	342	347	352	358	
01	363	369	374	380	385	390	396	401	407	412	
02	417	423	428	434	439	445	450	455	461	466	
03	472	477	482	488	493	499	504	509	515	520	
04	526	531	536	542	547	553	558	563	569	574	
05	580	585	590	596	601	607	612	617	623	628	
06	634	639	644	650	655	660	666	671	677	682	
07	687	693	698	703	709	714	720	725	730	736	
08	741	747	752	757	763	768	773	779	784	789	
09	795	800	806	811	816	822	827	832	838	843	
810	849	854	859	865	870	875	881	886	891	897	
11	902	907	913	918	924	929	934	940	945	950	
12	90 956	961	966	972	977	982	988	993	998	*004	
13	91 009	014	020	025	030	036	041	046	052	057	
14	062	068	073	078	084	089	094	100	105	110	
15	116	121	126	132	137	142	148	153	158	164	
16	169	174	180	185	190	196	201	206	212	217	
17	222	228	233	238	243	249	254	259	265	270	
18	275	281	286	291	297	302	307	312	318	323	
19	328	334	339	344	350	355	360	365	371	376	
820	381	387	392	397	403	408	413	418	424	429	
21	434	440	445	450	455	461	466	471	477	482	
22	487	492	498	503	508	514	519	524	529	535	
23	540	545	551	556	561	566	572	577	582	587	
24	593	598	603	609	614	619	624	630	635	640	
25	645	651	656	661	666	672	677	682	687	693	
26	698	703	709	714	719	724	730	735	740	745	
27	751	756	761	766	772	777	782	787	793	798	
28	803	808	814	819	824	829	834	840	845	850	
29	855	861	866	871	876	882	887	892	897	903	
830	908	913	918	924	929	934	939	944	950	955	
31	91 960	965	971	976	981	986	991	997	*002	*007	
32	92 012	018	023	028	033	038	044	049	054	059	
33	065	070	075	080	085	091	096	101	106	111	
34	117	122	127	132	137	143	148	153	158	163	
35	169	174	179	184	189	195	200	205	210	215	
36	221	226	231	236	241	247	252	257	262	267	
37	273	278	283	288	293	298	304	309	314	319	
38	324	330	335	340	345	350	355	361	366	371	
39	376	381	387	392	397	402	407	412	418	423	
840	428	433	438	443	449	454	459	464	469	474	
41	480	485	490	495	500	505	511	516	521	526	
42	531	536	542	547	552	557	562	567	572	578	
43	583	588	593	598	603	609	614	619	624	629	
44	634	639	645	650	655	660	665	670	675	681	
45	686	691	696	701	706	711	716	722	727	732	
46	737	742	747	752	758	763	768	773	778	783	
47	788	793	799	804	809	814	819	824	829	834	
48	840	845	850	855	860	865	870	875	881	886	
49	891	896	901	906	911	916	921	927	932	937	
850	92 942	947	952	957	962	967	973	978	983	988	
N	0	1	2	3	4	5	6	7	8	9	Prop. Parts

Prop. Parts:

6
1	0.6
2	1.2
3	1.8
4	2.4
5	3.0
6	3.6
7	4.2
8	4.8
9	5.4

5
1	0.5
2	1.0
3	1.5
4	2.0
5	2.5
6	3.0
7	3.5
8	4.0
9	4.5

Prop. Parts	N	0	1	2	3	4	5	6	7	8	9
	850	92 942	947	952	957	962	967	973	978	983	988
	51	92 993	998	*003	*008	*013	*018	*024	*029	*034	*039
	52	93 044	049	054	059	064	069	075	080	085	090
	53	095	100	105	110	115	120	125	131	136	141
	54	146	151	156	161	166	171	176	181	186	192
	55	197	202	207	212	217	222	227	232	237	242
	56	247	252	258	263	268	273	278	283	288	293
6	57	298	303	308	313	318	323	328	334	339	344
1 0.6	58	349	354	359	364	369	374	379	384	389	394
2 1.2	59	399	404	409	414	420	425	430	435	440	445
3 1.8	**860**	450	455	460	465	470	475	480	485	490	495
4 2.4	61	500	505	510	515	520	526	531	536	541	546
5 3.0	62	551	556	561	566	571	576	581	586	591	596
6 3.6	63	601	606	611	616	621	626	631	636	641	646
7 4.2	64	651	656	661	666	671	676	682	687	692	697
8 4.8	65	702	707	712	717	722	727	732	737	742	747
9 5.4	66	752	757	762	767	772	777	782	787	792	797
	67	802	807	812	817	822	827	832	837	842	847
	68	852	857	862	867	872	877	882	887	892	897
	69	902	907	912	917	922	927	932	937	942	947
	870	93 952	957	962	967	972	977	982	987	992	997
	71	94 002	007	012	017	022	027	032	037	042	047
	72	052	057	062	067	072	077	082	086	091	096
5	73	101	106	111	116	121	126	131	136	141	146
1 0.5	74	151	156	161	166	171	176	181	186	191	196
2 1.0	75	201	206	211	216	221	226	231	236	240	245
3 1.5	76	250	255	260	265	270	275	280	285	290	295
4 2.0	77	300	305	310	315	320	325	330	335	340	345
5 2.5	78	349	354	359	364	369	374	379	384	389	394
6 3.0	79	399	404	409	414	419	424	429	433	438	443
7 3.5	**880**	448	453	458	463	468	473	478	483	488	493
8 4.0	81	498	503	507	512	517	522	527	532	537	542
9 4.5	82	547	552	557	562	567	571	576	581	586	591
	83	596	601	606	611	616	621	626	630	635	640
	84	645	650	655	660	665	670	675	680	685	689
	85	694	699	704	709	714	719	724	729	734	738
	86	743	748	753	758	763	768	773	778	783	787
4	87	792	797	802	807	812	817	822	827	832	836
1 0.4	88	841	846	851	856	861	866	871	876	880	885
2 0.8	89	890	895	900	905	910	915	919	924	929	934
3 1.2	**890**	939	944	949	954	959	963	968	973	978	983
4 1.6	91	94 988	993	998	*002	*007	*012	*017	*022	*027	*032
5 2.0	92	95 036	041	046	051	056	061	066	071	075	080
6 2.4	93	085	090	095	100	105	109	114	119	124	129
7 2.8	94	134	139	143	148	153	158	163	168	173	177
8 3.2	95	182	187	192	197	202	207	211	216	221	226
9 3.6	96	231	236	240	245	250	255	260	265	270	274
	97	279	284	289	294	299	303	308	313	318	323
	98	328	332	337	342	347	352	357	361	366	371
	99	376	381	386	390	395	400	405	410	415	419
	900	95 424	429	434	439	444	448	453	458	463	468
Prop. Parts	N	0	1	2	3	4	5	6	7	8	9

N	0	1	2	3	4	5	6	7	8	9	Prop. Parts
900	95 424	429	434	439	444	448	453	458	463	468	
01	472	477	482	487	492	497	501	506	511	516	
02	521	525	530	535	540	545	550	554	559	564	
03	569	574	578	583	588	593	598	602	607	612	
04	617	622	626	631	636	641	646	650	655	660	
05	665	670	674	679	684	689	694	698	703	708	
06	713	718	722	727	732	737	742	746	751	756	
07	761	766	770	775	780	785	789	794	799	804	
08	809	813	818	823	828	832	837	842	847	852	
09	856	861	866	871	875	880	885	890	895	899	
910	904	909	914	918	923	928	933	938	942	947	
11	952	957	961	966	971	976	980	985	990	995	
12	95 999	*004	*009	*014	*019	*023	*028	*033	*038	*042	**5**
13	96 047	052	057	061	066	071	076	080	085	090	1 0.5
											2 1.0
14	095	099	104	109	114	118	123	128	133	137	3 1.5
15	142	147	152	156	161	166	171	175	180	185	4 2.0
16	190	194	199	204	209	213	218	223	227	232	5 2.5
											6 3.0
17	237	242	246	251	256	261	265	270	275	280	7 3.5
18	284	289	294	298	303	308	313	317	322	327	8 4.0
19	332	336	341	346	350	355	360	365	369	374	9 4.5
920	379	384	388	393	398	402	407	412	417	421	
21	426	431	435	440	445	450	454	459	464	468	
22	473	478	483	487	492	497	501	506	511	515	
23	520	525	530	534	539	544	548	553	558	562	
24	567	572	577	581	586	591	595	600	605	609	
25	614	619	624	628	633	638	642	647	652	656	
26	661	666	670	675	680	685	689	694	699	703	
27	708	713	717	722	727	731	736	741	745	750	
28	755	759	764	769	774	778	783	788	792	797	
29	802	806	811	816	820	825	830	834	839	844	
930	848	853	858	862	867	872	876	881	886	890	
31	895	900	904	909	914	918	923	928	932	937	**4**
32	942	946	951	956	960	965	970	974	979	984	1 0.4
33	96 988	993	997	*002	*007	*011	*016	*021	*025	*030	2 0.8
											3 1.2
34	97 035	039	044	049	053	058	063	067	072	077	4 1.6
35	081	086	090	095	100	104	109	114	118	123	5 2.0
36	128	132	137	142	146	151	155	160	165	169	6 2.4
											7 2.8
37	174	179	183	188	192	197	202	206	211	216	8 3.2
38	220	225	230	234	239	243	248	253	257	262	9 3.6
39	267	271	276	280	285	290	294	299	304	308	
940	313	317	322	327	331	336	340	345	350	354	
41	359	364	368	373	377	382	387	391	396	400	
42	405	410	414	419	424	428	433	437	442	447	
43	451	456	460	465	470	474	479	483	488	493	
44	497	502	506	511	516	520	525	529	534	539	
45	543	548	552	557	562	566	571	575	580	585	
46	589	594	598	603	607	612	617	621	626	630	
47	635	640	644	649	653	658	663	667	672	676	
48	681	685	690	695	699	704	708	713	717	722	
49	727	731	736	740	745	749	754	759	763	768	
950	97 772	777	782	786	791	795	800	804	809	813	
N	0	1	2	3	4	5	6	7	8	9	Prop. Parts

Prop. Parts	N	0	1	2	3	4	5	6	7	8	9
	950	97 772	777	782	786	791	795	800	804	809	813
	51	818	823	827	832	836	841	845	850	855	859
	52	864	868	873	877	882	886	891	896	900	905
	53	909	914	918	923	928	932	937	941	946	950
	54	97 955	959	964	968	973	978	982	987	991	996
	55	98 000	005	009	014	019	023	028	032	037	041
	56	046	050	055	059	064	068	073	078	082	087
	57	091	096	100	105	109	114	118	123	127	132
	58	137	141	146	150	155	159	164	168	173	177
	59	182	186	191	195	200	204	209	214	218	223
	960	227	232	236	241	245	250	254	259	263	268
	61	272	277	281	286	290	295	299	304	308	313
5	62	318	322	327	331	336	340	345	349	354	358
1 0.5	63	363	367	372	376	381	385	390	394	399	403
2 1.0											
3 1.5	64	408	412	417	421	426	430	435	439	444	448
4 2.0	65	453	457	462	466	471	475	480	484	489	493
5 2.5	66	498	502	507	511	516	520	525	529	534	538
6 3.0											
7 3.5	67	543	547	552	556	561	565	570	574	579	583
8 4.0	68	588	592	597	601	605	610	614	619	623	628
9 4.5	69	632	637	641	646	650	655	659	664	668	673
	970	677	682	686	691	695	700	704	709	713	717
	71	722	726	731	735	740	744	749	753	758	762
	72	767	771	776	780	784	789	793	798	802	807
	73	811	816	820	825	829	834	838	843	847	851
	74	856	860	865	869	874	878	883	887	892	896
	75	900	905	909	914	918	923	927	932	936	941
	76	945	949	954	958	963	967	972	976	981	985
	77	98 989	994	998	*003	*007	*012	*016	*021	*025	*029
	78	99 034	038	043	047	052	056	061	065	069	074
	79	078	083	087	092	096	100	105	109	114	118
	980	123	127	131	136	140	145	149	154	158	162
	81	167	171	176	180	185	189	193	198	202	207
4	82	211	216	220	224	229	233	238	242	247	251
1 0.4	83	255	260	264	269	273	277	282	286	291	295
2 0.8											
3 1.2	84	300	304	308	313	317	322	326	330	335	339
4 1.6	85	344	348	352	357	361	366	370	374	379	383
5 2.0	86	388	392	396	401	405	410	414	419	423	427
6 2.4											
7 2.8	87	432	436	441	445	449	454	458	463	467	471
8 3.2	88	476	480	484	489	493	498	502	506	511	515
9 3.6	89	520	524	528	533	537	542	546	550	555	559
	990	564	568	572	577	581	585	590	594	599	603
	91	607	612	616	621	625	629	634	638	642	647
	92	651	656	660	664	669	673	677	682	686	691
	93	695	699	704	708	712	717	721	726	730	734
	94	739	743	747	752	756	760	765	769	774	778
	95	782	787	791	795	800	804	808	813	817	822
	96	826	830	835	839	843	848	852	856	861	865
	97	870	874	878	883	887	891	896	900	904	909
	98	913	917	922	926	930	935	939	944	948	952
	99	99 957	961	965	970	974	978	983	987	991	996
	1000	00 000	004	009	013	017	022	026	030	035	039
Prop. Parts	N	0	1	2	3	4	5	6	7	8	9

Index

519

PERIODIC TABLE OF THE ELEMENTS

GROUP

PERIOD	1A	2A	3A	4A	5A	6A	7A	8	8	8	1B	2B	3B	4B	5B	6B	7B	0
1	1 H 1.0080																	2 He 4.003
2	3 Li 6.940	4 Be 9.013											5 B 10.82	6 C 12.010	7 N 14.008	8 O 16.0000	9 F 19.00	10 Ne 20.183
3	11 Na 22.997	12 Mg 24.32											13 Al 26.98	14 Si 28.09	15 P 30.975	16 S 32.066	17 Cl 35.457	18 A 39.944
4	19 K 39.100	20 Ca 40.08	21 Sc 44.96	22 Ti 47.90	23 V 50.95	24 Cr 52.01	25 Mn 54.93	26 Fe 55.85	27 Co 58.94	28 Ni 58.69	29 Cu 63.54	30 Zn 65.38	31 Ga 69.72	32 Ge 72.60	33 As 74.91	34 Se 78.96	35 Br 79.916	36 Kr 83.80
5	37 Rb 85.48	38 Sr 87.63	39 Y 88.92	40 Zr 91.22	41 Nb 92.91	42 Mo 95.95	43 Tc [99]	44 Ru 101.7	45 Rh 102.91	46 Pd 106.7*	47 Ag 107.880	48 Cd 112.41	49 In 114.76	50 Sn 118.70	51 Sb 121.76	52 Te 127.61	53 I 126.91	54 Xe 131.3
6	55 Cs 132.91	56 Ba 137.36	57 La 138.92 (58 to 71)	72 Hf 178.6	73 Ta 180.88	74 W 183.92	75 Re 186.31	76 Os 190.2	77 Ir 193.1	78 Pt 195.23	79 Au 197.2	80 Hg 200.61	81 Tl 204.39	82 Pb 207.21	83 Bi 209.00	84 Po 210	85 At [210]	86 Rn 222
7	87 Fr [223]	88 Ra 226.05	89 Ac 227 (90 to 98)															

58 Ce 140.13	59 Pr 140.92	60 Nd 144.27	61 Pm [145]	62 Sm 150.43	63 Eu 152.0	64 Gd 156.9	65 Tb 159.2	66 Dy 162.46	67 Ho 164.94	68 Er 167.2	69 Tm 169.4	70 Yb 173.04	71 Lu 174.99
90 Th 232.12	91 Pa 231	92 U 238.07	93 Np [237]	94 Pu [242]	95 Am [243]	96 Cm [243]	97 Bk [245]	98 Cf [246]					

The number above the symbol of the element is the atomic number. The number below the symbol of the element is the atomic weight.